Metallurgy & Plastics

for Engineers

Merle C. Nutt

Professor Emeritus of Engineering
College of Engineering Sciences
Arizona State University

Associated Lithographers
Phoenix, Arizona

Distributed outside North America by Pergamon Press

U.K.	Pergamon Press Ltd., Headington Hill Hall, Oxford OX3 0BW, England
CANADA	Pergamon of Canada Ltd., 75 The East Mall, Toronto, Ontario, Canada
AUSTRALIA	Pergamon Press (Aust.) Pty. Ltd., 19a Boundary Street, Rushcutters Bay, N.S.W. 2011, Australia
FRANCE	Pergamon Press SARL, 24 rue des Ecoles, 75240 Paris, Cedex 05, France
FEDERAL REPUBLIC OF GERMANY	Pergamon Press GmbH, 6242 Kronberg/Taunus, Pferdstrasse 1, Federal Republic of Germany

Copyright © 1976 by Merle Caro Nutt.

ISBN 0 08 021684 6

. . . To those Metallurgists,
Engineers, Scientists
and all others
who have made this earth
on which we live
a little bit better . . .

Library of Congress Catalog Number:
76-19249

Printed in the United States of America

From *Liftoff* to *Touchdown* on the Moon, all systems were 'Go' on Apollo 17. Pictured is Scientist-Astronaut Harrison H. Schmitt next to the deployed U.S. flag during lunar surface extravehicular activity at the Taurus-Littrow landing site. The highest part of the flag appears to point toward the Earth, which can be seen in the far distant background. This picture was taken by Astronaut Eugene A. Cernan, Apollo 17 commander. Schmitt was the mission's lunar module pilot. Astronaut Ronald E. Evans, command module pilot, remained with the Command and Service Modules in lunar orbit while Cernan and Schmitt descended in the Lunar Module 'Challenger' to explore the lunar surface.

Preface

The purpose of this book is to provide an introductory course in the fields of metallurgy, plastics, adhesives and elastomers all of which are extremely important in materials sciences. It is imperative that engineers in this space age, design, select and use metals and alloys as well as plastics, that will perform with maximum dependability in all environments. The principles and problems of various types of corrosion are developed as well as a study of metal fatigue and fractures, along with the correct and accurate methods of testing to determine the suitability of metals, plastics and elastomers to fit the job.

An important chapter is devoted to the joining of metals including the conventional methods such as soldering, brazing, arc and gas welding and also the newest techniques and processes of electron beam and laser welding. Heat treating is developed in another chapter.

Powder metallurgy is covered in detail including, not only methods of producing the powders but also the fabrication of desirable parts along with the advantages of powder metal parts over cast, forged and machined parts for certain applications.

Strength-to-weight ratio of metals has brought into sharp focus, the need for more serviceable light metals and alloys, one chapter being devoted to aluminum, magnesium, titanium and other light metals and alloys.

The application of electronic computers in solving metallurgical problems is included, with actual problems and solutions. Computers have made it possible to examine thousands of metals and alloys as well as plastics, as to their physical and mechanical properties, leading to the selection of the best ones for various applications that will give maximum performance under a given set of conditions.

Polymers have come into major importance, plastics, adhesives and elastomers (rubbers) now being specified with safety in supersonic aircraft, and these subjects are covered in the last chapter.

Although it is impossible to include every detail and phase of the various areas covered in the text, it is hoped and believed that the reader will emerge with a set of "tools" and knowledge in these important fields that will encourage him toward further study in materials science.

To all who have in any way been of assistance in the writing of this book, I am most grateful and indebted. Although space does not permit a listing of the names of such individuals, appropriate credits and recognitions are given to many persons, industries and facilities of the Armed Forces who gave me their cooperation.

Merle C. Nutt
Tempe, Arizona
1976

Contents

Chapter 12. EQUIPMENT AND TECHNIQUES USED IN METALLURGICAL INVESTIGATIONS 295

Contents

xiii

Chapter 19. PLASTICS, ADHESIVES AND ELASTOMERS (RUBBERS)

XV

History of Metallurgy

1-1   Primitive Man's First Uses of Metals

Several Biblical references to man's early uses of metals point to the fact that primitive man adapted them to his own purposes. In Genesis, for example, there is a reference to Tubalcain as "an instructor of every artificer in brass and iron." It is not certain if this "iron" was wrought iron or cast iron. Again, in the Book of Job there is reference to the early iron age, giving a glimpse of man's first venture into the mysterious world of ores and fire that he found and used—the ores from underground and the fire from his own ingenious making. This passage from Job relates:

> Iron is taken out of the earth,
> and copper is smelted from the ore.
> Man put an end to darkness, and
> searched out to the farthest bound
> the ore in gloom and deep darkness.
> They open shafts in a valley away
> from where men live:
> they are forgotten by travelers,
> they hang afar from men, they
> swing to and fro. As for the earth,
> out of it comes bread: but underneath it is
> turned up as by fire.

Going back much farther than the writings of the Bible it is revealed from the writings and artifacts of prehistoric days that cavemen 20,000 years ago worked with stone and bone to make their tools and weapons. Man undoubtedly learned to use metals in a limited way not later than 5500 years ago when the Egyptians made and wore copper beads and their rulers bathed in water conveyed by copper pipe from the river Nile to their private pools. Copper nuggets and meteoric iron, as well as gold and silver, were used; the gold, in the form of nuggets found exposed along the river beds, being pounded into crude ornaments with a stone hammer. Unlike copper, gold did not harden appreciably with this pounding, and man was therefore unable to use it for his tools. Native silver was also used in rings, bracelets and other fine ornaments, but not to the extent of gold. We have discovered that goldsmiths were among the first metal workers, as revealed by some of the oldest archaeological excavations in Egypt, Iraq and Crete.

Man discovered the art of smelting ores to produce metals near the end of the Stone Age and, from what we can learn, this discovery did not revolve merely about copper, the first industrial metal, but actually engaged man in chemistry that revealed to him, in rather quick sequence, the existence of silver, lead, tin, and probably iron. We find that tin revealed itself as the ideal addition to bronze only after long and undoubtedly unintentional trials with such impurities as antimony and arsenic.

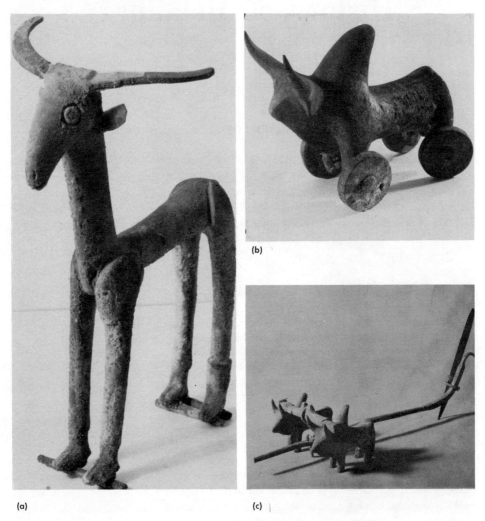

(a)   (c)

Fig. 1-1. *Metals as art. (a) Bronze mountain deer. Length, 5.3 cm. (b) Bronze humped cow mounted on four wheels. Length 11.5 cm. (c) Bronze oxen with yoke and plow. Overall length about 35 cm. These items are from the recent Marlik excavations in Iran (about 1200–1000 B.C.) (Courtesy of Theodore A. Wertime.)*

Fig. 1-2. *Bronze lion incense burner. Seljuk, 12th century. 11-3/8 in. long (Print through courtesy of Smithsonian Institution.)*

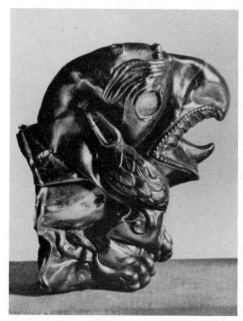

Fig. 1-3. *Gold protoma of a lion. Ziwiye 7th century B.C. Weight 57 g. (Print through courtesy of Smithsonian Institution.)*

Fig. 1-4. *Bronze battle club, Iran, Luristan 8th–7th century B.C. (Print through courtesy of Smithsonian Institution.)*

Fig. 1-6.   *Large gold beaker with two pairs of winged bulls. Height 7-1/4 in., Marlik Ca. 1200–1000 B.C.*

Fig. 1-5.   *Nude bronze goddess (back). Height 24.5 cm. Width 4 cm.*

Fig. 1-7.   *Gold necklace Marlik Ca., 12–1000 B.C. Length 12-1/4 in. (Prints through courtesy of Smithsonian Institute)*

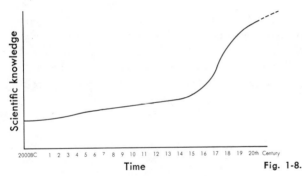

Fig. 1-8.

Early man was confronted with a large assortment of ores, copper ores alone being found in some seven or eight forms. This leads us to conclude from the colors he recorded of them, that he found the yellow of chalcopyrite and the ruby red of cuprite, the green of malachite, the bright blue of azurite, the purple of bornite, the purplish-brown of native copper, and the gray sparkle of chalcocite.

The actual discovery of metals appears to have begun in the sixth millenium, as man's uses and recordings of them became reasonably well advanced by the year 2000 B.C. This did not occur in only one locale or area, but through an area stretching from western and central Anatolia (Turkey), across the flanks of the Taurus and Zagros mountains, over to the edge of the central desert of Iran.

A look at the probable evolutionary stages in man's first efforts to treat metals is pieced together only after looking at the evidence (and, in many cases, the lack of evidence). For example, the idea that pyrometallurgy was somehow confined exclusively to the various phases of working copper until bronze and later iron came into their own, is debatable, for the reason that artifactual evidence often becomes very misleading. Iron and silver all too frequently have corroded away or, perhaps, have been overlooked in their oxide or chloride forms. We find also that early man looked upon lead as being worthless.

A look at the four stages in the development of man's treatment of native copper is of interest to us today as they reveal how much was known many centuries ago, much of which has been utilized down through the ages.

1-2   Four Stages in Early Man's Treatment of Native Copper

1. **Hammering.**   The earliest use of natural copper involved an extremely limited Stone Age technique by which small, specially selected pieces of metal through cold forging were made into beads and possibly awls, pins, or hoops. Early man's attempts to cold-hammer small pieces of native copper show varying degrees of success. Cold-working gave very limited improvement over the native copper itself.
2. **Annealing.**   The potentialities of stoneworking techniques, such as simple shaping, greatly increased when the smith learned to produce copper of a more malleable form by the process of annealing—which he did by a softening, slow heat. This was a step toward the subsequent melting of copper.
3. **Puddle Casting.**   When early man discovered that melted pieces of copper formed a single puddle that would reharden, he had found a way of using scrap, thereby enlarging his effective supply of metal.

4. **Open Mold Casting.** Man's first efforts to shape the molten metal that accumulated in crevices in the hearth consisted of cutting forms in slabs of stone, or molding forms in clay. To fill these molds, the smith transferred the molten metal to a crucible, which might be merely the new bottom for the hearth. Therefore, he was able to shape objects readily, and to save the time required for hammering and annealing.

1-3 Metallurgy and Pyrotechny

When we look at the activities of early man from the viewpoint of metallurgy and pyrotechny, we conclude that the smith of the late fourth millenium B.C. must have been remarkably sophisticated in a practical way regarding the individual phenomena of metallurgy. He undoubtedly knew the effects on metals of hammering, annealing, oxidation, melting, and alloying; he must have been aware of the phenomena of simple decomposition of ores, their reduction, double decomposition, and metathesis (exchange of impurities), and he undoubtedly knew something of the miscibility and immiscibility of solutions. Following his trail into these arcane revelations is indeed an exciting, and occasionally a rather bewildering quest.

Study in the twentieth century of the early history of metallurgy has been hampered by a rather singleminded attention to firing temperatures as the key to the first appearance of metals. Thus, by this rather absurd reasoning, the Copper Age precedes the Iron Age by some 4000 or 5000 years, because copper melts at only 1083C, whereas the melting point of iron is 1537C. However, early smiths viewed not one element at a single temperature, but the whole of matter on an ascending scale of heat.

We can imagine the bafflement of the first men when they attempted smelting when we review some facets of chemistry which would have seemed to them utterly contradictory. At 100C oxide films first appear on some metals. At 330C silver oxide and pyrites begin to decompose, while pure tin and lead have melted. At 500C sulfide ores (in air) begin to roast, while cold-worked copper and bronze have fully recrystallized and become soft. It is also significant that at 600C clay pottery develops moderate hardness and some types begin to develop a vitreous finish. Some glazes are molten at this temperature, but more heat is required for metallurgical slags to run properly. At this or even at a lower temperature, it is relatively easy to reduce copper, lead, and iron from pure oxide minerals by contact with charcoal; but the reduction of an ore is not metallurgically practical unless the metal can be separated from the rocky impurities. This, of course, requires that the metal be melted, and it is usually also necessary for the ore to reach a temperature high enough to fuse the earthy matter contained in it. Common early slags for all metals were composed of iron silicates or calcium-iron silicates melting at about 1200C. Copper, lead, and tin conveniently melt below the temperature of fusion of the slags; iron does not melt when the slag does (its melting point when pure is 1539C), but even at a dull red heat it is reduced to a metallic sponge which can easily be consolidated by hammering to weld the particles together when the slag melts and can be expelled.

1-4 Transition of Metallurgy from an Art to a Science

Although primitive man did master the complex skills of practical pyrotechny, as previously explained, its scientific lessons eluded him for many millenia. It may be said that artisans discovered the metals and the metallurgical processes in a practical way, but did not identify them scientifically. The pseudoscience of alchemy was a natural consequence of the first dazzling successes in transmuting base elements to metals. Even non-speculative workers continued to look upon tin, antimony and arsenic as having some connection with lead and retained such Latin terms as *plumbum candidum* (tin) and *plumbum cinereum* (antimony) until the time of Agricola (1494 to 1555). Steel was not known at all. The word *kassiteros* originally meant ores containing no tin as well as ores containing tin.

It was not until the eighteenth century A.D. that man finally began to slough off his misconceptions and to appreciate the complex chemistry of metallurgy. Even at that time, many recognized scholars continued to believe that certain irons gave a "coppery" quality. Of significance to us today is the fact that our knowledge about the structural and physical properties of metals has been acquired even more slowly. Metallography of real importance is only a century old, and X-ray diffraction, which elucidated the atomic structure of metals for us, is only fifty years old.

The actual start of the Iron Age is believed to have taken place about 1500 B.C. with the first smelting of iron ore. During this era, man-made iron was used mainly for coins, cooking utensils and implements of war. During the early days of the Iron Age, metallurgists, no doubt, discovered the cementation process for making steel and the art of quenching steel for hardening and tempering weapons.

The progress of metallurgy was slow until about 1300 A.D., when the Catalan forge was developed in Spain. This was most significant as it was the forerunner of the modern open-hearth furnace of our day. For the first time in history it was possible for man to produce a sizeable tonnage of iron in one heat. The forerunner of the blast furnace as we know it today was the continuous shaft furnace, developed in Germany about 1323 A.D. The product of this furnace, with its high carbon content, was known as "cast iron" and it broadened the use of iron castings considerably.

It was early in the sixteenth century that man's natural curiosity gave birth to modern science in metallurgy; however, the transition of metallurgy from an art to a science was rather slow when we compare it to the technological progress in other fields through the years. Developments in mining and processing of ores revealed ore sources at locations and depths that previously had been unknown and inaccessible to man. The improved steam engine of James Watt in 1780 made it possible to remove mine water; in fact it was the earlier work on the steam pump in 1704, and its use in the removal of mine water from the mines, that aided Watt in the accomplishment of perfecting his steam engine. This marked the beginning of the Power Age and the coming of the Industrial Revolution.

With the Power Age came the demand for larger tonnage of metal and at the same time the production of still greater power for larger production. A man named

Henry Cort, who wanted to make England independent of foreign countries for the supply of iron, erected an iron works at Gosport, Hampshire, and in 1700, at the age of 39, Cort perfected his processes for puddling and rolling iron. This was the beginning of the rolling mill and was a big step forward in the production of iron and steel in bars, shapes, and sheets. Because the cementation process of making crucible steels was very costly for large scale consumption, the predominant structural metal in those days was wrought iron, and remained so until the invention of the Bessemer converter in 1855 by another English scientist, Henry Bessemer. Bessemer developed the process during his search for an improved material for guns. Previously steel had been scarce and expensive, made chiefly by the crucible process. It was reserved for special purposes, while wrought iron, cast iron, and bronze were used for structures, engines and ordnance. Bessemer read an important paper before the British Association at Cheltenham on 13 August, 1856, entitled "The Manufacture of Malleable Iron and Steel Without Fuel." His was a new and cheap process of making steel rapidly from pig-iron by blowing a blast of air through it when in the fusion state to clear it of all carbon, then adding the requisite quantity of carbon to produce steel. As a result of this and other inventions, he was knighted. Bessemer's application for a patent on his process disclosed that William Kelley, an American, had also worked on a similar method since 1847; a patent was later granted Kelley in 1857.

1-5 Contributors to Science of Metallurgy, Past and Present

In order to explain countless phenomena in the art of metallurgy which had been ignored or regarded with ignorance down through the ages, scientific man set out to broaden his knowledge by experimentation in the laboratory. Several scientists of the eighteenth and nineteenth centuries, including such men as Faraday, Lavoisier, Volta, Davy, Mendeleef, Gibbs, Sorby, Priestly and others, led the march that transformed both chemistry and metallurgy from an art to a science, thereby providing the basis for these technologies today. In fact, it was the English clergyman Joseph Priestly who first prepared oxygen by focusing the sun's rays on mercuric oxide and later observed that a candle burned most brilliantly in oxygen. When Priestly told Antoine Laurent Lavoisier (1743–1794) about his experiment, the French chemist suspected that the gas (oxygen) was intimately connected with his theories about calcination and combustion.

The contributions of each of the aforenamed scientists to chemistry and metallurgy were substantial. Alessandro Volta first developed an apparatus for chemically producing electricity and electric current. In 1800 Volta developed the electric battery and thereby made it possible to separate the light metals; this was the origin of electrometallurgy. Dimitri Ivanovitch Mendelyeev, the Russian chemist, made many contributions to chemistry and metallurgy, not the least of which were the periodic table and the periodic law of the elements, in 1868, after exhaustive study of existing data and theories on the similarity of properties of the elements. Arranging the known chemical elements in the order of their atomic weights, he discovered a periodic repetition of properties among the elements. Then he classified the elements in eight groups, to show the similarity of properties of the elements within each group. It was only after radioactivity was discovered that his classification was shown to be slightly in error for a few of the elements. So nearly perfect was his classification and so fundamental was his understanding of chemistry that Mendeleef predicted the existence of several undiscovered elements and also their approximate weights and their principal properties. When we stop to consider that 76 of the 104 presently known chemical elements are metals, we can readily appreciate the impetus which Mendeleef's periodic table gave to the advancement of metallurgy, as well as to chemistry.

Although science was growing up, communication among scientists was not always direct. By way of example, from 1864 to 1869 a German chemist and physician by the name of Julius Lothar Meyer (1830–1895) worked on the classification of the elements and prepared an incomplete table in 1864 which he did not publish. By 1869 he had completed his table, but neither Meyer nor Mendelyeev knew anything of the other's work prior to 1869. Today, Meyer is acknowledged as a co-discoverer of the periodic system.

In the twentieth century one finds the contributions to the science of metallurgy of Sauveur, Martin, Hall, Austin, Grossman, Cohen, Bain, Jominy and others. Although the work of some of these contributors will be further discussed, it should be noted here that Charles Martin Hall was the founder of the electrolytic process of refining aluminum, and that Walter E. Jominy investigated the effect of furnace atmospheres on scaling and decarburizing of iron and steel. He developed the important method, which bears his name, of testing the hardenability of steels. Edgar Collins Bain was a physical metallurgist of this century who contributed to the knowledge of crystal structure and allotropy in metals and alloys of steel, including high-speed and tool steels. The structure, Bainite, which in carbon steels occurs by a nucleation and growth process in the transformation from austenite— usually formed at a constant temperature—was justifiably named for Bain.

From the foregoing mention of the important scientists of the eighteenth, nineteenth and twentieth centuries it will be recognized that metallurgy very definitely has its roots in both chemistry and physics, as well as in crystallography, and is not an independent science.

1-6 Fundamental Divisions of Metallurgy

Metallurgy might well be defined as the art and science of the preparation and application of metals and alloys of metals. Metallurgy has been classified into two subdivisions, i.e., process metallurgy and physical metallurgy. It is somewhat broader, however, than this concept and may well be classified into three categories: 1) extractive, 2) physical, and 3) mechanical, all of these being somewhat interrelated. Although more will be said in detail in later chapters regarding these three divisions of metallurgy, it is well to set out here just what each embraces.

Extractive metallurgy is concerned with the extraction of metals from natural deposits in the earth's crust, those metals extracted from ores, natural brines, or sea water being known as primary or virgin metals. This branch of metallurgy has also been referred to as *chemical* and *process* metallurgy; however, throughout this text this phase of metallurgy will be termed extractive metallurgy. (The first work to be published on ore reduction and applied metallurgy was the *Pirotechnia* of Vannoccio Biringuccio, which appeared in 1540 AD.)

Physical metallurgy is the science concerned with the nature of the physical and mechanical properties and characteristics of metals and alloys; this category includes other facets of the subject, such as metallography, mechanical testing, and the heat treatment of metals. The study of the microstructure of metals by means of the metallurgical microscope and the electron microscope is highly important, and is known as metallography. By means of X-ray diffraction study and determination of the atomic structure of metals and alloys are possible. The techniques and processes of changing the physical and mechanical properties of metals are also included in this category of metallurgy.

Mechanical metallurgy is that branch of metallurgy that involves any and all mechanical treatments of metals, whether by rolling, drawing, forming, or extrusion that change the *shape* of the metal. It is very essential that the engineer who is to be concerned with, and is responsible for, the selection of metals and alloys in industry should have a fundamental knowledge of chemistry, physics, thermodynamics, dynamics, and mechanics to be most effective. Although he obviously will not be able to qualify as an expert in all these fields, he should know how they are interrelated and just how they relate to physical metallurgy, and the selection, treatment, working, and ultimate use of metals and alloys. Every engineer, regardless of the particular field in which he is going to specialize, should have a working knowledge of metallurgy and the physical aspects of the same.

1-7 Summary of the Growth of Scientific Learning

A graph such as that shown in Fig. 1.8, showing scientific learning plotted against time since the beginning, would reveal that although primitive man and his early discoveries were very significant and did mark certain guideposts for those who followed him, the tremendously impressive accumulation of scientific knowledge occurred during the nineteenth and twentieth centuries. The early history of metallurgy with its "metal ages" provides very useful categories for the broad sweep of history, but they tell little or nothing at all about the true origins of metallurgy. Some of the information contained in this chapter was abstracted, with his permission, from an excellent article by Theodore A. Wertime of the U. S. Information Agency, that appeared in the December 4, 1964, edition of *Science* magazine.

QUESTIONS

1. Who were the first to use metals, and when?

2. When did man first learn to recover metals from ores?

3. What were the first metals smelted by man, and for what purpose?

4. Do we find many artifacts made from copper, tin, silver and lead in primitive man's early developments? Explain.

5. How did early man record the finding and use of the several types of copper ores?

6. Is it believed that pyrometallurgy was confined to the various phases of working copper? Give the reasons for your answer.

7. Name and describe the four stages of the development of native copper by early man as related to present-day practice.

8. Explain some of the problems confronting primitive man in his attempts to use firing and smelting temperatures as a basis for separating and purifying metals.

9. Was it a rapid step from the mastery of the practical skills of pyrotechny and the discovery of metals and metallurgical processes, to the scientific approach and understanding?

10. When did man finally begin to understand and appreciate the complex chemistry of metallurgy?

11. About when was the Catalan forge first developed? Where was this accomplished and of what significance to us is it today?

12. Of what importance to mining and metallurgy was James Watt's improved steam engine? What preceded the steam engine of Watt and what part did it play in mining? Give dates of both.

13. Who developed of the processes for puddling and rolling of iron? Give details.

14. Describe the details of the development of the Bessemer converter, including reasons for its importance in the field of iron and steel making.

15. Many men contributed in a major way to the art and science of metallurgy during the eighteenth and nineteeth centuries. Give the names of eight such men and explain something of their work.

16. Into what three categories may metallurgy be classified?

17. The engineer who is going to be responsible for the selection of metals for specific applications must be familiar with certain areas of knowledge to be most effective. What are these areas?

References

Braidwood, Robert J., Joseph E. Burke, and Norman H. Nachtrieb, "Ancient Syrian Coppers and Bronzes," *Journal of Chemical Education*, 28 (1951), 87–96.

Coghlan, Herbert and Henry, *Notes on the Prehistoric Metallurgy of Copper and Bronze in the Old World*. Oxford: University Press, 1951.

Forbes, Robert James, *Metallurgy in Antiquity; a Notebook for Archaeologists and Technologists*. Leider: E. J. Brill, 1950.

Job 28: 2–5, *Holy Bible, Old Testament*.

Ley, Willy and Werner Von Braun, *The Exploration of Mars*. New York: Viking Press, 1956.

Peake, Harold, "The Copper Mountain of Magan," *Antiquity* 2 (1928), 42.

Stronach, David, "Excavations at Beycesultan: An Early Metal Hoard from Beycesultan," *Anatolian Studies*, IX (1959) 47–50.

Tylecote, R. H., *Metallurgy in Archaeology; a Prehistory of Metallurgy in the British Isles*. London: E. Arnold, [1962].

Von Braun, Werner, "Conquest of Outer Space," an address to the Cleveland Post, American Ordnance Association, December 8, 1959, Cleveland, Ohio: The Cleveland Post, American Ordinance Association, 1960.

————, Fred L. Whipple and Willy Ley, *Conquest of the Moon*. New York: Viking Press, 1953.

Wertime, Theodore A. "The Coming of the Age of Steel," and "Man's First Encounter with Metallurgy," *Science Publication*, Washington, D.C., U.S. Information Agency, 1964.

Extraction of Metals from Ores

2-1 Sources and Availability of Metals

Locating the sources of metals as they occur in nature and then extracting those metals is not an easy task. It requires the services and knowledge of engineers, metallurgists, geologists, and miners working cooperatively toward a common end. Because of this the engineer must know where metallic ores are abundant as well as the complex problems that are involved in the extraction of the metals from the ores.

As a first consideration of the availability of metals, it is well to study the average composition of the earth's crust—that outer silicious shell of the globe on which man dwells, approximately ten miles in thickness. We have first-hand knowledge of the composition of the rock deposits in this outer shell as shown in Table 1, and it is from this shell or crust that we obtain our metallic ores and other mineral products.

Few metals are found in a pure state in the crust of the earth, but when and where they are found, they are termed *native metals*. Although they, of course, are not chemically pure, they are in the elemental state and not locked up as oxides, sulfides, silicates, etc. As a rule the metals are found in the form of compounds which we call *minerals*. A large deposit of metallic minerals that can be suitably and economically worked to extract the metal from the ores is called an *ore deposit*. Although the minerals that make up an ore are usually numerous and varied in nature, they are classified as values, impurities, and gangue, the *values* being all of the valuable minerals, the *impurities* constituting the elements that are chemically combined with the *values*, and the *gangue* being all those minerals that are mechanically in combination with the *values*. It is necessary to determine the relative amounts of the fractions that are present in an ore deposit, the size or extent of the deposit, and the location of the deposit, before a decision can be reached as to whether or not the extraction of the metals will be economical and sound.

TABLE 2–1. Average Analyses of Igneous Rocks*

Element	Per Cent	Element	Per Cent
Oxygen	46.59	Lead	0.002
Silicon	27.72	Thorium	0.002
Aluminum	8.13	Cobalt	0.001
Iron	5.01	Beryllium	0.001
Calcium	3.63	Molybdenum	0.000, n
Sodium	2.85	Arsenic	0.000, n
Potassium	2.60	Tin	0.000, n
Magnesium	2.09	Antimony	0.000,0 n
Titanium	0.63	Cadmium	0.000,0 n
Manganese	0.10	Mercury	0.000,0 n
Zirconium	0.026	Silver	0.000,00 n
Nickel	0.020	Platinum	0.000,000, n
Vanadium	0.017	Gold	0.000,000, n
Copper	0.010	Iridium	0.000,000,0 n
Uranium	0.008	Palladium	0.000,000,00 n
Tungsten	0.005	Radium	0.000,000,000 n
Zinc	0.004		

The rocks of the earth's crust may be classified as *igneous, metamorphic,* and *sedimentary.* Igneous rocks are those that have been subjected to extremely high heat and solidified from a state of fusion. The metamorphic rocks have, in their formation, been subjected to extreme pressure as well as to heat and, therefore, are more dense and compact (crystalline) in nature. The sedimentary rocks are those that have been formed by or from deposits of sediment, especially of fragments of other rocks transported from their sources and deposited in water, e.g., sandstone and shale; and also at times and under certain conditions, precipitated from solutions, as in the case of gypsum and rock salt. Sedimentary rocks may also be formed from calcarous remains of organisms, as is the case in the formation of limestone deposits.

Despite the fact that there are many methods employed in the extraction of metals from their ores, because of the forms and conditions of the metallic minerals, nonetheless, in general, all metals are subjected to a sequence of operations that are similar. First of all, the *ore* is *mined* in an appropriate manner depending on the nature of the ore, and this is followed by *concentration, purification, reduction to metal,* then a *refining* process, which yields the desired *commercially pure metal or alloy of metal.* The nature of the metal and mineral involved and the cost of the operation will usually dictate and determine the process of purification and refinement. The comparatively low grade copper ores must be extensively concentrated and purified before final refinement thermally or electrolitically, while aluminum ores contain impurities which can be removed with less cost prior to, rather than after, reduction. At the other end of the comparison, iron ore contains only small amounts of impurities that can be profitably removed from the metal during the smelting, and refining operations, therefore, are not, as a rule, necessary except in the case of high purity irons and steels.

---

* F. W. Clarke and H. S. Washington, *Composition of the Earth's Crust.* U. S. Geological Survey Professional Paper 127, 1924.

2-2 Mining

The mining of ores bearing the metals we desire may be accomplished by the *open-pit* or the *under-ground* method, depending on many variables. Often a mining operation will commence with shafts or underground methods, and then in time, when the vein has been developed, it is converted to an open-pit operation as this permits a wider use of machinery and is more economical in many instances.

Before an open-pit mining enterprise can get under way, it is usually necessary to remove any *overburden* (barren rock or soil that covers the desirable ore), and this is often very costly. In those instances where the desirable ore is under water, dredging and pumping operations are used to bring it to the surface for further working.

Shaft or underground mining is used when the ore is either in veins or pockets and also when it is deep in the earth's crust; however, as previously stated, these mines are more costly in their operation. Wherever possible, mining companies turn to open-pit operations, as this type of mining is more economical in many ways, not the least of which is safety.

2-3 Ore Dressing

After the ore is removed from the ore deposits, it is then subjected to milling, mineral dressing or beneficiation, all of these terms referring to *ore dressing*. Almost all of the nonferrous ores and many iron ores are subjected to ore-dressing procedures of one type or another. By the term *ore-dressing* we mean the mechanical separation of the grains of ore minerals from gangue minerals, in order to arrive at a richer concentration that will contain most of the ore minerals, and a discard principally made up of tailings that may or may not be reworked for more of the sought-after metallic minerals.

When the ore comes out of the mines it ranges in size from large boulders to "fines" and before any further work is done it must be crushed and sized by screening. The end particle size will depend on the size of the mineral particles in the form of values and gangue, the degree of purification that must be done, and the particular process or method to be used. The smaller the particle size of the minerals and the more extensive the purification required are the determining factors as to the fineness of the ore in the grinding operations. Many steps are usually required to accomplish the best degree of fineness involving several crushers, grindings, both wet and dry, and final screening in numerous steps.

The difference in properties between the values and gangues—density, wettability, chemical reactivity toward some reagents, magnetic properties, and other factors—dictates the concentration methods to be used.

2-4 Crushing of Ore

There are almost always two or more stages of crushing used in most ore-dressing plants since this has been found to be more economical and more efficient than attempting to accomplish this comminution with only a single stage operation. First the ore is placed in the first stage or primary crushers, such as the Blake-type heavy jaw crushers or gyratory crushers, so that the mine-run ore may be reduced to a size sufficiently small to be accommodated by the next crushing operation performed by *secondary crushers*. Between the jaw-type and the gyratory crushers we find, in general, the former being used more in smaller operations, and the gyratory being used in larger mining facilities. The basic reason for this is the fact that the discharge from the gyratory crusher is of a more uniform nature, since the crusher is designed to prevent the passage of large flat slabs and to permit the passage of uniformly crushed ore, suitable for secondary crushing. The secondary crushers are either of the roll-type or, in some instances, modifications of the jaw or gyratory primary crushers. It is understood that since these secondary crushers are working on finer material than the first, primary stage, there is considerably more power needed for the operation. There is also more wear and tear on the equipment in secondary crushers, so that preventive maintenance becomes a "must" at all times.

2-5   Concentration Methods

Although there are several methods of concentrating minerals, it will be recalled from our previous statement that the method to be used will be determined by the difference in properties between the values and the gangues—the density, wettability, chemical reactivity toward certain reagents, etc. There are many instances of the use of *gravity* separation processes that may range from crude sluicing after panning of the material to the Wilfey tables and classifiers. All of these *gravity* methods have as their main objective the faster settling of the heavier minerals in a stream of water. Sink-or-float methods are also used, and these achieve their purpose by the suspension of the ore in a liquid with an intermediate density between the values and the gangues.

Another type of concentration is *magnetic concentration*, which can obviously only be used when either the values or the gangues have magnetic properties. As a result, this type of concentration is found largely in the processing of iron ores which are either inherently magnetic or which can be made so by a roasting process.

The more popular and more effective method of concentration is the *flotation* method, even though this method requires that the ore must be ground down to a very fine mesh to be adaptable to this method. The *flotation* method of concentration is dependent on the reagents used that become affixed to the important minerals and thereby prevent them from becoming wetted by water. These reagents, called oilers or collectors, assist in the flotation of the finely-ground minerals. Although in most cases ore minerals can be floated if they are of a mesh of from 48 to 65, in modern flotation practice we are able to treat successfully material that is ground as fine as 1500 to 1800 mesh.

The operation of the mechanical flotation cell is quite simple; the ore-water pulp feeds into the unit and is kept agitated and in circulation by an impeller that is mounted at the bottom of the vertical shaft. This rotating impeller generates sufficient vacuum to draw air down the standpipe that surrounds the impeller shaft, the impeller dissipating the air throughout the pulp in the form in tiny bubbles. Those materials that float are carried upward by the bubbles and eventually accumulate in the froth above the pulp on top. Those minerals that do not float stay in the main body of the pulp, as they have no ability to adhere to the bubbles on their upward movement. Automatic scrapers remove the mineral-laden froth containing the concentrate.

After the values have been taken out, the depleted pulp that contains the tailings flows out of the flotation unit. As a rule we find the flotation units operated in series, with the pulp flowing from one cell to another in continuous fashion, some of the flotable minerals being given up at each cell.

2-6   Frothers

We have already mentioned the use of *collectors* or, as they are sometimes called, "oilers," and although there are several of these that are used effectively, we find that the sodium xanthates are most popular as they seem to give a more water-repellent surface to the minerals than the others. In the case of the frothers, whose sole purpose is to cause a thick layer of froth to form on the surface of the bath, we find most common frothers are pine oil and cresylic acid or derivatives of them. Only a small amount of the frothers is needed and they in no way seem to have any effect on the ability of the minerals to float, their sole purpose being to form a stable froth that will hold until the froth containing the minerals can be scraped off into the concentrate launders. From the launders, the concentrates move on to the filters that are either a continuous or an intermittent type, where the moisture is extracted from the concentrates and are then ready to move on to the reduction of the compounds to metals. This can be accomplished by two distinct types of reactions; the pyrometallurgical and the hydrometallurgical processes.

2-7   Pyrometallurgical Processes

As the name indicates, this method involves the use of fire, and in most instances it is accomplished by smelting in large smelting furnaces that resemble the open-hearth furnace of the steel industry. The pyrometallurgical process is used, for example, in the reduction of the compound of the copper sulfide ores, and also for low-grade manganese from the oxidized ores; however, in the case of the oxidized copper ores and manganese ores of higher purity, the hydrometallurgical method of reduction is found to be more suitable.

In the smelting operation used to reduce compounds to the metallic state, two things are accomplished: first, the reduction of the metal, and second, the separation of the metal from the impurities. In order to do this, some additions must be made to produce the desired reducing effect. Other additives are also necessary to bring about the physical separation of the metal from its impurities. For the usual smelting operations, the ore, ore-concentrates, reducing agents, and flux are placed in the smelting furnace. A high degree of heat during smelting must be maintained, either from an outside source or from the combustion of the reducing agents added. In the case of electric-arc furnaces used for smelting, this heat is supplied from the arc. In smelting such metals as vanadium in the reduction of vanadium oxide with aluminum, the exothermic heat evolved by the reaction is sufficient for the smelting operation, and after it has started, it will continue to completion of the process.

Undoubtedly the most important pyrometallurgical piece of equipment is the *blast furnace*, which basically consists of a vertical steel shaft resembling an inverted boiler in which the ore, coke, and flux are charged at the top and then progress downward through the shaft. In this descent the charge of the furnace meets the blast of intensely hot gases that are rising from the bottom, having come in through the tuyeres. Although we think of the blast furnace as being particularly used in the smelting of iron ores, it is also used for the roasted lead ores, tin ores, and high-grade oxidized copper ores. Because of the lower temperature requirements of these non-ferrous materials, the equipment is not as elaborate as in the case of the higher temperature needs of the iron blast furnace, where there are both endothermic and exothermic reactions taking place. (It is of note that the weight of air used in the blast furnace operation is greater than the total weight of all of the ore, flux, and coke used.)

2-8   Hydrometallurgy

As the name implies this is *water metallurgy* and is basically used in large-scale operations, separating the soluble materials from those that are insoluble, by means of a solvent. In other words, this is an extraction process and the solvent used may be either water or some aqueous solution. In some instances, nonaqueous solvents are used in order to remove dissolved metals from the aqueous leaching solutions.

In every hydrometallurgical operation there are two essential steps required: first, leaching to dissolve the metal, and secondly, a precipitation to remove the dissolved metal from the leaching solution. In general, it may be stated that hydrometallurgy is not only comparatively low in cost of operation, since it requires little fuel, except where it is necessary to perform a roasting operation in advance, but is also a method capable of producing sizeable quantities of the metals—a most desirable asset. Hydrometallurgical techniques do not require expensive equipment, the main cost being the chemical reagents required. Even these, in some instances, such as in the leaching of copper, are regenerated by means of precipitation.

Oxidized copper ores, also the ores of gold, oxidized uranium and vanadium, are all treated by hydrometallurgical methods. It is a fact that, despite the many advantages that derive from the use of hydrometallurgical methods, many minerals simply will not permit and respond to leaching methods; consequently, as stated previously, hydrometallurgy is not as effective as pyrometallurgical techniques, and the chances of it ever replacing the latter are very remote, This is due to the fact that it is used, primarily, on low-grade ores and such other materials as ore-concentrates, artificial sulfides or metals (matte), the artificial arsenides and antimonides (speiss) as well as the alloys of some metals. All of this hydrometallurgical processing must be done on a large scale in order to prove profitable.

Obviously, the nonferrous ores, such as copper and zinc, lend themselves to leaching methods and subsequent precipitation treatments.

2-9   Electrometallurgy

Electrometallurgy is essentially the electrorefining of metals after they have been produced by the many techniques of pyro- and hydro-metallurgy previously mentioned. The principle use of electrorefining is to produce an extremely high purity metal from the anodes that have been produced prior to going to the electrorefinery. In this case, the anode, such as copper, is placed in an electrolyte of copper sulphate in large cells, into which are also placed what are known as "starting sheets" of pure copper. An electric current is then passed through the cell which causes a galvanic action, a dissolving of the anode metal, and a redeposition of the same onto the extremely high purity starting sheets. During this process, the impurities that are present in the anodes will either dissolve in the electrolyte or be deposited at the bottom of the cell, and in either case some of these "impurities" are valuable and are extracted profitably, such as gold and silver, in the case of the electrorefining of copper, which cannot be recovered by pyrometallurgical methods.

Electrorefining is based on Faraday's Law which states, essentially, that the quantity of a substance that is liberated at an electrode is directly proportional to the quantity of the current that is flowing through the electrolyte. Also, that the quantities of different substances which are liberated at the cathode by the same quantity of electric current passing through solutions of different electrolytes, are proportional to the equivalent weights of the substances that are liberated.

In addition to copper, nickel, lead, and tin are also refined by the electrorefining method with highly satisfactory results. Electrolytically refined metals are required for highest purity products.

2-10 Hall Process of Refining Aluminum

This process was invented by Charles Martin Hall (1863–1914) and is still the only commercial method used in the production of the metal aluminum. Because aluminum is produced in greater tonnage than any other metal except iron, this is a very important process.

A rectangular steel cell about 8 ft long, 5 ft wide, and 2 ft deep is the *cell* or *pot* that is used in the extraction (or smelting) of aluminum. Fig. 2–1 is a section of this cell with all essential parts identified. Buried in the carbon lining is a collector plate to conduct the current—the entire carbon lining being the cathode of the cell. Carbon anodes are attached to metal rods, as shown, these hanging from the superstructure. The carbon anodes are oxidized and consumed and must be replaced at regular intervals. The *carbon plant* is a large part of any aluminum smelter, as it prepares the anodes, attaches the supporting rods, and prepares the carbon linings of the cells. About 0.7 lb of carbon is consumed for each pound of metal produced. The anodes are made from a mixture of high-grade petroleum coke, tar pitch, and used electrode scrap. These materials are crushed, blended, and shaped in hydraulic presses; the green electrodes are then heated and baked, and the metal supporting rods attached.

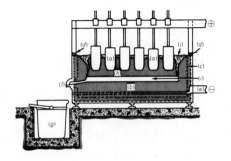

(a) Carbon anodes
(b) Carbon lining (cathode)
(c) Thermal insulation
(d) Electrical insulation
(e) Collector plate
(f) Tap hole
(g) Ladle
(h) Molten electrolyte
(i) Molten aluminum
(j) Frozen crust

Fig. 2-1. Reduction cell for aluminum. (From Bray, *Non-Ferrous Production Metallurgy,* John Wiley & Sons)

The electrolyte is molten *cryolite*, Na_3AlF_6; this is a very stable compound that will dissolve about 20 per cent Al_2O_3. As long as there is sufficient Al_2O_3 in solution, there is little or no liberation of fluorine or other decomposition of the electrolyte. The electrolyte is made from natural cryolite mineral and/or from artificial sodium and aluminum fluorides. The operation is conducted at 900C. A crust of frozen electrolyte forms on top of the cell during the operation.

There is a drop in voltage across a cell of from 6.5 to 7.5 v with a current density of 650 to 750 amp per sq ft of cathode surface, and a cell will draw from 8,000 to 30,000 amp. The power requirement, based on the theoretical decomposition voltage of Al_2O_3, is 5 kwhr per lb of aluminum. Actually, it is between 12 and 13 kwhr per lb of aluminum, this being due to the heavy current density; however, this is essential because sufficient heat must be generated to keep the electrolyte in a molten state.

Aluminum is liberated at the cathode, where it collects in a pool. At the anodes there is a liberation of oxygen which combines with the carbon to form CO and CO_2. Al_2O_3 is stored in hoppers above each cell, and it is usually dropped onto the electrolyte crust by gravity to be warmed prior to adding it to the cell. When replenishment of Al_2O_3 is necessary in the bath, the crust is broken and the powder allowed to fall into the bath.

When the cell is operating normally, the electrolysis proceeds continuously; Al_2O_3 is added, anodes are replaced as needed, and the metal is tapped according to a regular schedule. The aluminum produced from Hall cells is commercially pure aluminum and requires no further refining. Special high-grade aluminum is made by using especially pure Al_2O_3 and carbons.

Because of the considerable power required by the Hall cells, aluminum smelters are located in areas where electric power is abundant and of low cost. This very often is at some distance from the ores and the market.

QUESTIONS

1. Referring to Table 2–1, giving the average analyses of igneous rocks of the earth's crust, what are some of the significant factors that you observe?

2. What are metals called when and where they are found in the pure or native state? Are most of the metals found in nature in the pure state? Explain.

3. Just what is meant by the term "ore deposit"?

4. How are the minerals that make up an ore classified?

5. Into what categories are the rocks of the earth's crust classified?

6. Because of the forms and conditions of metallic minerals as they are found in nature, is it possible to give a basic outline of the handling of the same from ore to the final metal or allory of the metal? If so, make such an outline and if not, state why not.

7. In general, there are two basic processes of mining. What are they?

8. Before open-pit mining can be started, what important operation is usually necessary?

9. When is it more economical to adopt shaft or underground mining in preference to open-pit mining? Which is the more costly method?

10. Describe the following terms as used in the mining industry: "values," "impurities," and "gangues."

11. After the ore is removed from the mine, what is the next step? Describe it.

12. How is the proper method of concentration of the ores determined?

13. Describe the crushing methods used on most ores to prepare them for concentration.

14. When is it possible to use the magnetic concentration method in the processing of ores?

15. Describe fully the flotation method of concentration of ore and explain when and why it is used.

16. What two objectives are accomplished in the pyrometallurgical process of smelting of ore?

17. What is the basis of the hydrometallurgical method of the reduction of oxidized copper ores and manganese ores of higher purity? Why not use the pyrometallurgical process on such ores?

18. Name and describe the two essential steps required in every hydrometallurgical operation.

19. Define what is meant by the term "electrometallurgy" and describe the primary use of this method of refining metals.

20. Upon what important law is electrorefining based? Define the law.

21. An aluminum plant has five series of cells with 60 cells in each series. Each series takes 28,000 amp and 450v. The current efficiency is 88 per cent. Using this information, find:
    a. The annual capacity of the plant, in pounds.
    b. The kilowatt-hours consumed, per pound of metal produced.
    c. The voltage absorbed by the chemical reaction, assuming that one-third of the oxygen from Al_2O_3 goes to CO, two-thirds to CO_2. (Assume room temperature for this problem.)
    d. The rate of heat production in the cell, in calories per minute.
    e. The total volume of gases liberated in each cell every 24 hours.

References

Hayward, Carle Reed, *An Outline of Metallurgical Practice*, 3d, ed., Toronto, New York: D. Van Nostrand Co., Inc.

Metal Statistics. New York: American Metal Market, 1908–1966.

Newton, Joseph, *Extractive Metallurgy*. New York: John Wiley & Sons, 1959.

Parsons, Arthur Barrette, *The Porphyry Coppers in 1956*, 1st ed. New York: American Institute of Mining, Metallurgical and Petroleum Engineers, 1957.

United States Steel Corporation, *The Making, Shaping and Treating of Steel*, edited by Harold E. McGannon, 8th ed. Pittsburgh: U.S.Steel Corporation, 1964.

Van Arsdale, George D. (ed), *Hydrometallurgy of Base Metals*, 1st ed., New York: McGraw-Hill Book Company, 1953.

The Structure of Matter

3-1 Atomic Structure

The smallest and most basic unit of matter is the atom, which is composed of three distinct particles: neutrons, protons, and electrons. Although the nucleus is made up essentially of protons and neutrons, and carries a positive charge, there are known to be still other particles in the nucleus, including what are called *a-particles*—some of these are referred to as the "strange particles" by some atomic scientists. Other particles making up the nucleus of the atom are the *isotopes*, which have the same atomic number as the elements but have different atomic weights. Still another is the *isobar* of elements, which have the same atomic weight but different atomic numbers. The particle known as the *neutron* within the nucleus of the atom has a mass slightly greater than that of the proton, and has no charge, while the proton has a mass of $1.66 \cdot 10^{-24}$ g and carries a charge of $4.80 \cdot 10^{-10}$ esu. It is the number of protons present in the nucleus that determines the charge on the nucleus, and this, in turn, identifies the element involved. The atomic number as shown in the periodic table of elements in Fig. 3–13 also indicates the number of protons in the nucleus.

The energy of the electrons is constant within the orbit as they revolve around the nucleus in their orbits. No more than two electrons can fit into any one orbit, and in order to fit together, they must spin in opposite directions according to the Pauli exclusion principle. Pauli found that no two electrons in an atom can be in exactly the same state as defined by all four quantum numbers, n, l, m_l, and m_s these being a measure of the energy of the electron in the particular state indicated. The quantum number l is a measure of the angular momentum and may therefore have values from 0 to $n - 1$. The principal quantum number is n, this being a measure of the total energy of the orbit. The electron is not at rest when $l = 0$; however an angular momentum is not created by the movement involved. The quantum number represented by m_l is a measure of the component of the angular momentum in a specified direction, and may have any value from $+1$ to -1, as well as a 0 value. The quantum number m_s indicates the electron spin and, depending upon the direction of the spin, may have a value of either $+1/2$ or $-1/2$. (The negatively charged electrons with a mass of $1/1836 \cdot$ the mass of the proton, have a charge of $-4.8 \cdot 10^{-10}$ esu, and these electrons revolve around the nucleus.)

The quantum numbers n, l, and m may, according to the Pauli exclusion principle, be identical for two electronic states of an atom, but the value of one of the two states must have an m_s value of $+1/2$ and the other state must have an m_s value of $-1/2$.

Each orbit in which the electrons move around the nucleus differs from the others by one or more energy quanta, the energy level increasing with the distance of the orbit from the nucleus. The orbits are grouped in shells, and within the shells there are subdivions referred to as energy levels. The shells are also related to energy levels since they are specified by quantum number n. The maximum number of electrons that can be accommodated in each shell may be expressed by the term $2N^2$ where N is the number of the shell. Accordingly, the first shell contains a maximum of two electrons, the second shell a maximum of eight, the third, eighteen, the fourth, thirty-two, etc.

In their movement around the nucleus, the electrons tend to move to the lower energy-level orbits, corresponding, as a rule, to the energy levels in the inner shells. The inner shells are filled before electrons move on to positions in the next shell. In some instances, the upper energy levels of an inner shell in elements may be higher that the lower energy levels of the adjacent shell, in which case the electrons take positions in the outer shell prior to filling the inner shell. Such is the case of the transition elements—iron, vanadium, cobalt, and others. Shells that are completely filled are stable, but unfilled shells are unstable, tending to become filled either by the formation of chemical compounds or by the formation of molecules.

3-2   Crystal Bonds and the Nature of Interatomic Forces

All materials are made up of millions of atoms that are bonded together in a cohesive fashion, and the cohesion between the atoms depends upon the nature of the elements involved. In the liquid state, metals are noncrystalline and the atoms, while free to move about, are said to possess *short-range order*, which will be discussed in a later chapter; briefly, however, it is the greater-than-average tendency for *unlike* atoms of metals above the critical temperature to leave the long-range order and assume an atomic distribution that is more or less random. Although in some cases the atoms will be found to be close enough to each other, and in the proper locations, to form a space lattice; being surrounded by the correct number of other atoms, they do not form such a lattice since each atom is moving freely, so that the bonds between the atoms become broken easily and then are reformed. Such random distribution is characteristic of metals in the liquid state. When some liquids are cooled, they become increasingly viscous and ultimately become firm and rigid as glass. In such cases of undercooled liquids, since the random distribution of atoms still persists just as it did in the liquid state, undercooling results in what are called *amorphous* substances, as differentiated from true solids. Amorphous materials, while *rigid* in form, may therefore be identified as being without a regular, ordered form, since their atoms are arranged randomly. The atoms of a metal arrange themselves in a three-dimensional distinct pattern in space, referred to as a *space lattice,* but more properly identified as a *crystal structure.* All true solids possess a crystal structure; however, there is a considerable difference in the properties of metals within the solid state, due substantially to the way in which the atoms are bound to one another in the solid state.

Although it is true that atoms do make up the crystals, it is easier and more convenient to consider a set of imaginary points which has a fixed arrangement and relation in space to the atoms of the crystal, and may therefore be regarded as a skeleton or framework on which the actual crystal is constructed. If space may be assumed to be divided by three sets of planes, with each plane parallel and spaced equally in each set, the result will be a set of cells, each one identical to its neighbors in size, shape, and orientation. Each of the cells is a parallelepiped, having its opposite faces parallel and each face being a parallelogram. The planes in space will intersect each other in a set of lines, and these lines in turn intersect in the set of points, as stated before. The construction of a set of points in the aforenamed manner constitutes what is known as a *point lattice;* this is essentially *an array of points in space arranged so that each point when viewed in any particular direction from one lattice point, would have the exact same appearance when viewed in the same direction from any other point in the lattice.*

Inasmuch as all of the cells of such a lattice are identical, any one may be selected and referred to as a *unit cell.* Such a point lattice is shown in Fig. 3–9, and any one of the cells shown in this point lattice may be considered as a *unit cell.*

As was stated previously, the wide difference in the properties of metals within the solid state is due largely to the way in which the atoms are bound to one another in the solid state. There are four types of binding: metallic, Van der Waals forces, ionic, and covalent, each of which is shown in Fig. 3–2.

Metallic bonding is the principal attractive force that holds the atoms of a metal together. This results when each atom in the metal shares its valence electrons to form an electron cloud that permeates the solid metal. The other three types of binding will be discussed; however, it is important to note that one of the types of binding predominates in a particular instance and the others are, in such instances, of lesser importance.

In the metallic bond there is complete freedom of movement by the outer shell electrons when an aggregate of atoms become associated with each other. There are not enough electrons in each atom to fill the outer shell entirely, so that the shared electrons can move freely from one atom to another. However, there is interference in such movement of the electrons because of collisions of electrons with one another in their rapid movement, collisions with vibrating ions, and defects that may be present in the crystal. However, the electrical and thermal conductivity of metals is largely accounted for by this relatively free movement of electrons, while the collisions which interfere with the flow of electrons explain the resistivity in metals.

With the exception of helium, the inert gases are formed when a stable quantum shell becomes completely filled with electrons, thus accounting for the fact that eight electrons in the outer shell insure the existence of a stable condition. As was stated in 3–1, the most stable state of any atom is that in which its energy is a very minimum, and that when an atom is in an excited state, it is in a higher energy state. It is also important to recall that when each of the quantum shells is filled to its stable configuration, an unusually stable element is obtained. Provisional stability exists when the third and higher shells contain eight electrons each.

Atoms of the nature of the inert gases are not affected by the presence of other atoms either of the same type or of some other type. In other words, they are entirely chemically inert. Atoms of the inert gases do not bond together easily and exist in the liquid and solid states (except helium which does not appear in the solid state), even though they do not combine with other elements. Cohesion between the atoms is entirely dependent upon the character of the particular elements involved. The cohesion that exists in the case of inert gases is due to what are known as *Van der Waal's forces (polarization)*, these being the forces that attract the atoms, resulting from the harmonized electronic motion of two atoms. In the inert gases such as argon, neon, helium, etc., Van der Waal's forces are the only attractive forces balancing the repulsive forces that are caused by the electrostatic attraction of the electrons.

Because of the difference in character in the electronic state, the bond formed between atoms other than those found in inert gases is of a different type. For example, in many materials the bond is electrovalent in character and is known as an *ionic bond*, such as the bond found in the compound NaCl, where valence electron of the sodium atom enters the single 2_p state of the chlorine atom. Such a bond is also said to be *polar* where the ions of a crystalline solid are held together by coulombic forces. In the case just stated, when sodium chloride is formed, one valence electron of the sodium atom is given up to the chlorine atom, so that the electronic configuration of the sodium ion becomes the same as that of a neon atom with a positive charge. These two inert gas-like ions with positive and negative charges are held together by coulombic forces.

As shown in Fig. 3–1, the space lattice of sodium chloride consists of two face-centered cubic sublattices with each ion surrounded by six nearest neighbors of the same charge. In this space lattice, each unit cell consists of four sodium ions and four chlorine ions.

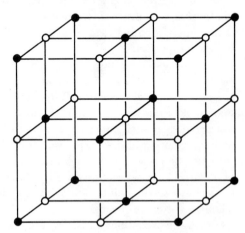

Fig. 3-1. *Ionic arrangement in sodium chloride. Open circles represent chlorine anions and filled circles represent sodium cations.*

Numbers of atoms that have three or more valence electrons are bound in their crystal structures by *covalent or homopolar bonds* resulting from forces arising from the sharing of electrons. According to the determinations of G. N. Lewis, as set out in his "Valence and the Structure of Atoms and Molecules," in some elements and compounds the electrons in the outermost shells of the atoms are shared in order to build up stable shells containing a maximum of 2, 8, 18 and 32 electrons. These are designated as the K, L, M, and N shells, respectively, each of them being successively farther away from the nucleus. For example, each chlorine atom has seven electrons in the M-shell and requires one more to complete a stable outer shell with an even number of electrons. When two free atoms are in close proximity, each supplies the other with one electron to establish the stable M-shell. Thus, each atom in a molecule of chlorine, Cl_2, has six unshared and two shared electrons in the M-shell. In order to complete the requirement of eight electrons needed for atomic stability, electrons must be shared with $8 - N$ (8 minus N) neighboring atoms, where N represents the number of valence electrons in the particular element under consideration. A classical example of covalent (homopolar) crystal binding is the diamond-cubic structure shown in Fig. 3–3, where each carbon atom has four nearest neighbors, thereby complying with the $8 - N$ requirement applied to its four valence electrons.

A similar type of covalent bonding exists in silica, as shown in Fig. 3–4 where a silicon atom is surrounded by four oxygen atoms situated at the corners of a tetrahedron. Each oxygen atom shares one of its two electrons with the silicon atom and so the resulting tetrahedron has four negative charges. However, in an assembly of these tetrahedra, as shown in Fig. 3–5, the corners and not the edges are shared. That is, each silicon atom has four oxygen neighbors and each oxygen atom has two silicon neighbors, so the resulting assembly of Si-O network in silica can be represented by the stoichiometric formula SiO_2. The four types of binding in solid materials explained in this section of the chapter—metallic, van der Waals' (polarization), ionic and covalent (homopolar) are shown graphically in Fig. 3–2 with the significant characteristics of each identified.

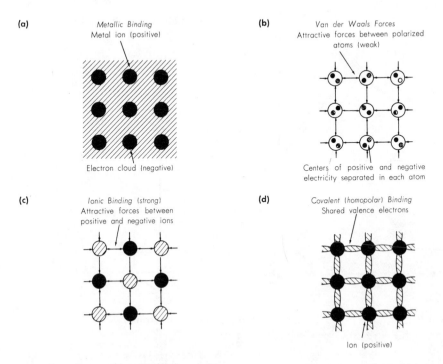

Fig. 3-2. *The four types of binding of atoms in solids: (a) metallic binding; (b) van der Waals' forces; (c) ionic; (electrovalent); (d) covalent (homopolar) binding.*

Shown in Fig. 3–6 is another of the covalent type binding, this being of the crystal structure of the arsenic type. In this case, a given atom is observed to share its valence electrons with three of its nearest neighbors, as shown.

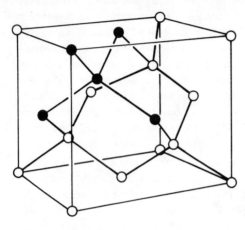

Fig. 3-3. *Covalent crystal binding in the case of diamond-cubic structure with each carbon atom having four nearest neighbors, thereby fulfilling the 8—N rule as it applies to its four valence electrons. Metals of the covalent type of binding are usually low in electrical conductivity and have a high degree of hardness.*

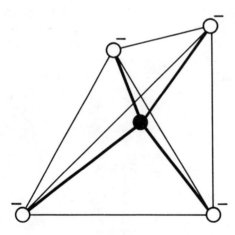

Fig. 3-4. *Tetrahedral distribution of oxygen atoms, indicated by open circles around silicon atoms (dark circle) in silica.*

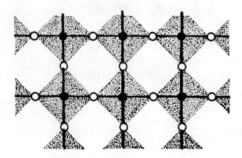

Fig. 3-5. *Two-dimensional illustration of an assembly of tetrahedra; the corners and not the edges are shared. That is, each silicon atom has four oxygen neighbors, and each oxygen atom has two silicon neighbors. The resulting assembly of this Si-O network in silica can be represented by the stoichiometric formula SiO_2.*

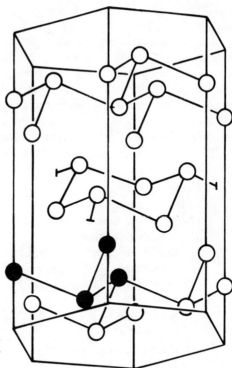

Fig. 3-6. *Arsenic-type crystal structure, this being another of the covalent type solids with covalent or homopolar binding.*

3-3   Space Lattices and Crystal Structure

All elements crystallize according to a particular symmetrical pattern or arrangement of atoms which is repeated at specific and regular intervals to form a crystal. An idealized representation of such a regular arrangement of atoms in the solid state is termed the *space lattice*. Those elements which have the characteristic of forming a three-dimensional, orderly arrangement of the atoms in crystal formation may be considered as having a latticework of imaginary lines between the atoms; such arrangement is the space lattice for the element under consideration. The metallic space lattices are, in general, highly symmetrical in character, although it is true that those of manganese, uranium, tin, plutonium, and antimony are rather complex and less symmetrical. Such complex lattices are also found in some of the alloys, as will be discussed later in the text. As illustrated in Fig. 3–7 (12), in the case of the simple cubic space lattice, a single atom occupies each corner of each unit cube with each of the atoms in the eight corners being shared by seven other unit cubes. Therefore, since only one-eighth of each corner atom can be considered as belonging (or effective) to any specific unit cell, it follows that each simple unit cube contains only *one effective atom*. The smallest repetitive geometric prism which possesses the complete symmetry of the entire crystal is called a *unit cell*. By definition, each unit cell in a space lattice is identical in shape and orientation with every other unit cell. Space lattices are characteristic of all crystalline materials. The type and dimensions of most of the unit cells of the elements have been determined by X-ray diffraction and are recorded in the *Metals Handbook* of American Society for Metals, as well as in various books on X-ray diffraction.

3-4 Types of Space Lattices

A space lattice is formed when there is a distribution of lattice points in three dimensions with every lattice point having identical surroundings. There are numbers of possible ways in which the lattice points may arrange themselves in a manner that will satisfy the definition of a space lattice; however there are fourteen arrangements that are more commonly recognized, as shown in Fig. 3–7. These fourteen fall into seven crystal systems, each of which has certain characteristics, such as equality of angles, lengths of coordinate axes, etc.

The fourteen types of space lattices, illustrated by a unit cell of each in Fig. 3–7, may be described as follows:

1. Triclinic, simple
2. Monoclinic, simple
3. Monoclinic, base-centered
4. Orthorhombic, simple
5. Orthorhombic, base-centered
6. Orthorhombic, body-centered
7. Orthorhombic, face-centered
8. Hexagonal
9. Rhombohedral
10. Tetragonal, simple
11. Tetragonal, body-centered
12. Cubic, simple
13. Cubic, body-centered
14. Cubic, face-centered

(Courtesy of *Metals Handbook*, American Society for Metals.)

It is important to note that the most useful pure metals are found to crystallize in one of three distinctly different types of space lattice, as follows:

1. Cubic System: three equal axes, mutually perpendicular.
2. Tetragonal System: two equal axes perpendicular to each other and to a third (unequal) axis.
3. Hexagonal System: two equal axes inclined at an angle of 120° and a third (unequal) axis perpendicular to their plane.

The base length of these lattices is known as the *lattice parameter* and is approximately four Angstrom units (on the order of $1.6 \cdot 10^{-8}$ inch). The total size of a particular space lattice depends upon the metal in question, and also upon its temperature at the time under consideration.

Where the atomic radii of the atoms are known, the exact dimensions of the crystal lattice may be calculated by applying the Pythagorean theorem. By way of example, the radius of an aluminum atom is 1.428 Å, and aluminum has a face-centered cubic structure. The base length (lattice parameter) of the aluminum atom may be determined by the equation:

$$(4r)^2 = a^2 + a^2$$

where a is the lattice constant which is related to the atomic radius. Then

$$a = \frac{4r}{\sqrt{2}} \quad \text{(face-centered cubic)}$$

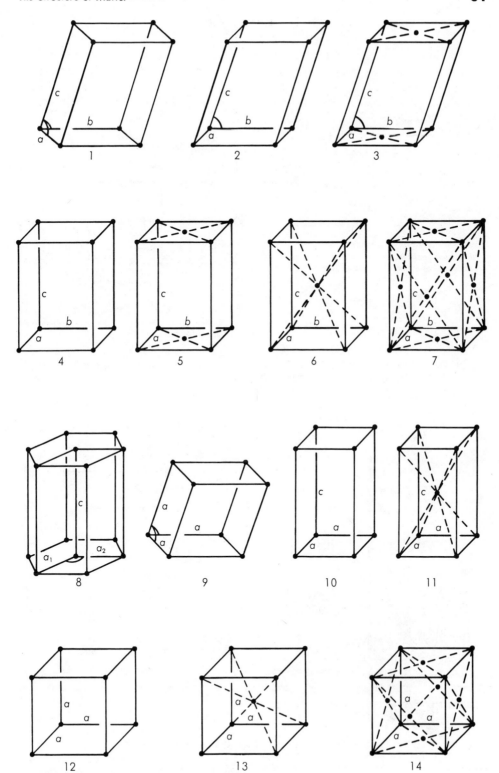

Fig. 3-7. *Fourteen space lattices illustrated by a unit cell of each.*

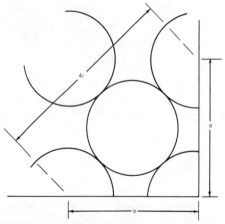

Fig. 3-8.   *The (100) plane of a face-centered cubic unit cell such as aluminum, copper, etc.; a, the lattice constant is calculated as shown in equations on p. 30.*

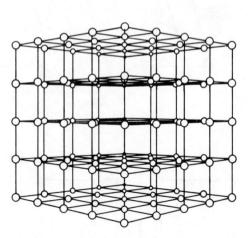

Fig. 3-9.   *One view of a portion of a simple cubic lattice. The (110) planes are the prominent vertical planes, as shown here.*

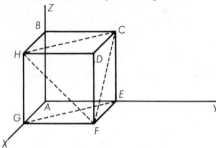

Fig. 3-8A.   *Diagram of cubic crystal imposed on the X, Y, Z axes.*

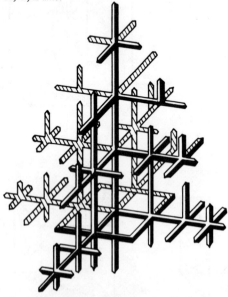

Fig. 3-10.   *A graphic description of an idealized crystal formed during the solidification of the cubic systems. Due to the fact that it resembles a tree, the crystal formation in the initial stages is called a* dendrite, *the word of Greek derivation, meaning bush or tree.*

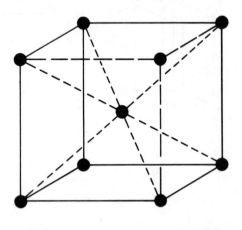

Fig. 3-11.   *The unit cell of a body-centered cubic metal in which are seen the 8 atoms at the corners, each one of which is shared with other adjacent atoms so that these 8 atoms are the equivalent of only one atom, which, with the atom at the center of the cell, makes this unit cell have 2 effective atoms in all.*

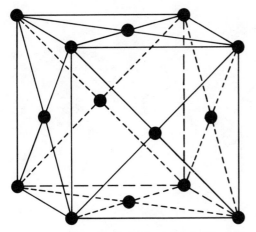

Fig. 3-12.   *The unit cell of a face-centered cubic metal which has 8 atoms at the corners, all of them shared with adjacent atoms, thereby having the effect of 1 atom which, with the 6 atoms at the center of each face, each of which is also shared, gives them the equivalent of 3 atoms, resulting in a total of 4 atoms in the face-centered cubic unit cell.*

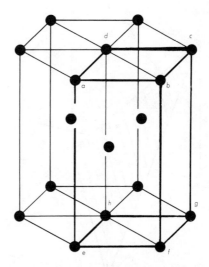

Fig. 3-13.   *The unit cell of the hexagonal close-packed lattice contains only one-third of the hexagon shown here, represented by lines connecting the points a, b, c, d and e, f, g, and h. Accordingly, the hexagonal close-packed unit cell has 8 atoms at the corners as shown, all of which are shared, thereby having the effect of a single atom, and the single atom shown at the center of the cell makes a total of 2 atoms in the unit cell.*

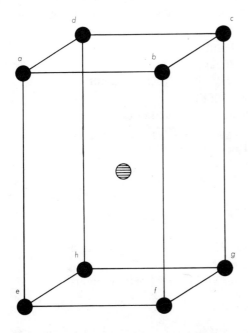

Fig. 3-14.   *The unit cell of the body-centered tetragonal space lattice with two equal and one unequal axes at right angles to one another. This is one of the six more common space lattices found in metals and alloys. (The distance from one atom to the next measured along one of the axes used in describing the crystal structure is referred to as the* lattice constant *or* lattice parameter. *This is true for all space lattices.)*

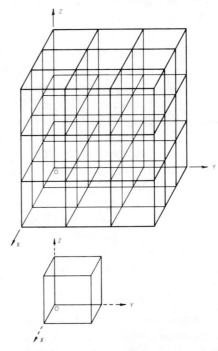

Fig. 3-15.   *Cubic space lattice and unit cell. This kind of lattice may be thought of as being formed by the intersection of three sets of equally spaced and mutually perpendicular sets of planes. The points where three planes intersect, as well as the three points where three lines intersect, are called lattice points.*

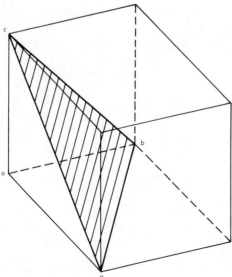

Fig. 3-16. *Cubic model with very important plane in face-centered cubic metals. Here the plane abc may well be imagined to pass through corners of a cubic model as here illustrated from back to front in the drawing.*

The lattice constant *a* between the adjacent corners of the unit cell of aluminum is found to be 4.035 Angstroms, which is the lattice parameter for the aluminum atom (1 Å $= 10^{-8}$ cm).

Depending upon the temperature, some metals can exist in several lattice forms. For example, of the commercially important metals, iron, cobalt, manganese, tin, chromium, and titanium are all found to exist in more than one lattice arrangement, as follows:

Iron   —Body-centered cubic *a* (below 1670F)
                Face-centered cubic γ (1670 to 2552F)
                Body-centered cubic δ (2552 to 2795F)   (melting point)

Cobalt   —Close-packed hexagonal (below 788F)
                Face-centered cubic (788 to 2723F)   (melting point)

Manganese—Cubic, 58 atoms per unit cell *a* (below 1252F)
                Cubic, 20 atoms per unit cell β (1252 to 2012F)
                Tetragonal γ (2012F to 2080F)
                Tetragonal δ (2080F to 2273F)   (melting point)

Tin   —Cubic *a* (gray below 55.8F)
                Tetragonal β (white from 55.8F to 450F)   (melting point)

Chromium —Close-packed hexagonal β (below 68F)
                Body-centered cubic α (68F to 3270F $\pm$ 90F)   (melting point)

Titanium —Close-packed hexagonal α (below 1615F)
                Body-centered cubic β (1615F to 3140F)   (melting point)

Allotropy

When metals such as those listed above exist in more than one lattice form, they are said to exhibit *allotropy*. A good example of allotropy is carbon, which occurs in the form of the diamond, graphite, lampblack, and charcoal. When no change in composition is involved, crystal changes are called *allotropic transformations*. The most widely used metal which undergoes allotropic transformations is iron, changing, as it does, from body-centered cubic lattice at room temperature up to

1670°F, then transforming to face-centered cubic; then at 2552°F the iron lattice reverses itself to the body-centered cubic lattice.

In general, changes in crystal form are accompanied by substantial changes in crystal properties, these changes being utilized by industry, as will be discussed in a later chapter on heat treatment.

When a metal crystallizes in two or more different forms of lattice, it is said to be polymorphic (in more than one form). Those metals which occur in two or more forms, characterized by either different crystal structures, as previously discussed, or by marked differences in energy content, or both, are said to be polymorphic (allotropic).

3-5 Miller Indices

Since it is essential to devise a method for describing the faces of a crystal or the atomic planes within a crystal or space lattice, and in a quantitative way, sets of numbers that identify given planes are used, these sets of numbers being known as *Miller indices* of the plane. These special planes and directions within the crystal of metals serve an important function in the study of hardening reactions, plastic deformation, and other areas of the behavior of metals under various conditions. These numbers are also useful in X ray and other investigations of metals. Shown in Fig.3–17 is an illustration of the method for determining the Miller indices of a given plane. The procedure for arriving at indices shown in this figure are as follows:

1. After designating the three crystal axes, x, y, and z, determine the intercepts of the plane in question on these axes, expressing the same in terms of the number of axial lengths of said intercepts from the origin. $X/2$ $Y/3$ $Z/1$ Axis/intercepts.

2. Establish the reciprocals of these numbers: $1/2$, $1/3$, $1/1$.

3. Reduce these reciprocals to the smallest integers that are in the same ratio:

$$\frac{1}{2} = \frac{3}{6}, \quad \frac{1}{3} = \frac{2}{6} \quad \text{and} \quad \frac{1}{1} = \frac{6}{6}$$

(or 326)

From this procedure it may be observed that the position of the plane of atoms shown is described by the Miller indices 3, 2, 6, (326).

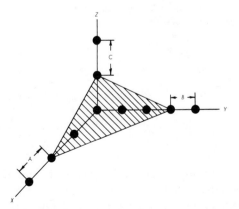

Fig. 3-17. *Diagram showing the intercepts of a plane of atoms on the three crystal axes. Only a very few of the infinite number of atoms constituting the space lattice are shown, and these are indicated along the three crystal axes as shown.*

A few of the simpler crystal planes in cubic crystals are illustrated in Fig. 3–18, including not only the cubic but also the octahedral and dodecahedral, as noted.

It should be noted that a set of these Miller indices as shown in Fig. 3–18 not only describes a single crystal plane but also an entire family of planes that are parallel to the plane used in the procedure for determining the correct set of indices. Another plane parallel to the (326) plane used in the illustration would be one with intercepts 4, 6, and 2, and this plane would also have intercepts (326) the same as the first used.

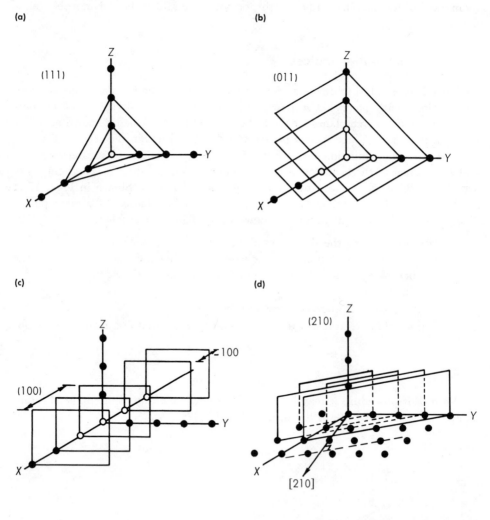

Fig. 3-18. *Some of the simpler crystal planes in cubic crystals. Additional ways of designating these planes are (a) octahedral, (b) dodecahedral, and (c) cubic. The relation of the [210] direction to the (210) plane is shown in (d) above.*

Referring to Fig. 3–8A illustrating a cube (crystal) imposed onto the X, Y, and Z axes, it is observed that the plane *CDFE* intersects the X axis at infinity (∞), since it is parallel to it, and also that this same plane intersects the Y axis at 1 unit from the origin (A). This *CDFE* plane similarly intersects the Z plane at infinity (∞), being parallel to that axis. Therefore, the Miller indices of this *CDFE* plane are:

$$\text{For the } X \text{ axis} = \frac{1}{\infty} = 0$$

$$\text{For the } Y \text{ axis} = \frac{1}{1} = 1$$

$$\text{For the } Z \text{ axis} = \frac{1}{\infty} = 0$$

The Miller indices for this *CDFE* plane are therefore determined to be (010). In like manner, the Miller indices for the *HDFG* plane are found to be (100), and for the *HGEC* diagonal plane they are (110).

Since the atom designated as the "origin," for purposes of determining the Miller indices, could be any atom, it is apparent that there is actually no physical difference between planes such as (100) and the similar plane on the other side of the point of origin. Consequently, the plane on the opposite side of the point of origin is designated as the negative plane, and it is indicated as ($\bar{1}$00). The numbers are the same, but the negative sign is placed over the first digit of designation.

In using the Miller indices, a specific plane is enclosed by parentheses (100) while a family of planes of like form are shown in curved brackets {100}, which designation simply means (100), (010), (001), ($\bar{1}$00), ($0\bar{1}0$), and ($00\bar{1}$). A certain direction or line in a crystal is designated by a square bracket [100]. The indices of a certain direction are the smallest integers that are proportional to the coordinate differences in terms of parameters between equivalent points that lie on a crystal line. For this reason, reciprocals are not used in the determination of the indices of a direction of a plane. A complete set of equivalent directions (similar forms) is designated by carets such as ⟨100⟩, which represents [100], [010], [001], [$\bar{1}$00], [$0\bar{1}0$], and [$00\bar{1}$]. The cubic system is the only one in which each direction is perpendicular to a plane of the same indices.

3-6 Analysis of Crystals by Means of X-ray Diffraction

Because few crystals are found formed under conditions permitting the full development of the faces, perfectly formed crystals, particularly in metals, cannot be obtained. Therefore, it is necessary and essential to utilize X rays or other very short wavelength rays, such as beams of electrons or neutrons (used for special purposes), for studying the structure of crystals, particularly their innner structure. Inasmuch as the atomic spacings in crystals are only a few Angstroms, it is understandable that X rays play an important part in the study and research of crystal structures.

When certain geometric conditions are satisfied, as expressed either by Bragg's Law or alternately by Laue's equations, a beam of X rays is diffracted from a crystal. (It should be recognized that the intensity of the diffracted beam is not given in Bragg's Law.) By using these relationships, the positions of the diffracted beams forming the diffraction pattern can be studied and analyzed to give the size, shape and orientation of the unit cell of the crystal. In order to determine the way in which the atoms are arranged within the unit cell, it is necessary to analyze the intensities of the reflected X-ray beams. The most accepted method of doing this is by using the structure-factor equation, which bears a relationship between the position of each atom and the intensities of all reflections.

Certain correction factors are often necessary in the actual determination of crystal structure by X rays, these being applied in the reading of the film in order to arrive at the true intensities. Tables of correction factors will be found in various X-ray handbooks, including the textbook, *Elements of X-ray Diffraction*, by B. D. Cullity.

When an X-ray beam passes over an atom, the electric field of the beam acts upon each electron of the atom, thereby accelerating each electron with a resulting motion of vibration. An electric charge undergoing an oscillation of this nature becomes the source of a new set of electro-magnetic waves similar to the alternating

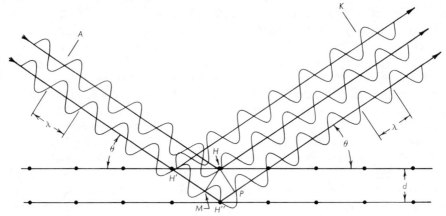

Fig. 3-19. *Parallel planes of atoms from which an X-ray wave is diffracted revealing that the waves may be reflected from an atom at* H *or* H' *or remain in phase as* K. *(Courtesy of Addison-Wesley Publishing Co.)*

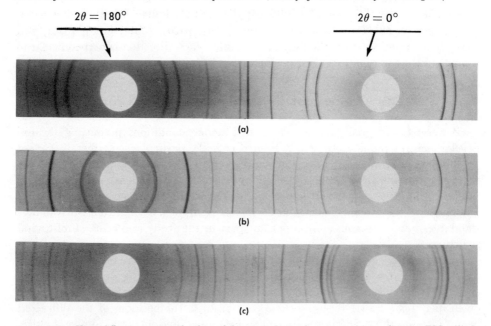

Fig. 3-19A. *X-ray diffraction patterns for three of the principal crystal structures.* (a) *is of copper, FCC;* (b) *is of tungsten, BCC;* (c) *is of zinc, HCP. The lattice constants and the crystal structures may be calculated from patterns such as those shown above. Further reading in B. D. Cullity's* Elements of X-ray Diffraction *is recommended. (Courtesy of Addison-Wesley Publishing Co.)*

electric current in the antenna of a radio transmitter sending out electromagnetic waves of radio frequency in the case of coherent scattering. Such waves radiating from the vibrating electrons have the same frequency and wavelength as the incident beam that originated the vibration. Each electron involved, in effect, subtracts a small amount of energy from the impinging beam and scatters it in all directions. These various scattered waves from the individual electrons of an atom combine and may be looked upon as a single set of radiating waves which, in most instances, can be considered as originating from a single point. The difference in the nature of the scattering by a number of electrons assembled at a single point, and the same number of electrons distributed in a cloud around the nucleus of an atom, is sufficiently different so that an analysis of the scattering reveals the dimensions of the cloud and the distribution of the electrons within it.

An X-ray tube operates on the principle that high-speed electrons striking the target metal in an X-ray tube knock out some of the electrons from the inner levels. X rays typical of the target metal are then generated when electrons from outer levels fall into positions that are vacant in the inner levels. X-ray wavelengths are about equal to the distance separating the atoms in a solid, so diffraction effects are produced when a beam of X rays strikes a crystalline material. The X rays directed at such a crystalline material are diffracted by the planes of atoms or ions within the crystal.

Reference to Fig. 3–19 shows that the diffraction angle depends upon the wavelength of the X rays and the distance between adjacent planes. Considering the parallel planes of atoms in Fig. 3–19 from which a wave is diffracted, it is observed that the waves may be "reflected" from an atom at H or H', or remain in phase at K. X rays, however, are not only reflected from the surface plane, but also from subsurface planes, and if these reflections are to remain in phase, the distance $MH''P$ must equal one or more integral wavelengths of the rays. Therefore, it follows that:

$$n\lambda = 2d \sin \theta$$

where λ is the wavelength of the X ray, d is the interplanar spacing and θ is the angle of incidence. The value n so obtained is known as the *order* and indicates the number of waves which occur in the distance $MH''P$. In general, the higher *order* reflections are weaker reflections. This equation is Bragg's law of reflection from crystal planes. (Bragg's law gives the *conditions* for diffraction to occur, but does not give the *intensity* of the diffracted beam.) The order of reflection n may be 1, 2, 3, 4, etc.; the interplanar spacing of a given (*hkl*) plane may be, for example, for plane (100) or (110) or (210), etc.

The unit-cell parameter of most crystals is on the order of 4.0 Å, and the d values will be equal to or less than this value. The maximum value of $\sin \theta$ is unity; therefore, if diffraction is to occur, λ must be 8.0 Å or less if just the first order of diffraction from the (100) planes is to be obtained.

It is significant to note that the direction of the diffracted beam is governed entirely by the geometry of the space lattice and is independent of the kind of atoms occupying positions on or within the unit cell. The size and shape of the unit cell determines where the diffracted beam will appear, since the d in the Bragg equation is a function of the lattice parameters of the cell under investigation. For example, in the simple cubic cell the distance between (100) planes is a, the lattice parameter of the cell. The distance between parallel (110) planes passing through lattice points is $a/\sqrt{2}$: for (111) planes, $a/\sqrt{3}$. In general, it may be said that the distance between parallel planes of indices (hkl) in terms of the parameter a for the cubic system is as follows:

$$d^2 = \frac{a^2}{h^2 + k^2 + l^2}$$

Similar relationships may be derived in which d can be related to the lattice parameters for each of the crystal systems, as follows:

TABLE 3–1. Interplanar Spacing of Simple Lattices*

Cubic:
$$\frac{1}{d^2} = \frac{h^2 + k^2 + l^2}{a^2}$$

Tetragonal:
$$\frac{1}{d^2} = \frac{h^2 + k^2}{a^2} + \frac{l^2}{c^2}$$

Hexagonal:
$$\frac{1}{d^2} = \frac{4}{3}\left(\frac{h^2 + hk + k^2}{a^2}\right) + \frac{l^2}{c^2}$$

Rhombohedral:
$$\frac{1}{d^2} = \frac{(h^2 + k^2 + l^2)\sin^2\alpha + 2(hk + kl + hl)(\cos^2\alpha - \cos\alpha)}{a^2(1 - 3\cos^2\alpha + 2\cos^3\alpha)}$$

Orthorhombic:
$$\frac{1}{d^2} = \frac{h^2}{a^2} + \frac{k^2}{b^2} + \frac{l^2}{c^2}$$

Monoclinic:
$$\frac{1}{d^2} = \frac{1}{\sin^2\beta}\left(\frac{h^2}{a^2} + \frac{k^2 \sin^2\beta}{b^2} + \frac{l^2}{c^2} - \frac{2hl\cos\beta}{ac}\right)$$

Triclinic:
$$\frac{1}{d^2} = \frac{1}{V^2}(S_{11}h^2 + S_{22}k^2 + S_{33}l^2 + 2S_{12}hk + 2S_{23}kl + 2S_{13}hl)$$

* Used by permission of Addison-Wesley Publishing Co., Inc.

As an example of the importance and use of X-ray diffraction in the determination of interplanar spacings present in the crystals under investigation, suppose the X-ray diffraction analysis of a crystal is made with X rays having a wavelength of 0.58 Å. Also, that reflections are observed at angles of (a) 6.45°, (b) 9.15°, and (c) 13.0°. To find the interplanary spacings present in the crystal, Bragg's equation is used as follows:

$$n\lambda = 2d\sin\theta ,$$

$$\frac{d}{n} = \frac{\lambda}{2\sin\theta}$$

Then

(a) $= \dfrac{0.58}{2(\sin 6.45°)} = 2.575\,\text{Å} ,$

(b) $= \dfrac{0.58}{2(\sin 9.15°)} = 1.82\,\text{Å} ,$

(c) $= \dfrac{0.58}{2(\sin 13.0°)} = 1.29\,\text{Å} .$

It will be observed in (a) that d/n is twice the value of d/n in (c); therefore, angles 6.45° and 13.0° must represent different orders of the same interplanar spacing. In this case n could equal 1 in (a) and 2 in (c) and d would therefore be 2.58 Å. Inasmuch as no other reflections are stated, it can be assumed that n equals 1 in (b). As a result of this, it will be observed that there is a second d with a value 1.82 Å.

3-7 Periodic Table of the Elements

In Fig. 3–20 is a listing of the elements, originally constructed by chemists, based on the similarity of the chemical behavior of certain groups of elements. In the discussion of the states of the electrons in the elements, it was emphasized that elements having similar electronic states have other properties that are also similar. Recognizing the periodicity of the elements, Dmitri Mendelyeev, a Russian chemist, arranged them into a periodic table. He did this before the turn of the present century, and since then, as a result of studies of atomic structural behavior, the gaps and anomalous behavior of certain elements in the periodic table have been reconciled. A considerable amount of information on the behavior of the elements can be obtained from their location in the periodic table.

A study of the periodic table of the elements in Fig. 3–20 will reveal that the elements are arranged into *groups* in the vertical rows and into periods in the horizontal rows. Furthermore, the elements are found to be arranged in the order of increasing atomic number from left to right in each of the periods. Of the seven periods, one period contains hydrogen and helium, two short periods are present with eight elements in each, two long periods contain 18 elements each, and a very long period contains 32 elements. There is an incomplete period containing elements with atomic numbers 87 through 101. Plotting certain properties of the elements in the table as a function of their atomic numbers, reveals that there is a systematic change and a definite periodicity of the elements taking place. The atomic numbers are shown in the upper right next to the element, and the atomic weight of the element is shown just below the chemical symbol for the element.

Those elements with atomic numbers 21 through 28 in the first long period, and those with atomic numbers 39 thorugh 46, are known as the transition elements, since they have inner shells that are not filled in the regular order as is found in the other elements. The elements with atomic numbers 57 through 71 are designated the *rare earth metals* or lanthanons, while those with atomic numbers 90 through 98 are identified as the actinons.

Undoubtedly the most striking feature of the periodic table is the repeated occurrence of the noble gases helium, neon, argon, krypton, and others. The atomic number of these gases is given by the series $Z = 2(1^2 + 2^2 + 2^2 + 3^2 + 3^2 + 4^2 \ldots .)$. The electronic configuration, except for helium, is $ns^2\ np^6$, where n is the principal quantum number. A regularity of this type would seem to indicate a symmetrical arrangement of electrons about the nucleus. The known properties of the noble gases, including their low freezing points, lack of chemical reactivity, etc., would indicate that they are unique, in that their weak force fields are associated with the symmetrical arrangement of their electrons.

In the left and central part of the periodic table are found the *metals* while the *nonmetals* are found in the right portion of the table. Beginning with group 3 and and passing diagonally down to the right through boron, silicon, germanium, arsenic, antimony, tellurium and polonium, there is a transition from metals to nonmetals; those elements having properties between the two are known as metalloids.

The periodic table is frequently used in research and development investigations to determine what, if any, elements can be substituted for other elements to give the same or closely similar properties in the development of alloys. For example, sulfur, which has been known to be important in the improvement of the machinability of steel for many years, can be replaced by selenium and tellurium to an advantage in stainless steels and nonferrous alloys. In like manner, tungsten can be replaced by molybdenum to provide good resistance to softening of steels at elevated temperatures and, to a lesser degree of effectiveness, by chromium in certain

Fig. 3-20. Periodic Table of the Elements

	0	I	II	III	IV	V	VI	VII	VIII
		1 H 1.0080							2 He 4.003
		3 Li 6.940	4 Be 9.013	5 B 10.82	6 C 12.01	7 N 14.008	8 O 16.00	9 F 19.00	10 Ne 20.183
		11 Na 22.991	12 Mg 24.32	13 Al 26.98	14 Si 28.09	15 P 30.975	16 S 32.066	17 Cl 35.457	18 A 39.994

0	I a	II a	III a	IV a	V a	VI a	VII a		b	b	b	b	b	b	b	b	VIII
18 A 39.994	19 K 39.100	20 Ca 40.08	21 Sc 44.96	22 Ti 47.90	23 V 50.95	24 Cr 52.01	25 Mn 54.94	26 Fe 55.85 / 27 Co 58.94 / 28 Ni 58.71	29 Cu 63.54	30 Zn 65.38	31 Ga 69.72	32 Ge 72.60	33 As 74.91	34 Se 78.96	35 Br 79.916	36 Kr 83.8
36 Kr 83.8	37 Rb 85.48	38 Sr 87.63	39 Y 88.92	40 Zr 91.22	41 Cb 92.91	42 Mo 95.95	43 Tc (98)	44 Ru 101.1 / 45 Rh 102.91 / 46 Pd 106.7	47 Ag 107.880	48 Cd 112.41	49 In 114.82	50 Sn 118.70	51 Sb 121.76	52 Te 127.61	53 I 126.91	54 Xe 131.30
54 Xe 131.30	55 Cs 132.91	56 Ba 137.36	57 La to 71 138.92	72 Hf 178.68	73 Ta 180.95	74 W 183.86	75 Re 186.22	76 Os 190.2 / 77 Ir 192.2 / 78 Pt 195.09	79 Au 197.0	80 Hg 200.61	81 Tl 204.39	82 Pb 207.21	83 Bi 209.00	84 Po 210	85 At (211)	86 Rn 222
86 Rn 222	87 Fr (223)	88 Ra 226.05	89 Ac 227	90 Th 232.06	91 Pa (231.1)	92 U 238.07	93 Np (237)	94 Pu (242) / 95 Am (243) / 96 Cm (243)	97 Bk (245)	98 Cf (251)	99 E (254)	100 Fm (253)	101 Mv (256)	102 No (254)	103 Lw (257)	
0	1	2	3	4	5	6	7	8 / 9 / 10	11	12	13	14	15	16	17	18

Rare Earth Metals

58 Ce 140.13	59 Pr 140.92	60 Nd 144.27	61 Pm (145)	62 Sm 150.35	63 Eu 152.0	64 Gd 157.26	65 Tb 158.93	66 Dy 161.51	67 Ho 164.94	68 Er 167.27	69 Tm 168.94	70 Yb 173.04	71 Lu 174.99

alloys. These and many other relationships that appear in the periodic table make the work of the early chemists who developed it invaluable in our day and in the years to come.

3-8 Crystal Chemistry of Metals and Alloys—Solid Solutions

The physical properties of all gases, liquids, and solids are determined by the way in which the atoms are bound together, as discussed in paragraph 3–2 of this chapter. Another fundamental fact is that all metals are monotomic; that is, their crystalline structure as well as their liquid structure is made up of individual atoms and not of molecules. Metals are never made up of molecules, and the word *molecule* can never be correctly applied to metals.

In their pure form metals have limited applications in engineering work; how-ever, when alloying elements are added to pure metals, the resulting alloys find many uses and possess important and useful properties. Although elements may combine in numbers of ways to form alloys, the elements making up alloys are usually soluble in the liquid state and dissolve in each other, the same as water in alcohol. A different situation obtains in the solid state, as in this condition the ele-ments may combine to form mechanical mixtures, compounds, or *solid solutions*. When alloying elements are added to pure metals, the dimensions of the lattice struc-ture of the base metal (solvent) is usually altered, and at the same time the type of the lattice itself may be changed. The position of the alloying elements (solute) in the space lattice of the resulting alloy, and the changes that take place in the size and type of the unit cell, are of great importance in determining the properties of the alloy and its reaction to heat treatment and other methods of processing.

In some cases the solute atoms take the place of certain solvent atoms in the lattice structure, in which case there results what is referred to as a *substitutional solid solution*. This occurs when the atoms of the solvent and the solute metals are of comparable size. (The first requirement for the formation of a *solid solution* is that the second, or alloying, element must dissolve in the solid metal.)

In other cases the solute atoms are of such size that they can and do fit in between the spaces or interstices between the solvent atoms; in such cases the resulting alloys are called *interstitial solid solutions*. There are not many relatively small atoms that can be accommodated in the interstices of the lattice between the matrix atoms', however, elements such as carbon, nitrogen, hydrogen, boron, and oxygen do form interstitial solid solutions with numbers of the metals. One of the most common examples of interstitial solid solutions is that of the solid solution of carbon in gamma iron to form austenite.

3-9 Hume-Rothery Rules and Vegard's Law

Studying the solid solubility of metals, William Hume-Rothery made empirical observations and general rules governing the formation of substitutional solid solu-tions. These rules are most helpful in making the proper selection of alloying ele-ments. In brief they are as follows:

a. *Relative Size Effect.* Upon the investigation of the sizes of two metallic atoms revealed in a measure by their lattice constants, if they are found to differ by less than 15 per cent, the metals are concluded as having a favorable size factor for the formation of a solid solution. If the comparative size factor is greater than 15 per cent, the formation of a solid solution is severely limited, being only a fraction of one per cent.

b. *Relative Valence Effect.* In cases where the alloying element has a different valence from that of the base metal, the number of valence electrons per atom (*the electron ratio*) will be modified as a result of alloying. Inasmuch as crystal structures are more sensitive to a decrease in the electron ratio than to an increase, a metal with a high valence will dissolve only a small amount of a metal with a lower valence, although the lower valence metal may have satisfactory solubility for the higher valence metal.

c. *Chemical Affinity Factor.* This involves the electropositivity of the metals; the greater the chemical affinity of two metals, the more restricted will be their solid solubility. Those metals that differ greatly in electropositivity will usually form intermetallic compounds rather than solid solutions. In cases where an unusually stable metallic intermetallic compound is formed, the solid solubility is somewhat restricted.

These Hume-Rothery empirical observations are extremely important in metallurgy in the consideration of binary alloys. All ferrous metallurgy depends, essentially, on the interstitial solid solutions of carbon in iron. Here, the atomic radius ratio is too large, so that the solubility is restricted. The Fe atoms, therefore, enter between the C atoms in the lattice interstitially, since they cannot enter on a substitutional basis.

The conditions for interstitial solubility are as follows:

1. The size of the solute atom must be less than 59 per cent of that of the solvent atom.

2. The solvent involved must be polyvalent.

Numbers of the electron compounds (where the intermediate phases appear at definite compositions in certain binary equilibrium diagrams, and depend on the ratio of electrons to atoms at those compositions) have properties that are similar to those of solid solutions. Included among them are a wide range of composition, high ductility, low hardness and, at times, random distribution of atoms. The *nickel-arsenide* type of compound might be said to be the link between the electron compounds and the chemical valence compounds. Compounds of this type form at the electron-atom ratio of approximately 5:2 and are combinations of metals such as cobalt, nickel, copper, gold, etc., and also with high valency elements such as selenium, arsenic, tellurium, antimony, and tin. These compounds are of the hexagonal lattice type, are very high in hardness and brittleness, and possess a relatively high electrical conductivity.

Upon melting or freezing, metals are found to change volume. This is a very important phenomenon from a practical standpoint, since it is an expression of the change in density of the metals at the melting point, between the solid and liquid phases. A few examples of how metals change volume on melting are shown in Table 3–2.

TABLE 3–2. Volume Changes upon Melting*

Element	% Increase in Volume	Element	% Increase in Volume
Na	2.5	Al	6.0
K	2.55	Ga	− 3.2
Cu	4.15	Si	−12.0
Ag	3.8	Ge	−12.0
Au	5.1	Pb	3.5
Mg	4.1	Sn	2.8
Zn	4.2	Sb	− 0.95

* From Frost, B. R. T., *Progress in Metal Physics* 5, Chalmers, Bruce, and King, R., Eds., Pergamon Press, London, 1954, p. 98.

In the case of substitutional solid solutions, the density is somewhat different than in pure metals, for the reason that the lattice parameter and the average mass of the atoms are both changed. It is understandable that when an atom of a larger diameter enters the lattice site and substitutes for one of a smaller diameter, the lattice parameter usually changes, and vice versa in the case of an atom with smaller diameter entering the lattice site and substituting for an atom of larger diameter. This follows *Vegard's Law* which states, in general, that the lattice parameter of a solid solution varies linearly with the concentration in atomic per cent.

When the components of an alloy have no solubility in each other and have no tendency to combine with each other, *mechanical mixtures* are formed. In such cases each metal of the alloy freezes independently of the other, not allowing the other to enter into its crystal lattice. The solid that is formed under such circumstances consists of individually separable regions of the pure components of the alloy, in the form of a mechanical mixture instead of a solid solution or compound.

When a terminal substitutional solid solution is formed, the lattice parameters will, of necessity, change from that of the pure solvent to that of the alloy. The change in the parameter, in numbers of cases, is a linear function of the atomic per cent of the metal addition, such as is found in the case of the variation of the lattice parama-ter of magnesium, plotted as a function of the atomic per cent of certain solutes, including MgAg, MgCd, MgIn, etc., as discussed in G. V. Raynor's *Progress in Metal Physics*, Vol. 1, London, Pergamon Press. This linear relationship is usually referred to as Vegard's Law, due to the fact that Vegard studied the phenomenon that, theoretically, the parameter of the lattice of the solution is linearly propor-tional to the amount of the solute present. In numerous cases the plots of parametric distances vs. atomic per cent reveal negative or positive deviations. These devia-tions can be corrected in many cases by plotting the cube of the lattice parameter or the volume of the unit cell vs. the atomic per cent. In fact, in many respects this is a more desirable procedure, since an atom going into solution affects the entire lattice volume and not just one of the lattice dimensions.

3-10   Order-disorder Transformations

When a solid solution alloy with a random distribution of atoms undergoes an ordering by which the atoms of each component in the solid state assume definite positions, an *order-disorder transformation* takes place. It is most common in those alloys which are completely miscible in the solid state, such as copper-nickel, gold-platinum, antimony-bismuth, copper-gold, etc. In general, the maximum amount of ordering takes place at some simple ratio of the two alloys, such as 1:1, 2:1, 3:1, etc. Within such specific ranges of composition, the atoms in a solid solution may, at certain temperatures, assume a definite arrangement in the nature of an *ordered structure*. Shown in Fig. 3–21 is an equilibrium diagram for the order-disorder transformation of the copper-gold system, indicating the occurrence of an ordered structure at 25 and 50 atomic per cent (50.9 and 75.5 weight per cent) gold, at 745°F and 795°F, respectively. From a study of order-disorder transformations it is clear that perfect ordering of a solid solution can occur only if the two kinds of atoms are present in certain ratios, as indicated above. In the case of the copper-gold alloy shown in Fig. 3–21, the ordering takes place when the phase boundary is reached on cooling. There will, however, be a region with two phases present on each side of the areas marked as a' and a''.

The ordered phase often has the same structure as the disordered solid solution, the only change being the rearrangement of atoms. In certain cases such as is true in the copper-gold alloys, there will also be a different structure in the ordered phase, but the lattice parameter has changed very little.

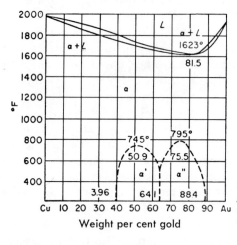

Fig. 3-21.   *Order-disorder transformation in a copper-gold alloy system.* (Physical Metallurgy for Engineers, by Clark and Varney, Courtesy of D. Van Nostrand Company, Inc., Princeton, New Jersey.)

The properties are affected only slightly, if at all, in most cases, the only exception being in the electrical conductivity, which is considerably higher in the ordered phase. Due to the negligible effect on the properties of the metals and alloys, the order-disorder transformations are not utilized extensively in industry.

3-11   Solidification of Pure Metals and Alloys—Coring

In changing from a liquid to a solid state certain changes take place in the mechanisms that are of great importance in metallurgy. When pure metals solidify from a molten bath of metal, crystallization begins, and at times this may be initiated at various places within the melt. Because of the random motion of the atoms in the liquid metal and their close proximity to each other, it is thought that a small group of atoms, from time to time, become arranged in the proper geometric arrangement resulting in a small amount of the metal in the form of a solid. In cases where the temperature of the liquid is above the temperature of solidification, this grouped arrangement of the atoms is unstable and therefore loses its configuration. When the temperature of solidification is reached, however, those groupings of atoms that have been formed in the proper arrangement for crystallization are pulled together by a cohesive bonding force between the atoms, resulting in a solidification, and the formation of nucleus or nuclei for further solidification. In other words, solidification begins with the formation of a lone unit cell within the metal, often referred to as a "nucleus." Then solidification continues by means of grain growth, one cell upon another, one layer on another. Another concept of this solidification that has won more support, is that it is unneccessary for an entire unit cell to be formed first; it is only necessary for a portion of the unit cell or lattice to be formed, and then additional atoms add themselves until the proper arrangement of the lattice is completed. Only the requirement that each atom attach itself to the growing crystal to assure the growth of the lattice, is neccessary for solidification to continue.

Fig. 3–22 shows a cooling curve for a pure metal wherein it will be seen that pure metals freeze at a constant temperature thereby forming a horizontal thermal arrest. Solidification commences when the liquid metal is cooled down to its freezing temperature, and the temperature remains constant until freezing of the metal is completed. While freezing has progressed, a *latent heat* of solidification is being given off in just sufficient amount to maintain a constant temperature.

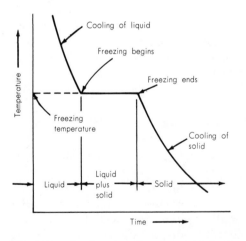

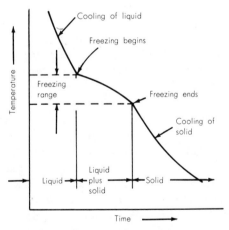

Fig. 3-22. *A cooling curve for a pure metal showing that a pure metal freezes at a constant temperature and that the thermal arrest for a pure metal is a horizontal line. (Ideal equilibrium conditions.)*

Fig. 3-23. *A cooling curve for a solid-solution alloy showing that in this case freezing occurs over a temperature range and not at a constant temperature, as in the case of pure metals. (Ideal equilibrium conditions.)*

Although it is understood that the ideal situation would not be possible in commercial practice so far as uniform cooling solidification is concerned, even if this were possible, and crystals could be generated throughout the melt, the newly-formed crystals would not be found to grow uniformly in all directions throughout the melt. Rather, it would be found that crystal growth would proceed in a tree-like manner, with branches forming throughout. This tree-like growth is known as *dendritic* growth or *dendritic crystals*, with the several branches of the dendrites growing in a three-dimensional pattern, each branch forming new branches until an interlocking crystal system is formed. Surrounding each of the dendritic branches is liquid metal that is continuously freezing to form new and smaller branches and thickening those branches that had been formed earlier in the freezing process. Nearly all metals freeze in a dendritic manner, as do the alloys of metals.

Although pure metals freeze at constant temperatures, solid solution alloys are found to freeze over a wide range of temperatures, as is shown in Fig. 3–23. The mechanism of freezing in the case of the solid solution alloys is quite similar in the early stages to what takes place in the freezing of pure metals; however, the the first solid metal that is formed in the alloy is richer in the constituent with the higher melting point, and the last metal to freeze is richer in the metal with the lower melting point. This phenomenon is called *coring* and is found in the microstructure of many of the cast alloys. Coring is the variable composition of solid solution dendrites; the center of the dendrite is richer in one element, as shown by the pertinent solidus-liquidus lines in the phase diagram. Furthermore, in a typical solid-solution system such as copper-nickel, which is not at all unique in solidifying to produce a single, solid-solution phase (the silver-gold is another that involves only solid-solution freezing), decided variations in mechanical and physical properties appear with change in chemical composition. Properties that are affected only very little by atom interactions vary more linearly with composition. A few examples of such properties of the solid solution are thermal expansion, specific heat, specific volume, and the lattice constant.

Alloys that solidify at the usual cooling rates found in commercial casting operations are not in equilibrium; consequently, a very undesirable, inhomogeneous (coring) structure develops in the course of solidification. Because of an inadequate length of time for diffusion in the growing particles of solid alloy, the inhomogeneous, cored structure is the expected result of mechanism of freezing in the solid-solution systems. By extended heating of the solidified alloy at a temperature below the melting range of the component elements, the equilibrium condition can be approached and, in some cases, accomplished.

When liquid metal freezes, on cooling, to a solid, the crystals that make up the solid metal are referred to as *grains* and where the crystals or grains come together and make contact with one another, the formation of grain boundaries takes place. These grain boundaries are important in metallurgy, and especially in metallography where studies of the grain boundaries are pursued in order to determine just what takes place when the liquid metal or alloy becomes a solid. The size of the grains, and thus the amount of grain boundary present in the metal, has a decided effect upon the properties of the metals. As will be discussed in a later chapter, it is highly important when making microstructure studies of polished specimens in the metallographic laboratory to obtain a scratch-free surface prior to etching the specimen, in order to eliminate the possibility of mistaking scratches in the surface for grain boundaries.

QUESTIONS

1. Every solid substance exists in one of what three forms? Define each of the three forms.
2. Define the following terms: space lattice, unit cell, crystal.

3. How has it been possible to determine the type and dimensions of most of the unit cells of the elements?

4. Make a sketch of each of the 14 types of space lattices of the crystal systems, describing each.

5. What means do we use to determine and describe the faces of a crystal or space lattice?

6. Name and describe the three steps used in determining the Miller indices of the planes for the atoms in a crystal.

7. State the Miller indices of a plane in a cubic structure that intersects the X axis at 3 and Y the axis at 1 and is parallel to the Z axis.

8. Give the Miller indices of a plane in a cubic structure that intersects the Y axis at 1/2, the Z axis at 2, and is parallel to the X axis. Draw the cubic structure and shade or cross-hatch the plane involved.

9. State the Miller indices of a plane in a cubic structure that is perpendicular to the YZ plane and intersects the Y plane at 1 and the Z axis at 1/2.

10. Referring to Fig. 3–20, showing a reproduction of the periodic table of the elements, describe the three classes, Class I, II and III. On what, essentially, is this classification based?

11. What is meant by the Coordination Number of atoms? Why is this important in metallurgy?

12. Name the four categories of the interatomic forces that bind the atoms in elements and in the aggregation of like and unlike atoms, and describe each.

13. Define the term, "dendrite" and tell how it got its name.

14. Basically, what is it that determines the physical properties of gases, liquids and solids?

15. Metals are said to be *monatomic*. What does this mean?

16. What happens to the lattice structure of a metal when we add an alloying element? How does this affect the properties of the resulting alloy?

17. Define the following terms: substitutional solid solution, interstitial solid solution, mechanical mixture, intermetallic compounds.

18. Some metals may exist in more than one lattice form, possessing the ability to shift from one crystal structure to a different atomic arrangement with changes in temperature. What is this type of lattice change called?

19. Draw a cooling curve for a pure metal and also for a solid solution alloy, properly marking it to show the important differences.

20. Explain what happens when liquid metal freezes to a solid. Why is the study of this phenomenon of interest to us in metallurgy?

21. Define the term allotropy, and give one example where allotropy is desirable and another where it is objectionable.

22. Lead has an atomic diameter of $3.492 \cdot 10^{-8}$ cm and is face-centered cubic in structure. What is the volume of the unit cell of lead?

23. The atomic radius of silver is 1.441Å and it is face-centered cubic. Calculate the size of the side of the unit cell.

24. A sodium chloride crystal is used to measure the wavelength of some X rays. The diffraction angle is $5.2°$ for the (111) spacing of chlorine. What is the wavelength if the lattice constant is 5.63 Å?

References

American Society for Metals, *Metals Handbook*. Cleveland, Ohio, 1961.

Clark, Donald Sherman, *Engineering Materials and Processes*. Scranton, Pennsylvania. International Textbook Co., 1959.

Clark, Donald S. and Wilbur R. Varney, *Physical Metallurgy for Engineers*, 2d ed. Princeton, New Jersey: D. Van Nostrand Co., Inc., 1962.

Cullity, Bernard Dennis, *Elements of X-ray Diffraction*. Reading, Massachusetts: Addison-Wesley Publishing Co., 1956.

Guy, Albert G., *Elements of Physical Metallurgy*, 2d ed. Reading, Massachusetts: Addison-Wesley Publishing Co., 1959.

Hume-Rothery, William and G.V. Raynor, *The Structure of Metals and Alloys*, 3d ed. London: Institute of Physics, 1955.

Rogers, Bruce Allison, *The Nature of Metals*. Cleveland, Ohio: American Society for Metals and Iowa State College Press, Ames, 1951.

Van Vlack, Lawrence H., *Elements of Materials Science*. Reading, Massachusetts: Addison-Wesley Publishing Company, 1959.

4

Equilibrium Diagrams

4-1 Phases

A *phase* is defined as any substance which has a homogeneous structure bounded by definite surfaces. In other words, a heterogeneous system consists of two or more homogeneous systems, and any homogeneous part of a heterogeneous system is called a *phase*. A good example is the case of melting ice, which is a heterogeneous system consisting of two or three phases, i.e., either ice and water, or ice, water, and water vapor, respectively. A *system* is a combination of *components*, and the number of components of any system is the smallest number of independent variable constituents which are sufficient to define the composition of each phase under equilibrium conditions in a heterogeneous system. In the example given, although water consists of two types of elements, it consists of only one component, because the composition of ice, water, and vapor (at ordinary moderate temperatures) can be identified. Although the atomic arrangements of water (H_2O) are different in these phases structurally, nevertheless, the composition does not change. Still another example is in the calcination of calcium carbonate, wherein the equation is

$$CaCO_3(\text{solid}) = CaO(\text{solid}) + CO_2(\text{gas}). \qquad (4\text{--}1)$$

This is recognized as a heterogeneous system consisting of three phases: solid $CaCO_3$, solid CaO and gaseous CO_2 and only two components. Taking CaO and CO_2 as the two components, the composition of the third phase can be found from the stoichiometry of the reaction shown in Equation 4–1. Still another example of a system is the case of the reduction of hematite (Fe_2O_3) by means of hydrogen, to produce iron and water vapor. In this case, the system under consideration consists of solid hematite, solid iron, and a gas that contains hydrogen and water vapor. In other words, in this case there is a three-component system involved.

A crystal in the solid state with a definite lattice structure is considered as a phase. Another crystal of the same structure is the same phase; however, a crystal with a different structure is a different phase. Whenever a liquid solidifies, a change of phase takes place because of the formation of a new phase out of the liquid phase. This also occurs when a metal undergoes an allotropic transformation, since a crystal change has taken place.

A knowledge of the structure of an alloy is most helpful in the prediction of its properties, for the properties of a material are dependent on the nature, number, and distribution of the phases which compose it. Phase diagrams, also known as *equilibrium diagrams* and *constitution diagrams*, graphically indicate the form the constituents of the alloys takes, with respect to the temperatures involved. Such an equilibrium diagram is actually a plot of the composition of the phases as a function of temperature in any system of alloys under equilibrium conditions.

In the case of an alloy with two elemental components, the phase diagram is called a *binary diagram*, and, where there are three elements in the alloy, it is a *ternary diagram*. With four elements in the alloy a *quarternary diagram* is used to describe the various facts concerning the alloy, including melting and boiling temperatures, allotropic transformations, etc.

Inasmuch as metallurgical systems are essentially condensed systems (solid and liquid systems), the effect of external pressure on the phase equilibria is not perceptible, at least under normal atmospheric conditions. Since all the phase equilibrium diagrams are predicated on a constant pressure of one atmosphere, the only remaining variables of the system are temperature and compositions.

4-2   Phase Rule and Systems of One Component

Every system has certain variable factors, and the number of these variables, which define the state of the system, is called the *degrees of freedom*. From thermodynamic principles of equilibrium, Gibbs gave us the *phase rule* which is extremely important in metallurgy and particularly in physical metallurgy. Gibbs showed that, provided the equilibrium between any number of phases is not influenced by external forces, such as gravitational, electrical, magnetic, etc., but only by temperature, pressure and composition, the number of *degrees of freedom* (F) of a system at equilibrium is related to the number of components (C) and of phases (P) by the following equation:

$$F = C - P + 2 \qquad \text{(This is known as the Phase Rule.)}$$

The application of the phase rule to heterogeneous equilibria is shown by considering the solid-liquid-vapor equilibria for a system of one component. Then for a single phase system, such as water, $C = 1$, and $P = 1$, so that the number of degrees of freedom $(F) = 2$; this is what is known as a bivariant equilibrium, where both temperature and pressure can be established or changed arbitrarily. For a water-water vapor, water-ice, or ice-water vapor system, $C = 1$, $P = 2$ and $F = 1$. In other words, in this univariant equilibrium system, either temperature or pressure is the independent variable. When the three phases, ice, water, and water vapor are in equilibrium, $F = 0$ and this is an *invariant system*. A pressure/temperature phase diagram for a single component system as shown in Fig. 4–1 can be constructed, using the information obtained from the phase rule. Fig. 4–2 shows a pressure/temperature phase equilibrium diagram for a single component system which sub-

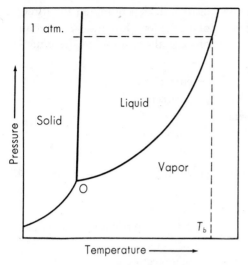

Fig. 4-1. *Pressure/temperature equilibrium diagram for a single component system which has a normal boiling temperature.*

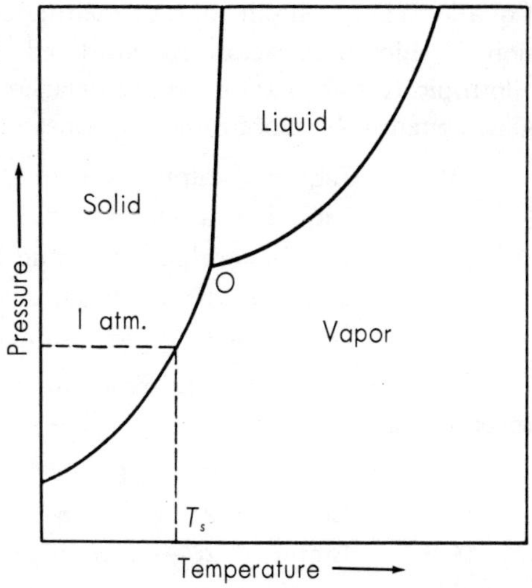

Fig. 4-2. *A pressure/temperature phase equilibrium diagram for a single component system which sublimes at atmospheric pressure. (Diagrams courtesy of U. S. Steel Corporation)*

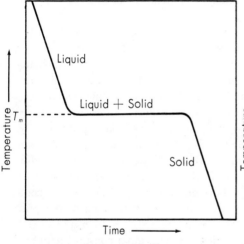

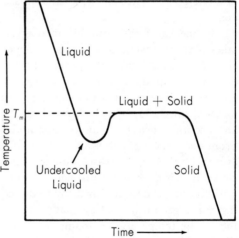

Fig. 4-3. *Temperature-time plot for the solidification of a single component melt without any undercooling taking place.*

Fig. 4-4. *Temperature-time plot for solidification of a single component melt where undercooling has taken place. (Plots courtesy of U. S. Steel Corporation)*

limes at atomspheric pressure. In Fig. 4–3 will be seen a temperature-time plot for the solidification of a single component melt without any undercooling taking place; in Fig. 4–4 another temperature/time plot is of a single component system where undercooling has taken place. The invariant reactions in a system are important, since they often control the structure of the polyphase alloys. Disregarding the vapor phase and related transformation in a system containing only one component, two types of invariant reactions are possible:

(1)   Liquid $\rightleftharpoons$ alpha   (reversible reaction)
(2)   alpha $\rightleftharpoons$ beta   (reversible reaction)

Equation (1) is solidification or melting of the constituent, depending on the direction in which the reaction is considered. The second reaction (Equation 2) is of an allotropic transformation. Many invariant reactions are also possible in the binary alloy systems, the more important ones being

(3)	Liquid $\rightleftharpoons$ alpha + beta	(eutectic)
(4)	Liquid + alpha $\rightleftharpoons$ beta	(peritectic)
(5)	Liquid $\rightleftharpoons$ alpha + liquid beta	(monotectic)
(6)	alpha $\rightleftharpoons$ beta + gamma	(eutectoid)
(7)	alpha + beta $\rightleftharpoons$ gamma	(peritectoid)

In the ternary system several reactions are possible but the following are considered to be the more important:

(8)	Liquid $\rightleftharpoons \alpha + \beta + \gamma$	(eutectic)
(9)	Liquid $+ \alpha \rightleftharpoons \beta + \gamma$	(mixed eutectic and peritectic)
(10)	Liquid $+ \alpha + \beta \rightleftharpoons \gamma$	(peritectic)
(11)	Liquid $\rightleftharpoons \alpha + \beta +$ liquid γ	(monotectic)

The reactions that take place in a single component system may also take place in binary systems. Similarly, binary reactions may take place in ternary systems, etc. It should be remembered, however, that a two-phase reaction is invariant only in a one-component system; a three-phase reaction is invariant in a binary system, etc.

By means of the equilibrium diagrams a graphic description of exactly what takes place in reactions is obtained, depending on the type and number of phases and the invariant reactions between them. Several methods are used in the construction of phase diagrams, including thermal analysis, microscopic studies, and x-ray diffraction. The simplest and most generally used method is the thermal analysis method, since alloys may be slowly heated or cooled, regardless of their compositions, and accurate measurements of time and temperature may be taken quite readily. From such readings points are plotted on the graph to show the variation of temperature with time. In the case of the freezing of a pure metal, the latent heat of solidification that is liberated is just enough to maintain the alloy at constant temperature until freezing is accomplished. By so doing, a horizontal line is revealed on the cooling curve graph, indicating that throughout the cooling and freezing of the pure metal, the temperature remains constant. The latent heat that is liberated during the freezing of a solid-solution alloy is not sufficient to maintain a constant temperature, but does slow down the cooling rate of the alloy. In the case of the freezing of a solid-solution alloy, the thermal arrest is not a straight, horizontal line on the cooling curve, but a curve such as is shown in Fig. 3-23, showing discontinuous changes in the slope with changes that take place in the phases.

The changes in phases that take place in an alloy can also be determined by studies under the microscope by heating a small specimen up to the desired test temperature and quenching the same down to room temperature very rapidly. Observing the microstructure of the quenched specimen under the microscope, one may assume that the observed structure is the same as that which prevailed at the higher temperature, prior to the quenching operation. By doing this with several specimens, quenching the same at various temperatures, the temperatures at which phase changes occur can be observed and plotted in the form of a phase or equilibrium diagram. X-ray diffraction methods are also used in determining the phases that are in evidence, as well as some of the other changes that have occurred, thereby adding to the knowledge obtained from thermal and microscopic procedures.

4-3 Equilibrium Diagrams of Binary Systems

As previously stated, an equilibrium diagram of a system of alloys is a complete set of temperature-composition curves, connecting solubility limits and freezing and melting points under equilibrium conditions. Another definition states that an equilibrium diagram is a plot of the composition of phases as a function of temperature in any alloy system under conditions of equlibrium.

Equilibrium diagrams are classified according to the degree of mutual solubility of the constituent metals involved. On this basis, there are six types of systems, as shown in Figures 4–5, 4–6, 4–7, 4–8, 4–9, and 4–10, which may be described as follows:

1. Where the constituent metals are partially soluble in the liquid state but are insoluble in the solid state.
2. Where there is complete solubility in both the liquid and solid states, so that the constituent metals form an entire series of alloys.
3. Where there is complete solubility in the liquid state, but insolubility in the solid state.
4. Where there is complete solubility of the component metals in the liquid state and partial solubility in the solid state.
5. Where there are systems of chemical combinations at some temperatures and compositions, as well as any of the first four types mentioned above.
6. Where the components are completely insoluble in the liquid state and also insoluble in the solid state.

A close study of the six types of binary alloy equilibrium diagrams is important, as these are the basis of the development of many highly significant and useful alloys at various temperatures and in varying degrees of composition.

Inasmuch as an equilibrium diagram is merely an exact presentation of experiment data determined for a given alloy system of metals, it is obvious that the original data can be obtained again by referring to the diagram. Under equilibrium conditions, it is possible to tell, (1) the phases present, (2) the chemical composition of each phase, and (3) the quantity of each phase present.

A system of Type 1 where there is partial solubility in the liquid state and insolubility in the solid state is shown in Fig. 4–5. Alloys of Fe-Cu, Zn-Bi, Al-Pb,

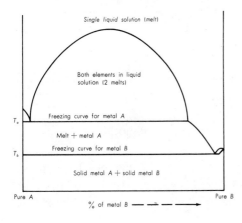

Fig. 4-5.

Cu-Pb, and others are of this type. Although in the case of the Zn-Bi alloy there is a homogeneous liquid solution above the upper curve (*liquidus*), in the case of the Fe-Cu system of the Type 1 series there are two distinct liquids at higher temperatures above the liquidus; however, as the temperature drops and cooling proceeds, a homogeneous liquid region is observed in the equilibrium diagram.

As may be seen in Fig. 4–6, antimony (Sb), cooling from the molten state, solidifies at a constant temperature, T_{Sb}, of 1167F. For the solid solution alloy of 25 per cent Bi, cooling continues at a uniform rate until the temperature reaches 1095F, then more slowly as a break occurs at X. Then as the rate of cooling decreases to the point Y (this is called the *recovery point*), the normal rate of cooling resumes. From these graphs it is observed that pure metals solidify at a constant temperature and their cooling curves show only a horizontal "hold," whereas the cooling curves of solid solution alloys show a break and then a recovery.

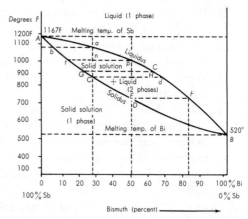

Fig. 4-6. *Type 2 Binary Alloy where there is complete solubility in both the liquid and solid states.*

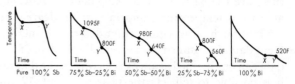

Fig. 4-6a.

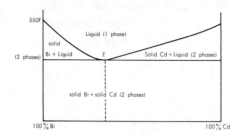

Fig. 4-7. *Bismuth and cadmium equilibrium diagram.*

Shown in Fig. 4–7 is a Type 3 system illustrating complete solubility in the liquid state and insolubility in the solid state. This is known as a *eutectic* system, since a eutectic occurs at a certain point in the cooling (solidification) diagram, as indicated. (A *eutectic* is a mechanical mixture of two phases which differs from a solid solution, where we find alloys that form over a wide range of compositions.) The eutectic is a specific point that varies with the alloys involved. Many of the physical properties of eutectic alloys (at the eutectic point) are quite similar to those of the pure metals. As indicated in the equilibirium diagram above, we find a eutectic at 60 per cent Bi—40 per cent Cd. This alloy in the solid state is composed of an intimate mechanical mixture of grains of Cd and grains of Bi. This is the eutectic alloy of this system. (Actually, a eutectic reaction is the isothermal reversible reaction of a liquid that forms two different solid phases [in a binary alloy system] during cooling.)

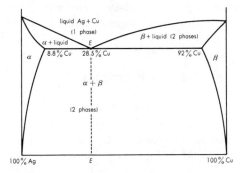

100% Ag   E   100% Cu **Fig. 4-8.** *Equilibrium diagram of silver and copper.*

A Type 4 equilibrium diagram which is also a eutectic system is shown in Fig. 4–8. In this system a binary alloy is one where there is complete solubility in the liquid state, but only partial solubility in the solid state. This is the most common and, therefore, the most important system. Fe-C, Cu-Ag, Pb-Sn, and several other alloys belong to this type. Present in this system are the monophase and biphase fields along with the invariant reaction at the eutectic point E.

Alloys to the left of the eutectic (E) are usually referred to as *hypoeutectic*, inasmuch as their content of metal B is less than that of the eutectic. Alloys to the right of eutectic (E) are called hypereutectic, since their content of metal B is greater than that found at the eutectic composition.

Type 5 alloys are chemical combinations of metals at some temperatures and compositions, together with any of the first four types mentioned. In the Type 5 system of alloys there is transformation from two phases to one phase on cooling; this transformation is referred to as a *peritectic reaction*. This may be thought of as an inverted eutectic system. In the eutectic system, the transformation is from one phase to two phases, on cooling the melt. Many useful alloys for structural purposes in engineering are of the peritectic reaction type, such as the copper–zinc, gold–bismuth, and other binary alloys. A typical example of a peritectic reaction with partial formation of solid solutions is shown in Fig. 4–9, where the peritectic reaction occurs at the peritectic temperature between the solid solution α with composition C and liquid P, forming a solid solution β of the composition D. Within

Fig. 4-9. *Peritectic reaction in a binary system with partial solubilities.*

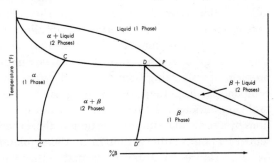

the field $CDC'D'$ there are two phases, α and β, the compositions of which change with temperature along the solubility curves CC' and DD' respectively. Reactions of the peritectic type are usually slow, due to the fact that they depend largely upon diffusion of the atoms of the liquid metal through the compound to the crystals of component A of the system.

In the Type 5 systems *eutectoid* transformations are also encountered, these being the isothermal, reversible reactions, wherein a single solid phase transforms into two phases, as designated by E in the Fe-FeC equilibrium diagram shown later in Fig. 7-2. This will be developed further in Chapter 7.

4-4   Ternary Alloy Systems—Tie-line Principles

The ternary alloys systems are the three component systems, and in making the equilibrium diagram of such a system the data are plotted within a triangle, as shown in Fig. 4–10, with each side of the triangle being the composition abscissa for the system A-B, B-C, and C-A. The composition of point M in Fig. 4–10 is 50 per cent A, 20 per cent B and 30 per cent C.

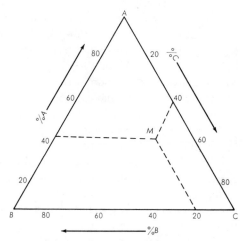

Fig. 4-10.

In the case of the temperature/composition diagram for a ternary alloy system, a prism with a triangular base is constructed for the composition and the height for the temperature scale. Where there is complete miscibility of the three components in the system, a very simple type exists, since only two phases are formed, these being a liquid and a solid. For complete solubility of the three components in each other, they must also be soluble two by two, and the corresponding diagrams are of the solid solution type. In actual engineering applications, the simple binary alloy systems are seldom utilized. Most of our alloys contain more than two components, so it is necessary to construct diagrams that show the phase relationship that exists over a range of temperatures for such a three-component (ternary) system. The problem of visualizing such a phase diagram for a system containing three or more components, and then representing such systems graphically, presents quite a problem, although the ternary system can be partially represented in two dimensions by a series of isothermal sections of the ternary diagram, with compositions represented by points either within or on the equilateral triangle shown in Fig. 4–10, and by temperatures by distances normal to this plane. In order to represent the equilibrium of a particular solid composition along with the appropriate liquid composition involved, however, it is essential to use *tie lines*, as shown in Fig. 4–11, such as TT'. This ternary diagram is a fairly simple one since no intermediate phases are present.

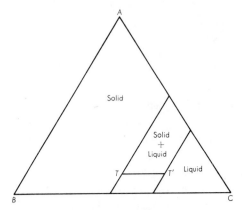

Fig. 4-11. *A simple ternary system showing tie lines.*

A tie line is an isothermal line drawn through a given point in the ternary phase diagram; the intersections of the tie line with the boundaries of the two-phase region determine the composition of the phases present. At a constant temperature and pressure, a three-phase system in a ternary alloy will have phases with fixed compositions. On the other hand, a ternary alloy containing only two phases will always have the compositions of those phases variant, i.e., they are not fixed.

4-5 The Lever Rule

Referring to the binary phase diagram in Fig. 4–12, at any given temperature T, a mixture of liquid and solid solutions coexist. The composition of a liquid phase may be obtained by determining the intersection of a horizontal line corresponding to T temperature with the liquidus line; the intersection of this same horizontal line with the solidus line denotes the composition of the solid phase. The relative proportions of the phases that coexist can be determined by applying the *lever rule*. The lever rule is a geometric construction by which proportions of components and phases can be determined by calculation.

For example, considering an alloy of two components, A and B, as shown in Fig. 4–12, and specifically one with a composition Z, at a temperature T, this alloy will consist of the mixture of a liquid with composition X_1 and a solid with composition Y_2. Assuming the fraction of the component B in this alloy to be designated as z, and the amount of solid present as s, then the amount of B in the solid phase is sy, and the amount of B in the liquid is $(1 - s)x$. Inasmuch as the amount of B in the alloy must be equal to the amount of B in the liquid, plus the amount of B in the solid, an equation can be written:

$$z = sy + (1 - s)x \qquad (4\text{–}2)$$

In the same manner, the relative amount of solid can be determined:

$$s = \frac{z - x}{y - x} \qquad (4\text{–}3)$$

Inasmuch as $z - x$ designates the portion of the horizontal line LO and $y - x$ is the portion LS, then the relative amount of solid will be found to be equal to the length LO divided by LS, so it may be said that $s = LO/LS$. By the same reasoning it may be determined that the relative amount of liquid present will be

$$l = \frac{y - z}{y - x} = \frac{SO}{SL} \tag{4-4}$$

Noting the above as percentages it may be stated

$$\frac{LO}{LS} \cdot 100 = \text{the per cent of solid present} \tag{4-5}$$

and that

$$\frac{SO}{SL} \cdot 100 = \text{the per cent of liquid present} \tag{4-6}$$

This geometric construction is called the *lever rule* because the amount of a given phase multiplied by its lever arm is equal to the amount of the other phase multiplied by its lever arm. By using such geometric relations, the proportion of solid corresponds to the length of the portion adjacent to the liquidus line, and the fraction of the liquid present corresponds to the length of the portion adjacent to the solidus line. In such cases, the isotherm can be seen to resemble a tie line inasmuch as it "ties" the composition of the two phases in equilibrium at a specific temperature. In Fig. 4–12, the areas above the liquidus line and below the solidus line are bivariant, inasmuch as

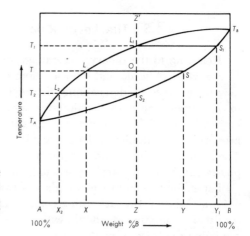

Fig. 4-12.   *Illustration of the lever rule with the point L_1 indicating the composition of the liquid X_1 and with the point S_2 indicating the composition of the solid Y_2. It is obvious that distances X_1 and Y_2 are equal to the original composition Z.*

there are two components although only one phase is present. It follows, therefore, that both temperature and composition can be varied without the appearance of any new phase or the disappearance of such. This system is univariant in the area between the liquidus and solidus since it is a two-phase region in that area. It is observed, then, that either temperature or concentration can be varied without the disappearance of a phase. It may therefore be said that for a constant temperature such as T, a series of alloy compositions is possible between x and y, and for a constant composition as represented by line $z'z$, the temperature may be varied from T_1 to T_2 as noted.

QUESTIONS

1. Define the following terms: phase, system, component.

2. What is a phase diagram? What is it also called?

3. How do we designate phase diagrams with only two elemental components? With three elemental components? Four components?

4. Due to the fact that metallurgical systems are essentially condensed systems (solid and liquid systems), how great is the effect of external pressure on the phase equilibria under normal atmospheric conditions?

5. Define what is meant by the term "degrees of freedom" of a metallurgical system.

6. Give and explain Gibbs' Phase Rule.

7. What do we mean by the term "invariant system"?

8. State the two types of invariant reactions that are possible in a system containing only one component, disregarding the vapor phase and related transformations.

9. In the ternary system (three components) several reactions are possible. State the ones that are considered the more important.

10. What are the several methods used in the construction of phase diagrams? Which of these is the simplest and most generally used?

11. In the case of binary alloys, how are equilibrium diagrams classified?

12. Draw an equilibrium diagram of a binary alloy where there is complete solubility in both the liquid and solid states. What can be said of a system of this type?

13. Draw an equilibrium diagram for bismuth and cadmium. What type of system is this combination?

14. What type of system is the combination of silver and copper? Draw an equilibrium diagram for such a system.

15. How is the cooling curve of a binary alloy determined? What is the significance of a hold, a break, and a recovery in a cooling curve for binary alloys?

16. In the Type 4 equilibrium diagram of a eutectic system what are those alloys called that are to the left of the eutectic point (E)? What are the alloys to the right of the eutectic point called?

17. Using the lever rule, draw a binary phase diagram for copper and nickel, and, assuming an average alloy composition of 70 per cent with a total weight of 100 g, determine the weight of both the solid and liquid phases.

18. Refer to Fig. 4–6 and explain in detail the steps that take place when an alloy of this type is heated from the solid state to the liquid state with a very slow heating procedure.

References

American Society for Metals, *Metals Handbook*, Cleveland, Ohio, Vol. 7, 1960.

American Society for Metals, *Metals Handbook*, Cleveland, Ohio, Vol. 8, 1961.

Barrett, Charles Sanborn, *Structure of Metals, Crystallographic Methods, Principles and Data.* 2d ed. New York: McGraw-Hill Book Company, 1956.

Chalmers, Bruce, *Physical Metallurgy*. New York; John Wiley & Sons, 1959.

Hansen, Max and Kurt Anderko, *Constitution of Binary Alloys*. 2d ed. New York: McGraw-Hill Book Company, 1958.

Jastryebski, Zkigniew D., *Nature and Properties of Engineering Materials*. New York: John Wiley & Sons, 1959.

Reed-Hill, Robert E., *Physical Metallurgy Principles*. New York: D. Van Nostrand Co., Inc., 1964.

Ricci, John Ettore, *The Phase Rule and Heterogeneous Equilibrium*. New York: D. Van Nostrand Co., Inc., 1951.

5

Hot and Cold Working
of Metals

5-1 Plastic Working of Metals

The term *plastic working* refers to the permanent deformation of metals that is brought about by the application of mechanical forces to the metal surfaces. The main purpose and objective of this working is usually to produce specific shapes and/or sizes (*mechanical shaping*), but in other instances plastic working is used to produce an improvement in the physical properties of the metal. This is termed *mechanical treating*, however, depending on the metals involved and the circumstances of the plastic working. Both of these end results, i.e., mechanical shaping and mechanical treating, are possible simultaneously.

The cornerstone for all metal-working processes, including forging, bending, deep-drawing, extrusion, hot-rolling, etc., is the nature of the plasticity of the metals being worked. Just how the single crystals and polycrystallin metals behave at various temperatures, i.e., what takes place when the metals are heat-treated, annealed, quenched, etc., is basic in metallurgy. When the subject of plastic deformation of metals is approached from the viewpoint of the physical changes that take place when the metals are deformed plastically, the procedure is termed *microscopic* investigation. In this phase, the relations of plastic behavior to the crystal structure and inter-atomic forces involved are discussed, as these are extremely important in the design of metals and alloys possessing superior plastic properties. The other approach to this subject, and of equal importance, is that of *macroscopic* considerations, which concern themselves with the relation of plastic behavior to applied stresses, temperature, and rate of deformation. These subjects are important to consider when designing metal-forming processes, structures, and/or machines. Within the framework of these areas of consideration, *cold working* and *hot working* of metals methods are studied. In the case of hot working, the forces needed to deform the metal are very sensitive to the rate at which the deforming forces are applied and the temperature changes that take place. In hot working, however, the basic strength of the metal after deformation has taken place is relatively unchanged. On the other hand, in cold working the forces that are applied are relatively insensitive to the rate at which the loads are applied and to any temperature variations. Here also, the basic strength is definitely and permanently improved.

Mechanical working of metals involves their permanent deformation by stressing them beyond their elastic limits. Employing mechanical working, ingots, billets, blooms, slabs, etc. are partially or completely shaped into bars, flats, plates, sheets, and other such useful objects. In addition to changes in shape of metals under mechanical working, we find changes that usually occur in the physical properties of the metals. Mechanical working can be carried out at or near room temperature or at elevated temperatures, and the effect on the properties will vary with the temperatures employed. Since the yield strengths of metals usually fall off with higher temperatures, a given amount of hot deformation is possible at much lower applied stresses in hot working than in an equivalent cold deformation. Where there is an appreciable change in shape to be made, as in fabricating large pieces, such as heavy crank shafts, axles, etc., it is best not to use cold work methods, as the forces required are too great, as a rule, for the equipment being used. It is obviously necessary to heat the metal billet prior to starting the deformation. As a result, the first shaping operations on large billets are usually done at elevated temperatures. When mechanical working is viewed from the standpoint of principal stresses involved, this becomes more understandable. The *elastic strain* (within the elastic limit) is reversible; however, the *plastic strain* (that performed beyond the elastic limit)

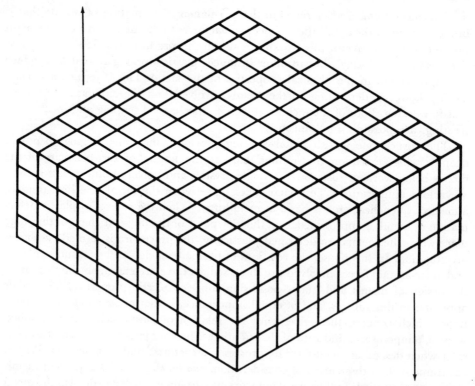

Fig. 5-1. *A hypothetical crystal containing no dislocations. Primitive cubic cells about to undergo slip on a 100 type of plane.*

is not reversible, but is permanent and irreversible. It can be said, therefore, that strain is elastic if the crystal lattice returns to its original shape when the stresses that caused the strain to occur are removed. Similarly, the strain is plastic when the amount of deformation is so great that the shear stress is greater than the ability of the atomic forces within the lattice to return it to its original shape.

Plastic strain is usually carried out at higher temperatures, but can be accomplished at room temperature or a bit higher under certain circumstances. Plastic strain may take place by a process known as *slip*, which involves a relative movement of layers of atoms within the crystal. A graphic description of slip is shown in Fig. 5–2 in which it is seen that deformation is taking place by a gliding or shearing action on certain planes of the crystal. This action within the crystal is discontinuous and it

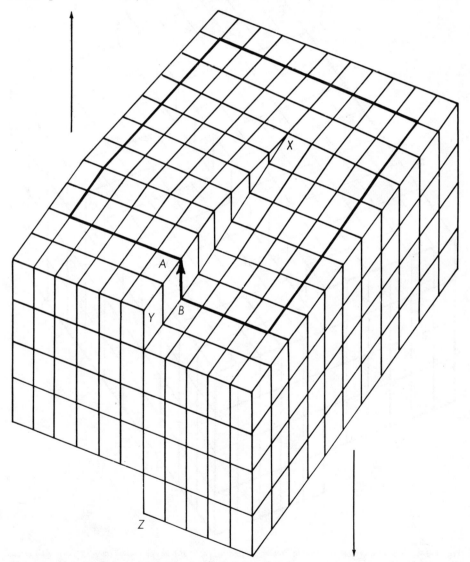

Fig. 5-2. *A crystal after slip action has started to take place. Slip started at the front of the crystal and has progressed toward the back as far as line W (W is directly below X) which is the dislocation line. This is a screw type dislocation, for the reason that a spiral path can be traced from the bottom plane to the top one, where the path encloses the dislocation line.*

takes place by a definite and distinct movement on certain planes. In Fig. 5–1 a
block of smoothly polished metal is shown prior to any deformation. Fig. 5–2 shows
the same block after deformation has started to take place. In Fig. 5–2 the intersection of individual *slip planes* with the polished surface is observed, thus forming
slip lines. The intersection of a cluster of slip planes with the surface is known as a
slip band. Shown in Fig. 5–3A is the same block of metal where slip had previously
occurred, but which had subsequently been polished on the surface, to show that

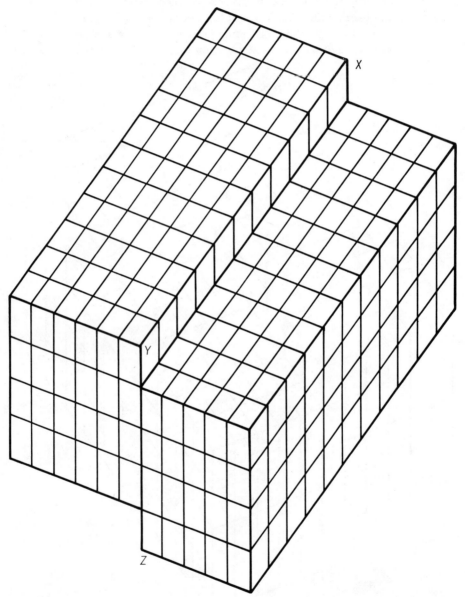

Fig. 5-3A.   *The same crystal as shown in Figures 5-1 and 5-2, after slip has progressed completely across the crystal.
Here, the dislocation has passed entirely out of the crystal, leaving the offset condition as shown. It is obvious why a
dislocation of the type just described should be termed a screw dislocation when one observes that a line beginning
on the top plane of Fig. 5-2 can follow an uninterrupted spiral path to the bottom plane. The first turn of the spiral
is marked by a heavy line in Fig. 5-2, as noted.*

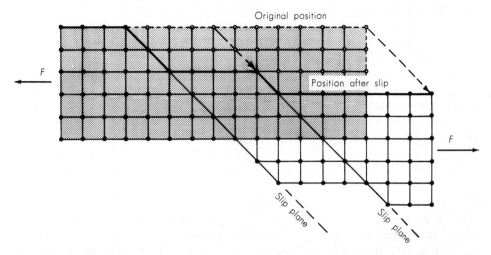

Fig. 5-3B. *Slip in a cubic structure where the orientation of the atoms remains the same subsequent to slip. Here are entire blocks of atoms that have slid along particular planes known as "slip planes." When slip takes place, the amount of the movement and spacing of the slip planes is considerably greater than shown here.*

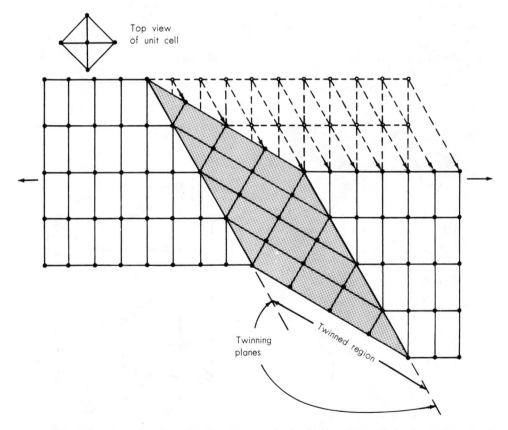

Fig. 5-3C. *The relationship of twinning in a face-centered cubic lattice structure. Each atom in the twinned area moves a particular distance, thereby providing a twinned region, which results in a structure much like the parent, but with a different orientation. This new orientation is a mirror image of the parent. Because of their different orientation, twins remain visible even after repolishing and re-etching of the specimen.*

slip does not change the orientation of unit cells; this is evidenced here by the fact that repolishing removes all evidence of slip planes.

Those planes within a crystal having the greatest atomic density will be the planes of easiest slip potential. The reason for this is that slip planes (the planes of atoms on which slip takes place) are the planes in the lattice which are generally farthest apart from each other. Therefore, the bond between these planes is weakest, and as a consequence they are the ones in which movement takes place more easily when an external force is applied to the crystal, assuming that the force, or at least a component of the force, is in the proper direction. In the case of the face-centered cubic lattices, the {111} planes will slip most readily, while in the body-centered cubic structures the slip planes are found to be {110}, {112}, or {123}. In the hexagonal close-packed systems, the {0001} plane is the plane of easiest slip. It is also significant that the *direction* of easiest slip is also the direction that corresponds to the greatest atomic density, as previously stated. Therefore, for the face-centered cubic structure, it is a $\langle 101 \rangle$ direction; in the body-centered cubic structure it is $\langle 111 \rangle$, and in the hexagonal close-packed structure the direction of easiest slip is $\langle 11\bar{2}0 \rangle$. The plastic behavior of metals is due largely to the nature of the metallic bond of the metal involved. For example, atoms may be displaced with respect to each other without breaking the atomic or metallic bond; however, this is not true in covalent and ionic bond type structures.

Referring to Fig. 5–3D (a), (b), and (c), showing the crystal structure of the face-centered cubic, body-centered cubic, and hexagonal close-packed cells reproduced here from Hume-Rothery's treatise on alloys, it will be seen that the *face-centered cubic* structure has the highest degree of atomic concentration and symmetry found in any lattice. Following the lines drawn through the center of the atoms at each corner and in the center of each face, we see that an equilateral triangle is formed in each

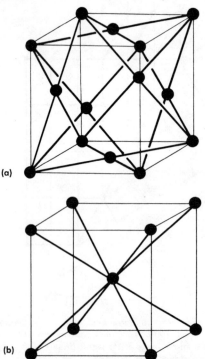

(a)

(b)

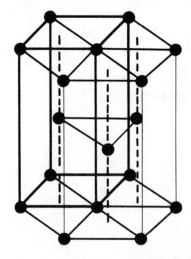

(c)

Fig. 5-3D. *Atomic arrangement in: (a) face-centered cubic, (b) body-centered cubic, and (c) hexagonal close-packed unit cells. (It will be seen that neighboring atoms are joined by heavy lines.)*

instance. Eight similar close-packed planes are observed in which each atom is in the center of a hexagon formed by lines through the centers of its six equidistant neighbors. Because the eight planes, if extended, would form the faces of an octahedron, they are called the octahedral or {111} planes. There are only four series of {111} planes, since the opposite faces of the octahedron are parallel. The three rows of close atom packing on the {111} planes are the sides of the equilateral triangles or the ⟨110⟩ directions which are normal to the faces of the regular octahedron. Since, as previously stated, the face-centered cubic lattice has the highest degree of atomic concentration and symmetry that is found in any lattice, it is found to have four close-packed planes {111} and twelve close-packed directions ⟨110⟩. It follows, therefore, that those metals of the FCC type are ductile, easily formed, and good conductors of heat and electricity. Copper, aluminum, and silver are metals of this type.

The body-centered cubic unit cell, as shown in Fig. 5–3D (b), by the same analysis, will be found to have large voids or interstices between the atoms, and therefore it is not one to have close-packed planes such as are found in the face-centered cubic unit cell. As a result, the body-centered cubic metals do not have a well-defined slip plane, but instead deform by movement along various planes {110}, {112}, {123}, depending on the relation of stresses involved, as well, as on the temperature of deformation and the important directions ⟨111⟩. It is observed, therefore, that with no close-packed planes and only four close-packed directions, this condition does not permit a high degree of plasticity, so that metals of this BCC type, including tantalum, columbium (niobium), have great strength and just medium ductility.

Analyzing the *close-packed hexagonal lattice*, it is observed that the close packing is similar to that of the face-centered cubic unit cell; however, the upper and lower horizontal planes reveal the hexagonal grouping of one atom intimately surrounded by six neighbors in its own plane. In this case, these planes of high atomic concentration are the basal planes {001} or {0001}, and the lines of close-packing on these planes are parallel to the edges of the first-order prism faces ⟨210⟩. Since the opposite faces of the hexagon are parallel, there is only one close-packed series of planes {001}, and three important rows ⟨210⟩ (direction). Consequently, it would be expected that slip may be expected along specific planes in this type of structure, but not with the same freedom as in the case of the face-centered cubic lattice. The elements falling into this type, such as magnesium, cadmium, and zinc, can accommodate their structure to stresses by another mechanism, known as *twinning*, an alteration which generates additional slip planes {001}, thereby approximating the plasticity found in the face-centered cubic lattice metals and surpassing that of the body-centered cubic metals. The hexagonal close-packed metals are anisotropic, such anisotropy depending on the symmetry of the crystal.

Any force applied to the surface of a crystal is transmitted by interatomic reactions across each crystallographic plane. The force that is transmitted across a particular plane can, in general, be resolved into a component normal to the plane and a component tangent to the plane. This tangent component can, in turn, be resolved further into components that correspond to definite crystallographic directions of the plane. By this means a definite force component for each slip system can be determined. It has been shown that slip in a particular system will take place if this force exceeds a critical value on a unit area of the slip plane. This is known as the *critical shear stress law*. The critical value or *yield stress*, as it is better known, is essentially independent of the normal force on the slip plane; however, it does depend on the particular type of slip system involved. Whenever a system of forces is applied to the surface of a polycrystalline metal, slip takes place first in that crystal and in that system where the critical shear stress is reached first. In the case of complex plastic deformation, however, slip occurs in several systems within each of a number of crystals. Although the critical shear stress decreases somewhat as the temperature increases, it is not very temperature-dependent in low temperature ranges of 200K to 500K. Since the melting point of a metal is that temperature at which thermal energy is just sufficient to cancel the bonding forces so that the atoms are no longer held together at the melting point, the critical shear stress there is zero. At temperatures just below the melting point, there is a finite critical shear stress, and as the melting point is approached and finally reached, there is an abrupt decrease to zero. Since metals deform by slip only on certain planes of atoms, it follows that anything that interferes with the slip process hardens the metal. For a given volume of precipitate, more slip planes could contain precipitate particles acting as *mechanical keys* to prevent slipping rather than just a few large slip planes. This later became known as the *keying theory*. A contradiction of this theory came with the work of Fraenkel and Seng in 1920, and Schmidt and Wasserman in 1926, when they were studying the electrical conductivity and lattice parameters of atoms during age-hardening. While the removal of solute from solution really should increase the conductivity of electrical energy, Fraenkel and Seng found, rather, that there was actually a *decrease* in conductivity for low-aging temperatures. It was also determined that for the Duralumin alloys (aluminum-base alloys with 3-1/2 per cent Cu, 0.20 per cent Si, 0.50 per cent Mg and 0.50 per cent Mn) the lattice parameter decreased steadily as the Cu dissolved in the Al decreases, whereas it actually should rise.

Although foreign atoms in the structure of a single crystal usually have a pronounced effect on its strength characteristics, the exact value of critical resolved shear stress is strongly dependent on the purity and perfection of the lattice. In fact, in polycrystalline substances foreign atoms may, and usually do, have a distinct effect on their strength characteristics.

The critical shear strength of a single crystal is increased by plastic deformation, such as work hardening in which the critical shear stress increases as the amount of elongation increases.

Metals also deform by a process known as *twinning*, as stated previously. Although it is true that less is known about twinning than about *slip*, it is known that in twinning a section of the crystal takes a new orientation with respect to the parent orientation. This new orientation is such that the twin is the mirror image of the parent. Therefore, the use of the term *twin* is more descriptive than factual, for although the twin may be thought of as being formed by a 180° rotation of a section of the crystal about the twinning axis, no actual rotation is involved.

In the case of slip, entire blocks of atoms slide past one another along definite crystallographic planes for quite a substantial distance, and in a certain direction. However, the orientation and the crystal structure are not destroyed in the action. The *slip plane* and the *slip direction* make up the *slip system*. In the twinning action, each plane of atoms in a twin band moves a slight amount with respect to that next to it, in such a way as to bring about the same crystal lattice but with a configuration that is a mirror image of the untwinned part. The *twin system*, then, is the twin plane and the direction of movement that takes place.

The criteria that determine which mechanism, slip or twinning, takes place under a given stress, are the actual orientations of the various systems with respect to the applied stress, and also the critical shear stress that is rquired on each system, slip or twinning, to initiate the deformation. In twinning, the rows of atoms parallel to what is termed the twinning plane are displaced along the plane by a distance that is proportional to the distance from the twinning plane. Thus, a formation takes place in the structure producing a mirror image of the lattice on the opposite side of the twinning plane. Plastic deformation by twinning has been found to occur mainly in body-centered cubic and hexagonal close-packed metals; however, experimenters have found deformation by twinning to occur also in face-centered cubic metals at very low temperatures of from 4K to 12K.

5-2   Imperfections in Crystals—Dislocations

Most metals and alloys are polycrystalline and are not composed of only a single crystal. Therefore, the crystals in the structures have different orientation, so that where two crystals meet, the atomic planes are mismatched, with grain boundary material existing between the different crystals. Not only is this mismatching found in the crystal or grain boundaries, but it is also present, at times, within the crystal itself in what is known as *subboundaries* and *mosaic* structures. Each crystal, therefore, can be thought of as being made up of millions of atoms with enough mismatching between them to act as individual units, in a way, but not enough to cause the formation of actual grain boundaries between them. Foreign atoms such as, as *point defects*, are found to exist in even the purest metals, such atoms of varying diameters themselves acting as sources of imperfection, inasmuch as the lattice around them has become distorted.

All imperfections in a lattice that result from a mismatching of atomic planes are known as *dislocations*. Even though dislocations are usually too small to be recognized even with the aid of the metallurgical microscope, evidence of their existence is obvious and explains phenomena in metals which could not otherwise be readily comprehended. The electron microscope is an excellent research tool in revealing the existence of dislocations; the etch-pit technique has also aided in such research. More will be discussed on the many uses of the electron microscope in Chapter 12. For example, the mechanism resulting from plastic deformation, vapors, and the actual strength of metals, can now be explained in the light of the presence of dislocations. Grain boundaries and subboundaries can be looked upon as being arrays of dislocations.

In addition to the distortion of the lattice caused by dislocations due either to foreign atoms in the lattice or to mismatching of the atomic planes in the crystal, it has been found that still another type of imperfection exists in crystals, i.e. that caused by *point defects* (vacant sites) in the lattice. These are places in the lattice where one or more atoms obviously are missing and do not fill in as might be expected, inasmuch as they have been found to be stable. It has also been found that equilibrium is reached in a system in accordance with to the number of vacancies that are present in the lattice, and that the number of such vacancies increases with an increase in temperature.

Imperfections and distortion of whatever cause or nature have decided effects on the crystal's properties and therefore on the physical and mechanical properties of metals and alloys. Shown in Fig. 5–4 is a sketch of a dislocation caused by mismatching of atomic planes, an example of edge dislocation.

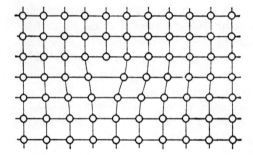

Fig. 5-4. *A dislocation caused by mismatching of atomic planes. This is an example of edge dislocation.*

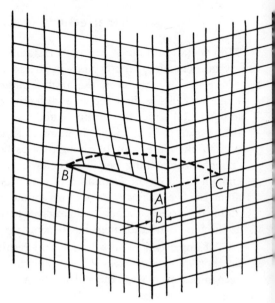

Fig. 5-4(a). *A screw dislocation in a simple cubic crystal lattice.*

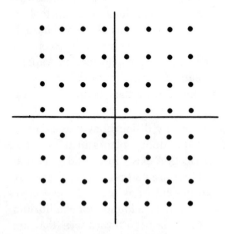

Fig. 5-4(b). *An example of edge dislocation due to mismatching of atomic planes. This is a positive edge dislocation since the extra row of atoms is above the dislocation line. (Courtesy U. S. Steel Corporation.)*

Shown in Fig. 5–4(a) is a single dislocation line, *BC*, in an otherwise perfect simple cubic lattice. There are in a typical metal crystal as many as 10^7 to 10^9 such lines that cross a sq in. of area everywhere in the crystal. The fact that dislocations of this type create internal forces between the atoms is one of the characteristics of such dislocations. They may be likened to the internal stresses found in a perfect

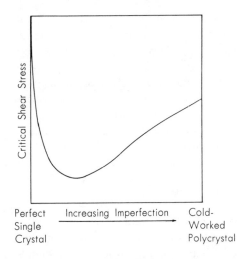

Fig. 5-5. *The effect of imperfection on the critical shear stress. As shown here, a perfect crystal has a high yield strength, but a crystal with only a few imperfections has a very low yield strength. As the density of imperfections becomes larger, the yield strength again become larger (Courtesy U. S. Steel Corporation.)*

elastic body if a cut were made in it such as *ABC* in Fig. 5–4(a). When the upper portion in this figure is displaced just one atom distance (b), and the cut is cemented together, such a dislocation can be visualized, this being what is known as an *edge-type dislocation,* the simplest type to occur. It is as if there were an extra plane of atoms just above or below the dislocation line. In cases where this extra plane of atoms is *above* the dislocation line, it is arbitrarily and by custom referred to as a *positive edge dislocation.* If the extra plane of atoms is *below* the dislocation line, it is termed a *negative edge dislocation.*

An edge dislocation might also be considered as a structure in which one plane of atoms above or below the dislocation line is missing. In the case of an edge dislocation, it is one that extends through the lattice perpendicular to the plane of the paper indicated in the Fig. 5–4(b).

Shown in Fig. 5–1 is a hypothetical crystal that does not contain any dislocations whatever and is therefore in the undeformed state. Assuming that this crystal has a basic cubic unit cell, and that it undergoes slip on a {100} type plane, it will be seen that any stresses that might be imposed upon it have not, as yet, produced deformation in the crystal.

Another type of dislocation is produced if a shearing stress is exerted on the crystal, as shown in Figures 5–2 and 5–3A. In these illustrations no atoms are shown, but it may be assumed that they lie at the intersections of the lines that are shown. In Fig. 5–1 the condition of the undeformed crystal in Fig. 5–2 is shown after slipping action has started to take effect and has extended as far as line *XW.* (*W* lies immediately below *X.*) In Fig. 5–2 *XW* is the dislocation line and is the boundary between the slipped and unslipped portions of the crystal. It will be observed here that in the *screw dislocation* shown in Fig. 5–3A, the dislocation line is parallel to the direction in which the shearing forces are applied, whereas in the previously described edge dislocation it was perpendicular to them. In Fig. 5–3A it will be observed that the dislocation line has progressed completely across the crystal, passing completely out it, leaving the condition of offset as shown in the illustration. This type of dislocation is properly referred to as a *screw dislocation* by reason of the fact that a line starting at the top of Fig. 5–3A can follow a spiral path to the bottom in an uninterrupted manner. The same path can also be followed in the reverse direction.

By a combination of an edge dislocation and a screw dislocation within a crystal, a *dislocation loop* is formed. It is significant that an edge dislocation can terminate in a screw dislocation, and the reverse is also true. Dislocations in crystals are can multiply, so that dislocations can be generated and modified considerably by foreign elements present or introduced into the lattice structure. Carbon or nitrogen in iron, for example, may retard and restrain the development of a dislocation, so that it will require higher stresses to produce any appreciable deformation. (In body-centered cubic metals, yield point, blue brittleness, and other mechanical phenomena are caused by the interstitial-dislocation interaction.)

5-3   Macroscopic Nature of Metals

As has previously been stated, microscopic plasticity commences with certain observations related to the arrangement of atoms in the crystal lattice, developing a knowledge and understanding of the detailed mechanism of plastic flow of metals. On the other hand, *macroscopic plasticity* begins with certain observations related to plastic deformation of polycrystalline metals in such mechanical tests as simple tension and compression, leading to an understanding of gross plastic flow. In the macroscopic concept, the metal is looked upon as a continuum having such properties as density, stress, and velocity at all points within its outer structural surface. The main advantage of the continuum concept is that it permits the physical quantities, such as density, stress, and velocity to be treated as functions that are continuous, thereby making possible the handling of these functions by means of a wide use of mathematics based on these functions.

In the continuum concept stress and strain are two important factors, as they describe the behavior of the average way in which the forces function between the atoms and the deformation of the lattice in the crystal. Stress, as has been stated previously, is a quantity that represents the force per unit area on an internal plane of the crystal. It is obvious, however, that the stress at a point in a continuum cannot be defined by a single number, as it varies for different planes that pass through the point. Strain rate represents the *relative* velocities of neighboring internal planes. It may therefore be seen that it, too, varies for the different planes that pass through any particular point. Stress and strain are quantities that are referred to as *tensors* and may be thought of as mathematical quantities, or numbers, but with far more complex properties.

Macroscopic plasticity, in theory, depends substantially on three macroscopic observations concerning stress and strain rate. The first of these is that *the volume remains essentially constant during gross plastic deformation.* We conclude from this that the sum of the principle strain rates, stretches, and compressions, is zero, i.e.,

$$\epsilon_1 + \epsilon_2 + \epsilon_3 = 0 \text{ (i.e., the principal true strain is zero.)}$$

This is what we might expect, for the main mechanism of plastic flow is consecutive slip of adjacent rows of atoms, and this mechanism does not require any change of volume.

Another basic observation is that *plastic flow or yielding occurs at a point only after the maximum shear stress in some direction on some plane reaches the critical value* k. We know from a study of the stress tensor that the greatest shear stress occurs on the two planes that are halfway between planes of greatest and least principal stress. The magnitude of this shear stress is one-half the difference between the greatest and least principal values. By this, we see that the second observation for plastic flow to take place may be stated:

$$\frac{\sigma_1 - \sigma_2}{2} = k \text{ (in the case of ductile metals).}$$

A third basic observation of total plastic flow is that *the directions of greatest shear strain rate coincide with the directions of greatest shear stress.* From this we can see that although shear straining is similar to slip, the observation is, essentially, that the most slip occurs in the directions of greatest shearing stress, which is what we would expect to be the case.

5-4   Principles of Metal Working

One of the most valuable characteristics of metals is their ability to be plastically deformed, permitting us not only to produce metal plates, shapes, sheets, etc., but also to manufacture by means of rolling, drawing, and extrusion, rods, strips, tubes, and other shapes so useful and essential to industry. This characteristic also makes it possible for us to form parts from solid metal, with an increase in such physical properties as strength, hardness, and toughness.

In order to get an improvement in strength by means of plastic deformation, it is necessary that higher stresses be applied, particularly if the deformation is to be continued with further plastic deformation resulting. The unique atomic structure of metals is the key to our ability to deform them without the danger of fracture. Metals, as we will recall, consist of atomic nuclei surrounded by electron gas, and it is this structure that permits the shifting of the bonds between the atoms and an interchange of electrons, both essential to plastic deformation.

Inasmuch as individual ions of an atom are not rigidly attached to any particular electrons, it may be seen that it is relatively easy to shift the ions along particular crystallographic planes. By means of plastic deformation of the metals, the electron-to-ions bonds are readily altered, making it possible to change the shape of metallic parts without severing the atomic bonds. By virtue of this characteristic of metals, an entire section of a metal crystal is able to move in relation to the balance of the crystal by slipping along atom planes without a fracture occurring in the area being deformed. The metal is thereby made capable of being deformed as desired by progressive deformation along numbers of such atom planes, resulting in a change of dimensions and shape without causing a fracture of the metallic part.

When we consider the application of the principles of plastic deformation to the design of products by means of metal-working, we must define the factors that not only assist in such deformation, but also those that limit and, in some cases, prevent such deformation. The first of these limiting factors is *instability* which brings about undesirable forms of deformation, usually because of small and often unavoidable irregularities in the metal or, possibly, in the load application. The *instability* factor can be divided into two fundamental types: those related to compressive stresses, which we call *buckling*, and those related to tensile stresses, termed *necking*. In Fig. 5–6 we can observe these two types of instabilities, the example being a deep-drawn metal cup. In this instance, if the flange is too thin or not supported sufficiently, the compressive forces around the circumference may cause buckling or wrinkling. On the other hand, if metal walls are too thin, the axial

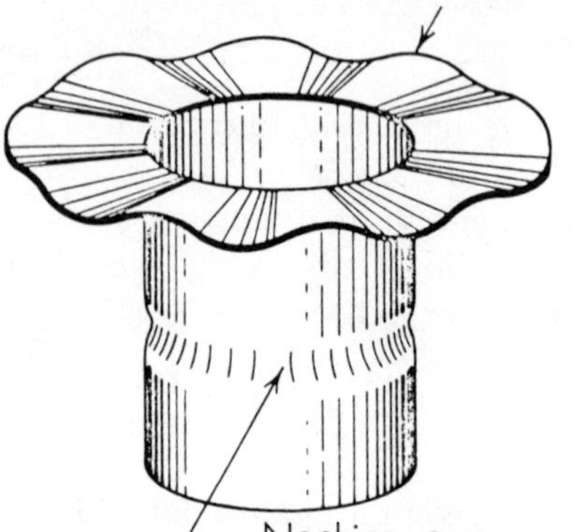

Buckling or
Compressive Instability

Fig. 5-6. *Examples of forming instabilities in a deep-drawn metal cup illustrating both buckling and necking. The former is one of compressive instability and the latter of tensile instability. Factors which have a tendency of spreading plastic deformation will reduce the likelihood of instability.(Courtesy of United States Steel Corporation.)*

Necking or
Tensile Instability

tensile stresses may cause necking, or local thinning. Regarding this matter of *instability*, we can say that those factors that have a tendency to spread plastic deformation minimize the probability of instability. Such factors may be work hardening and mechanical design properties, such as the shape of the load and method of applying it.

The other main factor limiting the deformation of metals is *fracture*, which brings about entirely new surfaces, such as cracks, holes, and actual separation into two or more parts. Fracture may be looked upon as the separation of the crystal lattice because of tensile forces strong enough to overcome the interatomic cohesion. Macroscopic studies of many fractures indicate that they are connected or associated with the reaching of some critical tensile stress within the metal. From this observation we arrive at one of the most important principles of metal working, i.e., *the amount of plastic working is usually enhanced by the use of compressive, rather than tensile, methods.* It is because of this fact that larger reductions in shape are possible by means of forging operations than by stretching methods and, similarly, by single-pass rolling rather than single-pass drawing. Still another factor that is important in the design of metal-working operations is the ability to bring about some particular properties in the part that we desire, such as directional properties, anisotropy, etc. We may want to produce a product with little or no residual stresses, or one that has only certain prescribed residual stresses. Residual stresses, by means of hotworking, can be minimized by actually destroying any work hardening that may be present.

5-5   Crystallization and Recrystallization

The attraction which produces crystals is one of the fundamental properties of matter. It is identical with the cohesion of ordinary solidification, for there are in fact very few cases outside of the kingdom of life in which solidification takes place without some degree of crystallization. (There are solids, such as glass, which when undercooled in the liquid state do crystallize, as pointed out in Chapter 3.) The "cohesive attraction" is, in fact, the organizing or structure-making principle in organic matter, since it produces specific forms for each species of matter, just as life does for each living species. For example, a bar of cast iron right from the mold is rough and granular in surface because of its angular crystalline grains, which the iron assumed when solidification took place. A fragment of marble such as is mined in Vermont (ferro-silicon and also ferro-manganese) glistens in the sunlight because of the reflection of light from the hundreds and thousands of crystalline surfaces. Every single grain in the entire mass has its own crystalline structure. Just as water cannot solidify without crystallization, neither can iron, or lead, or any other mineral material. It can be said, then, that crystallization produces masses made of crystalline grains when it cannot produce separate and distinct crystals. The granite mountains of Vermont are mountains of crystals (consisting essentially of quartz and orthoclase), each particle of them being crystalline in nature and structure.

When the lava currents from volcanic eruptions cool, they become masses of crystalline grains. In fact, the earth itself may be said to have crystalline foundations, based on the profound beauty of the universal law of symmetry which, when conditions of environment permit, leads to the perfect crystal, with regular angles and facets.

In Chapter 3 the structure of matter was discussed and it was stated that a metal in the liquid state (unless undercooled as in some cases of glass) is noncrystalline in that the atoms are fairly free to move about randomly, with little regard for interspacial distances. The exception to this is the fact that there is at times an activation energy for diffusion in solids, and this energy, which such atoms inherently possess internally, interferes with their approaching one another closely enough to succumb to the control of the electrostatic fields of force of other atoms. In fact, atoms may be close enough to other atoms, in many cases, and surrounded by the proper number of atoms to set up a lattice. However, being in the liquid state, and with every atom having free energy to move at random, no structure is created; each atom's bonds are broken and reformed with ease, as is usually the case when matter is in the liquid state.

As long as fifty years ago metallurgists were already aware that a cold-worked metal, when heated up to a high temperature for a sufficiently long period of time, would form new unstrained grains that in time would supplant the cold-worked structure. It was also known then that variations in the amount of cold work, and in the composition of the metal, affected the recrystallization temperature and the size of the resulting grains that were formed. Furthermore, the phenomenon of recovery, which is the removal of residual stresses by localized plastic flow, resulting from low-temperature annealing of cold-worked metals, had already been discovered at about the turn of the century. Indeed, engineers had observed the effect of critical strain on the size of the recrystallized grains that were formed.

Engineers and metallurgists during the past fifty or sixty years have expended a great amount of time and effort on the study of the processes of crystallization, recrystallization, and recovery; these are fundamental and must be understood to permit development of metals and alloys producing materials with superior properties for industry and the military.

In the annealing of cold-worked metals, three types of mutually distinguishable phenomena take place. These are, in the order in which they occur in the annealing process, *recovery*, *grain growth* and *recrystallization*. Briefly stated,

1. *Recovery* is the first stage of the softening process of a metal. This is accompanied by a change in physical properties—particularly those determined by the

state of strain of the cold-worked metal at low annealing temperatures, the change being unaccompanied by any detectable change in microstructure of the cold-worked metal. Stress-free grains begin to form in the slip planes, no doubt as a result of the residual distortion energy of the crystal lattice. As the annealing continues, the nuclei grow to visible size as new equiaxed, stress-free grains; here the original plastically deformed grains begin to gradually disappear.

2. Grains that were severely deformed in the recovery period may be thought of as eaten away by the stress-free grains during their period of growth. *Grain growth* is the result of the tendency of the atoms in the smaller crystals, with higher energy, to become a part of larger crystals. It occurs in completely recrystallized metals, as it is a continued growth of recrystallized grains. In cases where there has been a limited amount of deformation in the lattice, there is likely to be an exaggerated grain growth upon annealing, called *germination*. Diffusion is the controlling factor in grain growth, and since diffusivity increases exponentially with elevated temperature, increasing the temperature speeds up grain growth substantially. Another consideration in this connection contributing to grain growth is that of the grain-boundary energy, which renders the small grains unstable. The result is that the small grains have too high a surface-to-volume ratio and therefore become smaller and are consumed by the stress-free grains enlarging the latter.

3. *Recrystallization* occurring at elevated temperatures is a process of the formation and growth of unrestrained grains, supplanting entirely the cold-worked structure. Metals that have been cold-worked are in a non-equilibrium condition because of the distortion of their lattices. Although an internal force tends to bring the metal to equilibrium, the movement of the atoms is so small that this internal force cannot bring about the movement necessary to break up the distortion of the lattice. When the metal is heated, the internal force changes only slightly, but the movement of the atoms increases sharply. In time a temperature is reached at which movement of the atoms can start, and they can arrange themselves into lattices that are not distorted. This degree of heat is known as the *recrystallization temperature*, and it is quite variable even for the same metal.

Recrystallization of metals is actually of two types: that due to heating of the cold-worked metal, as just explained, and that due to the allotropic changes that occur in some metals, as pointed out in Chapter 3, wherein it was stated that iron, cobalt, manganese, tin, chromium, and titanium contain more than one lattice structure. Recrystallization due to allotropic transformations without changes in composition are, in reality, changes in crystal form are usually accompanied by appreciable changes in crystal properties.

All three of the aforenamed annealing phenomena depend on time and are not instantaneous. The rate at which each operates increases with an elevation in temperature. It is true that when the temperature to which the cold-worked metal has been subjected is sufficiently high, these processes work with such rapidity as to appear to be instantaneous; however at lower temperatures the time-dependence is readily detected.

Recovery, grain growth, and recrystallization are all processes leading to the softening of the metal. In the past it was conventional to study these phenomena by putting cold-worked samples through a series of elevated temperatures and holding them there for a sufficient period of time, usually from 15 minutes to two hours, subsequently measuring the physical properties at room temperature.

The *recrystallization temperature* is important to recognize—this being the lowest temperature at which equiaxed, stress-free grains appear in the structure of a metal that was previously plastically deformed. The recrystallization temperature depends upon several factors, including the following:

1. The severity of plastic deformation
2. The grain size prior to plastic deformation
3. The temperature at which plastic deformation was performed
4. The time in which the plastic deformation was accomplished and during which the plastically deformed metal was heated in order to attain recrystallization
5. The presence of dissolved or undissolved elements in the alloy

Upon completion of recrystallization, a grain growth occurs because of the process of coalescence and reorientation. With the increase in grain size a decrease in strength and hardness takes place. In those instances where the metals have not been uniformly deformed plastically, or in cases where the composition is not uniform throughout the alloy, an extremely large and non-uniform grain size results. In the production of these abnormally large and non-uniform grains, the phenomenon is referred to as *germination*, which is the same result produced by very slow heating after moderate deformation has been applied. Obviously, this production of coarse grains after re-crystallization has occurred is not desirable, as a lower ductility results along with other impairment of desirable physical properties. Metallurgical experimenters, like James B. Austin, Administrative Vice President, Research and Technology, United States Steel Corporation, and others, have broadened the understanding of these processes and in fact have greatly enhanced our knowledge by the use of the electron transmission microscope and by the use of highly pure, zone-refined iron. Prior to the electron microscope, our investigations of cold-worked iron were seriously hampered by the limited resolution of the light microscope. Even at high magnification using the conventional metallurgical light microscope, there was little to see except a mass of elongated grains, along with occasional twin structures. As shown in Fig. 5–7, an examination of deformed polycrystalline iron with an electron microscope, using transmission techniques, reveals the severely deformed structure much more clearly at 12,000 diameters. In this photograph the dark irregular "jagged" lines are visible evidence of misalignment of atoms or dislocation caused by cold-working the metal. As the metal is worked these dislocations move through the material, concentrating in certain regions. The broad dark lines in the picture (Fig. 5–7) are high concentrations of dislocations; few dislocations exist within the "cells" outlined by these bands.

Fig. 5–8 shows the structure of iron strained at three levels, 5, 9 and 30 per cent, and it is instructive to be able to trace the development of the cell structure in poly-crystalline iron as it is so strained by rolling at room temperature. As shown in this photograph, the material strained at 5 per cent reveals dislocations formed in a relatively random distribution—at least we cannot see any apparent pattern here. In the photo showing the iron strained at 9 per cent level, we see that the dis-locations are concentrating in high density regions separated by areas of low density. In this manner embryonic cells form, their diameters averaging about 3 microns, which is much less than the diameter of unworked grains. In the bottom photo in

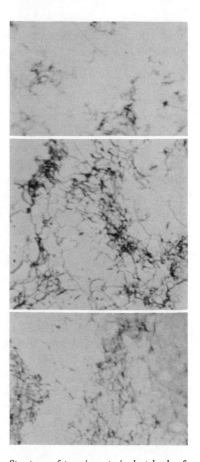

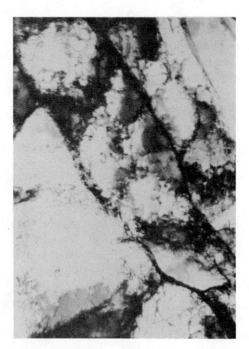

Fig. 5-7. *Electron microscopic photo of cold-worked material, a structure of severely deformed (70 per cent) iron. The jagged lines are dislocations which result from misalignment of atoms.*

Fig. 5-8. *Structures of pure iron strained at levels of 5, 9 and 30 per cent (top to bottom) and revealing dislocations in varying concentrations. In the lightly strained material, dislocations are distributed randomly, while further straining concentrates dislocations into embryonic cell borders, until definite subgrains appear, as in structure in bottom photo. (All photos taken at 30,000 diameters.)*

Fig. 5–8 we see iron which was strained 30 per cent and observe that very few dislocations exist in the matrix. However, the average dislocation density has increased, largely because of the extreme concentration of dislocations in the walls of the cell. The cell diameter is now approximately one micron.

Where the strain rate is greatly increased or the deformation temperature is lowered, there is a tendency for cell formation to decrease, both of these effects shown in Fig. 5–9, In the photo at the left, the specimen was shock loaded to 70 kilobars (one bar is 14.5 psi) at room temperature; the specimen shown at the right in Fig. 5–9 was rolled to 2 per cent reduction in area at −320F (−196C). As is evident here, under such deformation conditions, dislocations are uniformly distributed throughout the matrix. Also, increasing the deformation temperature raises the cell-forming tendency and the density of the dislocations in the cell walls.

Recent investigations by scientists at U.S.Steel Corporation laboratories at the Monroeville, Pa. plant revealed changes in average dislocation density and the

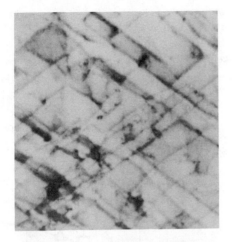

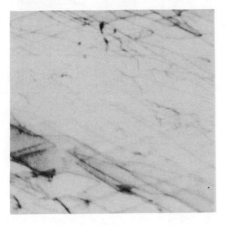

Fig. 5-9. *How variations in processing conditions affect the distribution of dislocations. On the top, the pure iron has been subjected to shock-loading (to 70 kilobars); the bottom photo shows iron rolled 2 per cent at −320F. Each of these treatments distributed the dislocations evenly throughout the material. 32,000 diameters.*

recovery of yield stress of zone-melted iron, as functions of the amount and temperature of deformation and the time and temperature of the recovery anneal. Analyzing these factors separately, it is found that the average dislocation density (N per sq cm) varies with the amount and temperature of deformation. In Fig. 5–10 we see that average dislocation density (in iron tested at room temperature) rises with increasing strain. This average density, however, is independent of deformation temperature, for in this chart the points for deformations at −95F and +480F fall on the curve, which leads us to another conclusion. Since the density of dislocations in cell walls increases with deformation temperature, as stated before, dislocations must necessarily move from cell interiors to cell walls with rising temperature.

In Fig. 5–11 the changes are shown in dislocation density and distribution that take place during recovery of a metal. In this experiment the specimens were strained at 16 per cent at room temperature and then heated to 1025F several times. At the top of Fig. 5–11 the cell structure in the deformed material is quite evident. Heating for 15 minutes at 1025F as shown in the center photo reveals how the dislocations become straightened, the average dislocation density being lessened and a regular dislocation network established. After 16 hours at temperature, the recovery was substantially completed and the formation of well-defined subgrains observed. These subgrains, it will be observed, are the same size as the dislocation cells in the deformed iron. A snake-like configuration is also noted here, typical of the structures of boundaries between subgrains in a fully recovered iron. The diamond-shaped markings are actually hexagons with two short sides that are believed to result from an interaction between two sets of parallel dislocations.

It has been found by experimentation in the laboratory of U.S.Steel Corporation that recrystallization takes place through a process of subgrain coalescence. Fig. 5–12 shows some of the subgrain boundaries gradually disappearing (from left to right) as the time at temperature (1350F in this instance) is increased. Furthermore,

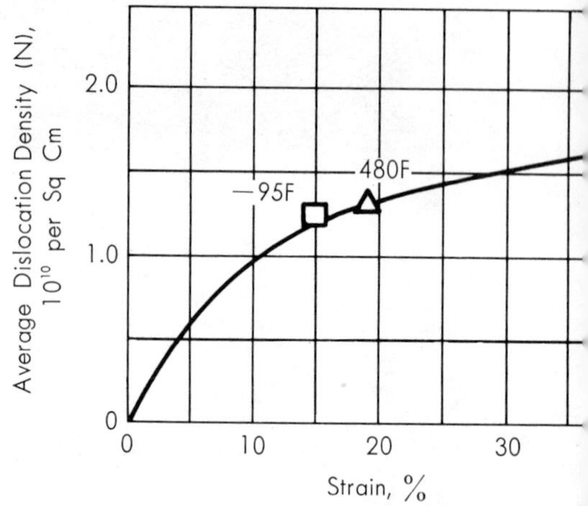

Fig. 5-10. *Illustration of dislocation density rising with strain, increasing rapidly at first, then leveling off. Since dislocation densities measured in material strained at low and high temperatures fall on the curve, (determined at room temperature), the effect is apparently independent of temperature.*

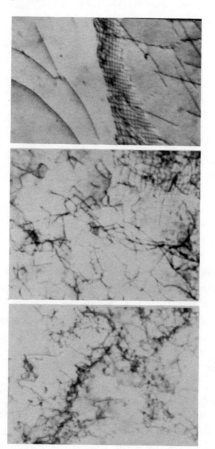

Fig. 5-11. *Pure iron when strained 16 per cent at room temperature forms many jagged dislocation lines, as shown at the top. Heating at 1025F for 15 minutes (center) and for 16 hours (bottom) straightens and redistributes these dislocations and causes subgrains to form. Recovery is substantially complete after 16 hours.*

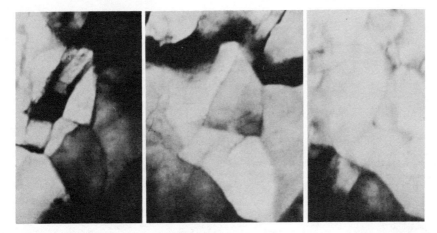

Fig. 5-12. *How, during the annealing process, the subgrains coalesce. Here a cold-worked iron-silicon has been heated at 1350F for 30 sec., 2 min., and 3 min. respectively. As coalescence takes place, the differences in orientations among subgrains disappear. (Photo taken at 40,000 diameters.)*

the contrast between adjoining grains becomes minimal, indicating that their orientations have merged, one with the other.

Reviewing the steps in this process briefly, we see that the subgrains form as a result of polygonization when a cold-worked crystal is annealed. With further annealing, the dislocations making up these subgrain boundaries move out to the intersecting or connecting boundaries. In the meantime, the subgrains rotate by lattice diffusion, merging into a common orientation. Then, in the next step, geometrical adjustments take place in boundaries because of increased angular misfits in the coalesced subgrain boundaries. Subsequently, coalescence of the larger subgrains may take place. Further action will form new high angle boundaries around the coalesced subgrains which have now become a *recrystallized grain* at an early stage of formation. Further growth takes place through migration of the high angle boundaries, at the expense of the polygonized matrix.

The recrystallization of austenite is now assuming considerable importance, due to the fact that it is associated with thermo-mechanical treatments commer cially significant. Working with AISI 1040 steel, a grade in which austenite is stable at elevated temperatures but is not retained in appreciable quantities on cooling to room temperature, it has been found that certain formations take place that are important. (It should be here stated that this stability of austenite at elevated temperatures and lack of retention on cooling to room temperature, is characteristic of most commercial steels.) Following the processing of these steels by rolling or forging at elevated temperatures, it is found that although these operations do deform the austenite present at such temperatures, recrystallization takes place very rapidly, and in most instances no trace of elongated austenite grains remains at room temperature.

The newly formed austenite grains are smaller, as a rule, than those which existed at the start of hot rolling. Figure 5-13 illustrates the relation between various mechanical properties and austenitic grain size in the AISI 1040 steel.

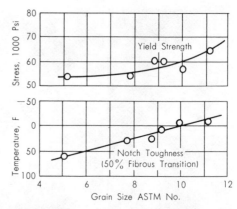

Fig. 5-13. *In AISI 1040 steel, smaller grain sizes mean enhanced yield strength and toughness. Decreasing the grain size, however, does not affect the tensile strength, elongation or reduction in area—these values remaining at averages of 88,000 psi, 25 per cent and 51 per cent, respectively, throughout all grain sizes.*

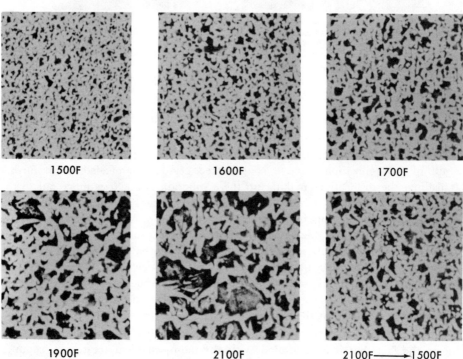

Fig. 5-14. *The heating of AISI 1040 steel at progressively higher temperatures results in larger grain sizes. These specimens were heated and forged at the same temperatures, except the one in the lower right hand corner. It should be noted that forging at 1500F did not completely refine the grain size that was developed at 2100F. Photomicrographs were taken at 200 diameters. (Picral was used as the etchant for these pictures.)*

Tensile strength, reduction in area, and elongation, as shown by these tests with AISI 1040 steel, are independent of grain size, but yield strength and notch-toughness improves significantly as the grain size decreases. It is therefore apparent that it is of considerable commercial importance to obtain the finest possible grain size for best results in commercial steels. It has also been found that a very fine-grained product can be produced by controlling the hot-working process to govern the three factors that affect the recrystallized grain size:

1. Prior austenite grain size
2. The amount of deformation that is being applied
3. The recrystallization temperature

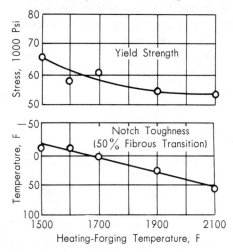

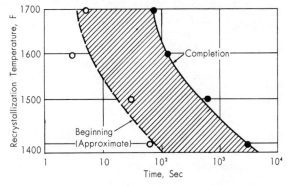

Fig. 5-15. *The results of mechanical tests made on specimens of AISI 1040 steel, photomicrographs of which are shown in Fig. 5-14. Higher forging temperatures are detrimental to yield strength and to notch toughness, an effect which is associated with the concomitant increase in grain size. Tensile strength, elongation, and reduction in area were not affected, being 88,000 psi, 25 per cent and 46 per cent respectively.*

Fig. 5-16. *After a specimen of AISI 51B60 is austenitized at about 1700F and rolled to a 65 per cent reduction, it will recrystallize at various times and temperatures according to this pattern. In general, sufficient time is available, especially at the lower temperatures, to permit further heat processing before recrystallization starts. Just as might be expected, recrystallization takes place more rapidly at higher temperatures, but even at the highest temperature studied (1700F), the time period is quite substantial. At lower temperatures within the stable austenite region, recrystallization proceeds slowly enough to be amenable to control by heat treatment after deformation has taken place.*

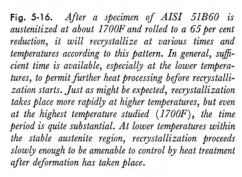

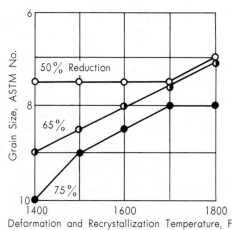

Fig. 5-17. *With increasing working at given temperature in the austenitic zone, the grain size becomes finer. We also see that the lower the deformation and recrystallization temperature, the finer the grain size will be.*

---

* Figures 5–7 through 5–17 used by permission United States Steel Corporation.

Since all three of these variables can be controlled in the laboratory, it is felt that they may also be controlled in actual practice, so that a maximum amount of grain refinement can be obtained by heating and deforming at the lowest temperature at which the austenite is stable. In the tests on rectangularly shaped specimens of AISI 1040 steel, heated at temperatures from 1500 to 2100F and upset with a single blow in a high energy rate forming machine, the resulting microstructures as shown in Fig. 5–14 were obtained. These show quite clearly that the lower the heating and forging temperature, the finer the recrystallized grains will be. Also, it should be noted in Fig. 5–14 that heating to a high temperature (2100F) and then forging at a lower temperature (1500F) was not completely effective in bringing about a desirable refinement in the grain structure.

5-6   Determination of Grain Size

Grain size may be expressed in terms of the grains per unit area or volume. In many nonferrous metals, particularly alpha brasses, grain size is expressed in millimeters average diameter and is determined by comparison with standards at 75 diameters of magnification. Estimation of grain size or grain counting is accomplished by viewing a polished *plane* section under the microscope; the boundaries of the grains as viewed lay out a network on a plane surface. The number of grains per unit area so sectioned on a plane, or the average area of these rough polygons, serve as well, as a measure of grain size. The usual terms for reporting grain size are

1. Grains per sq mm
2. Average area of grain (in sq mm)
3. Mean diameter of grain (in mm)
4. Arbitrary numbers (exponential) such as ASTM standards based on the formula:
    Number of grains per sq in. at $100X = 2^{N-1}$ where N is the index of the grain size involved.

In summarizing the subject of recrystallization of metals, and especially steel, the following conclusions may be reached:

1. The larger the austenite grain size produced by heating prior to hot working, the slower will be the rate of recrystallization and the larger the recrystallized grains resulting.
2. Lowering the recrystallization temperature reduces the rate of recrystallization and results in smaller recrystallized grains.
3. Where all other factors are constant, larger amounts of deformation favor faster recrystallization and smaller grains, which, in turn, improve yield strength and notch-toughness—two properties that are desirable in most instances.

5-7   Hot Working of Metals

Whereas cold working is plastic deformation *below* the recrystallization temperature, hot working entails plastic deformation at temperatures where no strain hardening takes place. There are two basic reasons for hot working: to shape metals into useful parts, and to accomplish better physical properties than are possible with castings. At the same time that hot working is progressing, the metal is being subjected to an annealing process, and immediately after plastic deformation takes place, recrystallization occurs. This self-annealing process reduces the possibility of hardening and an accompanying loss of ductility, such as we find is the case in cold working. At the higher hot-working temperatures, the yield strength of metal is substantially lowered, thereby permitting plastic deformation at lower stress values.

The principal purpose of hot-working is to deform metal plastically into a required shape and with as low an energy output as possible, and to impart to the metal the best possible mechanical properties. For these reasons hot working is highly desirable for comparatively large deformations that would be impossible, or uneconomical, by a cold-working method. Furthermore, much less force is necessary and lower capacity equipment is required in the hot working of metal, in comparison to the working force and capacity of equipment needed for making the same deformations by means of cold-working processes.

Although various defects, such as internal porosity, gas pockets, blowholes, and segregation may be present in the metal parts or billets to be hot-worked, these are substantially eliminated or reduced by the impacting and resulting increase in the density of the parts. Plastic deformation at the elevated hot-working temperatures brings about a definite effect on segregation due to slipping along crystallographic planes, which results in a mingling of atoms, helping to reduce and eliminate any microsegregation, as well as coring. Furthermore, the elevated temperature of hot working speeds up diffusion. Diffusion entails the migration of atoms through a metal at elevated temperature from an area of high atomic concentration toward an area of low concentration of similar atoms. This driving force of diffusion has a tendency to eliminate concentration gradients within the metal and to result in a homogeneous material.

When the solute atoms are considerably smaller than the solvent atoms, the smaller atoms are able to migrate rapidly through the interstices of the solvent atoms, resulting in the formation of interstitial solid solutions. The rate of diffusion of the solute atoms in an interstitial solid solution is found to be very rapid, as might be expected. Diffusion also occurs in the case of substitutional solid solution alloys because of the thermal vibration of the metallic atoms and the presence of vacancies, permitting the atoms to migrate from their original positions. Because of the increased temperature, there is also an increase in diffusion.

The best properties of hot-worked parts are obtained when the hot-working technique orients the direction of *flow* in relation to the direction of stress required. Areas of varying composition and nonmetallic inclusions are elongated and flattened with the elongation of the main portion of the metal, so that there is a dispersion of detrimental effects due to these factors. These areas of nonmetallic inclusions and varying compositions are referred to as *fibers*, and the way in which they orient themselves within the metal is called *flow*. They indicate the direction of metal flow as well as direction of elongation of the structure of the metal. These flow lines within hot-worked metal may be either detrimental or beneficial, depending on whether they are properly utilized and oriented with respect to the subsequent stress direction imparted to the part in question. Shear stress and bending stress should be transverse to the fiber (flow) direction for best results, A highly desirable result is also obtained when the segregated regions of alloying elements and nonmetallic inclusions are elongated and lined up parallel with the direction of an applied tensile stress.

Along with the many advantages of hot working over cold working, there are also some limitations to hot working, due primarily to the elevated temperatures required. Formation of oxides on the metallic surface at the time of heating and hot working gives rise to rough surfaces on the finished products, along with weight loss resulting from scaling on the surface. There is also an expansion of volume in the metal during heating and a corresponding shrinkage during cooling, so that it becomes difficult to obtain a highly smooth finish on the surface. Furthermore, close tolerances of dimensions, such as we are able to realize with cold working, are not possible.

Another serious limitation of hot working is the decarburization that occurs on the surface of the metal, due to the loss of carbon taking place inside the heating furnaces, as well as to the period of time when the hot stock is handled in the air. The result is the formation of a layer of low-strength steel that is decarburized on the surface of many manufactured hot-worked parts. This results in a surface weakness very detrimental in many cases, particularly where the parts are to be subsequently subjected to repeated stress, as this often leads to fatigue failures. Failures of this nature are usually initiated at the surfaces of the metal and not from the internal portion of the metal part. Fatigue cracking is also prevalent in decarburized parts, cracks that originate at a weak surface, propogating easily into the stronger metal underneath the surface. This condition can be eliminated or minimized by the complete removal of a layer of the surface metal from the billets and blooms, either by chipping, machining, or flame scarfing, etc. if it is deemed necessary to do so to protect the surface and render the surface of the part to the same composition and properties as the metal below the surface.

5-8   Hot-Working Temperature

The lowest temperature at which metal may be satisfactorily hot worked is the lowest temperature at which no strain hardening takes place during the plastic deformation process. With a steady reduction of temperature, a point is reached at which recrystallization with softening are out of phase with the plastic deformation that is taking place. As a result of working the metal at too low a temperature, strain hardening results. Actually, in commercial hot-working processes, metal is worked at a much higher temperature than theoretical minimum to be sure of good working plasticity. The yield strength and resistance to deformation are lessened with elevated temperature, permitting much lower working forces or pressures on the part of hammers, rolls, etc. For obvious reasons, the maximum hot-working temperature should be well below the point of burning because of preferential grain-boundary oxidation, or the potential of melting at the grain-boundaries, both of which are caused by excessively high temperatures. And undesirable large grains are formed when the hot-working temperature is permitted to become excessive.

5-9   Control of Grain Size

The main control over grain size is close regulation of the temperature at which hot working is completed; this is called the *finishing* temperature. Recrystallization of the deformed metal part takes place with only a minimum of coalescence

Fig. 5-18. *Newly recrystallized grains of larger size brought about by elevation of the temperature of cold-worked metal. This transformation of the smaller grains into newly recrystallized grains that are larger than originally present, is due to* coalescence. *(500X)*

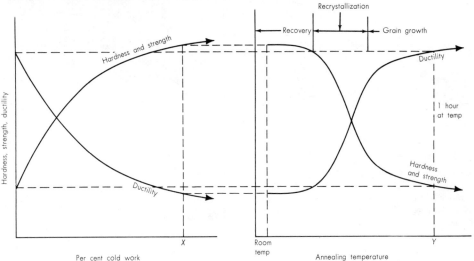

Fig. 5-19. *The cold-work annealing cycle showing that metal is hardened and strengthened by cold deformation but that ductility is decreased. Prior to metal fracture, cold-working is stopped at point X; however, if the metal which has been previously deformed to point X is reheated for 1 hour at temperature Y, the ductility and strength it originally possessed will return. In order to achieve intermediate properties, the metal should be annealed when sufficiently oversize so that desired properties may be achieved during the finishing procedure.*

of the newly recrystallized grains, when the finishing temperature is about the same as the minimum hot-working temperature at which no strain hardening takes place.

5-10   Principal Methods of Hot-Working

Hammering, pressing, rolling, and extrusion are the basic methods used in the hot working of metals. The first two methods employ *forging* which is accomplished by the use of hammers, dies, and drop-forging equipment either in mechanical presses and upsetters or by the method known as *roll forging*. By *pressing* we usually refer to the manufacture of parts forged by hydraulic presses. This type of press

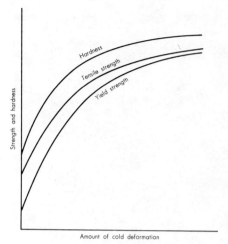

Fig. 5-20. *Effect of cold deformation on the strength and hardness of metal. It will be seen that the spread between the yield strength and tensile strength curves becomes less with greater amounts of deformation and a consequent reduction in ductility.*

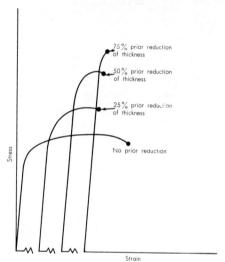

Fig. 5-21. *Stress-strain curves for metal subsequent to varying degrees of prior cold working. It will be observed that cold working brings about an increase in tensile and yield strengths and a decrease in elongation prior to fracture.*

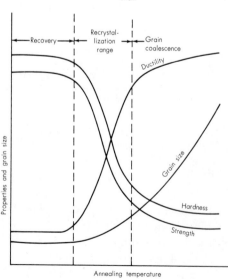

Fig. 5-22. *The change in properties of cold-worked metal resulting from annealing. Longer annealing time moves the curve to the left. Metals that are made harder and stronger by cold working may be returned to their softer condition by proper annealing.*

Fig. 5-23. *The forged steel bolsters shown are for holding rectangular die blocks by means of convenient toe clamps at front. The dies are for producing anchor chain. One pair of blocks is for edging and flattening the round-cornered square stock to dispose of scale; a second pair is for blocking, and the third pair is for finishing. The blank blocks at right would accommodate additional operations required. (Courtesy of United States Steel Corporation.)*

is also used in the extrusion of metals, by means of which the hot plastic metal is forced through a die of the configuration required. Rolling is done in rolling mills of various types, depending on the nature of the metal involved and the amount of area reduction desired. Prior to the hot working of metals, regardless of method used, it is essential to select the correct size of stock to be used, round bars, square or rectangular, round-cornered square, tubing, etc. The stock selected is first cut to the desired sizes and then brought up to the proper temperature prior to fabrication.

5-11 Mechanical Forging

Either billet or bar stock is worked progressively into the shape required by the use of dies with the various cavities and contours previously cut into them. There are several specific steps used in the production of closed-die forgings, including *fullering, edging, rolling, bending, blocking, finishing,* and *trimming*. Fig. 5–24 shows a typical forging die with several contours and shapes machined into it, both top and bottom, prior to mounting in the forging machine. The cross-section at the center of the stock is reduced by means of *fullering*, at which time the material is also stretched to length. Next follows the *edging* or *rolling*, these being very similar, except that

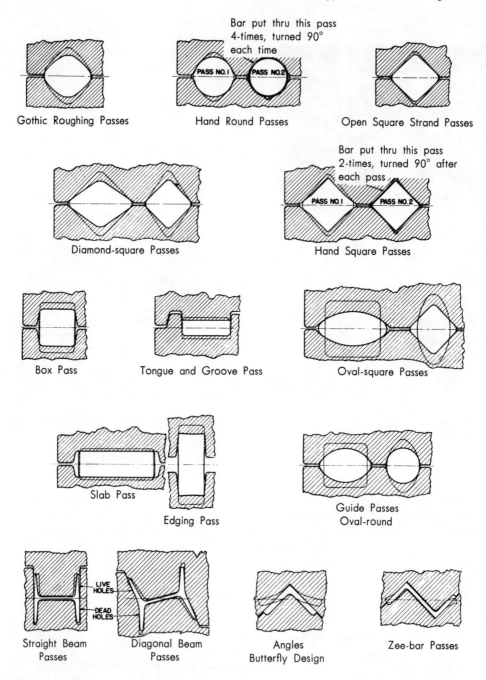

Fig. 5-24. *Some common types of roll grooves or passes, with the axial sections of the roll bodies shown in cross-hatching and the dotted lines indicating the cross section of the piece entering each pass. (Courtesy U.S. Steel Corporation.)*

rolling results in a nearly circular cross section, whereas edging produces more of a rectangular cross section. It is not always necessary to incorporate the bending operation, but it is used, as a rule, where the axis of the end product is not in a straight line. It is essential that every cavity of the die be completely filled, yet there should not be an excess of metal, which could result in a detrimental condition for proper forging. Usually the *blocking* operation follows, in which the stock is deformed to approximately the shape of the end product but in a rather rough form that must be subsequently worked in the *finishing* portion of the die cavity. A small amount of excess metal is provided in the design of the dies and stock, so that the cavities are well-filled yet without an excessive amount to be later removed by shearing off the flash metal. The flash is cut off by means of a special trimming die, after which the forging is complete so far as fabrication is concerned.

5-12 Hot Rolling

Forging rolls are used to shape metal into long, thin sections; these rolls are semicylindrical, with several grooves machined into them through which the stock is passed progressively from one size groove to the next. By placing the metal stock between the rolls in a specific groove and permitting the same to roll toward the operator, the stock conforms to the size and shape of the groove, and with the proper contouring of the grooves the heated stock may be formed into either tapered or straight sections as desired. The process of hot rolling consists of passing the hot metal between two rolls that are revolving at the same peripheral speed but in opposite directions, i.e., clockwise and counterclockwise, and so spaced that the distance between them is slightly less than the section of stock entering the rolls.

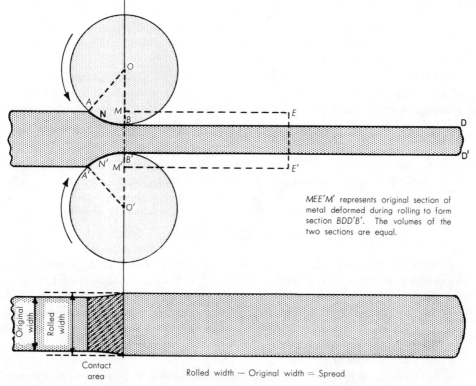

MEE'M' represents original section of metal deformed during rolling to form section *BDD'B'*. The volumes of the two sections are equal.

Rolled width — Original width = Spread

Fig. 5-25. *Diagram showing action of plain rolls upon a bar of hot, plastic steel of originally square cross-section. (Courtesy United States Steel Corporation.)*

Fig. 5–25 shows the action of plain rolls upon a piece of hot, plastic metal that had an original square cross-section. As may be seen, the extent of side or lateral *spread* depends mainly upon the amount of reduction and configuration of the cross section entering the rolls; therefore, in rolling rather wide plates, the actual total spread is independent of the width and in some instances may be less than that resulting from the first pass, as in the case of the reduction of small, square billets. This is particularly true if the percentage of reduction in cross-sectional area is substantial in the small, square billets.

A frictional force is introduced by the turning rolls in contact with the work, and this acts along the arcs *AB* and *A'B'* as shown in Fig. 5–25. This force is proportional to the pressure between the rolls and the workpiece. It is this action that pulls the work into the opening between the rolls against the wedging action of the larger tapered section that is entering the rolls. The work is delivered at a higher speed than the speed of the roll-surface, having entered at a velocity lower than the roll-surface speed. The arc *AB* is called the *contact arc*, and its included angle *AOB* is termed the *contact angle* or *rolling angle*. This angle is referred to as the *angle of bite* when it is the maximum at which the work piece will enter without being pushed or forced. The area of metal under the contact arc is called the *contact area*, shown in Fig. 5–25 to reveal the spreading that may take place. The force that is exerted against the rolls by the work piece pushing against them is referred to as the *separating force*.

The temperature of rolling has a marked effect on the physical dimensions of the work piece going through the rolls, both the degree and uniformity of heating being very influential in this respect. In the case of the hot-rolling of steel, additional plasticity given to the steel by only relatively slight elevations of temperature results in a lowering of the amount of power required for rolling, and increases the ease with which it can be made to flow plastically in the directions desired.

It is also true that the diameter of the rolls has a decided effect on the amount of force required, small diameter rolls requiring less force than larger ones for a given amount of reduction in a section of workpiece. Fabricators take advantage of this fact in four-high and other mills that use small-diameter work rolls backed up by heavier rolls, for two reasons:

a) the area of contact is less, so that, for a given pressure, the total pressure is less, and
b) the required average pressure against the work is less because of the smaller area of contact, reducing the frictional forces involved.

5-13 Principles of Cold Working

Plastic deformation below the recrystallization temperature is called *cold working*. By means of cold working, a good surface finish and dimensionally close tolerances, are possible. There is also no loss of weight or scaling because of oxidation. Cold working metals brings about high internal energy, thereby rendering them unstable. By heating these cold worked metals we then transform them into a more stable condition by an annealing process, as described in paragraph 5.4, by recovery, recrystallization and grain growth.

The immediate result of reheating cold-worked metal is the reduction of internal stress without much change in mechanical properties. Reheating of cold-worked metal is most often done until a complete recrystallization takes place. At that time the recovery period has passed and all signs of recovery have disappeared. By means of X-ray diffraction techniques we are able to detect some evidences of recovery, thereby revealing the elimination of internal stresses. Evidences of recovery can also be detected by small changes in physical properties of the metal, including the electrical its resistivity.

Cold working is less expensive for the ductile metals than hot working; however, in the case of the harder, more brittle metals it requires much more energy. As a result it is more expensive than hot working, from this standpoint, as might be expected.

In cold working the temperature of the metal being worked is very close to room temperature, so that it is not necessary to correct measurements of thickness for possible thermal contraction. The tools used in cold working can be kept clean and with good, smooth surfaces, resulting in brighter end products. The grain size of the end product can be controlled by cold working; in fact, pronounced reduction in grain size can be obtained, increasing the strength of the metal being worked.

Cold-worked metal held above the recrystallization temperature after recrystallization has been completed, develops a growth of some of the crystals that have recrystallized, while other crystals become smaller; this process is known as *grain growth* or *coalescence*. By this process, during which some grains become larger at the expense of others that eventually disappear, the end result is a larger average grain size with fewer total number of grains. Due to the fact that properties of metals important to engineers are related to grain size, it may be seen that the control of grain growth is highly important in cold working and annealing metals.

Grain-boundary migration is one of the fundamental reasons for some crystals' growing during coalescence while others get smaller and disappear. This migration of boundaries between the grains is not so pronounced when the boundary is fairly plane; in such cases there is less tendency for one grain to become large at the expense its neighbor. The boundaries that are not plane seem to migrate inwardly toward the center of the curvature of the boundary. This results in some grains becoming larger and others becoming smaller until they disappear altogether. It is also held that there is a tendency for grains to grow in certain crystallographic directions in a preferential manner to growth in other directions.

Fig. 5–19 shows the cold-work annealing cycle, wherein it is seen that cold working hardens and strengthens metals but at the expense of decreasing the ductility. It is also revealed that when cold working is excessive, it results in the fracture of the metal prior to reaching the size and shape that are desired. A study of Fig. 5–19' cold-work anneal cycle is recommended for full understanding.

5-14 Principal Methods of Cold Working

Cold-working processes are, in general, used to fabricate finished products. They are used instead of hot working because of the ability to fabricate an end product with a superior, smooth finish, better mechanical properties, and closer dimensional tolerances, as well as better control of the finished size and shape desired. Better machinability and the ability to produce thinner gages of metal than by hot-working processes, are also possible and economically achieved. For the most part, cold working uses the same techniques as hot rolling, and the forces of the metal passing through the rolls are much of the same type as in hot rolling; however, the magnitude of these forces is much greater. Cold rolling is usually done on relatively thin sections, due to the fact that the surface friction effect and the resistance of the metal to cold deformation are greater. Those forces trying to separate the rolls becomes greater, and the elastic deformation of the rolls, roll housings, bearings, and frame of the machine are all greater than in the case of hot-working operations.

Cold working by means of cold rolling consists of passing unheated, hot-rolled bars, sheets, or strip, free from scale, through a set of rolls several times, as a rule, until the desired size is reached. The result is a smooth, dense surface that may or may not be heat treated in order to produce an end product with controlled mechanical properties. In the modern nomenclature of the steel industry, cold rolling implies a rolling operation in which the thickness of the steel is reduced a relatively small amount—usually just enough to produce a superior surface or to give the steel desired mechanical properties in the rolled product.

A special form of cold rolling is *cold reduction*, in which the original thickness of the product is reduced by relatively large amounts in each pass through a single-stand cold mill or a series of passes through a tandem cold mill. Therefore, in the production of most cold-rolled strip, cold sheets, and black plate, the cold reduction process is used to reduce the thickness of the starting material between 25 and 90 per cent. A substantial tonnage of such products, after cleaning and annealing, is subjected to a cold-rolling operation referred to as *temper-rolling*, in which the thickness is reduced only a small per cent, but during which some desirable mechanical properties and improved surface characteristics are imparted to the material.

Prior to cold reduction, low-carbon, rimmed steel, in the form of hot-rolled breakdowns, has more or less equiaxed ferritic structure wherein the carbides are visible as pearlite or cementite (depending on whether the steel was coiled hot or cold); it is therefore relatively free from internal stresses, particularly so if coiled hot, whereby it is self-annealed. Cold reduction, however, elongates the grains from one to ten times and at the same time distorts the crystal lattice. Heavy internal stresses are induced, resulting in a hard product with very little ductility remaining. Because of this high degree of plastic deformation, the steel is rendered capable of returning to equilibrium conditions so far as the microstructure is concerned recrystallizing during heat treatment at temperatures considerably below the zone of the conventional phase transformation. When such recrystallization is allowed to continue to completion by holding the steel at the proper temperature long enough, the resultant structure will again consist of clearly defined equiaxed ferrite grains with undistorted lattices. This will render the steel with its carbon in the form of cementite; either small scattered spheroids, in the case of coils of hot-rolled breakdowns, or massive agglomerates, regardless of the state of the hot-rolled product prior to cold-working. Where sufficient time is given at the annealing temperature, steel given a heavy cold reduction will begin to recrystallize at a somewhat lower temperature, will complete recrystallization more quickly, and finish with a finer ferrite grain structure than steel that is given a light amount of cold reduction. The reason for this is that the former material is more distorted prior to annealing and, therefore, has more centers of nulceation and higher localized stresses to induce the crystalline realignment.

Continuous annealing of light-gage, cold-reduced steel in a deoxidizing atmosphere has come in for serious attention, since the modern cold-reduction process has permitted the manufacture of continuous single lengths of material in the continuous mill, thousands of feet in length. In this treatment, a single length of steel that has been cold-reduced to the thinness of tin plate travels at a very high speed through a heating zone with a controlled atmosphere. Here it is quickly brought to a temperature just above the lower critical, when it crystallizes almost instantly, then passes through a cooling zone, and emerges into the air cool enough to eliminate the possibility of any oxidation. From an engineering standpoint, the continuous-annealing operation is made practical by building the heating and cooling zones as towers, thus increasing the effective length by threading the steel back and forth around rolls at the top and bottom of the towers. This type of continuous-annealing line is designed to operate at a strip speed of 1500 ft per minute. At this speed, less than two minutes (112 seconds) elapses from the time a given section of strip enters the heating zone until it leaves the fast-cooling zone at the end of the operation. Such automated production enables American steel producers to compete on a very favorable basis with foreign producers despite the lower wages paid in the other countries.

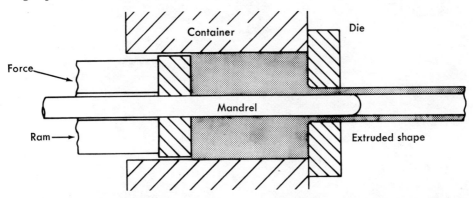

Fig. 5-26. *Diagram of extrusion of seamless tubing showing smaller plunger, termed the mandrel, operating inside the main ram of press and moved in relation to it. Billets that have been heated first are used in this process, hot metal being forced through annular area between the die and mandrel, under pressure transmitted through the outer rim.*

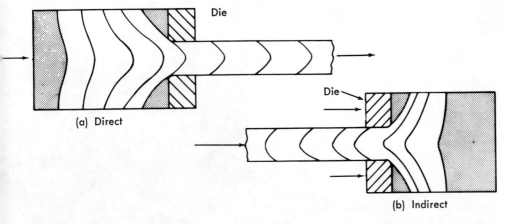

Fig. 5-27. *Illustration of the flow of metal by direct and indirect extrusion, both of these methods having their place in industry and both developing a high degree of grain flow in the direction parallel to axis of extrusion, resulting in high tensile strengths in this axis of the tubing.*

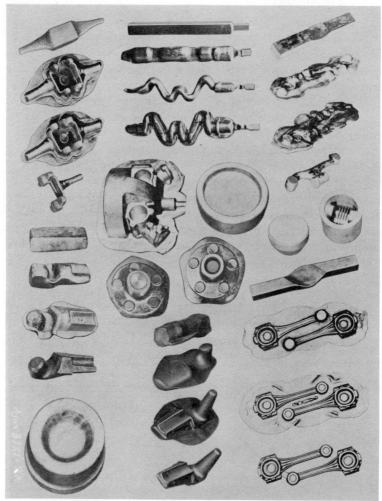

Fig. 5-28. *Progressive operations of press forgings made with Ajax machines.*

Fig. 5-29. *A 2-1/2 in. Ajax Air Clutch Forging Machine—one of many in the Ajax line where the output is limited only by the operator's ability to feed stock to the machine. (Capacity of 55 strokes per minute of 2-1/2 in. diameter stock.) (Ajax Manufacturing Co., Cleveland, Ohio.)*

Fig. 5-30.   *A 7 in. Ajax Air Clutch Forging Machine with a capacity of 25 strokes per minute, of 7 in. diameter stock.*

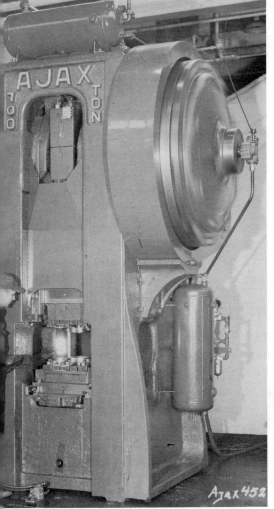

Fig. 5-31.   *An upright Ajax 700-Ton High-Speed Forging Press with a capability of 80 strokes per minute.*

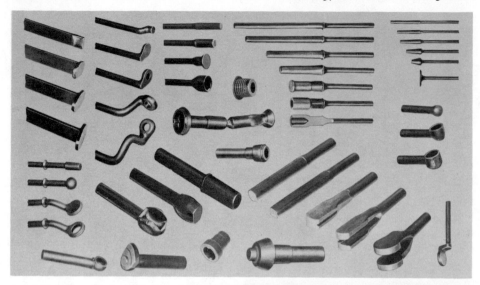

Fig. 5-32. *Upset Forgings including some progressive upsetting and piercing operations made on Ajax Forging Machines.*

Fig. 5-33. *Hydraulic forging press in operation, hot working a massive ingot supported on a porter bar which, in conjunction with the chain-link support, permits handling and turning of the ingot as desired. (Courtesy United States Steel Corporation.)*

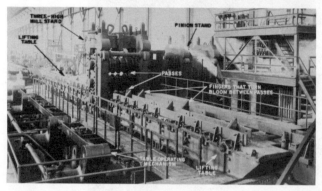

Fig. 5-34. *A 40-inch, three-high blooming mill, forming an intermediate stand that rolls roughed-down ingots (from another mill stand) into blooms that are supplied to the 28-inch billet mill in far left background. (Courtesy United Engineering and Foundry Company.)*

Fig. 5-35. *Over-all view of 45-inch universal slabbing mill, designed and operated solely for producing slabs. This type mill, is designed to increase production rate for wide slabs of eliminating expenditure of time required for vertical edging passes in a blooming mill. It is provided with a vertical pair of rolls in addition to the pair of horizontal rolls, the edging being accomplished by the vertical rolls.*

Fig. 5-36. *A 53-inch, high-lift, two-high reversing blooming and slabbing mill at the United States Steel Corporation's South Works. (Courtesy U. S. Steel Corporation.)*

Fig. 5-37. *A 46-inch two-high reversing blooming mill in Lorain Works of United States Steel Corporation. This mill exists in a wide range of sizes and is designed to roll ingots of square or nearly square cross-section up to 34 inches, and can edge vertically, in a grooved pass, a piece of about 40 inches maximum width. (Courtesy United States Steel Corporation.)*

QUESTIONS

1. What is "plastic working" of metals? What is its main purpose?

2. What is the cornerstone of all metal-working processes?

3. Explain the difference between *microscopic* and *macroscopic* considerations in the study of plastic deformation of metals.

4. What takes place in the grain structure and grain size in *hot working* and also in *cold working* so far as the ultimate strength of the metals is concerned?

5. In mechanical working of metals what other changes take place in addition to changes of shape?

6. What effect does temperature have on the resulting properties of metals undergoing mechanical working?

7. Explain what occurs to the yield strength of metals undergoing hot deformation, as compared to cold-working deformation.

8. Is cold working a satisfactory method of fabricating for crankshafts, where appreciable changes in shape are desired? Explain the reasons for your answer.

9. What is the difference between *elastic* and *plastic* deformation?

10. Define the term "slip" and explain how it occurs in plastic deformation of metals.

11. How can we determine the planes of easiest slip potential within a crystal?

12. State the planes of easiest slip potential in face-centered cubic lattices; in body-centered cubic lattices; in hexagonal close-packed systems. Also, name the direction of easiest slip for these three structures.

13. Explain what is referred to as the *critical shear stress law*. What happens to critical shear stress with an increase in temperature?

14. At what point is the critical shear stress of a metal zero?

15. Do foreign atoms in the structure of a single crystal have any effect on strength characteristics? What effect do such foreign atoms have on the critical shear strength of single crystals? Explain fully.

16. What effect do foreign atoms have in polycrystalline substances?

17. Explain the phenomenon of *twinning* and tell how it differs from *slip*.

18. What constitutes the *slip system* of crystal structure?

19. Explain the phenomenon of *edge dislocation* in an otherwise perfect simple cubic lattice and state the difference between *positive* and *negative* edge dislocations. Illustrate each type with a sketch.

20. Explain *tensors* when applied to the usual behavior of the forces between atoms and the deformation of the crystal lattice.

21. In theory, macroscopic plasticity depends substantially on what three macroscopic observations concerning stress and strain rate?

22. As a rule, is the amount of plastic working augmented or lessened by the use of compressive rather than tensile methods? Why?

23. What is the term for plastic working of metals below the recrystallization temperature?

24. Define and explain the terms *recovery, recrystallization, coalescence.*

25. What is the principal purpose of hot working metals?

26. What can be said about the direction of flow in relation to the direction of stress required, so far as properties of hot-worked parts are concerned?

27. Are flow lines in metals an advantage or a detriment? Explain.

28. What is the main control over grain size in hot working of metals?

29. In the hot, plastic working of steel bars, what is the *separating force*?

30. Define the term "cold-working" and give some of the advantages of this process in steel.

31. What happens when cold-worked metal is reheated? Why?

32. Explain in detail the cold-working of metal by means of cold rolling. Is this the same as "cold reduction"?

33. What is "temper rolling"? When is it used?

34. Describe the newer method of continuous annealing of light gage, cold-reduced steel in a deoxidizing atmosphere and state its advantages, if any, over more conventional methods.

References

American Society for Testing and Materials, *Part I, Ferrous Metals: Part II, Nonferrous Metals*. Philadelphia, Pa., 1964.

Barrett, Charles S., *Structure of Metals*, 2d ed., New York: McGraw-Hill Book Company, Inc., 1952.

Clark, Frances Hurd, *Strength of Materials under Combined Stresses*. New York: Reinhold Publishing Co., 1950.

Fisher, J. G. *et al.*, eds., *Dislocations and Mechanical Properties of Crystals*. New York: John Wiley & Sons, 1957.

Guy, Albert G., *Elements of Physical Metallurgy*, 2d ed. Reading, Massachusetts: Addison-Wesley Publishing Co., Inc., 1959.

McGannon, Harold E., Ed., *The Making, Shaping and Treating of Steel*, 8th ed., Pittsburgh, Pa., United States Steel Corporation, 1964.

Metal Interfaces, American Society for Metals, Cleveland, Ohio, 1952.

Metals Handbook, American Society for Metals, Cleveland, Ohio, 1961 edition.

Reed, W. T., Jr., *Dislocations in Crystals*, New York: McGraw-Hill Book Company, 1953.

Properties of Metals and Alloys

A description of specifications for the properties of metals must be clear and complete, as the *properties* of metals are very closely related to their *structure*. Knowing the atomic, crystal, or phase structure of metals and alloys makes it possible to draw some conclusions about their properties; those most useful in selecting and applying them in industry with greatest effectiveness. Knowledge of the nature of the structure of materials is important; however, it is only a prologue to the determination of their properties since there are a great many properties, most of them very important. The properties of materials are usually divided into three categories.

6-1 Physical Properties

The characteristics that are used to describe a material under conditions that exclude any external forces are called *physical properties*. In other words, they are those properties that are within the material itself. These include density, melting temperature, or melting range, coefficient of thermal expansion, thermal and electrical conductivity, specific heat, and electrical resistivity.

6-2 Mechanical Properties

Within this category are listed the characteristics of materials that describe their behavior under various and varying external conditions and forces. Included in this category are tensile strength, yield strength, elongation, hardness, endurance limit, compressive yield strength, shear strength, bearing strength, bearing stress,

creep strength, fatigue strength, etc. Resistance to corrosion is still another important mechanical property; however, this is often classed under the category of
chemical properties.

6-3   Chemical Properties

Included in this important category are the solubilities, corrosion properties
and characteristics, and actual chemical analysis, with emphasis on the way materials
behave under certain chemical conditions and in various environments. Under
this heading is considered the combining tendencies of metals to form alloys, as
some metals will combine with certain others metals in both the liquid and solid
states and in all proportions, while others will be miscibile in the liquid state but
only partially, or not at all, in the solid state. Deterioration in varying degrees
because of chemical reactions resulting from environmental conditions, is one of
the most troublesome properties engineers have to cope with in the selection and
application of metals and alloys for structural purposes. The subject of corrosion
will be discussed in greater detail in Chapter 13.

6-4   Density of a Material

The ratio of the mass of a material's homogeneous portion to its volume is
known as the *density* of the material. The density of the elements is given in the
Periodic Table, shown in Fig. 3–20, listed in the lower right hand corner of the
box, in grams per cubic centimeter. When the results obtained from X-ray diffraction analysis are studied, as outlined in paragraph 3–6 of Chapter 3, in the light of
a common property, such as *density*, they become meaningful and valid. Using
iron as a basis, with body-centered cubic structure, X-ray analysis reveals that the
unit cell has a lattice constant of 2.86 Å. Calculating the volume from this parameter, and remembering that the body-centered cubic unit cell has only two
effective atoms, since the eight atoms at each corner are shared by eight adjacent
unit cells, the weight of each unit cell, and thus the density of the material, can
be calculated in the following manner:

$$\text{Density} = \frac{\text{weight/unit cell}}{\text{volume/unit cell}} \qquad\qquad (6\text{--}1)$$

$$= \frac{(\text{no. of atoms/unit cell})(\text{weight of the atom})}{(\text{lattice constant})^3} \qquad (6\text{--}2)$$

Therefore, in the case of iron:

$$\text{Density of iron} = \frac{2[55.84/(6.02 \cdot 10^{23})]}{(2.86 \cdot 10^{-8})^3} = 7.9 \text{ g/cm}^3$$

The value of this figure (7.9 g/cm³) is proved by the fact that, in experiments
involving buoyancy tests, the density of iron has been established at 7.87 g/cm³.

Another important physical property of metals is the *melting temperature* or *melting
range* which, in the case of pure metals, is represented as a straight horizontal line
on the time-temperature graph, indicating that the temperature remains constant from the time the first drop of molten metal is formed until the entire mass
becomes liquid. This horizontal thermal arrest is present only in the case of pure
metals and for eutectic alloys right at the eutectic point. In binary alloys, the melting
occurs over a range of melting temperatures from the time of formation of the first

drop of liquid until the entire mass is liquid; however, in this case the thermal arrest is not a straight horizontal line, but a sloping line, depending on the nature of the component metals in the alloy. The melting point is closely associated with the strength of the atomic bond, since the melting point corresponds to the temperature at which the atoms have sufficient kinetic energy so that they are not permanently established in the lattice positions, but are free to move about freely with respect to each other. Since the atomic diameter is inversely proportional to the strength of the bond, within a certain period, it has been determined that a similar relationship prevails between atomic diameters and the melting points of metals. Table 6–1 shows the relationship between the melting points and atomic diameters of certain metals in Group A of the Fourth Period of the Periodic Table.

TABLE 6–1. Relationship of Atomic Diameter and Melting Points of the Elements in Group A of the Fourth Period of the Periodic Table

Element	Atomic Diameter (Å)	Melting Point °C
K	4.62	63
Ca	3.93	850
Sc	3.20	1,400
Ti	2.93	1,725
V	2.63	1,735
Cr	2.49—2.71	1,890
Mn	2.24—2.96	1,245
Fe	2.48	1,540
Co	2.51	1,495
Ni	2.49	1,455

From *Modern Theory of Solids*, by F. Seitz, McGraw-Hill Book Company, 1940. Used by permission of the publisher.

It will be observed from Table 6–1 that the atomic diameter is inversely proportional to the melting point, where the atoms have such kinetic energy as to leave their fixed positions in the lattice and to move about at rates that are determined by the temperature involved. For example, at the melting temperature, although the mobility of the atoms in the liquid is greater than in the solid state, in the absence of convection they will move through the molten metal very slowly. The diffusion coefficient in the liquid is usually a factor of 10 to 100 times larger than the diffusion coefficient in the solid, but it is still extremely small and usually of the order of 10^{-5} to 10^{-6} cm^2/sec.

6-5 Specific Heat

The amount of heat required to raise a gram-mol of a metal, 1K at a constant pressure (C_p) or at a constant volume (C_v) is known as the *specific heat* of the metal. The actual difference between the specific heats for most solids at constant volume and constant pressure is practically nil. In Fig. 6–1 the potential energy of an atom is sketched as a function of the lattice spacing. In the case of large lattice spacing (large total volume), the potential energy is seen to be arbitrarily set at zero, since the atoms then act negligibly with respect to each other. With decreasing lattice spacing the potential energy is observed to decrease. This is understandable, since solids exist even in the absence of external restraints. The important region is the one near the minimum, as there is no net force exerted there on an atom by its neighbors. Where all the atoms of the solid except one are fixed in position, and the atom in question moves in the x direction, then unbalanced forces develop between the neighboring atoms along the x axis. Thus, Fig. 6–1 shows the energy change when the distances to *all* the neighbors of an atom vary; if only one varies, the energy $E_a(x)$ must be divided by z, where z is the number of nearest neighbors. (The potential energy for atoms farther away than the nearest neighbors may be ignored.)

Another consideration of note is that of the comparison of the Debye heat-capacity, a curve of which is shown in Fig. 6–2, along with the observed heat capacities of Ag and Al. The constant θ_D is termed the *Debye temperature*, which has a different value for each solid; at $T = \theta_D$ the heat capacity reaches about 96 per cent of its final value. The Debye temperatures for a few materials are shown in Table 6–2.

TABLE 6–2.   Examples of Debye temperatures. (Values of θ_D in $°K$)

Metals:		Semiconductors:	
Hg	75	Sn (gray)	260
Pb	95	Ge	250–400
Na	160	Si	650
Au	170		
Sn	200		
Ag	230		
W	270	Insulators:	
Cu	340	H	100
Fe	360	AgBr	150
Al	375	NaCl	280
Be	1200	Diamond	1850

From *Modern Theory of Solids* by F. Seitz, McGraw-Hill Book Company, 1940. Used by permission of the publisher.

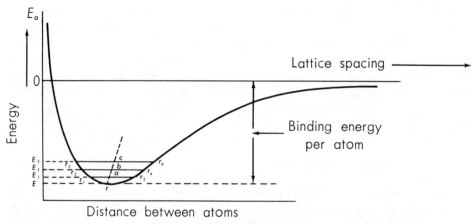

Fig. 6-1.   *The potential energy of an atom,* E_a *in a solid containing* N *atoms, as a function of the lattice spacing of the solid.   It is observed that the solid assumes the lattice spacing corresponding to the lowest energy. For large lattice spacing (i.e., large total volume) the potential energy is arbitrarily set at zero,   since the atoms then interact negligibly with each other ("r" is the atomic distance.)*

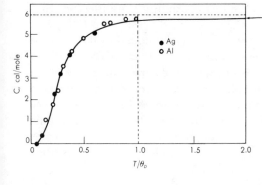

Fig. 6-2. *A comparison of the Debye heat-capacity curve and the observed heat capacities of Ag and Al. It will be noted that at absolute zero the heat capacity is zero, and at temperatures just above zero the heat capacity climbs rapidly and is proportional to* T^3 *in that region. At high temperatures it attains a nearly constant value of about 6 cal/g-mol* $°K$. *It is observed that this is a reduced temperature scale, i.e., it is* T/θ_D, *termed the Debye temperature, this constant having a different value for each solid. Debye temperatures are shown here for several materials for comparison. (After Seitz.)*

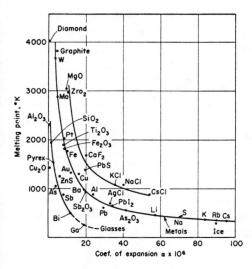

Fig. 6-3. *Curves showing the relation between the melting point and the thermal expansion coefficient, revealing that the higher the melting point of the material, the lower is the coefficient of expansion. (Zwikker, Physical Properties of Solid Materials, Pergamon Press, London.*

By using the *Law of Dulong and Petit,* which is an empirical relationship stating that gram-atomic specific heat (C_v) times the atomic weight of all elements is constant, the specific heat of a metal can be computed so long as it is near room temperature. It is also known that this gram-atomic specific heat is equal to three times the value of the universal gas constant, which is 1.986 calories/°C/mole. The specific heat approaches zero as the temperature approaches absolute zero. For example, the specific heat of Al at 20C Cal/g/°C is equal to 0.215 Btu/lb/°F or cal/g/°C. These concepts of specific heat apply only to pure metals, and not to alloys.

6-6   Thermal Expansion

When heat is applied to a metal, the balance between the attractive and the repulsive forces has been upset, which accounts for *thermal expansion* in metals. Whenever the atomic parameter of a metal structure is upset, there is a change in the dimensions which is manifested in the coefficient of thermal expansion. Many metals have crystal structures that are *anisotropic,* that is, they have directional properties that, if used correctly, may be beneficial for certain applications. These metals reveal anisotropy in the way they expand with the application of

thermal energy. *Anisotropy*, then, can be said to be the exhibiting of different properties when metals of this type are tested along axes in different directions. Fig.
6–1 shows a curve where the potential energy of a crystal is plotted in terms of the
interatomic spacing of the atoms. It will be seen in Fig. 6–1 that the configuration
of the minimum part of the curve determines the degree of expansion of the metal
under consideration. In the case of covalent solids, it will be seen that they develop
a steep curve on each side of the minimum; therefore these metals have very
small thermal expansions. This is also the case with materials that exhibit ionic
bonding. In the cases of materials with metallic bonding, there is a greater
thermal expansion, while in the category of molecular solids it is found that they
exhibit greater thermal expansion than all of the others.

Fig. 6–3 shows the relationship between the melting point and the coefficient
of expansion, wherein it is seen that there is a lineal relationship, not only in metals
but also in oxides, salts, glass, etc. Just as in the case of specific heat, it is apparent
that here the coefficient of expansion is dependent upon temperature. In fact, it
varies as the cube of the temperature nears absolute zero. It can be said, then,
that the higher the melting point, the lower the coefficient of expansion, a relationship that is used to advantage in the design of structures and in the selection
of metals for specific applications.

6-7 Thermal Elastic Effect

The thermal effect resulting from the elastic deformation of a metal is known
as the *thermal elastic effect*. As a rule, this is very small and may be ignored. Whenever
force is applied to a material, energy is expended and a change of volume usually
results. This energy is in the form of heat, and in the case of metals with low
coefficients of expansion, this heat (thermal elastic effect) is quite small.

6-8 Thermal Electric Effect

When two conductors of dissimilar materials are connected at each end and
are at different temperatures, a phenomenon known as the *thermal electric effect* is
observed. In such cases there is a potential difference between the two junctions,
known as the *Seebeck effect*. This effect is basic to the operation of all thermocouples.
Fig. 6–4 is a sketch illustrating the Seebeck effect. The electromotive force (emf)
produced by a temperature differential of 1C between the hot and cold junctions
of a thermocouple, is referred to as the *thermal electric power* of the material. When a
thermocouple circuit such as is shown in Fig. 6–6 is set up, and an external emf is
exerted at (1), heat will be evolved here and absorbed at (2). This is known as the

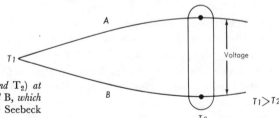

Fig. 6-4. *A temperature differential* (T₁ *and* T₂) *at
the junctions of two dissimilar metals,* A *and* B, *which
results in a potential difference known as the* Seebeck
effect.

Peltier effect. On the other hand, if a current is passed through a wire or bar that conducts heat, the heat will either be absorbed or evolved, depending upon the material and direction of the current flow. This is known as the *Thompson effect*, as shown in Fig. 6–5.

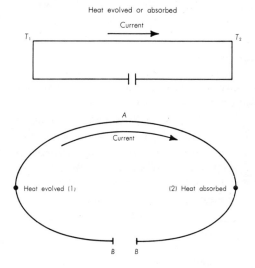

Fig. 6-5. *When an electric current passes through wire with a temperature differential, a heating or cooling of the wire results; this is known as the* Thompson effect.

Fig. 6-6. *A graphic description of the* Peltier *effect wherein a potential is impressed on the thermocouple producing a current flow resulting in the evolution of heat at one end* (1), *and the absorption of heat at the other junction* (2). *Such a phenomenon would be present in the case of a thermocouple composed of iron-constantan wire, such as is commonly used in heat-treating control units.*

6-9   Thermal Conductivity

Thermal conductivity is one of the important physical properties of metals and is another effect of applying heat to a metal or alloy. Whereas the specific heat is the physical property controlling the temperature increase, as discussed in paragraph 6.5, the *rate* at which heat can flow through a material under the influence of a certain temperature gradient is determined by the *thermal conductivity, k* of the material, and may be expressed by the equation

$$Q = k(T_2 - T_1)\frac{A}{l} \tag{6--3}$$

cal per sec, where Q = a given quantity of heat, T_1 = temperature of one surface of material involved, T_2 = temperature of other surface of material involved, A = area in which heat flow takes place, k = thermal conductivity of the material involved, and l = distance separating the surfaces that are at temperatures T_1 and T_2.

The transfer of heat (thermal energy) in solids can be explained in three different ways: by the free electrons that are present in the metals under consideration; by the molecules that may be present in organic solids; and by lattice vibrations resulting from electron transfer in the case of metals (although this is not the sole cause of lattice vibrations). Thermal conductivity is of major importance in the working of metals, and the magnitudes of this and other thermal properties depend a great deal on the nature of the solid phase and on its temperature. When a phase change takes place, the thermal properties of specific heat and thermal conductivity show abrupt changes. For example, when alpha iron transforms to gamma iron at 1670F, there is a sharp decrease in length and absorption of heat. Changes of this nature are the most difficult for the commercial heat-treater. Impurity atoms in metals lower thermal conductivity, so that many of our complex alloys have relatively poor thermal conductivity. They are used despite this fact because of their high-temperature strength and their resistance to oxidation. Metal furnace parts and chemical-petroleum vessels are examples of these applications.

6-10   Free Electron Theory

In an earlier chapter we discussed the nature of the metal atom and stated that it comprises a nucleus of matter and surrounding shells of rapidly moving electrons. In the lattice structure of a specimen of metal, the atoms tend to lose one or more of their outer electrons and become positively charged. These electrons form a so-called *electron cloud* of free electrons moving randomly through the metal with no particular electrons attached to specific atoms. Electrostatic forces between these negatively-charged free electrons and the positively-charged atoms in the lattice, and the free electrons, do not have enough kinetic energy to overcome these forces and rise to the surface of the metal.

Since the free electrons are continually moving randomly, the effect of the electrons moving in any specific direction through the metal will at all times be balanced by the effect of an equal number of electrons moving in the opposite direction. As a result of this, the net motion of all the electrons is zero, there being no flow of electric current through the metal. In the case of a perfect lattice structure in a metal, electrons could move with very little or no interference; however, all metal lattices have some degree of imperfections and the *electrical resistivity* of a metal is therefore affected by the mean free path of a given electron between these imperfections. The electrical resistivity of a metal is increased by any process that causes a distortion of the lattice, as the electronic mean free path is thereby decreased. It is therefore apparent that electrical resistivity is a function of the content of alloying elements, the stresses imposed on the metal, and the temperature; all three of these variables affect the structure of the lattice.

In many instances the flow of electrical conductivity is impeded by design and with purpose, and resistance to the flow is desirable (electrical appliances such as fry-pans, toasters, etc). For high voltage transmission lines, electrical resistivity is of course undesirable. The resistance to the flow of electricity depends on the configuration of the metal and the *resistivity* of that metal. The following equation can be used for a conductor of constant cross-section to determine the electrical resistivity of a metal:

$$R = \rho \frac{l}{A}$$

where R = resistance of the metal in ohms, l = length of metal in centimeters, A = area in square centimeters, and ρ = resistivity in ohm-centimeters.

Although, as has been stated above, the electrical resistivity of a metal is influenced by several factors, including foreign atoms, temperature, hot and cold working, etc., it has been found that cold working increases the resistivity only slightly; for this reason cold working is a very suitable method of strengthening metals and alloys used as electrical conductors.

6-11   Electrical Conductivity

Electrical conductivity is a function of the ease with which electrons move about among the atoms. Electrons circle the nucleus of the atom, which, it will be recalled, is composed of protons and neutrons, in orbits that allow the energy of the electrons to be constant within their orbit. Not more than two electrons can fit into any one orbit, and in order to fit together, they must spin in opposite directions; this is known as the *Pauli exclusion principle*. When an atom is in a higher energy state, it is in an excited state. Furthermore, each orbit differs from the others by one or more energy *quanta*. The electron states have been identified by two quantum numbers, n and k, the *principle quantum number* being n, which is a measure of the total energy of the orbit; k is designated as the *secondary quantum number*, and this is a measure of the angular momentum of the orbit and is equal to $kh/2$, where h is *Plank's constant* and is equal to $6.624 \cdot 10^{-27}$ erg sec. The secondary quantum number k can have any value from 1 to, and including, n. Niels Bohr was first to evolve the *quantum theory*, thereby correcting a very unsatisfactory situation that prevailed under previous concepts of electronic orbits, based on the assumption that one electron in hydrogen occupies a circular orbit and that the outward centrifugal force of electrons is balanced against the inward attraction of the nucleus of the atoms.

Each orbit differs from other orbits by one or more energy quanta, the energy level becoming greater with the orbit's distance from the nucleus. The orbits are grouped in *shells*, and inside the shells are subdivisions known as energy levels. The greatest number of electrons that can fit into each shell is determined by the expression $2N^2$, where N is the number of the shell. From this it will be seen that the first shell contains a maximum of two electrons; the third shell; eighteen; the fourth shell, thirty-two, etc. Electrons tend to migrate to the lower energy level orbits, which generally correspond to the levels in the inner shells. It follows, therefore, that the inner shells are filled before electrons move on and take positions in the next shell. At times, however, and in some elements, the upper energy-levels of an inner shell may be higher than the lower-energy levels of the next shell. In such cases electrons assume positions in the outer shell prior to filling the inner shell. It is significant and basic that filled shells are stable, but that unfilled shells are unstable, and tend to become filled either by the formation of molecules or by the formation of chemical compounds.

6-12   Semiconductors and Semiconductivity

The propensity of certain materials known as *semiconductors* to conduct electrical energy originates from certain structural imperfections or tiny quantities of chemical impurities introduced into the crystal. In a perfect crystal lattice, such as that of silicon, all four valence electrons are tied in place, forming covalent bonds, as described in Chapter 3. The energy of the valence electrons which bind the crystal together lies in the highest filled *energy zone*, called the *valence zone* (band). The empty zone or band, called the *conduction zone*, is separated from the valence zone by an energy gap, as shown in Fig. 6–7. The width of this forbidden energy zone, which is actually the magnitude of the energy gap, is characteristic of the particular lattice and varies considerably from one crystal to another. The transfer of an electron

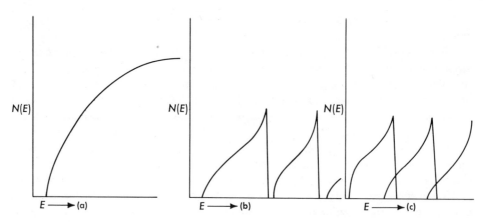

Fig. 6-7.　*Electronic energy levels in atoms. (a) Free atom. (b) Brillouin zones. (c) Overlapping Brillouin zones. As shown in Fig. 6-7 (c) in some cases where there is no gap between the zones and, in fact, where the Brillouin zones overlap, conductivity is possible even if the number of electrons is just enough to fill only the first zone; these materials are said to be good conductors of electricity.*

from the valence zone to the conduction zone requires high excitation energy to overcome the potential barrier of the forbidden energy zone. As a result, such elements act like insulators at low temperatures. When either heat or light is applied, however, enough energy may be provided to some electrons in the valence zone to excite them enough to cross the forbidden zone and into the conduction zone. The electrons in the conduction zone are now free to move under an applied electric field. In each case where an electron is excited from the valence zone to the conduction zone, a "hole" is left behind in, this term denoting a mobile vacancy in the electronic valence structure of a semiconductor resulting from the removal of one electron from the valence zone. *Holes*, in almost every instance, may be thought of as moving positive charges through a crystal that have an effective charge and mass of the same order as that of the electron. Under the applied field, however, only the electrons in the valence zone actually move into the holes, and this phenomenon can also be interpreted as the movement of holes into the original positions of the electrons. Such conduction, stemming from thermally or optically excited electrons, is called *intrinsic,* and those materials which possess such properties are known as *intrinsic semiconductors.* The conductivity of these intrinsic semiconductors usually takes place at higher temperatures, due to the fact that sufficient thermal agitation is necessary for the transfer of a sufficient number of electrons from the valence zone into the conduction zone.

The valence electrons in an atom are distributed at energy levels ranging from a minimum up to higher levels. If the number of energy levels $N(E)$ is plotted as a function of energy, E, a parabolic curve results such as is illustrated in Fig. 6–7(a), which shows that the number of energy levels increases with an increase of energy. Since only a few electrons can fit into the lowest energy level, as the number of electrons per atom increases, they must move on into higher and higher energy levels. Although such energy distribution can accommodate an infinite number of electrons, based on the simple free electron theory (due to the fact that the number of electrons in an atom are finite), only a portion of the curve is used in Fig. 6–7(a,)(b), and (c). Fig. 6–7(b) shows that where number of energy levels, $N(E)$, is again plotted against energy E, in this case due to the forbidden energy levels, the curve is broken up into several zones known as *Brillouin zones*, with intervals or spaces between them denoting forbidden energy levels.

In cases where the number of electrons only partially fills one of the zones, a slight potential can shift some electrons over to the higher energy levels, and conductivity of electricity is possible. Where a number of electrons entirely fill, one zone, conduction is possible only when the supply of energy is sufficient to permit electrons to jump over the forbidden gaps and to go on to the next higher zone. Since this usually requires potentials of tens of thousands of volts or higher, such materials are considered as *insulators*. As shown in Fig. 6–7(c), in some cases where there is no gap between the zones and, in fact, where the Brillouin zones overlap, conductivity is possible even if the number of electrons is just enough to fill only the first zone; these materials are said to be good conductors of electricity. At absolute zero, a semiconductor would become a nonconductor, since there would not be sufficient thermal energy to excite any electrons across the forbidden zone gap.

The conductivity of semiconductors at room temperature results from electrons and holes introduced by impurities in the crystal. The presence of such impurities lowers considerably the activation energy required to transfer an electron from the valence zone to the conduction zone. *Impurity semiconductors* are either the *p*-type or the *n*-type, the *p*-type semiconductor resulting when the impurity atoms have *fewer* valence electrons than the silicon or germanium atoms of the original crystal. The *n*-type semiconductor results from substitution of impurity atoms having *more* valence electrons than silicon or germanium atoms. Silicon and germanium are both covalent materials having a diamond microstructure. In the case of the trivalent elements (boron, aluminum, gallium, indium, and thallium), when substituted for a silicon atom, the resulting structure will be locally incomplete, and the impurity atom will acquire an extra electron from a nearby bond in the lattice, with a resulting nearly tetrahedral cloud distribution of the lattice. A positive hole is thus created that is localized near the impurity which will attempt to neutralize itself by taking an electron from another neighboring bond. Again a hole is formed in place of the electron, and it will, in turn, neutralize itself by taking another electron from the next neighboring bond. The final result of such sequences is the movement of holes through the lattice in the valence zone, causing the electronic conductivity. The impurity is referred to as the *acceptor*, and since the electronic conduction is the result of the motion of positive holes in the valence zone, such a semiconductor is called a *p*-type semiconductor. In cases where electrical conduction is effected by *holes* or vacant states at the upper end of the normally filled zone, such *holes* have been found to act as positive charges; materials of this type, as just stated, are called *p*-type semiconductors.

6-13 Magnetic Properties

Materials having a behavior similar to iron when they are placed in a magnetic field are termed *ferromagnetic*. These include alpha iron, cobalt, nickel, gadolinium and dysprosium, the last two being in the rare earth group of elements as nos. 64 and 65 in the periodic table of elements. Both of these are hexagonal close-packed. All these elements, with the possible exception of dysprosium, are in the transition group and have unfilled *d* shells of electrons. A number of the alloys of these metals are also *ferromagnetic*. In fact, we find that some alloys are ferromagnetic whereas their components are not. For example, the so-called Heusler alloys, with Cu, Mn, Al, or Ag, Mn, or Cu, Mn, and In, are of this type. A few nonmetallic materials, for example, *ferrites*, that have a structure like magnetite (Fe_3O_4), show ferromagnetic properties.

We know that with an increase in temperature, the ferromagnetic property of materials is lowered. When this ferromagnetic property reaches zero, the temperature is called the *Curie temperature*. In iron this temperature, where the magnetism reaches zero, is 1430F; for cobalt it is 2150F, and for nickel it is 690F.

Another phenomenon that takes place when a ferromagnetic material is magnetized is the elastic deformation that results. This is called *magnetostriction*. As an example, when nickel is magnetized, there is a contraction in all the principal lattice sites, whereas, when *permalloy* (80 per cent Ni and 20 per cent Fe) is magnetized, an expansion is found in all of the crystallographic directions. When we apply a stress to ferromagnetic materials like those just mentioned, we get a change in magnetization. It should be remembered that all metals react to a magnetic field— some more than others. In fact, they react differently to the magnetic field.

All materials can be found to be either *diamagnetic, paramagnetic* or *ferromagnetic*, depending on the way they behave under the influence of a magnetic field. Subclasses of ferromagnetic materials are those said to be *antiferromagnetic* and *ferrimagnetic*. Materials that are diamagnetic are made up of atoms which do not have permanent magnetic moments, but, rather, have weak induced magnetic moments. The ionic solids and molecular solids are of the diamagnetic type of materials, as a rule. Diamagnetic materials assume a position perpendicular to the direction of the applied field. In such cases, the *permeability* is less than that found in a vacuum. Included in this group are copper, bismuth, silver, etc.

In magnetic materials, atoms are grouped in *domains*, within each of which the third shell electrons have the same spins. Within a crystal, there are many domains, and since they have opposite spins, the material is not magnetic. When a magnetic field is applied, however, the domains orient themselves and magnetic properties appear. The force necessary to orient domains is a measure of the *magnetic permeability*, and the tendency of the domains to remain oriented is a measure of the *coercive force* of the material.

Where the tendency is for alignment parallel to the magnetic field, such metals are termed *paramagnetic*, and where this paramagnetic reaction is unusually strong such metals are said to be ferromagnetic. An important feature of ferromagnetic material is that it can retain its magnetization after the magnetic field has been removed.

Although electric motors, transformers, relays, etc. are more efficient where the magnetization of the alloy used is such that it follows very closely any change in the magnetizing field, and therefore performs best with *magnetically soft* materials such as ingot iron, steel with 1 per cent silicon, or Supermalloy (79 per cent Ni, 16 per cent Fe, 5 per cent Mo), there is an increasing need for more permanent magnets. These are known as *hard magnets* and they do not depend on an electric current for their constant magnetic field as do the magnetically soft materials, even though the most powerful magnetic fields are produced by means of electromagnets. Typical application of permanent magnets is for conversion of mechanical motion into electrical energy, as found in a phonograph pickup; for the conversion of electrical energy into mechanical motion, as found in electric clocks, meters, etc.; and for magnetic separation and mechanical fastening as found on latches for cupboard doors, and similar applications. Permanent magnets, such as those made from some of the *ferrimagnetics*, like Ferroxdur and Bismanol, as well as Alnico V, have the ability to retain magnetization after the magnetizing force has been removed. Small magnets made from these alloys are produced by means of powder metallurgy, compacting the powders and then sintering the compact in dry hydrogen. Magnetic properties of these alloys can be greatly improved by heat treatment in a magnetic field. The hard (permanent) magnets are usually quenched from about 1200C (2200F) and aged at 650C (1200F).

There are many other physical properties of materials, in addition to electrical, magnetic, thermal, and density, that are important in the consideration of the selection of the best material for specific applications, including considerations as optics, accoustics, color differentials, apparent gloss or shininess, haze measurement, etc. Since the scope of this book does not permit the development of all these physical properties, the reader is referred to *Materials in Design Engineering* magazine, published by Reinhold Publishing Corporation, as well as to *Metals Handbook*, published by American Society for Metals, and similar references.

6-14   Mechanical Properties of Metals and Alloys

All engineers must concern themselves with the way metals react and respond when external forces are applied to them. Such forces may be tension, compression, torsion, shock, vibration, shear, etc. or a combination of some of these. The manner in which metals act and react in the face of these external forces determines their *mechanical properties*. Knowing that metals used in engineering structures are usually made up of many crystals, i.e., they are *polycrystalline*, it is essential that a basic understanding be acquired as to how single crystals behave under externally applied forces. If an understanding of the basic behavior of single crystals is acquired, the mechanical properties and behavior of the polycrystalline materials will be better understood.

In a consideration of the mechanical properties of metals, it must be realized that such properties are sensitive to the crystal structure of the metal for the most part, whereas the physical properties, in general, are structure-insensitive. (There are a few physical properties, such as electrical conductivity, magnetic behavior, etc., which are structure-sensitive; however, for the most part they are not.) The mechanical reactions and properties of metals can be classified into two general categories: *strength* and *ductility*. The strength properties are related to the ability of the material to resist applied forces, while the ductility properties determine the ability of the material to undergo permanent changes of shape without rupture. Obviously, many mechanical characteristics or behaviors depend on both ductility and strength; however, even in such cases, an analysis and understanding of this complex behavior can best be acquired by looking at the individual contributions each makes to the material under consideration.

Mechanical reactions of metals to applied forces are very diversified and depend upon the exact nature of the forces and the conditions under which they are applied. In attempting to devise or select certain tests that will predict in advance what can be expected in the performance of a material, it is essential that all the variables possible be examined and understood. Obviously, the final answer as to whether a material, will be suitable for certain applications can only be found by running actual service tests. It is equally obvious that in most cases such service tests are impractical, so simpler tests must be adopted, particularly where frequent inspection of the materials is important. In doing this it is imperative that the type and severity of forces involved in the particular service application be known, i.e., whether the loading is one of compression, tension, bending, shearing, twisting, etc. It is also important that other characteristics of the loading be known, such as whether it is static or dynamic; in case it is dynamic, it is important to know the nature and rate of application and variation of the loading. In many cases, it is imperative that the temperature at which the loading is applied be known, whether there is a wide variation or fluctuation of temperature, and whether such temperatures are abnormally high or low.

In most cases engineering materials are used under elastic conditions; that is, when metals are deformed, the deformation is not permanent. When any force is applied externally to deform a single crystal of a metal, a deformation of the lattice structure takes place. In instances where this force is applied in only one direction, such as in compression, the distance between the atoms in the lattice is decreased in the direction of the applied force and increased in the directions at 90° to this force. The ratio of the transverse contraction of a strained test specimen to its longitudinal elongation is known as *Poisson's ratio*. It is essentially a statement of constancy of volume of the material during deformation. Although the atomic distances are altered slightly, the atoms in the lattice exert a resisting force which has a tendency to bring them back to their normal positions. This resisting force is termed *stress*, which can basically be defined as the internally distributed forces having a tendency of resisting deformation. If and when the externally applied force producing the deformation is removed, the crystal lattice returns to its normal dimensions so long as the deformation has not been great enough to cause permanent deformation.

The ability of a metal to return to its original form when it has been stretched, then the load removed, is known as elasticity. *Hooke's Law* states that stress is proportional to strain up to the proportional limit. The strains involved, however, must be very small in order for Hooke's law strictly to apply. The deviation from Hooke's law under normal engineering conditions is relatively small and may be ignored, but from a practical standpoint it is important that we recognize that there are deviations. It is the intensity of the atomic bond that controls the relationship between the *stress* and the *strain*, so that the differences in moduli are in reality governed by the characteristics of the various elements involved. Fig. 6–8 is an engineering stress-strain diagram for mild steel, showing the plastic behavior of a ductile material. It will be noted that the initial portion of the curve is a straight line representing the proportionality of stress to strain according to Hooke's law, where $s = Ee$; the factor of proportionality E is known as *Young's modulus* or modulus of elasticity; s is the stress and e is the strain. The point where the straight line ceases is the *proportional elastic limit* and it represents that point on the curve where elasticity ceases and beyond which the specimen will not return to its original length if the load is removed. Thus the elastic limit is the maximum stress that a material can undergo before taking a definite and permanent deformation or set. The *true elastic limit* often will differ from the proportional elastic limit; however, because of the difficulty in obtaining the true elastic limit, the proportional elastic limit is usually used for the true elastic limit in ductile metals, as it is only a little above the proportional limit. In fact, the elastic limit for mild steel will vary from about 32,000 psi to 120,000 psi for heat-treated alloy steel.

In the tensile test (using universal tensile testing equipment as shown in Chapter 12), as the load is increased beyond the elastic limit, a stress is reached at which the material continues to stretch (elongate) without application of any in-

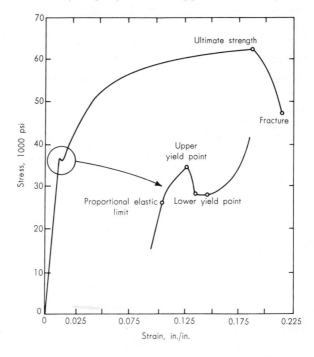

Fig. 6-8. *Engineering stress-strain diagram for a low carbon steel.*

creased load. This stress is termed the *yield strength.* For the most part, deformation beyond the elastic limit is *inelastic* or *plastic,* because it will be present in the metal after the load has been removed. For materials that do not yield sharply (as does mild steel), the yield point is described for a specimen with a 2 in. gage length as that stress *at which a permanent set of 0.2 per cent or 0.002 in. per in. takes place.* As will be noted on the diagram shown in Fig. 6–8, the *upper* and *lower* yield points are indicated, these being due to the peculiar behavior of mild steel. It is in this region during the stress fluctuation that distinct bands are discernible on the surface of tensile specimens of mild steel; these bands are inclined about 45° to the stress axis and are known as *Lüders' lines.* In deep-drawing operations of sheet metal, such as auto body and fender parts, these Luders' lines result in rough surface finishes, so they are undesirable. In order to avoid this, the steel is often cold rolled slightly prior to forming, in order to strain the material beyond the lower yield point and thus to prevent the formation of Lüders' lines during subsequent forming operations. A newer method of accomplishing these deep-drawing operations without the necessity of preliminary cold rolling is to process the steel by the *stretch-draw* method, which has several advantages, including the advantage of using smaller sized sheets at the outset, and also permitting a subsequent deep draw during the same set-up without producing the rough surface caused by the Lüders' lines.

Continuing the tensile test, as the specimen is strained beyond its yield point, the stress increases toward a maximum termed the *ultimate tensile strength* of the material. Brittle metals fail at this point, with a consequent fracture of the specimen. Ductile materials, however, begin to decrease (neck down) in diameter at some localized area until, ultimately, fracture occurs with an increase in loading.

Important items of information are obtained from the standard tensile, test for ductile metals like mild steel, including *percentage of elongation in 2 in., percentage reduction in area* of the specimen, *ultimate tensile strength, upper and lower yield points, point of ultimate fracture.* The percentage elongation is calculated as the difference in final and initial gage lengths divided by the original gage length, times 100. Percentage reduction in area is the ratio of decrease in area of the necked-down section of the specimen to the original area, times 100. Hard and brittle materials show very little, if any, elongation or reduction in area of specimen.

Modulus of toughness of a material is a term used frequently to denote the area under the engineering stress-strain diagram to the point of fracture, inasmuch as it actually represents the amount of energy (work) necessary to bring about failure per unit volume of material, this being a measure of the capacity of the material to absorb elastic and plastic energy under loading. It is recognized that the term *toughness* in this sense is only a qualitative description of the material and that other tests, including the *Charpy* or *Izod impact tests* are a more useful quantitative index. These and other tests, and testing equipment, are discussed at some length in Chapter 12.

6-15   Age Hardening and the Dislocation Theory

A discussion of imperfections and dislocations in crystals was introduced in Chapter 5 (5–2) where it was pointed out that particles that precipitate out from a supersaturated solid solution are many times too large or too small for the space they must occupy, and as a result they strain the matrix in their immediate vicinity. When a moving dislocation encounters a shearing stress that is not favorable to its passage, as some of the stresses around such particles often are, the dislocation is arrested until a stress is applied capable of overcoming the obstruction of the local stress. In cases where the dislocation is rigid and cannot yield or bend, and if it is long, compared with the average distance between particles, there will be nearly as many favorably directed stresses as there are opposing stresses along its length, so that little net obstruction to the dislocation motion will result. In cases where the dislocation traverses a region with widely spaced local stress centers, it will have a rather wavy form, following the contours of the stress field with resulting minimum energy, but with a slight curvature. If stress is applied, the dislocation stretches into loops between the points where it is caught on stress centers. In order to free this wavy dislocation from the stress centers, a stress sufficient to pull the dislocation through the center is required, without the help of other stress centers, under which condition the slip resistance will be high. This is much like the age-hardened condition, for the theory applying to the quenched condition is that the stress centers are so close together that the dislocation cannot bend sharply enough to follow the stress contours and, therefore, acts as a rigid dislocation, with aiding and opposing stresses cancelling each other, and with slip resistance very low. Only with a critical separation of the stress centers can maximum hardness result, these separations being found experimentally to be in the order of 100 atom spacings.

It is important to keep in mind that metals are weak because of the motion of dislocations in the crystal structure and that when this motion is retarded or prevented, the metal is strengthened. Commercial age-hardening alloys, such as those in the aluminum-copper system, where the maximum solubility of copper in aluminum is about 5.6 per cent of copper by weight at 1018F and less than 0.25 per cent copper in aluminum at room temperature, exhibit precipitation hardening tendencies under certain conditions.

By way of example, if an alloy of this aluminum-copper system containing 4 per cent copper is heated up to a temperature of about 1000F, the copper will be entirely dissolved in the aluminum. It the alloy is then allowed to cool very slowly to room temperature, a new phase will appear at the grain boundaries of the alpha solution, this being known as the theta solid solution and recognized as the compound $CuAl_2$. Upon slow cooling to room temperature, this alloy will have a tensile strength of about 36,000 psi. Then, if this same alloy is solution-treated by heating it up to between 970 and 1000F so that the copper goes back into solution again and then is cooled rapidly, the tensile strength will be found to have increased to about 46,000 psi and will have a hardness of approximately 55 to 57 BHN.

If this alloy is checked for hardness at intervals of about every 24 hours, a decided change will be found to be taking place; after about ten days, the hardness will be found to be up to 104 to 105 BHN and the tensile strength will be seen to be between 56,000 and 62,000 psi, these readings taken at room temperature. This phenomenon is known as *natural age hardening* and is common to those alloy systems which show limited solubility in the solid state. Some of the alloy systems aging at room temperature with an increase in tensile strength and hardness, proceed at such a slow rate that aging at a rather higher temperature is resorted to; this *artificial aging* is known as *precipitation hardening*.

6-16 Precipitation Hardening

Precipitation from the solid solution occurs to some degree in most alloys and to a marked degree in many alloy systems. In fact, by the addition of a properly selected alloying element, almost any metal can be made to precipitation-harden, and employing more than one alloying element, still further hardening should be possible. This is the process by which hardening of an alloy is effected by the precipitation of a constituent from the supersaturated solid solution, by heating to an elevated temperature. Precipitation itself is the decomposition of a solid solution into two phases of different composition, that is, the precipitate and the solid solution. The newly-formed solid solution shows a diminished solute concentration compared to that of the original solid solution. The phenomenon of precipitation can occur in only those alloys in which there is a decrease in solid solubility with decreasing temperature, resulting in a supersaturated solution. Since the supersaturated solution is unstable, it tends to decompose in the following manner:

$$\text{Supersaturated alpha} \longrightarrow \text{alpha saturated} + \text{beta}$$

where *alpha* indicates the solid solution, and *beta* the precipitate.

Precipitation is accompanied by changes in the physical, chemical, and mechanical properties of alloys. As a rule, electrical conductivity increases (with many alloys) and hardness also increases, attaining a maximum value, then decreases to a lower value. The higher temperature of aging, the earlier the maximum value is reached. Fundamentally, strength increases with hardness but not necessarily in proportion, while ductility decreases with increase in hardness. A change of volume of the material undergoing precipitation will result, and whether it is expansion or contraction depends on the relative specific volumes of the matrix and the solute. In some cases systems undergoing aging show a visible precipitation; however, in others there is no visible sign of aging until the optimum properties have been reached and passed, and by that time overaging has taken place.

Precipitation hardening may be attained in the very low carbon steels by quenching and then aging, the temperature of aging having a decided effect on the increase of hardness attainable, as well as the time necessary to bring about this change. In the case of low carbon steels the hardening is no doubt due to precipitation of iron carbide, iron nitride, etc. Thoroughly deoxidized steels do not usually have aging characteristics, so that oxygen in steel has a pronounced effect upon this reaction.

Precipitation hardening is used in industrial application in other alloys such as stainless steels, designated as the 17–7 PH, 18–8 PH, etc. The chemical analysis of 17–7 PH steel is as follows: 17 per cent Cr, 7 per cent Ni, 1.2 per cent Al, and 0.07 per cent C. This steel has properties that may be greatly improved by precipitation-hardening the properties before and after the treatment, as follows:

	Annealed State	*Precipitation Hardened*
Ultimate strength, psi	128,000	234,000
Yield Strength, psi	48,000	217,000
Elongation in 2 in. per cent	38.6	7.2
Rockwell Hardness	B86	C46

Alloys to be used at high temperatures have been found to be substantially strengthened by precipitation hardening, and this knowledge is used extensively in the selection of steels for certain high-temperature, high-strength applications.

"Quenching an alloy after solution heat treatment generally results in the lowest electrical conductivity, since a large part of the constituents present are retained in solid solution. However, in systems that age at room temperature, there may be a subsequent decrease in conductivity occurring during the initial stages of aging, attributed to Guinier-Preston zone* formation and related phenomena. By removing constituents from solid solution, aging (particularly at elevated temperatures) and, to a degree, annealing increase the electrical conductivity." (Aluminum: Volume I)

---

*Guinier-Preston zones. In a structure precipitating from solid solution, the two-dimension platelets that produce streaks on Laue X-ray photograms. These platelets form on specific crystallographic planes of the matrix lattice and produce the first discernible evidence of decomposition of a supersaturated solid solution.

QUESTIONS

1. In specifying the properties of a material, such as a metal or nonmetal, what are the three categories that must be given?

2. How do we define the *density* of a material?

3. In a study of the relationship of atomic diameter to melting points of the elements in group A of the fourth period of the periodic table, what do we observe?

4. Define the *specific heat* of a metal. How can it be computed?

5. Numbers of metals have crystal structures that are *anisotropic*. Explain what is meant by this term.

6. What do we mean by the thermal elastic effect in metals?

7. Explain the meaning of thermal electric effect and draw a sketch to illustrate the Seebeck effect.

8. What is the Peltier effect?

9. Draw a sketch of, and fully identify all components of, an electric circuit to show that when a current passes through a wire with temperature differential, we get a heating or a cooling of the wire. What term is used to identify such an effect?

10. The ability of metals to conduct electricity is due largely to what?

11. What are the Brillouin zones and how are they related to the conduction of electricity in metal wires?

12. Define the terms ferromagnetic, paramagnetic, and diamagnetic materials. Do *all* metals react to a magnetic field?

13. Define what is meant by the mechanical properties of metals and alloys.

14. Why is it essential to study the behavior of single crystals in order to better understand the mechanical properties of polycrystalline materials?

15. Upon what do the mechanical reactions of metals to applied forces depend?

16. What is the best and surest way to determine if a metal will be suitable for certain applications? Can this always be accomplished?

17. What is Hooke's Law? In order for Hooke's Law to strictly apply, should the strains involved be large or small?

18. What is the main difference between plastic and elastic deformation?

19. A term that is used a great deal is *critical shearing stress*. Exactly what does this term imply or mean?

20. What is the cause of strain hardening in a metal?

21. Why was the dislocation theory advanced?

22. Do groups of dislocations in metals and alloys remain static or can they move about or propagate within the material? How do we know?

23. Calculate the density of copper (FCC structure and atomic radius of 1.276 Å) and compare your answer with the density value obtained from *Metals Handbook*.

24. In order to remove all residual stresses in a laminated strip of copper and iron strips, it is annealed at 770F. This is followed by rapid coolimg to room temperature. (a) Determine the direction in which the laminated bimetallic strip will bend. (b) Given that the two elements are of the same thickness, calculate the stresses in each when the strip is restrained to an upright, straight position at room temperature. (The average coefficients of expansion over this temperature range for the two elements are $14 \cdot 10^{-6}$ and $18 \cdot 10^{-6}$ cm/cm/°C for the iron and copper respectively.) (The average modulii of elasticity for each of the metals are 30,000,000 and 16,000,000 psi, respectively.)

25. Assuming the dimensions of the bimetallic strip in the preceding Problem 24 to be a cross sectional area of 0.005 in.^{2} for the copper portion and 0.002 in.^{2} for the iron portion, calculate the stress that would be developed in each of these metals if they were treated exactly as indicated in the preceding problem.

26. Calculate the electrical conductivity of iron, (a) at room temperature, and (b) at 212F.

27. Assuming the maximum resistance of 1 ohm in a copper wire 25 ft long, determine the smallest diameter of wire which can be used.

References

Barrett, Charles S., *Structure of Metals*. New York: McGraw-Hill Book Company, 1952.

Bozorth, Richard M., *Ferromagnetism*. New York: D. Van Nostrand Co., Inc., 1950.

Clark, Donald Sherman, and Wilbur R. Varney, *Physical Metallurgy for Engineers*. New York: D. Van Nostrand Co. Inc., 1962.

Cottrell, Allan Howard, *Theoretical Structural Metallurgy*. New York: St. Martin's Press, 1957.

Goldman, Jacob E., *Science of Engineering Materials*. New York: John Wiley & Sons, 1957.

Kittel, Charles, *Introduction to Solid State Physics*. New York: John Wiley & Sons, 1956.

Metals Handbook, American Society for Metals, 8th ed., 1961.

Shockley, William, *Electrons and Holes in Semi-conductors*. New York: D. Van Nostrand Co., Inc., 1950.

Alloys of Iron and Carbon

7-1 Iron Carbon Alloys

Since carbon is one of the most important ingredients of steel, it is important to study the alloys of iron and carbon and the iron-carbon phase-equilibrium diagram. It is significant that only a small amount of carbon added to iron and subsequently heat-treated properly can raise the tensile strength of otherwise pure iron from 40,000 to 150,000 psi. Iron is seldom used in the pure state except in the laboratory for experimental purposes. The most common form of commercially pure iron, known as *ingot iron* is manufactured in the open-hearth furnace by the Armco Steel Corporation, among others. Such ingot iron is useful when fabricated into culverts, roofing, and as a base for porcelain enameled refrigerators, stoves, etc.

Iron and carbon alloys, with other elements added for specific purposes to improve the mechanical properties, constitute the important ferrous alloys referred to as *steels* and *cast irons*. Pure ingot iron is soft but can be readily toughened by cold working. By strain-hardening this iron can be strengthened substantially although not to the strength of alloys of carbon with iron, for reasons which will be explained later. Ingot iron is also used extensively in direct-current magnetic circuits because of its high magnetic permeability and low remanence.

A study of the cooling curve for pure iron shown in Fig. 7–1 reveals that there are three allotropic (polymorphic) forms, these being delta (δ), gamma (γ), and alpha (α), starting from the top of the curve at the melting point and descending to room temperature. Also shown in Fig. 7–1 is the atomic structure of these three allotropic forms of pure iron, which are: body-centered cubic (BCC), face-centered cubic (FCC), and body-centered cubic (BCC) respectively. It will be noted that alpha iron has two magnetic forms, being paramagnetic in the temperature range of 1414F to 1663F (770C to 910C) and ferromagnetic at temperatures

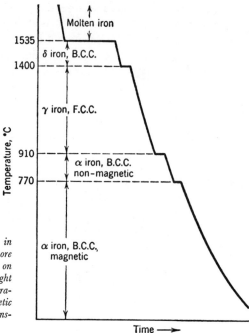

Fig. 7-1. *Cooling curve for pure iron. As shown in this curve, iron is allotropic and therefore exists in more than one type of crystal lattice structure depending on the temperature at which the iron is heated. The slight break in the cooling curve at 770C is merely the temperature at which iron changes from magnetic to non-magnetic (the Curie temperature) and is not an allotropic transformation, as it might appear in this diagram.*

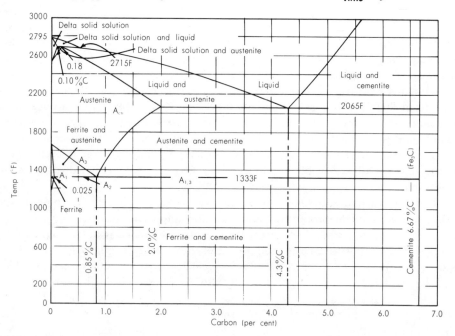

Fig. 7-2. *Equilibrium diagram of iron and iron-carbide.*

under 1414F (770C). This temperature at which iron changes from magnetic to non-magnetic is called the *Curie temperature.*

Due to the fact that carbon atoms are small compared to the relatively large iron atoms, they can dissolve interstitially in the iron lattices. It has been found experimentally that gamma iron dissolves about 2 per cent of carbon at 2065F (1130C); however, the maximum solubility of carbon in alpha iron is only 0.025 per cent at 1330F (723C). The interstitial solid solution of carbon in gamma iron is known as *austenite*, while the limited interstitial solid solution of carbon in alpha iron is called *ferrite*. Ferrite is soft, ductile, and practically carbon free. Its solubility for carbon decreases from a maximum of 0.025 per cent at 1333F to 0.008 per cent at room temperature. It has a tensile strength of about 40,000 psi and its hardness remains unaltered by heat treatment.

Referring to the iron-iron carbide phase equilibrium diagram shown in Fig. 7–2, it should be kept in mind that carbon is the most important element alloyed with iron. Intermetallic compounds are formed with iron and carbon, the most important being *cementite*, which has the formula Fe_3C and is very hard, being composed of iron and 6.67 per cent carbon. Like other intermetallic compounds, cementite is characterized by high hardness and extreme brittleness. In contrast to ferrite, whose hardness is about 80 Brinell, the hardness of cementite is approximately 1000. (On the basis of the commonly accepted formula of $TS = BHN \times 500$, the strength of cementite may be seen to be about 500,000 psi.) Because of the extreme hardness of cementite it is difficult to machine white iron castings, since cementite is its major constituent. Cementite contains 12 iron atoms and 4 carbon atoms in an orthorhombic crystal lattice.

When iron carbide in pure form breaks up into iron and graphite upon being heated to 2012F (1100C) or above, liquid plus cementite results, as shown in Fig. 7–2. Since carbon has the ability to alter the properties of iron materially when they are combined, the iron carbon alloys with from just a trace of carbon up to 1.7 per cent carbon by weight, and with minor amounts of other elements, are termed *plain carbon steels*. Iron with from 1.7 per cent up to 6.67 per cent carbon and with only minor amounts of other elements is referred to as *white cast iron*. Under equilibrium conditions the carbon in such alloys is in the form of the iron carbide compound, so that such a system is referred to as the iron-iron carbide system.

The iron-iron carbide diagram represents not only changes affecting physical states, such as liquid and solid, but also represents significant changes involving solid constituents. Inasmuch as such transformations are accompanied by either endothermic or exothermic reactions, temperatures at which these phenomena take place are designated *critical temperatures*. Furthermore, some of the transformations which occur at these temperatures are factors determining the response of steels to heat treatment, since solubility, diffusion, precipitation, and recrystallization are involved.

7-2 Designations of Critical Temperatures

The alpha to gamma transformation in steels is accompanied by an endothermic reaction; however, the gamma to alpha transformation is characterized by an exothermic effect. Since both thermal reactions interrupt normal heating and cooling rates, the temperatures at which these transformations occur are identified by the letter *A* as an abbreviation of the *arrest*. Transformations which occur during heating are further identified by the small letter *c*, while the small letter *r* is added to those transformations which occur during cooling. Thus the critical temperatures on heating are designated *Ac* and those on cooling as *Ar*. Furthermore, designations are given these critical temperatures at the loci as shown in Fig. 7–2. For example, the curve that separates the phases austenite and austenite with ferrite is termed the A_3 temperature, while the temperature at the point where magnetic transformation takes place, is termed the A_2. The eutectoid temperature is designated A_1 to indicate those alloys at the left of the eutectoid, and a designation of A_{3-1} indicates those alloys to the right of the eutectoid. Because the A_3, A_2, and A_1 points merge when the composition reaches 0.85 per cent carbon, the unified critical temperature is designated A_{3-2-1}, or more commonly as A_1. The *Ar* criticals occur at lower temperatures than the corresponding ones on heating, because of a hysteresis or atomic inertia, as the solid solution *austenite* decomposes into its constituents—ferrite and carbide (or carbon).

The *Acm* designation indicates the temperature at which cementite precipitates from austenite on slow cooling and goes into solution on heating. The *critical range* of temperatures is that area between A_1 and A_3 and is used frequently in discussing the heat treatment of iron-carbon alloys.

The eutectoid is a solid-state reaction wherein the decomposition of one solid solution takes place into different solid phases. In this case, the eutectoid (pearlite) containing 0.85 per cent carbon is made up of ferrite and cementite. Heat treating steel effectively is largely a matter of the proper control of this eutectoid reaction. Steels with less than 0.85 per cent carbon are usually referred to as hypoeutectoid steels, and those with more than 0.85 per cent carbon as hypereutectoid steels.

Considering the steel portion of the iron-iron carbide part of the equilibrium diagram, it is seen that a eutectoid reaction takes place at 1335F (725C) and a peritectic reaction takes place at 2719F (1495C). The eutectoid reaction is the more important of the two and is represented by the following equation:

$$\gamma(0.85\% \text{ C}) \rightleftarrows \alpha(0.025\% \text{ C}) + \text{Fe}_3 \text{ C}$$

The steel portion of the equilibrium diagram of iron and iron-carbide (with carbon up to 2.00 per cent) is shown in Fig. 7–8.

Referring to Fig. 7–2, showing the equilibrium diagram of iron and iron-carbide, it will be observed that the phases and structural constituents of the phases are as follows:

Austenite....................	Solid solution of carbon in face-centered cubic (gamma) iron
Delta solid solution	Solid solution of carbon in body-centered cubic (delta) iron
Ferrite	Solid solution of carbon in body-centered cubic (alpha) iron
Cementite	Intermetallic compound Fe_3C
Ledeburite	Eutectic mixture of austenite and cementite
Pearlite	Eutectoid mixture of ferrite and cementite

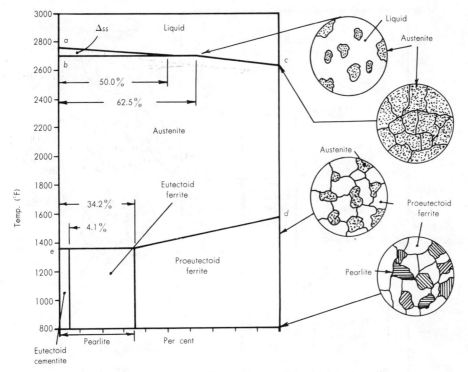

Fig. 7-3. *Phase transformation diagram for a 0.30 per cent carbon-iron alloy.*

The iron-iron-carbide equilibrium diagram should be studied to observe what happens when various alloys in this system change from the molten to the solid state, going through the process of solidification followed by cooling. In the equilibrium diagram it will be seen that there are three invariants in this system: the peritectic at 1488C, the eutectic at 1152C, and the eutectoid at 738C. Cementite (FeC) is in a metastable condition with the austenite, so that if sufficient time is allowed, iron-carbon alloys containing austenite and cementite will decompose and transform into austenite and graphite.

7-3   Transformation Diagrams.

Although the equilibrium diagram shows the composition and portions of the phases that will be in equilibrium at certain temperatures, it is more desirable if, by means of a graphic presentation, these changes can be determined in the proportions of the phases present. For this reason it is often desirable to construct a *phase transformation diagram*, plotting the temperature as a function of the percentage of the phases present. By so doing, the formation of phases and structural constituents present can be determined and shown in a graphic manner. As shown in Fig. 7–4, this diagram is rectangular in shape with the temperature shown as the ordinate, and the percentage of the phases or structural constituents shown on the abscissa. In the case of any phase or structural constituent making up 100 per cent of the structure, it is shown as the full width of the transformation diagram. Where the phase or structural constituent is less than 100 per cent, it is measured off

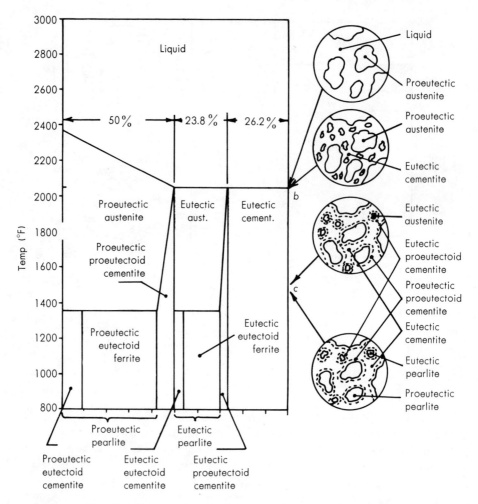

Fig. 7-4. *Phase transformation diagram for a 3 per cent carbon-iron alloy.*

accordingly for the exact amount of the phase or structural constituent that is actually present.

An example of the use of the equilibrium diagram in the construction of the phase transformation diagram follows. Referring to Fig. 7–2, showing the equilibrium diagram of iron and iron-carbide and particularly the eutectoid region of this Fe-C diagram, where the eutectoid occurs at 0.85 per cent carbon, if it were required to plot the percentage of ferrite, austenite, and carbide in an alloy of 0.60 per cent carbon and 99.40 per cent iron as a function of temperature, the solution would be

At 1334F

$$\text{the per cent ferrite} = \frac{0.85 - 0.60}{0.85 - 0.025} = 26 \text{ per cent}$$

At 1332F

$$\text{the per cent ferrite} = \frac{6.67 - 0.60}{6.67 - 0.025} = 91 \text{ per cent}$$

Phase transformation diagrams may be constructed from these results and also

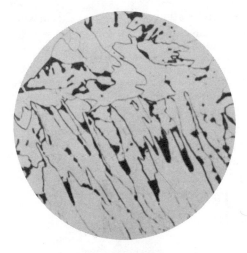

Fig. 7-5. *Microstructure of 0.20 per cent carbon steel, as-cast. Etched with Nital; 200X magnification.*

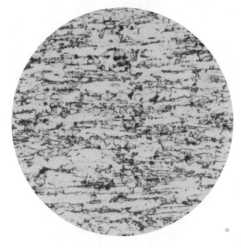

Fig. 7-6. *A microstructure of full-hard cold-reduced black plate steel after an 85 per cent reduction in area. Nital etch, magnification 200X. (Both cuts courtesy of United States Steel Corporation.)*

at other temperatures and for other phases, as detailed in the text and as shown in Figures 7–3 and 7–4.

An example of a phase transformation diagram of an iron-carbon alloy containing 0.30 per cent carbon is shown in Fig. 7–3, and in Fig. 7–4 is a similar transformation diagram for an alloy of iron and 3.00 per cent carbon. The percentages shown are by weight. Sketches of the microstructure of these two alloys with 0.03 and 3.00 per cent carbon in iron, respectively, are also shown in addition to the phase transformation diagrams. It will be noted that in the case of the alloy with 0.30 per cent carbon, the ferrite that forms prior to the formation of the pearlite is termed *proeutectoid ferrite,* whereas the ferrite that appears in the pearlite is called *eutectoid ferrite.* The cementite that is contained in the pearlite is termed *eutectoid cementite.* The two phases of ferrite and cementite in this alloy are found to be distributed in the following manner:

Eutectoid ferrite ....30.1 per cent
Proeutectoid ferrite ....65.8 per cent
Total ferrite present ....95.9 per cent
Eutectoid cementite present .... 4.1 per cent

Considering the phase transformation diagram of the alloy with 3.00 per cent carbon, shown in Fig. 7–4 and the accompanying sketches, it will be noted that several new terms and phases are introduced. The term eutectic is used as a prefix to describe the eutectoid ferrite, and eutectoid cementite to differentiate between these constituents and the eutectoid ferrite and cementite that were formed from the proeutectic components. Changes in structure that take place at the various temperatures and compositions will be noted. Referring to Fig. 7–7, showing a portion of the iron-iron carbide diagram, it will be noted that the alloys containing 1.7 per cent carbon and over are important in determining the transformations that take place, as well as the phases that are present.

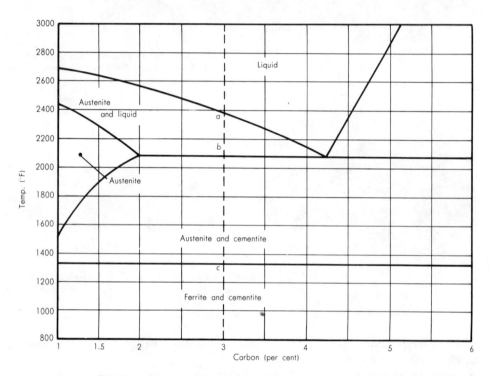

Fig. 7-7. *A portion of the equilibrium diagram of iron and iron-carbide.*

7-4. Structures Formed in Transformations of Iron-Carbon Alloys Containing over 1.7 Per Cent Carbon

Eutectic austenite .... Austenite that is formed when the eutectic liquid solidifies

Proeutectic austenite .... Austenite that is formed directly from liquid when cooled over a range of temperature prior to the formation of the eutectic

Proeutectic cementite .... Cementite formed from the liquid in cooling over a range of temperature before the formation of the eutectic

Eutectic cementite .... Cementite that is formed on solidification of liquid with eutectic composition

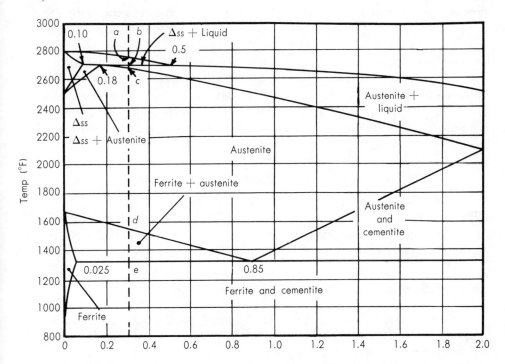

Fig. 7-8. *A small portion of equilibrium diagram of iron and iron-carbide up to 2.00 per cent carbon content.*

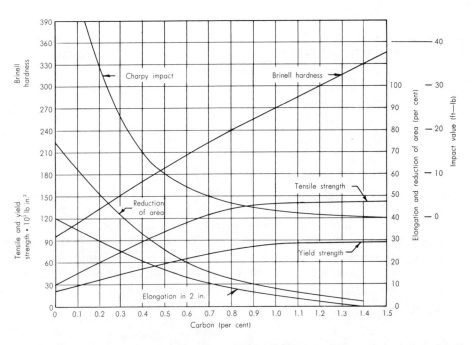

Fig. 7-9. *How carbon affects the mechanical properties of hot-worked steel. It will be noted that both the Brinell hardness and tensile strength of steel alloys show an increase with the increase in carbon up to 0.85 per cent; however, the elongation and reduction of area (ductility) show decreases with additions of carbon.*

Proeutectoid cementite . . . . .Cementite precipitated from austenite in cooling from eutectic to eutectoid temperature

Eutectoid cementite . . . . .Cementite formed on transformation of austenite with eutectoid composition

Eutectoid ferrite . . . . .Ferrite formed on transformation of austenite with eutectoid composition

Proeutectic proeutectoid cementite . .Proeutectoid cementite coming from proeutectic austenite

Eutectic proeutectoid cementite . . . .Proeutectoid cementite coming from eutectic austenite

Eutectic pearlite . . . . .Pearlite coming from eutectic austenite

Proeutectic pearlite . . . . .Pearlite coming from proeutectic austenite.

In the iron-iron carbide alloys under equilibrium conditions, the phases present are always ferrite and cementite at room temperature.

7-5   Alloys of Iron and Carbon

Although more will be discussed in Chapter 8 on the subject of the various alloys of iron and carbon, the following are of prime importance in industry and will be further developed in a later chapter:

> Ferritic gray cast iron
> Pearlitic gray cast iron
> Nodular cast iron
> Malleable cast iron
>
> Cast steel (as cast)
> Cast steel (normalized)
>
> Machine steel (0.20 per cent carbon)
> Hardenend and tempered steel (0.45 per cent carbon)
>
> Wrought iron
> Ingot iron
>
> Cold drawn steel (0.80 per cent carbon)
> Spheroidized steel (1.00 per cent carbon)
> Hardened and tempered steel (1.00 per cent carbon)

The above listing of the important iron-carbon alloys is somewhat related to cost for comparable parts with the cost of ferritic gray cast iron being the lower in cost, and hardened and tempered steel with 1.00 per cent carbon being the higher. In addition to iron and carbon, these alloys also contain other elements that improve their physical properties, and these will also be covered in Chapter 10. In fact, more will be discussed in Chapters 10 and 11 on the subject of steels and the heat treatment, surface treatment, etc., this chapter being given over to carbon steels and cast irons.

7-6   Cast Irons

The microstructure of several important iron-carbon alloys will serve as a simple and speedy evaluation of the more common cast iron, from the lowest to the

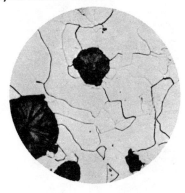

500X   Nital etch

Ferrite
in ductile iron

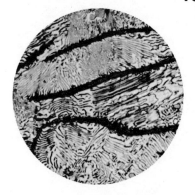

500X   Nital etch

Coarse pearlite
in gray iron

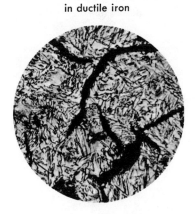

500X   Nital etch

Acicular structure
in gray iron

500X   Nital etch

Tempered martensite
in gray iron

500X   Nital etch

Fine pearlite
in gray iron

500X   Nital etch

Fine pearlite and iron carbide
in white iron

Fig. 7-10. *Matrix structures.*

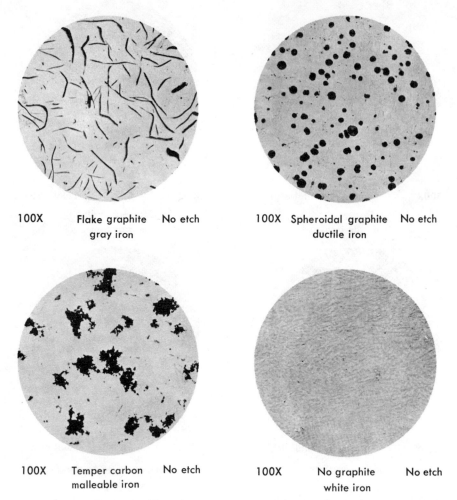

100X   Flake graphite   No etch
gray iron

100X   Spheroidal graphite   No etch
ductile iron

100X   Temper carbon   No etch
malleable iron

100X   No graphite   No etch
white iron

Fig. 7-11. *Types of cast iron as distinguished by graphite structure.*

highest tensile strengths. The lower strength cast irons have a ferritic matrix, while those of higher strengths have an acicular matrix as noted.

The reproductions of microstructures are excellent and typical, affording the student an opportunity to study them closely in the light of their physical properties, noted at the bottom of each page. It will be noted that all specimens were prepared on equipment and with supplies manufactured by Precision Scientific Company.*

Although steels, both carbon and alloy, will be further discussed in later chapters on it is well to set down here some information relating to and supplementing the microstructures shown on the previous pages of the text. It is an undisputed fact that the physical properties of metals are closely related to their microstructure, so that by studying the latter we can determine what took place at the time the metals solidified.

---

* All of the comparative microstructures of cast irons on this and subsequent pages are through the courtesy of D. G. Zimmerman, Chief Metallurgist, Precision Scientific Company, Chicago, Illinois.

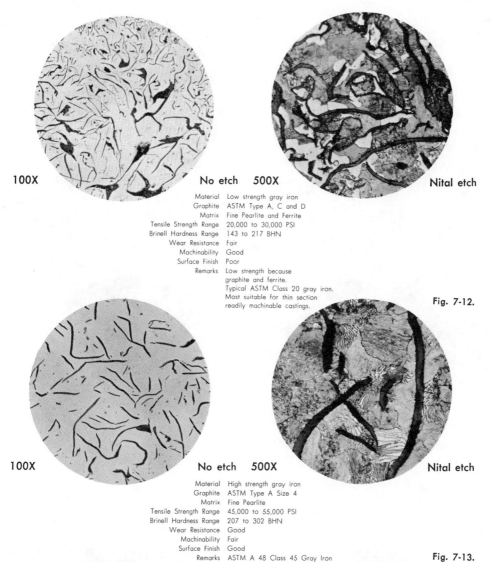

100X   No etch   500X   Nital etch

Material	Low strength gray iron
Graphite	ASTM Type A, C and D
Matrix	Fine Pearlite and Ferrite
Tensile Strength Range	20,000 to 30,000 PSI
Brinell Hardness Range	143 to 217 BHN
Wear Resistance	Fair
Machinability	Good
Surface Finish	Poor
Remarks	Low strength because graphite and ferrite. Typical ASTM Class 20 gray iron. Most suitable for thin section readily machinable castings.

Fig. 7-12.

100X   No etch   500X   Nital etch

Material	High strength gray iron
Graphite	ASTM Type A Size 4
Matrix	Fine Pearlite
Tensile Strength Range	45,000 to 55,000 PSI
Brinell Hardness Range	207 to 302 BHN
Wear Resistance	Good
Machinability	Fair
Surface Finish	Good
Remarks	ASTM A 48 Class 45 Gray Iron

Fig. 7-13.

The cast irons exhibit the influence of factors other than the equilibrium diagram in the determination of the final structure and properties of the alloy. This is, in fact, more significant in the cast irons than in steels. One of the most important behavior patterns of the cast irons is the fact that the iron carbide, Fe_3C, is very unstable. We find that at all temperatures the following transformation or reaction tends to take place:

$$Fe_3C \rightarrow 3\ Fe + C \text{ (in the form of graphite)}$$

At room temperature or in fact at low temperatures, the reaction takes place so slowly that iron carbide can and does exist for many years, and so is termed *metastable*. When cast iron is held at higher temperatures, this reaction can take place very rapidly; especially when silicon is present as an alloying element, we find a rapid graphitization of the iron carbide taking place. Silicon is extremely important to the graphitization of cast irons.

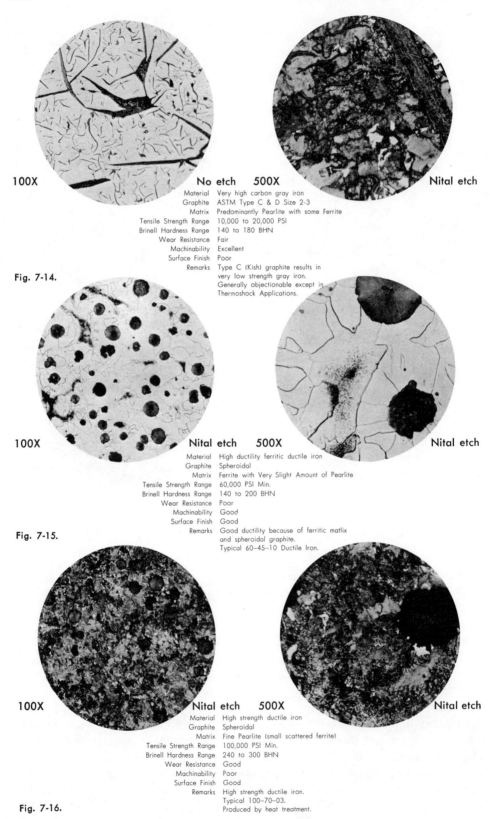

100X   No etch   500X   Nital etch

Material   Very high carbon gray iron
Graphite   ASTM Type C & D Size 2-3
Matrix   Predominantly Pearlite with some Ferrite
Tensile Strength Range   10,000 to 20,000 PSI
Brinell Hardness Range   140 to 180 BHN
Wear Resistance   Fair
Machinability   Excellent
Surface Finish   Poor
Remarks   Type C (Kish) graphite results in
                     very low strength gray iron.
Fig. 7-14.   Generally objectionable except in
                     Thermoshock Applications.

100X   Nital etch   500X   Nital etch

Material   High ductility ferritic ductile iron
Graphite   Spheroidal
Matrix   Ferrite with Very Slight Amount of Pearlite
Tensile Strength Range   60,000 PSI Min.
Brinell Hardness Range   140 to 200 BHN
Wear Resistance   Poor
Machinability   Good
Surface Finish   Good
Remarks   Good ductility because of ferritic matlix
                     and spheroidal graphite.
Fig. 7-15.   Typical 60–45–10 Ductile Iron.

100X   Nital etch   500X   Nital etch

Material   High strength ductile iron
Graphite   Spheroidal
Matrix   Fine Pearlite (small scattered ferrite)
Tensile Strength Range   100,000 PSI Min.
Brinell Hardness Range   240 to 300 BHN
Wear Resistance   Good
Machinability   Poor
Surface Finish   Good
Remarks   High strength ductile iron.
                     Typical 100–70–03.
Fig. 7-16.   Produced by heat treatment.

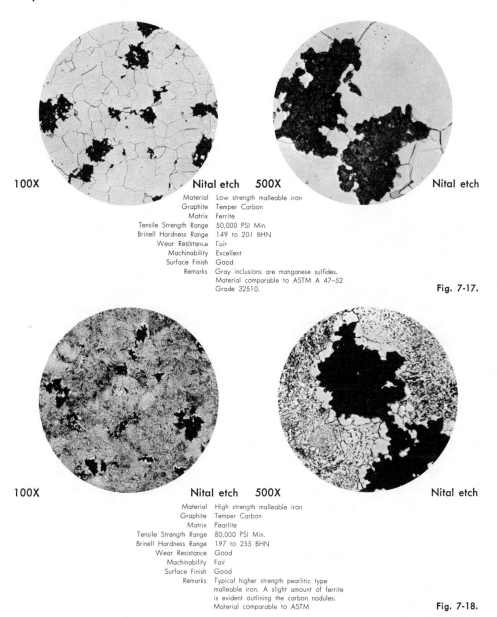

100X   Nital etch   500X   Nital etch

Material	Low strength malleable iron
Graphite	Temper Carbon
Matrix	Ferrite
Tensile Strength Range	50,000 PSI Min.
Brinell Hardness Range	149 to 201 BHN
Wear Resistance	Fair
Machinability	Excellent
Surface Finish	Good
Remarks	Gray inclusions are manganese sulfides. Material comparable to ASTM A 47–52 Grade 32510.

Fig. 7-17.

100X   Nital etch   500X   Nital etch

Material	High strength malleable iron
Graphite	Temper Carbon
Matrix	Pearlite
Tensile Strength Range	80,000 PSI Min.
Brinell Hardness Range	197 to 255 BHN
Wear Resistance	Good
Machinability	Fair
Surface Finish	Good
Remarks	Typical higher strength pearlitic type malleable iron. A slight amount of ferrite is evident outlining the carbon nodules. Material comparable to ASTM

Fig. 7-18.

7-7 White Cast Iron

When a cast iron with 3.0 per cent carbon, such as we discussed previously in this chapter, under phase transformation diagrams, is quickly cooled from the molten state, no graphitization takes place and the alloy that results is called *white cast iron.* The way in which solidification of a white cast iron takes place can be substantially determined from a study of the iron-iron carbide diagram in Fig. 7–2. Upon cooling to 2065F the austenite takes shape from the molten alloy in the form of dendrites, with approximately 50 per cent of the alloy solidifying in this manner. On arriving at 2065F, the molten mass reaches the eutectic composition with 4.3 per cent carbon, and at that point it solidifies as a eutectic mixture of austenite and cementite known as *ledeburite*. In both the matrix structures and microstructures shown on previous pages, this eutectic appears as white iron carbide, *cementite*, within the dendritic branches of austenite. Upon further cooling from 2065F to 1334F, a transformation takes place in which austenite, with a carbon content of 2.0 per cent, transforms to the eutectoid (pearlite), containing 0.85 per cent carbon, the iron carbide precipitating out. This additional iron carbide then builds up substantially onto the cementite (intermetallic compound of Fe_3C) particles that were already present at this temperature. The austenite at 1334F therefore transforms to *pearlite* (a eutectoid of ferrite and cementite). Rapid cooling prevents the graphitization of the cementite in white cast iron; however, if the casting of this composition is reheated to 1600F, flake graphite will be produced, very slowly, the alloy thus formed known as *malleable cast iron*. The matrix of such an alloy is preferably ferrite; however, it may also be found to be pearlite in case the alloy is cooled rapidly from 1334F or above, near the end of the heat treating process just mentioned. Alloys containing from 2.0 to 4.20 per cent carbon are known as *hypoeutectic white cast irons*; those with 4.2 per cent carbon are designated *eutectic white cast irons*, and the cast irons with from 4.2 to 6.67 per cent carbon are known as the *hypereutectic white cast irons*. In most cases the white cast iron castings are produced for subsequent conversion to malleable cast irons used by railroads, farm implement, automotive, and other industries where high strength, shock-resistant castings are required.

7-8   Malleable Cast Iron

Malleable iron castings consist almost entirely of ferrite and *temper carbon*. Temper carbon is graphite in a nodular form rather than in the flaky form found in gray cast iron. The carbon appears in the nodular form rather than flaky form because the graphite was separated from the cementite, Fe_3C, while the alloy was in the solid state, thereby preventing the growth of flakes.

While not strictly malleable, malleable castings are soft and can be bent without breaking. They are of two kinds, known as *white heart*, (European), and *black heart*, (American), these terms referring to the differences in the process and the products and countries of origin. In either type, the molten metal must have a composition that, when cast at the desired temperature into castings of the required size, will be free from graphitic carbon, and flakes will be absent from the melt. A charge consisting of malleable grades of pig iron (10 to 15 per cent), steel scrap (35 to 40 per cent) and cast-iron scrap (45 to 55 per cent), the latter consisting of feeders, runners, sprues, and defective castings, may be melted to obtain metal containing 2.25 to 3.00 per cent carbon, 0.3 to 0.50 per cent manganese, 0.05 to 0.08 per cent phosphorus, 0.06 to 0.11 per cent sulphur, and 0.60 to 1.15 per cent silicon. The exact composition, particularly in regard to silicon, may be varied according to the thickness of the section being made. If the carbon is under 2 per cent, graphitization in annealing is slow, and if the carbon is near 4 per cent, graphite may be formed in the casting. To prevent the latter occurrence, the silicon is lowered as the carbon is increased, particularly if the iron must be *white* all the way through after casting, with all of the carbon present in the combined form. As a rule, the manganese is approximately 1.7 times the sulfur content, plus an allowable excess of from 0.10 to 0.15 per cent. Although it is customary to hold the sulfur down to 0.05 or 0.06 per cent maximum, if the aforementioned ratio is adhered to, the sulfur can be permitted to go as high as 0.16 to 0.17 per cent without detrimental effects.

Malleable cast iron is usually manufactured in the reverberatory, or air-furnace, as it is sometimes called. The electric furnace is also used more extensively, and in either type furnace the metal is charged either with solid metal or, in some cases, in the liquid state from the cupola, where the *duplexing process* is utilized. Duplexed malleable iron is melted in the cupola and refined in electric arc or air furnaces. The metal charge for duplexing differs from cold melt practice, in that larger proportions of steel and less pig iron can be used. The reason for this is that the molten metal is carburized as it moves through the cupola and comes into contact with the incandescent coke. In cold melt furnace operations, all the carbon must be charged with the metal, and the metal charge and type of coke used for the cupola are carefully selected to produce the proper composition and metal characteristics in the iron. As a rule, the cupolas are operated to produce molten metal at low temperature (from 2700 to 2750F) to avoid excessive pick-up of carbon. The iron flows from the cupola into the elecric-arc or air furnace, where it is superheated to 2800 to 2900F and is there refined prior to tapping from the furnace and casting into molds. Although minor corrections in composition can be made in the refining furnace (electric arc or air furnace), the basic process control is in the cupola.

Upon solidification and cooling, the metal is in the form of white cast iron and, being hard and brittle, the gates, sprues, and risers can be readily removed from the castings. After the gates, etc., have been removed from the castings, the latter are ready to proceed to the heat treating process, and the gates, risers, sprues, etc., go back to the furnace for remelting.

Both malleable and pearlitic irons, which we will discuss next, are produced from base metal of approximately the following range of composition:

Carbon ....2.00 to 2.60 per cent.
Silicon ....0.09 to 1.60 per cent.
Manganese..................0.40 to 0.50 per cent.
Sulfur ....0.08 to 0.16 per cent.
Phosphorus ....0.03 to 0.10 per cent.

The air furnaces are fired with either powdered coal of high BTU, long-flame grade, or oil, to melt and superheat the iron with temperatures ranging from 2800 to 3100F depending on the composition of the metal and the nature of the castings being produced; the thickness of sections are an important factor. Heat treatment of the white iron castings to produce malleable iron is accomplished by a two-stage annealing process, as follows:

1. The first stage is done in either batch or continuous furnaces, depending on the rate of production required and the end use of the parts being produced. Where long annealing cycles are necessary because of low carbon or silicon, or both, the castings are generally packed in boxes made of iron or steel and annealed in a batch-type furnace. When the furnace is open-fired, so that hydrogen, water vapor, or decarburizing gases are present, the castings are often packed in sand, or gravel with carbonaceous material added to prevent attack of the surface of the castings during the long heat treating cycle involved. Where high production is required and large quantities of uniformly thick castings can be annealed in one cycle, continuous controlled-atmosphere furnaces are used, with roller hearths or roller trays,

the castings being packed into baskets or containers and pushed through the various zones of the furnace to accomplish the complete annealing cycle. Either electricity or radiant tubes fired with gas are used as a source of heat; in such cases the furnace is well sealed to exclude outside atmosphere. The atmosphere within the furnace is controlled to produce the desired carbon content on the surface of the final castings.

2. After the first stage annealing, the castings are cooled as rapidly as practical to about 1400F in preparation for the second stage of the annealing heat treatment. The rapid cooling cycle requires from 2 to 6 hours, depending on the type of furnace being used, after which the castings are cooled slowly at a rate of from 5 to 15F per hour. During this cooling, the carbon dissolved in the austenite is converted to graphite on the existing temper carbon particles, and a ferritic matrix is formed. Temper carbon is present in the form of nodules, with a nodule count of 70 to 90 discrete graphite particles in 20 sq in. of a photograph at 100X, for optimum desirability. This produces random particle distribution with short distances between particles.

Malleable iron castings are often preferable because of their high ductility (from 15 to 18 per cent elongation in 2 in.), shock-resistance, resistance to corrosion (due to an outside surface of almost pure iron as a result of decarburizing during annealing), and also their excellent machinability. Specifications for ferritic malleable iron castings, according to ASTM and SAE requirements, are

ASTM Number	Grade	Minimum Tensile Strength psi	Minimum Yield Strength psi	Minimum Elongation % in 2 in.
A47	32510	50,000	32,500	10
A47	35018	53,000	35,000	18
A197	Cupola	40,000	30,000	5

7-9 Pearlitic Malleable Iron

Whereas malleable iron, as stated previously, has a ferritic matrix with carbon (in the form of temper carbon) in nodules, pearlitic malleable has a matrix of pearlite (ferrite plus iron carbide). Pearlitic malleable iron is produced either by controlled heat treatment of the same base white iron used in the production of ferritic malleable iron, or by alloying to prevent decomposition of carbides dissolved in austenite during cooling from the first stage annealing temperature. Pearlitic malleable may be produced by air-cooling after first stage annealing and, subsequently, tempering to produce the specifications and hardness required, or by reheating, liquid quenching, and tempering to develop the desired specifications. It is possible to obtain a wide range of properties in pearlitic malleable iron by varying the base composition, melting practice, and heat treatment. There is a wide range of specifications and grades prescribed by ASTM, SAE and the Federal specification (MIL-I-11444) as follows:

Minimum Tensile Strength in psi	Minimum Yield Strength in psi	Minimum Elongation % in 2 in.
65,000 to 100,000	45,000 to 80,000	2 to 10%

The hardness of pearlitic malleable iron may range from 163 to 285 typical Brinell hardness range depending on end use of castings. It will be noted that while pearlitic malleable iron has potentially very high strengths, it is deficient in ductility and elongation. It contains a controlled quantity of combined carbon which may appear as lamellar pearlite, tempered martensite, or spheroidite in the metallic matrix, depending entirely on the heat treatment used in the process.

7-10 Nodular Cast Iron—Ductile Iron

Nodular cast iron, also referred to as ductile iron, spherulitic iron, and spherulitic graphite iron, is essentially cast iron in which graphite is present in the form of tiny balls or spherulites, rather than as flakes as in gray iron, or compacted aggregates (nodules), as in malleable iron. The chemical composition of unalloyed nodular irons is much like that of gray irons, and is somewhat as follows:

Total carbon	3.20 per cent
Silicon	1.80 to 2.80 per cent,
Manganese	up to 0.80 per cent
Sulfur	0.03 maximum
Phosphorus	0.10 maximum

In order to produce the spheroidal graphite structure, one or more alloying elements are added to the molten metal—usually magnesium, cerium, lithium, sodium, barium, or other elements. Magnesium and cerium are elements that are commercially important as additives for this purpose, the former being the cheaper and more versatile nodularizing agent of the two. Cerium, alone, is more effective in hypereutectic irons than in hypoeutectic irons. In most commercial applications both magnesium and cerium are used as alloying elements, with enough magnesium added to obtain a residual amount of magnesium of not over 0.08 per cent.

Although some nodular iron castings are used in the as-cast condition, in most cases they are given a heat treatment in the nature of a ferritizing anneal, or a normallizing treatment with quenching and tempering being used in some instances.

Nodular or ductile iron castings have a high shock-resistance, stiffness, and modulus of elasticity with the properties of large generators made from this material ranging as follows:

Tensile strength	65,000 to 85,000 psi
Elongation	13.5 to 4.5% in 2 in.
Hardness	163 to 228 Brinell
Modulus of elasticity	21.5 to 23.5 million psi

Prior to the nodularizing treatment, the base composition of a melt to be converted to nodular iron is made up of the correct amounts of steel and cast scrap, along with various grades of pig iron. It is essential that the ferrous components of the melt be low in phosphorus, chromium, titanium, copper, lead and other nonferrous metals that inhibit graphitization, as well as certain alloys that are commonly added to iron and steel. In other words, a melt for this purpose must be as pure an Fe-Si-Mn-C alloy as it is possible and practical to produce. The sulfur in the base iron should be especially low when magnesium or other nodularizing alloys are added to the melt. Sulfur may be controlled by using base metals low in sulfur, by desulfurizing the melt, or by a combination of both.

Furnaces for producing nodular cast iron may be of any type, including cupola melting with either an acid or basic slag or duplexing in an acid or basic cupola, followed by melting in an acid or basic electric-arc furnace, where certain needed adjustments in composition are made, after which the temperature of the melt is raised for treatment with magnesium alloy. The acid or basic electric-arc furnace is also used singly in some instances.

The magnesium alloys used as additions to the melt in production of nodular iron vary in composition and are selected on the basis of specifications, processing requirements, and foundry equipment in use with these alloys, currently employed:

Nickel-magnesium	40 to 80 per cent nickel content
Nickel-iron-silicon-magnesium	
Iron-silicon-magnesium	magnesuim from 8 to 50 per cent
Iron-silicon-magnesium-cerium	cerium from 0.50 to 1.5 per cent
and other combinations of the above.	

The three most widely used methods of adding magnesium to the melt are the following:

1. *The pressure ladle method*, consisting of a device with a cover and ram, with an attachment to hold an expendable capsule of magnesium alloy, making it possible to fasten and securely cover the ladle before the ram with its separate sealing device plunges the capsule into the melt.

2. *The immersion refractory basket*, in which a magnesium alloy container is anchored with the open end facing down. The ram-cover-shield arrangement moves over the ladle, and as the magnesium alloy is forced under the surface of the melt by the ram, the cover shield moves into position over the ladle.

3. *The ladle addition method*, employing the technique of adding magnesium to the melt by pouring or tapping base iron over magnesium alloy that has been charged into the bottom of an open receiving ladle, usually vented so that no pressure is created. This method uses more magnesium than the first two methods, since it is more difficult to recover much of the magnesium by this method.

The microstructure of nodular iron from the as-cast condition shows the matrix to be pearlitic, with considerable ferrite surrounding each graphite spherulite and usually with some cementite present. The relative amounts of pearlite, ferrite and cementite are dependent on the composition, type of innoculant used, the innoculant procedure, and the rate of cooling of the castings.

Nodular iron production involves the usual casting defects, such as are found in other types of castings including shrinkage, voids caused by entrapped gases, surface flaws due to nonmetallic inclusions, and failure to fill the mold adequately. In addition to these are some other unique problems and defects encountered in nodular iron castings, for instance carbon nodule segregation, which occurs when the carbon equivalent (CE) is incorrect for the thickness of castings being produced. The carbon equivalent of nodular iron is expressed:

$$CE = \%\text{total carbon} + 0.3(\%\text{Si} + \%\text{P})$$

For casting thicknesses 1 to 4 in., the carbon equivalent should not exceed 4.6, as otherwise nodule segregation will be incurred.

Another defect that sometimes occurs in nodular iron is that of subsurface inclusions, stemming from the formation of nonmetallic compounds subsequent to the additions of magnesium or magnesium-cerium alloy to the base iron. Because of their higher melting temperatures, these compounds may become entrapped in the metal near a mold surface when the metal solidifies. Slag inclusions are also found, in some instances due to the ignition of some of the magnesium. Desulfurization also leads to formation of excessive slag and consequent slag inclusions, so slag must be removed. This is accomplished largely by preventing the reversible reaction of sulfur compounds and by providing a suitable mold gating system with the proper use of runners to reduce the velocity of the stream of metal, thereby permitting the slag to be released from the stream to become trapped in the gates and runners, rather than in the castings themselves. Nodular iron castings have a good shock-resistance, and the corrosion resistance is about the same as common gray iron castings.

Depending on the end use of the castings, there is a need for all the various types discussed in this chapter; however, it is imperative that the engineer should become familiar with the properties of each of them, and, considering the nature and requirements of the end products, select the one that will give the most satisfactory service in the environments in which the parts will operate.

QUESTIONS

1. What is the most important alloying element combining with iron?
2. Why is ingot iron frequently utilized in direct-current magnetic circuits? What desirable properties does it possess?
3. Draw the cooling curve for pure iron, and identify all parts.
4. Define the term *allotropy* and relate it to pure iron.
5. What is the Curie temperature for pure iron? Explain fully.
6. Although there are many intermetallic compounds formed with iron and carbon, what is the most important one? Why?
7. Define the following in terms of iron and carbon: plain carbon steels, white cast irons.
8. Referring to the iron – iron carbide equilibrium diagram, Fig. 7–2, what solid-state reaction takes place at 1335F with a carbon content of 0.85 per cent? Why is this reaction of such importance?
9. How are steels containing less than 0.85 per cent carbon referred to?
10. What are steels containing more than 0.85 per cent carbon called?
11. Define the following terms: critical temperatures, critical range of temperatures, cementite, austenite, proeutectoid ferrite.
12. From a study of the iron-iron carbide equilibrium diagram, what can be said concerning alloys containing 1.7 per cent carbon or more?
13. With respect to the iron-iron carbide alloys under equilibrium conditions, in what form are the phases present at room temperature?
14. How does the increased amount of carbon in steel affect the mechanical properties of the steel?
15. How does graphite (carbon) appear in the following cast irons: gray iron, ductile iron, malleable cast iron, white iron?
16. Why is it essential that we be familiar with the microstructure of metals?
17. What is one of the most important behavior patterns of cast irons?

18. State the transformation (reaction) that takes place in the case of iron carbide at all temperatures. Does this reaction take place more rapidly at one temperature than at another?
19. Define the following and tell something about each: white cast iron, ledeburite, cementite, malleable iron.
20. Why is the carbon in malleable cast iron in nodular rather than in flaky form?
21. Discuss the advantages and disadvantages of *duplexing* in the manufacture of malleable cast iron.
22. Make an outline and discuss the manufacture of malleable cast iron from raw material to finished product.
23. What is pearlitic malleable iron? Be specific.
24. Explain the method of manufacturing nodular iron, and tell how it differs from gray cast iron and pearlitic malleable iron.
25. What castings would you specify for use by the railroads, where high strength, shock-resistance, and corrosion-resistance are of major importance?
26. Describe the phase changes which occur on heating a 0.20 per cent carbon steel from room temperature to 2200F.
27. Calculate the quantities of the phases at 100F intervals from 1200F to 1600F for the following steels: (a) 0.8 per cent carbon, 99.2 per cent iron; (b) 1.2 per cent carbon, 98.8 per cent iron. Construct phase transformation diagrams for each.
28. Calculate the per cent ferrite, carbide, and pearlite at room temperature in iron-carbon alloys containing (a) 0.5 per cent carbon; (b) 0.8 per cent carbon; (c) 1.5 per cent carbon.
29. Describe the phase changes that take place in a 3.0 per cent carbon and 97.0 per cent iron alloy is cooled from liquid state to room temperature.
30. Refer to Fig. 7–2 and state what happens to austenite containing 0.18 per cent carbon as it is heated above 2700F.

References

Briggs, Charles W. (ed.), *Steel Castings Handbook*. New York: Steel Founders Society of America, 1950.
Schwartz, Harry A., *Malleable Iron Castings*. Cleveland, Ohio: Malleable Founders Society, 1958.
Taylor, Lyman (ed.), *Metals Handbook*, Metals Park, Ohio, 7th ed. 1948 and 8th ed. 1961.

Production of Ferrous Metals

8-1 Blast Furnace Operation

As discussed in Chapter 1, the actual start of the Iron Age is believed to have been about 1500 B.C. with the first smelting of iron ore. Despite this early beginning, it was not until the fourteenth century that furnaces were developed and perfected that could not only reduce iron ore that was so necessary, but also could melt it at the same time, so that the product could be cast in molten condition. The modern blast furnace shown in Fig. 8–1 is the result of technical and engineering research and development dating back over 500 years. The blast furnace of today not only has a high productivity, but also a high efficiency, in order to produce large tonnages of *pig iron* and other ferrous alloys in increasing quantities, year after year, as shown in Table 8–1.

Pig iron is of major importance in the iron and steel industry since this is the intermediate form through which almost all iron must pass in the manufacture of steel. It is also used in foundries throughout the metals industry for the manufacture of many types and grades of iron castings. In general, pig iron is the term applied to the metallic product of the blast furnace containing over 90 per cent iron. Other blast furnace products, in addition to pig iron, are *ferromanganese* and *spiegeleisen*, these made from manganese ore and, in some cases, from mixtures of manganese ore and iron ore. Blast furnace products also include *ferrophosphorus* and alloy iron, as noted in Table 8–2. Although pig iron can be made in other ways than by the blast furnace method, i.e., in electric smelting furnaces or by melting steel scrap with an excess of carbon in the cupola, only small tonnages are made by these methods; the modern blast furnace is best by far for the production of pig iron, most of which is transferred to open-hearth, converters, electric furnaces, and other steel making methods and shops.

TABLE 8–1.   Yearly Production of Pig Iron and Ferroalloys (Net Tons)*

			Pig Iron					Ferroalloys
Year	Basic	Bessemer	Low Phos- phorus	Foundry	Malle- able	All Other, Including Direct Castings	Total Pig Iron	Ferroalloys and Silvery Pig Iron
1962	58,806,123	2,822,674	174,733	1,428,614	2,153,957	254,723	65,640,824	650,181
1961	58,149,520	2,601,146	176,077	1,362,215	2,102,724	239,005	64,630,687	664,199
1960	58,261,108	3,403,599	387,260	1,467,358	2,672,875	288,448	66,480,648	839,481
1959	52,114,297	3,055,776	374,479	1,881,228	2,487,851	280,415	60,194,046	635,337
1958	49,114,646	3,599,873	320,278	1,606,028	2,304,904	211,978	57,157,707	606,393
1957	65,377,744	6,344,106	580,013	2,279,256	3,459,331	334,928	78,375,378	963,554
1956	61,638,748	6,664,957	504,189	2,398,346	3,467,117	395,132	75,068,489	891,071
1955	62,484,889	7,436,354	263,036	2,754,641	3,531,420	387,077	76,857,417	932,267
1954	47,023,175	5,625,503	211,893	2,273,032	2,629,662	202,283	57,965,548	721,336
1953	59,882,512	8,110,881	297,065	2,500,996	3,784,458	325,517	74,901,429	955,443
1952	47,511,189	7,445,715	307,478	2,670,210	3,120,168	258,178	61,312,938	837,988
1951	54,212,509	9,045,954	314,725	3,050,626	3,363,369	287,095	70,274,278	953,472
1950	49,880,440	8,090,608	335,418	2,807,247	3,181,043	293,151	64,586,907	852,862
1949	40,905,356	7,059,416	301,520	2,503,912	2,409,436	232,922	53,412,562	762,972
1948	46,315,064	7,731,530	384,425	2,769,510	2,590,656	264,031	60,055,216	988,590
1947	44,804,743	7,182,207	331,118	2,953,405	2,874,752	182,687	58,328,912	985,436
1946	33,727,655	5,932,414	167,013	2,545,936	2,190,285	215,493	44,778,796	769,111
1945	39,866,982	8,255,513	314,063	2,248,887	2,350,076	187,648	53,223,169	943,313
1944	45,886,008	9,756,836	474,686	2,190,681	2,494,659	204,569	61,007,439	1,065,244
1943	45,374,662	10,258,788	538,832	2,059,501	2,393,241	185,646	60,810,670	1,109,644
1942	43,532,865	9,865,220	562,672	2,546,530	2,399,520	169,137	59,075,944	1,039,443
1941	39,759,841	9,522,343	474,428	2,760,827	2,417,137	165,975	55,100,551	969,955
1940	33,987,734	7,386,320	448,956	2,292,175	1,832,401	124,080	46,071,666	907,425
1939	25,437,868	5,755,806	214,828	1,910,868	1,386,337	102,975	34,808,682	587,796

*From American Iron and Steel Institute Statistical Reports for corresponding years.

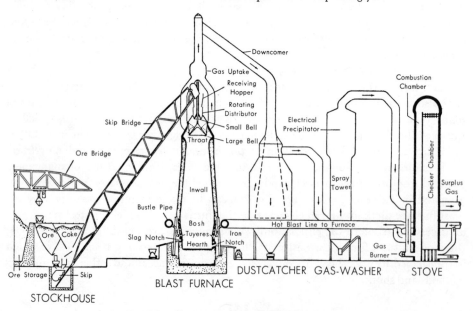

Fig. 8-1.   *Components of a modern blast furnace plant.*

In the form of molten iron from the blast furnace the metal is called *hot metal*; however, where it is to be used by foundries, the hot metal is cast into pigs and so it is called *pig iron*. The molds in which the pigs are cast are attached to a long conveyor from the pouring station to the point where the molds tip over, unloading the pig iron into waiting cars or trucks for further use. The equipment, consisting of the molds, the conveyor, etc., is called the *pig machine*. The term *pig iron* came about from the earlier method of pouring these chunks of iron into beds of molds in sand and arranged so that they were fed from a common runner; the entire group of molds resembled a litter of suckling pigs. As a result, the individual chunks of iron were referred to as *pigs*, and the runner as the *sow*.

Table 8–2 contains many different specifications for blast furnace products, falling into three fundamental classifications: (1) iron to be used in steel-making by a

TABLE 8–2. Chief Metallic Products of the Blast Furnace[a]

Product	Composition Range				
	Silicon (%)	Sulfur (%)	Phosphorus (%)	Manganese (%)	Total Carbon[b] (%)
IRON FOR STEELMAKING					
Basic Pig—Northern	1.50 max.	0.05 max.	0.400 max.	1.01 to 2.00	3.5 to 4.40
In steps of	0.25	—	—	0.50	—
Basic Pig—Southern	1.50 max.	0.05 max.	0.700 to 0.900	0.40 to 0.75	3.5 to 4.40
In steps of	0.25	—	—	—	—
Acid Pig, Bessemer	1.00 to 2.25	0.045 max.	0.04 to 0.135	0.5 to 1.00	4.15 to 4.40
Acid Pig, Open-Hearth	0.70 to 1.50	0.045 max.	Under 0.05	0.5 to 2.50	4.15 to 4.40
Oxygen Steelmaking Pig	0.20 to 2.00	0.05 max.	0.400 max.[c]	0.4 to 2.50	3.5 to 4.40
MERCHANT IRON FOR FOUNDRIES					
Low Phosphorus	0.50 to 3.00	0.035 max.	0.035 max.	1.25 max.	3.0 to 4.50
Intermediate Low Phosphorus	1.00 to 3.00	0.050 max.	0.036 to 0.075	1.25 max.	3.0 to 4.50
Bessemer	1.00 to 3.00	0.050 max.	0.076 to 0.100	1.25 max.	3.0 to 4.50
Malleable	0.75 to 3.50	0.050 max.	0.101 to 0.300	0.50 to 1.25	3.0 to 4.50
Northern Foundry	3.50 max.	0.050 max.	0.301 to 0.700	0.50 to 1.25	3.0 to 4.50
Southern Foundry	3.50 max.	0.050 max.	0.700 to 0.900	0.40 to 0.75	3.0 to 4.50
All grades in steps of	0.25	—	—	0.25	—
FERROALLOYS					
Spiegel (3 grades)	1.0 to 4.5	0.05 max.	0.14 to 0.25	16 to 30	6.5 max.
Standard Ferro-manganese (3 grades)	1.2 max.	0.05 max.	0.35 max.	74 to 82	7.5 max.
Ferrosilicon, Silvery Pig	5.00 to 17.00	0.06 max.	0.300 max.	1.00 to 2.00	1.5 max.
Ferrophosphorus	1.5 to 1.75	Under 0.05	15 to 24	0.07 to 0.50	1.10 to 2.0
FOREIGN PRACTICE					
Basic Bessemer (Gilchrist or Thomas)	0.3 to 1.00	0.20	1.9 to 2.5	0.7 to 2.5	3.50 to 4.0
Duplex Iron	1.2 to 1.75	Under 0.060	0.7 to 1.5	0.4 to 0.90	4.00 to 4.20

(a) Further information in: Steel Products Manual—Section 1—Pig Iron and Blast-Furnace Alloys, published by the American Iron and Steel Institute, 1951; and ASTM Standards 1961, Part I—Ferrous Metals (Specifications), published by the American Society for Testing and Materials.
(b) Carbon not specified.
(c) Up to 2.00 per cent phosphorus may be used by double slagging.

number of different processes; (2) iron to be used for the production of castings, including gray iron, malleable iron, ductile iron, etc., as referred to in Chapter 7; and (3) ferroalloys which contain a high percentage of one or more metallic elements and are used to regulate compositions of other ferrous metals, such as ferromanganese, spiegeleisen, ferrophosphorus, alloy iron, etc.

The process of manufacturing iron in the blast furnace is essentially one in which iron ore, coke and flux are charged into the top of the furnace, and air is introduced under pressure through the openings near the bottom edge, called *tuyeres*; the resulting gases, rich in carbon monoxide, rise through the descending burden of ore, coke and flux. The rising carbon-monoxide-rich gases serve to preheat the stock and to reduce the iron oxide in the ore. The carbon monoxide results from burning of the carbon in the coke in front of the tuyeres. The carbon in the coke is burned by oxygen in the air blast in accordance with the following reaction:

$$2C + O_2 \longrightarrow 2CO$$

Since this reaction takes place in front of the tuyeres and is completed before the air has penetrated by as much as 40 in. into the furnace, the combustion temperature in front of the tuyeres is approximately 3800F, assuming there are *stoves* provided to preheat the air blast up to 1300F in advance. The average temperature of molten iron in the hearth of a blast furnace producing basic iron is approximately 2700F, and the average temperature of the molten slag is slightly higher than that.

The components of a modern blast furnace are shown in Fig. 8–1 and an actual photograph of this is shown in Fig. 8–2. It is well to keep in mind the importance of the air blast used in every iron blast-furnace, for the actual weight of the air used is more than the total weight of all the other components combined, including iron ore, coke, and flux.

The carbon monoxide in the gas as it rises through the furnace reacts with the iron oxide in the ore in the approximate sequence of the following reactions, falling into the classification of "indirect reduction," and accounting for 85 to 90 per cent of the total reduction in an average blast furnace that is producing basic iron:

$$3\,Fe_2O_3 + CO \longrightarrow 2Fe_3O_4 + CO_2$$
$$Fe_3O_4 + CO \longrightarrow 3\,FeO + CO_2$$
$$FeO + CO \longrightarrow Fe + CO_2$$

It is true that iron oxide is also reduced directly by contact with solid carbon during the rising of the gases and the falling of the solid materials through the furnace, this being in accordance with the following reactions:

$$3\,Fe_2O_3 + C \longrightarrow 2Fe_3O_4 + CO$$
$$Fe_3O_4 + C \longrightarrow 3FeO + CO$$
$$FeO + C \longrightarrow Fe + CO$$

These reactions are called "direct reduction" reactions and account for approximately 10 to 15 per cent of the total reduction process.

The four main slagmaking constituents in the blast furnace burden are silica (SiO_2), alumina (Al_2O_3), lime (CaO), and magnesia (MgO). Inasmuch as the gangue or undesirable portion of the ore to be removed before it becomes commercially useful, is generally acid in character in the principal iron-producing districts of the

United States containing silica and alumina predominantly; we use lime in the form of limestone as the additive as a flux in the charge. This forms a slag with the required characteristics for ready fusibility in the process. The lime in the slag has the added purpose of removing the sulfur in the process in accordance with the following reaction:

$$CaO + FeS \longrightarrow CaS + FeO$$

Depending upon the amount of slagmaking constituents in the ore and coke, flux is added in the proper quantity to bring about a ratio of approximately 1 to 1 between total bases and acids in the slag. Any lower ratio than this usually requires a lower temperature for melting the slag, and any increase in flux raises the melting point of the slag, rendering it more viscous at constant temperature but, at the same time, improving its desulfurizing power.

Raw materials in the stockhouse bins are drawn into a scale car in specified weighed amounts and are then discharged into a cable-operated skip car which travels on an incline to the top of the blast furnace. Materials from the skip discharge over the small bell near the top of the furnace, which usually incorporates a device for periodic rotation of this compartment in order to compensate for any inherent differences in the trajectory and angle of repose of various materials, thereby making possible a uniform distribution of materials in the furnace. The small bell is then opened, permitting the materials to fall over the closed large bell. After a predetermined number of skips of material have been discharged onto the large bell, the small bell is held closed to prevent the escape of gases into the atmosphere. Then the large bell is opened, dropping the charge into the furnace. The top of the stock in the furnace is normally maintained at a level 6 to 10 ft below the bottom of the closed large bell.

An air blast is introduced into the furnace through tuyeres leading from the bustle pipe and disbursed peripherally around the hearth. The accumulation of molten iron in the hearth is "cast" at intervals of 5 or 6 hours by drilling through the clay plug of the tapping hole and then lancing the remaining iron skull with oxygen. Once a blast furnace has been started, it is operated continuously for many months. With the consumption of raw materials of coke, iron ore, and limestone, more of these materials are added at the top as previously described, in order to maintain the same volume of material inside the furnace.

Since the temperature of the furnace at the bottom is much higher than at the top as the charge descends through the furnace, many chemical reactions take place at different temperatures, as noted above. Although blast furnaces remove iron from its ore efficiently, only a limited amount of refining or purifying is done in the furnace. Most of the sulfur and silicon, and all of the phosphorus, that were originally in the ore will remain in the molten iron as it is tapped from the blast furnace. Also, iron in the furnace picks up 3.5 to 4.5 per cent carbon from the coke, as well as some sulfur while in the furnace.

Although several classes of blast furnace iron are produced, depending on the end use of the iron, the two principal classes are *basic iron*, which we expect to use in the basic open-hearth steel-making process, and *bessemer iron*, which we use in the acid bessemer process. The reason for these differences is that the various steel-making processes have their limitations of ability to remove impurities during the steel-making procedures. For example, the acid bessemer refining process, and the acid open-hearth process, both used extensively in the steel industry, are unable to remove phosphorus and therefore require low-phosphorus iron. On the other hand, the basic open-hearth process is able to remove phosphorus, so that iron made from higher phosphorus iron ore can be used in it. The charge of the blast furnace is such that for one ton of pig iron tapped and poured from the furnace, it takes 1.7 tons of iron ore, 0.90 tons of coke, and 0.40 tons of limestone.

Fig. 8-2. *Pair of large, modern blast furnaces and stoves.**

8-2   Metallurgical Coke Used in Blast Furnaces

The operation of the modern blast furnace requires metallurgical grade coke manufactured by two methods: the beehive process, and the by-product or retort process. In the beehive process, air is admitted into the coking chamber in controlled amounts in order to assist in the burning of volatile products distilled from the coal in order to generate heat for subsequent distillation. The physical properties of metallurgical coke, as well as its composition, depend largely upon the coal used and the temperature at which it is carburized. The coal must be of a special bituminous grade, as not all grades of bituminous coal will form coke suitable for metallurgical purposes. The most desirable blast furnace coke is made up of mixtures of high-volatile and low-volatile coals, pulverized and blended and then coked in ovens capable of heating the entire mass to a uniformly high temperature.

In the manufacture of steel today the use of by-product or retort processed coke is by far more prevalent. In the by-product method, air is excluded from the coking chambers and the necessary heat for distillation is supplied from external combustion of some of the gas recovered from the coking process. When modern by-product ovens are operated as they should be, all the volatile products liberated during coking are recovered as gas and coal chemicals, with about 40 per cent of the gas produced returned to the ovens for heating purposes.

Despite all the favorable advantages of the by-product coke ovens, the beehive process still serves a useful purpose in some instances, particularly during certain peak requirements, where the high investment of money in a by-product plant cannot be justified because of possible long periods of time when the plant is inoperative. If the beehive process could be altered to permit recovery of waste gases, it might be more useful; however, as it is, the by-product method is best and is far more in general use than the beehive. The best coke burns with an incandescence suited to the blast furnace operation. It serves two purposes, i.e., to reduce the Fe_2O_3 and Fe_3O_4 to Fe and O, and also to supply the heat needed to turn this reduced metal into a molten mass of iron. It is also very strong and will support the burden of ore and limestone without being crushed too severely. The composition of iron from a blast furnace will vary depending on the analysis of iron required as an end product, but will, in general, fall into one of the following categories or grades:

	Silicon	*Sulfur*	*Phos.*	*Manganese*	*Total C*
#1 Foundry pig	2.5 to 3.00	under 0.036	0.25–1.00	under 1.00	3.5–4.25
#2 " "	2.0 to 2.50	under 0.045	0.25–1.00	under 1.00	3.5–4.25
#3 " "	1.5 to 2.00	under 0.600	0.25–1.00	under 1.00	3.5–4.25
Malleable pig	1.0 to 2.00	under 0.050	0.20–0.90	under 1.00	3.5–4.25

The carbon picked up from the coke, and the sulfur and phosphorus that are in the ore from the beginning, will remain much the same in the final analysis of the pig iron.

8-3   Charging the Blast Furnace.

In charging the furnace the coke is usually put in first in several skip loads of 10,000 to 15,000 pounds each, and this is followed by iron ore and limestone. These two are usually mixed together prior to the charging. The whole charge of fuel, flux, and ore constitute what is called a "round." Because an even distribution of the charge is essential for best operating conditions, several rotating tops have been developed for this purpose to give a suitable mix. The weight of the air entering the blast furnace exceeds that of all other products in the charge combined.

8-4   Products of the Blast Furnace

As was stated, iron ore, coke, limestone, and air are the essential products going into the blast furnace. It is also important to review the products that come out of the blast furnace for a full appreciation of the entire operation. These are as follows:

1. Pig iron, which has been discussed. The main purpose of the blast furnace is to produce pig iron of suitable quality and grade for the purpose intended.

2. Slag, skimmed off into cars or into granulating troughs for subsequent use. Slag from the blast furnace was formerly discarded; now however, it is a

valuable ingredient used in the production of Portland cement. Crushed slag is also used in place of crushed rock as an aggregate in concrete. It is also used in the manufacture of building bricks, especially in Europe where it was first used in this manner.

3. Gas, which has the following approximate composition:

CO ......22 to 27 per cent
CO_2 ......10 to 17 per cent
N ......60 to 62 per cent

The calorific power of the gas coming from the furnace is about 900 cal per cu m.

All the coarse solids discarded with the gas are removed in a conical dust-arrester or dust-catcher, where water sprays remove most of the remaining dust. The cleaned gas is suitable for heating the stoves; however, any gas to be used in gas engines is further cleaned in bell or Theisen Washers. About 25 to 30 per cent of the gas is used to heat the stoves, while another 12 to 20 per cent is needed to operate the blowing engines, and the balance of the gas is available for general power purposes in the steel mill.

4. Flue dust is another product of the blast furnace, in the form of very fine particles of charge blown out of the blast furnace by the gas current, together with small quantities of volatile material. The coke fines make the flue dust rather high in carbon. In general, flue dust is caught and added in small quantities to the furnace charge; however, briquetting or some form of agglomeration such as sintering is more desirable and is used in many plants.

In summary, for a blast furnace with a capacity of 100 tons of pig iron per day, the following input and output products and quantities are, in general, correct:

Products going into the blast furnace:
For every
   2000 lb iron ore
   1000 lb metallurgical by-product coke
    600 lb limestone
   4500 lb air.
   ——————————
   8100 lb input

Products coming from the blast furnace:
   1120 lb pig iron
    800 lb slag
   6000 lb gases
   ——————————
   7920 lb of output

The most important element of control in the operation of a blast furnace is the height of the coke bed, as both the temperature within the furnace and the carbon content of the pig iron to come from the furnace are dependent on this factor.

8-5 Bottom-Blown Acid Process

The bottom-blown acid process of steel making, now generally known as the acid-Bessemer process, was the original pneumatic steel-making process. Millions of tons of steel have been produced by this process; in fact, from 1870 to 1910, the acid-Bessemer process produced most of the world's supply of steel. Inasmuch as the success of the acid-Bessemer steel-making process is dependent upon the quality of pig iron available which, in turn, demands reliable supplies of iron ore of relatively high purity, and also metallurgical coke, the importance of this process gradually declined with the depletion, over the years, of high quality ores abroad, especially the low-phosphorus ores. Still, in the United States, the Mesabi Range of iron ore in Minnesota has provided a source of relatively high grade ore for making iron by the acid-Bessemer process that should be productive for many years to come. Nevertheless, this process has, understandably, declined from a major to a minor steel-making method in the United States, the reasons being both metallurgical and economic.

At the present time the acid-Bessemer process is used principally in the production of steel for buttwelded pipe, seamless pipe, free-machining bars, flat-rolled products, wire, steel castings, and blown metal for the duplex process. Although most of the steel in this country is manufactured by the basic open-hearth process, the fact that the United States Steel Corporation built a new acid-Bessemer plant in Lorain, Ohio a few years ago, (and since this process is of importance in the use of the so-called "duplex" method of steel-making) makes it is important that the details of the equipment and process be pointed out in this chapter.

8-6   Acid-Bessemer Process of Steel Making

Molten blast furnace iron (pig iron) of the correct composition is poured into the Bessemer converter as shown in Fig. 8–3. This is a pear-shaped container mounted on trunnions, the converter tilted to receive the molten metal. There is usually between 5 and 30 tons of metal in the charge, depending on the custom and size of the plant. There is an acid refractory lining inside the converter so that the slags produced consist of more than 50 per cent silica, and it is for this reason that the process is called "acid-Bessemer" in this country. The process was named for Henry Bessemer, who discovered it during his search for a better grade of steel for the manufacture of guns in 1854–56. The early difficulties were largely due to the high phosphorous content of the pig iron used as the raw material in the converter. (As previously stated, Kelley, in this country also had done considerable work in the development of this process.)

Fig. 8-3. *Bessemer converter showing one of the three vessels "blowing." Slag pots and the bottom-hoist car operate on standard-gage tracks on the level below the vessels. (Photo by courtesy of United States Steel Corporation.)*

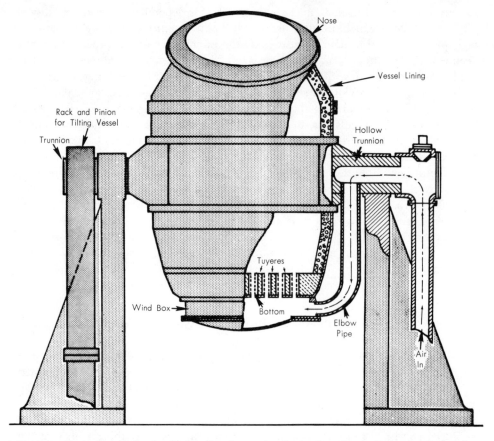

Fig. 8-4. *Construction details of a "bottom-blown" converter showing how the air blast enters it through a hollow trunnion, so that the vessel can be turned down without interrupting the flow of air (see Fig. 8-3 for actual photograph of a converter in operation). (Courtesy of United States Steel Corporation.)*

After the converter is charged with molten pig iron, air is introduced from the turboblowers, or blowing engines, from one of the two trunnions that support the vessel, into a blast box at the bottom of the converter. Air passes out of this box through many holes or tuyeres that are 1/2 to 7/8 in. in diameter into the interior of the converter; blast pressure of the air ranges from 20 to 35 psi. Automatic controls have now replaced the manual method in order to insure a uniform rate of air volume to avoid peaks and valleys that often prove detrimental, causing wide variations in depth of the bath, plugged tuyeres, etc. Converters of this type are known as "bottom-blown"; an example is shown in Fig. 8–4. The bottom of the converter receives the most wear and is therefore replaced frequently.

An adequate supply of replacement bottoms must be available at all times. On an average the life of the bottom will range from 25 to 35 "blows." As a result of extensive investigations of the use of an oxygen-enriched blast in the acid-Bessemer converter, there have been several improvements made in operation, including the following:

1. Shorter blowing time
2. Greater use of scrap and cold iron made possible
3. In the case of a blast with about 30 per cent oxygen content, the bottom and lining of the vessel are not worn as badly

4. Quality of steel very similar to regular Bessemer heats
5. Satisfactory pouring temperatures achieved, with flame temperatures readily distinguishable by the blowers in the system.

8-7 The Bessemer Blow in the Converter

The Bessemer blow is usually considered to be in three parts, the first period, the second period, and the after blow. Briefly, these are as follows:

1. First period, or *silicon blow*, commences as the blast is turned on at which time the converter is turned in an upright position. A short, transparent flame emerges from the mouth of the vessel and lengthens as the blowing continues after about four minutes when the second period begins.

2. Second period, or *carbon blow*. Air enters the bottom of the converter, giving out a long, brilliant flame, at which time there is a definite change in the appearance of the flame, indicated by a gradual shortening in the flame length and an apparent fanning out of the flame. Streaks of red appear at this point, as viewed through the colored glasses of the operator, followed by a change from golden yellow to a reddish flame. This change has been termed the *end-point*, and it usually occurs at the same carbon content so, that it has become a reference point for the proper control of the converter. In some cases, the blow is terminated and the converter shut down at the end-point, in which case the blows are said to be *young blown*. In other instances, for certain grades of steel, the blow is allowed to continue for from 15 to 20 seconds longer.

3. *After blow* is the interval of time between the *end-point* and the final turn, and heats of steel handled in this manner are said to be *full blown*.

Despite the fact that air is blown into the bottom of the converter, an action which might be thought to bring about a cooling of the metal, this blast actually brings added heat, through the exothermic chemical reactions of oxidation of carbon monoxide, silicon, etc. The chemical composition of the iron is a fundamental consideration in the control of temperatures, during the blow and later during the pouring operation.

Although the composition of the steel cannot be regulated satisfactorily by stopping the blow at an intermediate point, because of the speed of chemical reactions and other conditions, it is possible to blow a Bessemer heat to any desired carbon content, and with a more uniform chemical composition, by blowing to the drop of the flame and then making such carbon and manganese additions to the heat as are required. Metallic yield in the acid-Bessemer process is comparable to open-hearth practices and is, in the main, influenced by losses in metalloids, oxidation of iron, slopping, and other operational characteristics.

The fundamental factors that control the quality of the product of the acid-Bessemer converter are the characteristics of the flame at the end of the blow, and the deoxidation practice used in the process. Additions needed to produce various grades of acid-Bessemer steel are introduced during the deoxidation part of the process and may be added either to the vessel, ladle, or the mold into which the steel is poured. The acid-Bessemer process, unlike the open-hearth process, to be discussed next, taking several hours to refine the steel, accomplishes its refining action in a matter of a few minutes. It does have certain limitations, however, such as its inability to remove some of the undesirable elements usually found in pig iron, so that the end product of the acid Bessemer is somewhat limited to those products mentioned in paragraph 8–5 in this chapter.

The oxygen content of the blown metal is one of the most significant factors in the deoxidation of acid-Bessemer steel. The content of iron oxide is also related to the nitrogen content, in that both are increased by elevated temperatures and overblowing. In the production of liquid steel that has been deoxidized by additions of manganese, silicon, or aluminum, additives called *deoxidizers*, little or no dissolved oxygen remains in the steel to form blowholes or to produce a boiling action when the steel solidifies. Steel of this kind is called *killed* steel or *deoxidized* steel. In the production of killed steel, by the acid-Bessemer process, the deoxidation process is also affected by the fixation of nitrogen. For this reason, for proper deoxidation it is highly essential to control the temperature and end-point of the Bessemer blow. Actually, the oxygen is not removed by means of the deoxidizers but, rather, the deoxidizers combine with the dissolved oxygen, forming solid oxide products, and remain in the steel in the form of negligible inclusion that does not normally give any serious trouble.

Fig. 8-5. *A general view of the charging side of a group of modern open-hearth furnaces, showing a charging machine at left in background. (Courtesy of United States Steel Corporation.)*

During the solidification of metal in the ingot mold, many of the gases are rejected in the form of bubbles, with many of these being trapped within the ingot. Gases that form such blow-holes result in an ingot with a rather sound exterior surface, but with a rather porous interior, because of the trapped gases. Steel of this type is termed *rimmed* or *rimming* steel. Rimmed acid-Bessemer steels are usually fully blown and finished with a low carbon content. Since such steels are not completely deoxidized, a heavy evolution of gas occurs during the solidification in the ingot mold. Enough deoxidizer, such as aluminum, silicon or manganese is usually added, either in the ladle or in the mold, the silicon added in the form of ferrosilicon and the manganese as ferromanganese. The manganese, in addition to acting as a deoxidizer, also serves to improve the rolling characteristics of the steel.

Steel that has been fully killed, with gaseous oxygen completely removed, is the soundest metal for subsequent uses; however, rimmed steel with just the exterior surface in sound condition, and with the interior quite porous, also finds many uses. The expense and difficulty involved in the production of fully killed steel makes it second choice if rimmed steel can be used. Rimmed steel, with its clean and sound exterior surface, is very satisfactory in the fabrication of wire and sheets, where the internal blow-holes are welded shut during the several rolling operations to which it is subjected. In fact, for these and similar end products, rimmed steel is even more desirable than a completely killed grade of steel.

8-8   Basic Open-hearth Process

Although steel is produced in an acid open-hearth furnace in some plants, the tonnage produced by this method during the year 1962 was only 379,084 net tons as compared with 82,578,234 net tons produced by the basic open-hearth process, and 9,012,806 net tons by the electric furnace method. This discussion will therefore be based upon the basic open-hearth steel-making furnace, as shown in Fig. 8–5 and as graphically shown in Fig. 8–6.

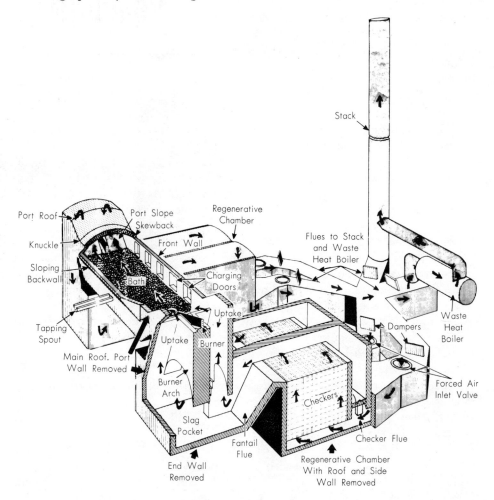

Fig. 8-6. *A diagrammatic illustration of the principal component parts of an open-hearth furnace with silica roof. The heavy curved arrows show the direction of the flow of the preheated flame, air, and waste gases when the liquid fuel is fired through a burner in the trench at the right end of the furnace. Although the charging floor is not shown here, the five doors that are shown are in the front wall of the furnace, and the checker chambers extend underneath this charging floor. (Courtesy of United States Steel Corporation.)*

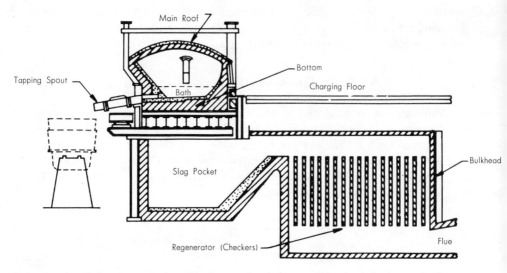

Fig. 8-7. *A vertical section across the width of an openhearth furnace. Although not drawn to scale, the names and relative locations of the component parts are indicated. The upper section is through the taphole of the furnace, while the bottom section is through the slag pocket and regenerator. (Courtesy of United States Steel Corporation.)*

The basic open-hearth furnace is rectangular in shape and is a brick structure reinforced with steel and supported on the sides and ends by steel *buckstays* in the form of steel beams, channels, or slabs bound together at their tops both longitudinally and crosswise above the furnace chamber, and ports by steel struts and tierods. The *hearth* refers to that part of the furnace below the charging door still level, including the *bottom* and *banks*. Some of the older furnaces have solid bottoms resting on concrete foundations; however, the more modern furnaces have "pan" bottoms of closely spaced steel beams covered with steel plates, so that the spaces between the beams and under the bottom are open to the air. Modern furnaces of more recent design do not have insulated bottoms, and the basic sub-hearth brick is 90 per cent magnesite instead of the chrome-magnesite or chrome brick formerly used. Most basic bottoms installed in large furnaces in recent years have been either burned-in grain magnesite or of all-rammed bottom construction. The latter type requires a shorter time for installation than other types. The specially grain-sized magnesite mixtures are rammed in over the top of the brick courses, using forms and careful tamping procedure.

There are five types of charges of raw materials for the basic open-hearth furnaces ranging from all-liquid iron generally, called *hot metal*, to all-solid scrap steel; however, the one most frequently used, especially by mills which roll their own steel ingots and have their own blast furnaces, is solid steel (steel scrap) and liquid iron, with some cold pig iron. In cases where the supply of scrap is limited, liquid iron may also be used to make up for the lack of local scrap. The amount of iron ore charged is proportioned to control the carbon content of the bath when it is entirely molten. Two of the more common types in this classification of charge are the 50–50 practice and the high molten pig iron practice. The 50–50 practice is a charge consisting of roughly 50 per cent pig iron and 50 per cent scrap, while the high molten pig iron method involves cases where the percentage of molten pig iron runs about 55 to 80 per cent of the total charge, leading to the use of a run-off or flush-off slag for more economical operation.

The melting period begins when the first scrap has been charged into the furnace. It is important to melt the scrap and other solid metallic elements in the charge as rapidly as possible in order to oxidize them with a sufficient supply of oxygen in the flame to produce a temperature and state of oxidation that will, on the one hand, keep the molten steel from chilling, because of the introduction of cold scrap, and, on the other hand, will not delay the oxidation of the metalloids of the pig iron by insufficient supply of oxygen from the oxidized scrap. For these reasons, a high rate of fuel supply at input is desirable, with a flame that will transfer the maximum number of heat units to the charge over the largest possible area.

Hot gases coming from the hearth are led through the checkerwork shown in Fig. 8–6 and are ultimately exhausted through the furnace stack. Actually the regenerative principle is employed whereby waste heat is utilized for the heating of the checker chambers on either side of the furnace. At the same time the air and gas entering the furnace are preheated by being passed through the previously heated checkers. The flow of these gases is periodically reversed, so that the hot chambers may be utilized for preheating purposes while the cooler chambers are again reheated through contact with the exhaust gases.

Steel scrap, pig iron (usually in a molten condition), limestone, and cast-iron scrap, along with other required materials, are charged into the furnace through the doors, and from time to time additions are made to the charge during the melting and refining process. Based on whatever ore practice is used in the furnace, today's modern, large, basic open-hearth furnace, with a capacity of from 200 to 225 net tons and fired with a liquid fuel (such as oil or tar), requires the amount of time for the various stages of the heat about as follows:

Melting down period (simultaneous with charging)	2.5 hr
Addition of the hot metal	0.5 hr
Ore boil	3.0 hr
Lime boil	1.5 hr
Working period	2.5 hr
Total time for the heat................................	10.00 hr

Using oxygen this time may be shortened by as much as 0.50 hr each for the meltdown time, as well as the working period; however, it becomes a matter of economics as to whether the expense of the oxygen can be justified. At the end of the period, the "heat" has become completely molten and refined so that it may be tapped and poured into either ingot molds or sand castings. The pouring temperature of the "heat" will depend upon the composition and grade of steel being made in the basic open-hearth, but in general, it is in the about 2900F.

8-9 Vacuum Degassing, Melting and Pouring of High Quality Steel

For several years, engineers and metallurgists have studied the problems and merits of vacuum melting, degassing, and pouring of steel, and have concluded that the prime reasons for this practice would be improved deoxidation and subsequent upgrading of the quality of electric furnace steels. The removal of hydrogen is considered a secondary objective, along with the removal of nitrogen, but these are considered to be more a function of melting practice and technique than of the equipment used.

Although it is known that carbon is a relatively weak deoxidizer of steel at atmospheric pressures and at normal steel melting temperatures, it is also known that carbon in the form of carbon monoxide gas does have a distinct advantage, in that after it has performed its task of deoxidation, it will leave the molten bath completely. This is found to be a very advantageous and much better than other conventional deoxidizers, such as aluminum and silicon, whose products of deoxidation remain partially in the steel as oxide inclusions. Furthermore, the effectiveness of carbon as a deoxidizer under vacuum is increased many times, largely due to the fact that vacuum levels required to deoxidize to very low oxygen content are much lower than any theoretical calculations indicate. By way of explanation, the *equilibrium constant* (K) for the reaction can best be expressed in terms of partial pressure of the CO (P_{CO}) and the percentages of oxygen and carbon in the bath as (C) and (O). Thus, the equation,

$$K \text{ (the equilibrium constant)} = \frac{P_{CO}}{(C)(O)}$$

The term "equilibrium constant" refers to the work done by C. M. Guldberg and Peter Waage (1864–67) and Henry Louis Le Chatelier (1885) and is based on the concept of mass action law, which, in turn, is based on the Gibbs free energy concept. In reference to vacuum melting and degassing, it means that the reactions involving gases and vapors may be expressed in terms of partial pressures of the reacting gases. (For further reading on the subject the reader is referred to Chapter 9 in *Physical Chemistry of Metals*, McGraw Hill, New York, 1953, and Chapter 12, Section 8 in *The Making, Shaping and Treating of Steel* (*Reaction Equilibria*) by United States Steel Corporation, 1964.)

Referring again to the equation for the equilibrium constant shown here, it is obvious that at low pressures, the product of (C) (O) should be reduced proportionately to P_{CO}. Since there is usually much more carbon than oxygen in medium carbon steels, the main effect of reduced pressure is a decided reduction in oxygen, which is greatly to be desired. One of the most essential requirements of vacuum melting and degassing is that of adequate stirring, by means of induction coils employed for this purpose. This insures optimum deoxidation, since there may be as much as two atmospheres of pressure at the bottom of the pouring ladle of steel due to the ferrostatic head alone. Induction stirring exposes effectively all portions of the bath to the vacuum, and in addition, alloy can be added and throughly stirred in after degassing is complete. In order for induction stirring to be feasible, the steel is held in ladles made of nonmagnetic stainless steel (type AISI 304) lined with a combination of high alumina brick. The direction and rate of stirring can be controlled by the operator.

To the users of steel, vacuum degassing is becoming more and more important. In fact, it has been stated that by 1975 over 80 per cent of steel produced will be manufactured by vacuum melting, degassing, and pouring methods. Gases in steel, such as oxygen, hydrogen, and nitrogen, lower its ductility so that by vacuum degassing, the steel's formability is greatly improved. This is also true of cold extruding of intricate components previously difficult if not impossible to make. To the makers of turbine-generators, vacuum degassing is of major importance. Steel made by this method can be made into forgings of highest quality by reason of the reduction of hydrogen content in the steel to less than 1 part per million, making much sounder forgings and improved ductility and there is an absence of flaking and thermal cracking. In addition, there are fewer chances for large non-metallic inclusions to occur, either from the slag entrapment or oxidation, during pouring. The tool and diemaker also prefers vacuum degassed steel because of its increased soundness and freedom from flakes, greater toughness and resistance to shock, and its improved cleanliness and much better machinability.

It is also true that vacuum degassed steel has improved transverse properties, and its grain size is more readily controlled. Along with grain size control is improvement in physical properties, including longer fatigue life, fracture toughness, fabricability, etc. The producers of metals to be used in semiconductor and transistor products, including germanium, silicon, gallium and others, learned long ago the importance of a high degree of purity, and the producers of steel have realised its significance and value in their industry. Many major improvements in quality and capabilities of steel are being achieved because of vacuum degassing, melting, and pouring. The aerospace industry urgently needs stress-bearing steel parts for missiles and jet aircraft able to withstand forces in extreme environments and often over long periods of time. In order to achieve this, reliability and consistency, possible only with vacuum melted, degassed, and poured steel, is the answer to the problem in most such cases. Tests have shown that the fatigue properties of vacuum degassed steels are far superior to those of comparable grades melted and cast in air. Although the degree of improvement varies with the technique and controls used, the aerospace industry has found that there will be, in general, from 5 to 10 per cent improved strength at the long life (10^7 cycles) end of the *SN* curve.

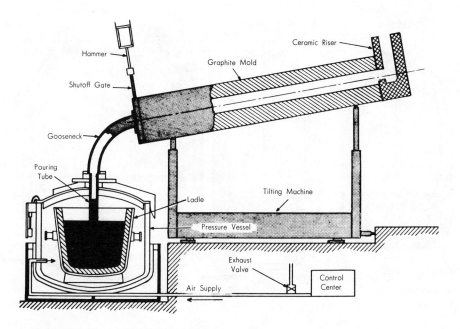

Fig. 8-8. *The principle of operation of the bottom-pressure casting methods as applied to the casting of slabs.* (*U.S. Steel Corporation.*)

Vacuum degassing, particularly when coupled with vacuum alloying, produces cleaner steels with less frequent and severe inclusions. This is an important feature, especially in the case of some of the more complex stainless steel types, in which it is possible to obtain superior properties as a result of closer controls and better balanced compositions.

8-10   Bottom Pressure Method of Casting Steel

Another method of attempting to bypass the ingot and primary-mill stages in the production of wrought steels is that of the bottom-pressure method, casting shapes similar to those produced by the primary rolling mills. The principle of the bottom-pressure casting method is shown in Fig. 8–8 , where is seen a ladle filled with molten steel placed in a pressure vessel, the latter being covered with a lid in which has been inserted a pouring tube that dips down into the molten steel almost to the bottom of the ladle. A gooseneck connects the pouring tube to the mold in the casting position. When air pressure is applied to the pressure vessel, the pressure of the air on the molten steel causes it to rise in the pouring tube and gooseneck and to enter the mold. The height to which the metal must be raised is that of the highest point to be filled with metal. The highest point depends on the length of the mold and riser, the height above the level of the metal in the ladle, and the angle above the horizontal at which the mold is set. Rate of casting is controlled by regulating the pressurized equipment to increase air pressure in the desired increments.

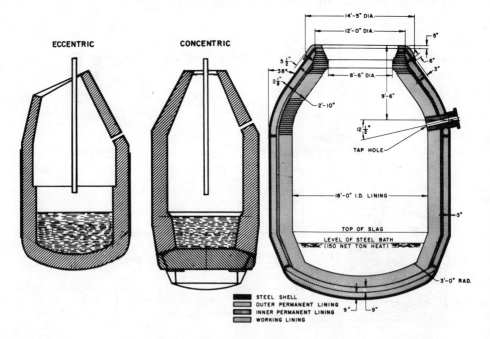

Fig. 8-9.   *Shown in (A) are schematic sections of two types of vessels used in blowing oxygen downward onto the metal through a water-cooled lance. At the right in (B) is a diagrammatic section of an actual concentric type of vessel. (Courtesy of United States Steel Corporation, Pittsburgh, Pennsylvania.)*

8-11 Basic Oxygen Process

In this process, substantially pure oxygen is introduced from above the surface of the molten metal in a basic-lined vessel. The equipment consists essentially of a vertical pipe or lance inserted through the mouth of a vessel like the Bessemer converter. This process was experimented with by C. V. Schwarz and R. Dirrer in Germany and by Durrer and H. Hellbrügge in Switzerland. The bottom-blown vessel proved unsuitable because the high temperature reached caused a rapid deterioration of the refractory tuyere bottom; subsequently this method gave way to the better one of blowing pressurized oxygen downward against the top surface of the molten metal bath. This method was found to convert the charge of steel with a high degree of thermal and chemical efficiency. Fig. 8–9 shows a schematic section of both the eccentric and concentric types of vessels where the oxygen is blown downward onto the surface of the metal by means of a water-cooled lance.

A principal advantage of the basic oxygen process is its flexibility in handling many types of raw materials, including both light and heavy materials, and the oxide charge, where used, may be dry ore, sinter, pellets, or mill scale. Substantially, the process can be used on any kind of hot metal that can be utilized in the basic open-hearth furnace. Oxygen steel-making plants around the world operate on blast furnace metal containing from 0.2 to 2.0 per cent silicon, from 0.4 to 2.5 per cent manganese, and up to 0.3 or 0.4 per cent phosphorus with a single slag proving to be adequate.

So far as the chemistry of the basic oxygen process is concerned, the process is characterized by the following factors:

1. It uses gaseous oxygen as the sole refining agent, thereby assuring that the refining reactions generate the maximum amount of heat.
2. The metallic charge is composed largely of blast furnace iron in the molten state, thereby reducing substantially the thermal requirements of the process.
3. The chemical reactions involved proceed rapidly in a molten bath of comparatively low surface-to-volume ratio, thus minimizing external heat losses.

These factors combine to provide an extremely versatile autogenous process that requires no external fuel does but provide a capability for melting a sizeable quantity of scrap (12 to 30 per cent). The use of pure oxygen for refining does not in any way alter the fundamental chemical reactions and equilibria in steel-making. The chemical reactions of major importance are those pertaining to carbon, silicon, manganese, phosphorus, sulfur, nitrogen, and oxygen. Unusually, the major problem in the top-blown basic oxygen process is one of *decreasing* rather than increasing the temperature. Obviously, this is associated with the use of oxygen rather than air for blowing the melt. The principal method used to control the temperature involves the regulation and control of the quantity of scrap additions. Steam is not used to any extent in cooling the bath.

There have been several variations of the basic oxygen process used by steel makers around the world, including the buffer-slag process, the Stora-Kaldo process, the Rotor process and others; however, the process described above in some detail has been found to be most satisfactory for the refining of steel in the United States and is used extensively by steel makers here. By way of example, in 1955 307,279 tons of steel for ingots were produced here by the basic oxygen process, and in 1965 this had risen to over 4,456,000 tons, according to the *Annual Statistical Reports* of the American Iron and Steel Institute.

8-12 Electric Furnaces

The two types of electric furnace which have proven to be most suitable for steel-making are the direct-arc furnace (series arc), developed originally by Heroult, and the high-frequency coreless induction furnace. Fig. 8–10 shows one of the modern three-phase Heroult-type furnaces, such as are used in many steel mills throughout the country. Fig. 8–11 is a schematic cross-section of this type of furnace,

Fig. 8-10. *Large, modern, three-phase Heroult electric furnace (Courtesy of United States Steel Corporation, Pittsburgh, Pa.)*

showing the component parts, with one half of the drawing illustrating an acid lining and the other half showing a basic lining. During World War II both the basic and acid processes for making steel in electric furnaces were used extensively; however, since then several technical and economic obstacles to the use of select scrap, and the increasing utilization of alloy steels, have greatly reduced the use of acid-lined furnaces. Practically all furnaces used for ingot steel production, and a large percentage of the foundry furnaces, are now basic-lined due mainly to the ability of basic-lined furnaces to use combinations of high-alloy steel scrap, lower grades of alloy scrap, and plain-carbon steel scrap to produce steels that will meet rigid chemical and mechanical properties and requirements of high cleanliness.

The direct-arc electric furnace most widely used by steel mills and foundries today receives the cold charge of scrap steel, etc., then an electric-arc is drawn between the electrodes and the surface of the charge to be melted. Electrodes are made either from graphite or amorphous carbon. When the arc is struck and is sprung from the electrodes to the metal bath, the metal is heated both by direct conduction from the arc and by radiation from the roof and walls of the furnace. The height of the electrodes above the bath, and consequently the heat input, is automatically controlled by winch motors in the system used to raise and lower the electrodes.

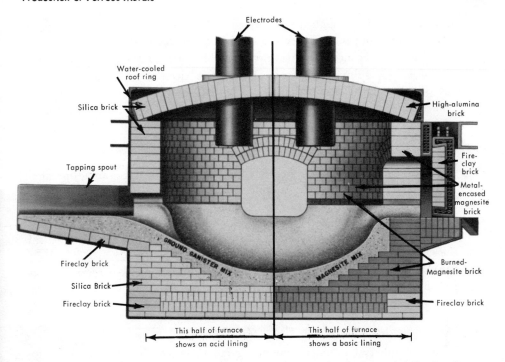

Fig. 8-11. *A schematic cross-section of a Heroult electric arc-furnace with a flat-bottomed shell 'and stadium-type sub-hearth construction. The typical refractories used in such furnaces are as indicated, the acid lining shown at the left and basic lining at the right. Although only two electrodes are shown in this section, furnaces of this type which operate on three-phase current have three electrodes. (Courtesy of U.S. Steel Corp. Pittsburgh, Pa.)*

It is essential to select the refractories used in the electric furnace with great care, as the hearth must be made of a basic material, such as magnesite or burned dolomite, in order to withstand the lime slags used in the basic process. In the acid process the slags are more siliceous than those in the basic process, so they do not remove phosphorus from the steel bath, which means that more expensive, carefully selected scrap and other raw materials of low phosphorus content have to be used. The basic slags react with and retain phosphorus, and practically all types of scrap and raw materials can therefore be used in the basic electric furnace. While acid melting is somewhat faster than the basic electric furnace process, it does not permit the reduction of sulfur or phosphorus, which means that these two elements must be held to a minimum in any charge going into the acid furnace.

The indirect-arc furnace is of the rocking arc type, so called for the reason that the arc is separate from the charge of metal. In this furnace heat is supplied to the metal by conduction and radiation—radiation from the hot refractory furnace walls, and conduction from the same hot refractory walls when the furnace is rocked and the molten metal washes over them. Although these furnaces are used more for melting copper and copper-base alloys, they are also used, at times, for melting cast iron and steel; however, with the high-temperature conditions that prevail the efficiency is comparatively low.

Advantages of the Electric-Arc Furnace

1. Most of the known grades of steel can be produced in the basic electric-arc furnace, including plain carbon steels, low-alloy and high-manganese

(up to 14 per cent), high-silicon (up to 5 per cent) and the entire range of stainless steels, super-alloy steels, and high-speed and other alloy tool steels.

2. It is the more economical steel-producing furnace under most conditions.
3. The greater desulfurizing power of the basic electric-arc furnace reducing slags facilitates the production of steels with lower sulphur residuals.
4. The absence of an oxidizing heat source permits heats that have been deoxidized in the furnace to be held without becoming rapidly reoxidized; this feature, coupled with the capability of using reducing slags, makes it possible to produce steels containing fewer nonmetallic inclusions.
5. Because it can be tilted to pour off slag, the electric-arc furnace can be operated with slag volumes controlled to a minimum (2 to 4 per cent of the bath weight); therefore the slag composition can be adjusted and controlled quickly by relatively small additions of slag-making, oxidizing, and deoxidizing materials. For this reason the steel may be treated under oxidizing, reducing, or neutral slags, or any succession of such slags.
6. Stirring the bath by either mechanical or magnetic-induction stirrer minimizes the time requirements for refining the steel.

Disadvantages of the Electric-Arc Furnace

1. Cost of auxiliary equipment, operating labor, power, electrodes and refractories are usually higher than similar costs in the open-hearth and other methods of melting steel.
2. Exclusive of net metallic charge, a cost study shows the electric furnace at a disadvantage; however, this can be overcome partially by faster heating time and greater efficiency.
3. The electric-arc furnace has a smaller capacity than the open-hearth furnace. This may be overcome to a limited extent by speeding up the electric-furnace operations; however, peak loads during melt-down periods may increase the difficulties of the power plants, which must maintain sufficient power for regular requirements during the same period of operation.
4. Although relative changes in cost of fuels and scrap materials, as well as hot metal or pig iron, have curtailed the economic advantage of the hot-charged open-hearth furnace over the electric-arc furnace, the recent advent of the basic oxygen steel-making process has introduced a new economic factor that accentuates the disadvantage of the electric-arc furnace for the production of plain-carbon and low alloy grades of steel.

8-13   Induction Electric-Furnace Processes

The melting procedure in steel plants using the induction furnace is substantially that of a crucible or "dead-melt" process. The charge is carefully selected to produce the composition desired in the finished steel with a minimum of further additions except, perhaps, small amounts of ferro-alloys, used as final deoxidizers. The charge may consist of a single lump of metal (ingot), a number of small pieces of selected steel scrap, or even turnings or other light scrap, mixed with a moderate amount of larger pieces, to provide initial conditions favorable to the generation of heat. Even with the closest packing, it is sometimes necessary to add some of the charge as the melting progresses.

As a rule, no refining is attempted in acid-lined furnaces, and it is seldom tried in basic-lined furnace. Very little oxidation actually occurs if the furnace is fitted with a tight cover over the crucible during the melting operation. Such a cover also serves to prevent cooling by radiation of heat from the surface of the molten metal. Because of this, from the standpoint of heat loss, the use of a slag covering to protect the metal is unnecessary. Nevertheless, slags are used successfully both during melt-down and refining in special cases.

Advantages of the Induction Melting process

1. The induction furnace is relatively low in cost compared to other types of melting units and, as a result, several furnaces can be installed at little added expense to operate from a single frequency changer.
2. Furnaces of different capacities can be used as required, or individual furnaces can be retained for making melts of special alloys, without danger of contamination or the necessity of making "wash heats."
3. Very little heat is radiated from the furnaces as they are water cooled. Furthermore, there is practically no noise in their operation.
4. In re-melting alloy-steel scrap, it is possible to make melts in less time than with other methods, minimizing the loss of very valuable alloying elements through oxidation.
5. Whereas standard equipment used to supply power to induction furnaces was, up until a few years ago, a rotary motor-generator set which supplied a frequency of abont 1,000 cycles, now mercury-arc frequency changers are used, giving several advantages over the older method. First, the efficiency is higher than that of the motor-generator sest, the static device presents no problems of vibration or air ventilation, and the cost is held to a minimum. Secondly, frequency output is determined by output circuit, so that if the frequency characteristic of the circuit changes during operation, the mercury-arc inverter will automatically supply the frequency required by the melting circuit.
6. Special alloys can be produced by melting in a vacuum, or under pressure in an inert-gas atmosphere, by enclosing the entire coreless induction furnace and mold in an airtight container which can be evacuated or put under pressure. Upon the completion of melting, the molten metal is poured into the mold; this is accomplished entirely by control elements outside the container that make it possible to tilt the container for pouring the furnace without opening the container. Then, after the metal has solidified, the container can be opened for emptying the mold and recharging the furnace for the next heat.

8-14 Ingot Molds

There are many types, shapes, and sizes of ingot molds; for example, in shape they will vary from round, square, and oblong to exceptional ones that have a cross-section roughly the same as the shape of the section into which the steel is subsequently to be rolled, i. e., a beam shape that may be ultimately finished as a large, wide-flanged beam. As a rule, ingots to be subsequently rolled have a square or oblong cross-section, corrugated or fluted in some cases to reduce the amount of cracking of the ingot as it solidifies and continues to cool.

The ideal ingot would be one that is homogenous both physically and chemically, would have a fine, equiaxed crystal structure, and would be devoid of chemical segregation, cavities, and nonmetallic inclusions. However, the physical laws that control the solidification of liquid metal operate against the achievement of the ideal conditions, for it is a fact that pipe, blowholes, chemical segregation, columnar crystal structure, and internal fissures form within the interior of the ingots in varying degrees.

The ingot mold into which the steel is poured is usually tapered from the top to the bottom, primarily to facilitate the stripping of the mold from the ingot after pouring. Shown in Fig. 8-12 are two types of ingot molds—those *big-end-down* and *big-end-up*. As indicated, the big-end-down molds are further classified into *open bottom*, *closed bottom*, and *plug bottom*, as illustrated in the sketch. The cap or bottom plate on which the ingot mold rests is called the *stool*, which serves as the bottom closure for the big-end-down mold cavities. The nature of the mold itself acts as the stool in the case of the closed bottom, big-end-up molds. The plug at the bottom of the plug bottom big-end-up mold is a refractory or metal plug that is closed just prior to pouring the ingot metal. Actually, the small hole at the bottom of this style of ingot mold with the plug bottom was originally intended to facilitate the use of a plunger in order to loosen ingots that sometimes stuck in the molds. Now, however, most plants do not use a bottom plunger, but the plug hole does permit easier cleaning of the mold, so that molds of this type are to be preferred to the closed bottom molds because of this feature.

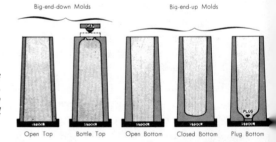

Fig. 8-12.   *Cross-sections (not to scale) of the five principal types of ingot molds used in steel mills today. Molds are usually cast from molten pig iron directly from the blast furnace. (Courtesy of United States Steel Corporation.)*

8-15   Ingot Structure Types

Shown in Figures 8-13 and 8-14 are several typical conditions found in commercial steel ingots, the dotted line indicating the height to which the steel was poured originally in each ingot. Here are shown the structures ranging all the way from *fully-killed* or *dead-killed*, as shown in ingot No. 1, to the violently rimming ingot shown in No. 8. The differences between structures in the eight types of ingots shown here are mainly due to the amount of gas that is evolved by the ingots as they become solidified. A look at the eight types of ingots reveals the following conditions:

No. 1 evolved no gas, so the top is slightly concave and right below the top is seen an intermittently bridged shrinkage cavity called *pipe*. This type ingot is almost always poured in *big-end-up* molds with a refractory top called a *hot-top*, in order

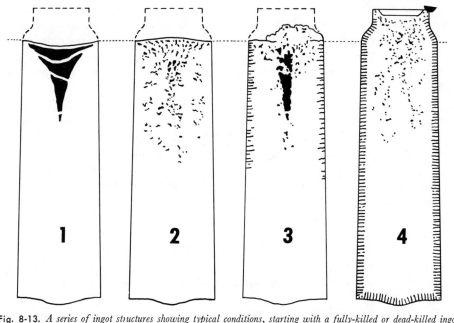

Fig. 8-13. *A series of ingot structures showing typical conditions, starting with a fully-killed or dead-killed ingot (No. 1) to an ingot (No. 4) where the gas has evolved so much as to cause a honeycomb of blow-holes, resulting in a rimmed condition near the top of the ingot. (See Fig. 8-10 for additional ingot structures.) (Courtesy of United States Steel Corporation.)*

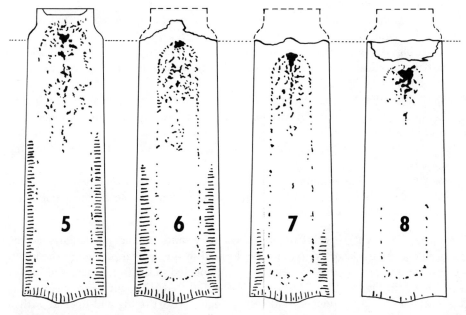

Fig. 8-14. *A further series of industrial ingot structures, with No. 5 representing a typically capped ingot and Nos. 6, 7, and 8 rimmed ingots. No. 8 illustrates a violently rimming ingot with low-metalloid steel. (Courtesy of United States Steel Corporation.)*

to confine the pipe cavity entirely within the hot-top portion that is subsequently cropped off and discarded; however it is included here for purposes of comparison. *No. 2* is an ingot typical of one that has been semi-killed, where only a slight amount of gas has evolved, but with enough blow-holes present to account for the shrinkage that took place during the solidification. Because of the hydraulic pressure exerted by the liquid steel due to gravity, blow-holes were prevented from forming in the bottom portion of the ingot. The rounded or domed top of the ingot was the result of the pressure caused by the trapped gases in the blow-holes.

No. 3 is an ingot where more gas has evolved than in No. 2 during its solidification, so that the resulting blow-holes have a greater volume than is required to offset the shrinkage caused by solidification. It is understandable that blow-holes are objectionable so close to the surface of the ingot, since they may well cause subsequent surface defects in later heating or rolling operations. Here, also, the gas pressure has ruptured the top surface that solidified first, forcing liquid steel up through the rupture where it froze; this phenomenon is known as *bleeding*.

No. 4 is an ingot that gave off so much gas that the top surface could not solidify immediately after pouring, causing many honeycomb blow-holes very close to the side surface of the ingot from top to bottom. This evolution of gas caused the steel to rise after pouring, producing a boiling action that we refer to as *rimming action*.

No. 5 is a typical capped ingot that has evolved so much gas that the resulting strong currents, upward along the sides of the ingot in the upper portion, removed the gas bubbles that might otherwise have formed there. Even in the lower half of the mold, the blow-holes were not permitted to form until the gas evolution had subsided somewhat.

No. 6 is a typical rimmed ingot where the evolution of gas, even though greater than in ingot No. 5, was enough to prevent the honeycomb blow-holes from exceeding the volume of metal required to offset solidification shrinkage, so that the top surface of this ingot rose slightly as it solidified in from the sides of the mold, as shown.

No. 7 is another rimmed ingot in which the evolution of gas was so strong that the formation of blow-holes was confined to the lower quarter of the ingot. The top of this ingot did not rise or fall, because the apparent increase in volume due to blow-holes offset the shrinkage that took place due to and at the same time as solidification.

No. 8 is a violently rimming steel ingot such as we find in low-metalloid steels. Honey-comb blow-holes could not form, so the top surface of the ingot fell a great deal during its solidification.

Reviewing the eight types of ingots shown here, and looking particularly at the the problem of shrinkage cavity, or pipe, located in the central portion of the ingot, we observe that this is largest and most deeply located in the two extremes of ingots, Nos. 1 and 8, in Figs. 8–13 and 8–14. If it is essential that the ingot be free from pipe, this is accomplished by pouring killed-steel ingots with the big-end-up and with a hot-top, as shown in Fig. 8–15, No. 1. Actually, the problem of shrinkage cavity, or pipe, is not too serious providing that the steel ingot is of higher carbon content

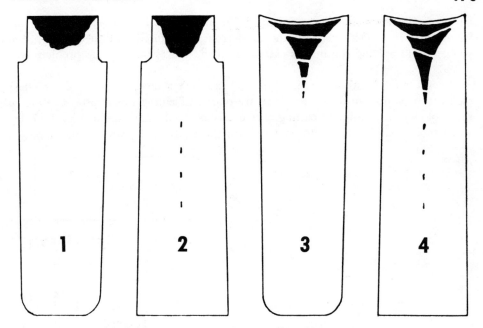

Fig. 8-15. *Four types of killed ingots of steel. (U.S. Steel Corporation.)*
1. Big-end-up, hot-topped
2. Big-end-down, hot-topped
3. Big-end-up, not hot-topped
4. Big-end-down, not hot-topped

and is to be subsequently reduced by rolling, such as is done in the case of lighter, flat-rolled products. In fact, under these circumstances, the big-end-down killed ingots, even when poured without a hot-top, often will have a lower, unoxidized portion of the pipe cavity sufficiently below the bridges, to be welded completely shut by the pressure and deformation of the steel during rolling operations.

8-16   Continuous Casting of Metals

About 1860 Sir Henry Bessemer conceived the idea of casting molten steel continuously into plate form by pouring it into the opening between two relatively closely-spaced horizontal rolls, as shown in Fig. 8–16. Flanges on the rolls prevented the escape of metal at the sides of the opening. Because of the inadequacy of engineering materials in Bessemer's day, the principle failed and, indeed, cannot be made to work even today with our improved construction materials. Engineers have experimented with continuous casting, and some headway has been made, as will be revealed in this chapter.

The many advantages of casting steel continuously, from the molten state into useful shapes, has led to a long series of efforts using various designs of machines. The process would make possible the elimination of the ingot and primary-mill stages of rolled steel production, which would bring important economies, as may be appreciated.

Because of the high melting point, high specific heat, and low thermal conductivity of steel, most attempts had to be dropped or were only partially successful for ferrous metals, although continuous casting has proved to be practicable for non-ferrous metals. In fact, success in the non-ferrous field caused continued study of the problems of applying continuous casting to steel, and eventually the problem was solved.

Even though continuous casting of steel (and even lower melting-point metals) seems to be simple in principle, there are many difficulties in the process. One of the problems in continuous casting of steel is shown schematically in Fig. 8–17, for when molten steel comes into contact with the walls of the watercooled mold, a

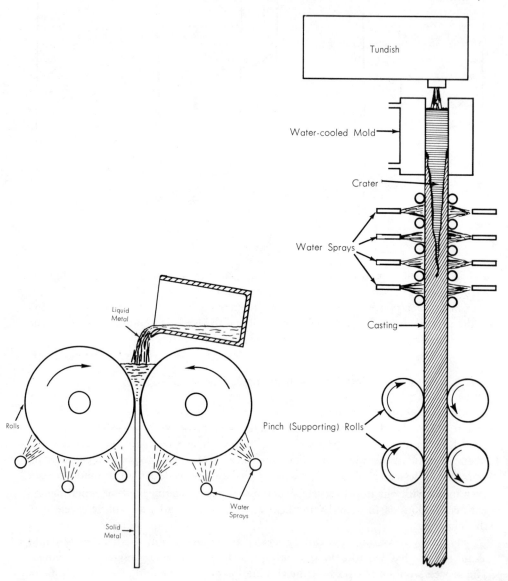

Fig. 8-16. *Schematic diagram of a method of continuous casting of steel, suggested by Sir Henry Bessemer. Here plates are being formed. (Courtesy of United States Steel Corporation, Pittsburgh, Pa.)*

Fig. 8-17. *Schematic diagram depicting how liquid metal persists in the center of a continuous casting for a considerable distance, after the casting leaves the water-cooled mold, forming a so-called "crater" at the center. (United States Steel Corporation.)*

thin, solid "skin" forms. Because of the physical characteristics of steel, however, and also because thermal contraction causes the skin to separate from the mold wall shortly after solidification, the rate of heat abstraction from the casting is so low that molten steel persists within the interior of the section for some distance below the bottom of the mold. The thickness of this skin increases because of the action of the water sprays as the casting moves downward, and eventually the entire section is solid. Shown in Fig. 8–18 are only three methods of arranging the principal components of existing continuous-casting machines. In this schematic drawing it should be noted that the machines are confined to designs that are constructed beginning at ground level, thereby necessitating a tall structure that requires hoisting of the steel ladle to considerable heights. A few machines have been constructed with their foundations deep in a pit, minimizing the height to which the steel ladle must be raised. Designs of this type require that there be some sort of conveyorized inclined plane or hoist arrangement to raise the product to plant floor elevation for further processing.

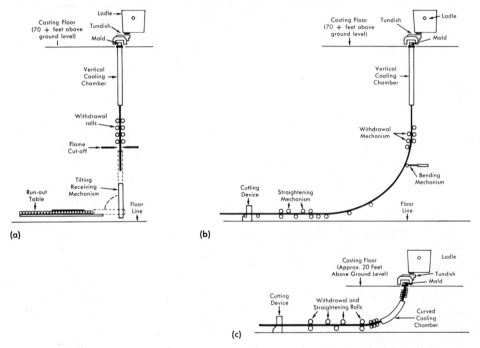

Fig. 8-18. *Three methods that have been successfully applied to the continuous casting of steel. (Courtesy of United States Steel Corporation.)*

The main difference between machines A and B in Fig. 8–18 is that in A the continuous length of casting is parted by a gas-cutting torch while the casting is supported in a vertical position, and the cut-off piece is caught in a tilting basket mechanism that lowers it to a horizontal position; whereas in B the continuous casting is bent by a series of rollers from the vertical to the horizontal position and cutting is then performed on the horizontal casting.

In Fig. 8–18C we see the design of a machine referred to as a semi-horizontal unit. Here, by use of an oscillating mold of a special design, and a curved cooling chamber, the height of the machine is reduced to about one-third that of the machines shown in Fig. 8–18A and Fig. 8–18B.

The importance of conserving and controlling the temperature of the molten steel makes it necessary to utilize preheated and insulated ladles, and also to preheat the tundish. Small ladles may even be heated to compensate for heat loss. The molten metal is poured into the tundish from either a stoppered or tilting ladle. The tundish may be equipped with one or more nozzles that feed the metal to the mold or molds (in the case of smaller sections, such as billets, multiple molds make it possible to cast more than one strand simultaneously). The molds in the machines are made of copper, fabricated from a solid block, or by assembling plates, and are cooled by the internal circulation of substantial amounts of water. But a small amount of solidification takes place in the mold, and water sprays below the molds perform most of the cooling of the exposed casting.

Several continuous-casting techniques have been employed successfully in the production of shapes corresponding to all of the basic semi-finished sections, including squares from 2 in. by 2 in. to 12 in. by 12 in., and slabs up to 8 in. by 60 in. Although some small rounds, such as reinforcing bars, are being produced, larger rounds, such as tube rounds, have presented some difficulty; however, this is being overcome. In fact, one plant is now successfully producing $8\frac{5}{8}$ in. rounds by the continuous method. Tool steel, stainless and alloy steels, as well as carbon steels, have all cast successfully using the continuous method. This technique presents great promise and will effect substantial savings wherever adopted.

8-17   Metallurgical Fundamentals of Casting Metals

The selection of the casting process best suited to any particular application depends on both technical and economic factors: that is, on such features of functional design as the size and shape of the part to be made, limitations of section thickness, the dimensional tolerances desired, and the surface finish required. Still other factors to consider are the number of parts required and the amount of subsequent machining and finishing necessary or desirable. It is of paramount importance also that the properties and inherent characteristics of the basic material be known and that it is considered, in the face of all of these various factors, whether it would be best to make the part of a ferrous or nonferrous material. The judicious selection of material and method of casting the part are highly important, as they have a decided effect on the cost of the part, as well as on the performance of the part when it is used.

The type of equipment used for melting and pouring the metal in question is of great importance, since not only the methods of directing the metal into the mold cavity and counteracting any tendency toward shrinkage, but also the production of sound castings with solidification in the correct directional manner, are of extreme importance. There are several ways of controlling directional solidification in order to try to obtain castings where freezing has started at the bottom and progresses uniformly upward, although it is difficult to attain this ideal result.

8-18   Melting and Handling of Metal

The initial step in the production of all castings is melting. Melting equipment and handling procedures can reflect greatly on casting procedures as well as on the final quality and cost of the castings. For all these reasons, the selection of equipment and the establishment of procedures and their control must be given careful consideration.

Before melting can take place it is necessary that the thermal activity of the atoms be greater than the strength of interatomic bonding, in order that the atoms may be free to move about in a random fashion. It is when the atoms are no longer held in a somewhat stable crystalline relationship, one with the other, that melting will take place. The temperature rises when heat is added to the solid metal, and this gives added vibrational activity to the metallic atoms; however, when the melting point of a pure metal is reached, it is necessary to add more heat to the metal, at constant temperature, before melting will take place. This additional heat, even after the melting point of the pure metal is reached, is called the *latent heat of fusion*; such heat is necessary to permit the metal to overcome the cohesive force holding the atoms in their regular crystalline positions, and to encourage the random atomic movement of all liquids, including molten metals.

As was discussed in an earlier chapter, alloys which melt over a temperature range, rather than at a constant temperature, as is the case of the pure metals, must also absorb the additional heat of fusion; however, this is accomplished over the entire melting temperature range and not at a constant temperature. When melting occurs, the regular crystalline metallic lattice is destroyed and a completely new liquid state appears which is characterized by the random movement of the atoms. Metals, for the most part, are not generally completely homogeneous, often consisting of more than one phase, and as a result they do not start to melt in all areas at the same time. Rather, melting commences in local regions, such as at the grain boundaries, areas of eutectic compositions, areas where lower melting point constituents predominate, or in other microscopic areas where the melting temperature is lowest. Commercially pure metals are not entirely uniform in microstructure, having some disarrangement of their atomic patterns at the grain boundaries so that, as a result, melting begins in such non-uniform areas first. The energy of metals in the solid state is lower than their energy content in the liquid state, even at the same temperature, and as a result solidification takes place with a release of energy. An interface is found to exist, however, between the liquid and solid phases, and in order to form this interface, more energy is required. The aggregates can solidify only when the energy released in freezing is greater than the energy needed to bring about the formation of the phase boundary. Solidification is possible when the aggregate is large enough, and when the total free energy of the system is lowered. Such a condition as this can obtain in pure metals within a specific time when the metal is considerably below its freezing point. Pure metals, in many cases, must be undercooled to about 250 to 430F before crystallization can be observed; this is true for metals which do not contain impurities, especially impurities in the solid state. By reducing the size of the boundary to be formed, impurities reduce the energy needed for the formation of interface, and by so doing, the rate of solidification is increased. The solidification process is also made easier, as it occurs at a higher temperature than in cases where no impurities are present. Therefore, in commercial metals and alloys in which impurities are always present, it is necessary to undercool only a few degrees in order to start crystallization in the melt.

The solidification of aggregates now act as nuclei or centers for further crystallization, and with the cooling of the metal continuing, more and more atoms tend to freeze. Such atoms may form new nuclei of their own, or they may attach themselves to nuclei that already exist. The important thing is that each nucleus grows by the addition of atoms as they continue to freeze. These atoms become attached to the nucleus in preferred positions, resulting in a growth of the nucleus more pronounced in certain directions than in others. It is this preferred growth that brings about the characteristic structure called a *dendrite* or "tree-like" structure. At the outset, the nuclei and the dendrites growing from them are surrounded by liquid metal and can grow in all directions, at random. Later the dendrites grow sufficiently and to a point where they meet, and grain boundaries are formed where this junction occurs. The free atoms still moving rapidly in the liquid state freeze within the branches of the dendrites, thereby closing up the gaps between them until finally all the metal is frozen and polygonal crystals are formed.

When solidification takes place, the size of the crystals formed is determined by the number of the nuclei that are formed. In cases where the number of the nuclei is large, a large number of small crystals will be formed and a fine-grained material will be formed. If only a few nuclei are formed, the crystals growing from them will be of larger size. The most important factor controlling grain size is the rate of cooling of the molten mass of metal. In case the heat is evolved very rapidly from the molten metal, considerable undercooling follows and numbers of nuclei are formed as a result. Few nuclei are formed if the temperature drops very slowly, and these grow to larger sizes. From this we can see that slow cooling results in coarse-grained metal, assuming a uniform temperature of the molten metal while solidification is taking place, and also that little or no differences in temperature from one point in the melt to another result from the cooling process.

When molten metal solidifies, it is invariably accompanied by shrinkage, finally resulting in separation of the outer portion of the casting from the mold itself, leaving a slight layer of air between the mold and the casting. The fact that the thermal conductivity of air is small alters solidification factors, as the heat from the metal evolves very slowly, with an abrupt curtailment in the escape of heat from the casting. This causes a slowing down of the columnar crystal growth to the point that, when the center of the casting has arrived at the freezing temperature, the formation of new nuclei commences and they grow until the entire casting is frozen.

Although the composition of the alloy has the greatest effect on the process of solidification, there are other factors that also appreciably affect the grain size resulting from solidification. In the equilibrium diagrams discussed earlier, we saw that when a particle of solid forms which is richer in metal A than the alloy, the liquid around the solidified metal becomes enriched with metal B. It follows that, until the liquid has been replenished by diffusion, no further growth of the solid can occur. The growth of the first nuclei formed is thus slowed down and a result is the origin of new nuclei, with an accompanying smaller final size of grains formed.

Still other factors appreciably affecting the grain size of the casting and the relative thickness of the three typical layers (surface, intermediate, and center zones of the casting) include the temperature of pouring, the temperature and type of the mold, the design of the casting, etc. The formation of fine, equiaxed grains is usually encouraged by (1) thin sections of castings, (2) pouring the metal at a temperature near the freezing point, (3) high conductivity of the heat of the mold, (4) substantial difference of composition between the liquid and solid phases and, (5) relatively high mold temperature. Coarse equiaxed grains are more in evidence with (1) low heat condctivity of the mold, (2) larger sections of the castings, and (3) metal that is poured at temperatures well above its melting point. Grains in columnar form are more prevalent when there is (1) a wide temperature difference between the metal and the mold, (2) favorable heat conductivity of the mold itself, and (3) a comparatively narrow range of solidification temperature of the alloy involved.

8-19   Ferrous Metals Foundry Practice

There are numerous types and sizes of equipment on the market for the melting of metals in the foundry. The choice of the proper melting method for a certain application depends upon several factors, including the following:

1. Amount or tonnage of metal required
2. Melting temperature of the metal in question
3. Type and cost of equipment required
4. Operational cost of the equipment
5. Amount of control needed during melting operation
6. Degree of refinement by the furnace expected in the metal.

The open-hearth is used in the production of large steel castings weighing over 10 to 12 tons each, as this tonnage of metal must be melted and poured at one time. In the production of castings, either cast iron or steel, in smaller foundries, the electric-arc furnace is found to be best; however, the induction type electric furnace is more generally used for smaller heats under 300 lb per heat. The cupola is generally used in smaller gray cast iron foundries because of the higher cost of electric furnaces. In the case of malleable iron casting foundries, we find some use of the air furnace, which is quite similar in type to the open-hearth furnace used in steel production, although much smaller; the idea is to have as large an area of the surface of the molten iron exposed to the source of the flame as possible, either powdered coal or oil, in order to provide a purification through oxidation of the same. In numerous malleable iron foundries we find the melting of the metal, either scrap or pig iron, or a mix of the two, accomplished in the cupola, and then from the cupola the molten iron is transferred to an air-furnace for purification. By this method, a much lower-cost mix of scrap can be used in the cupola than if it were melted down in the air-furnace or electric furnace. The cupola is a low-cost method of melting metal, being used, usually, in the production of common cast iron. Despite the fact that it is rather crude, being somewhat like a blast furnace in configuration, it is nonetheless capable of being closely controlled during the melting and pouring procedures. The cupola is a shaft-type furnace with a cylindrical shell of steel that is lined with refractory fire brick. Drop doors at the bottom of the shell close the shell, and these doors support the entire charge during the melting cycle. At the end of the heating-melting cycle, the residual coke and metal from the charge can be dumped through the drop doors. A large volume of air is necessary in the cupola operation, and this is introduced through several openings at the bottom of the cupola, called *tuyeres*. The air, blown in under pressure, serves to burn the coke, used as the fuel, and also to melt the iron in the heat. The entire charge, much like that in the blast furnace, consists of the coke fuel, limestone, flux, and metal (rather than iron ore, as is the case in the blast furnace), all this charge being introduced through the charging openings in the furnace. The limestone flux melts and causes a high degree of fluidity, purifying the metal as it travels through the coke.

QUESTIONS

1. Define and explain the significance of pig iron.

2. What are some of the products of the blast furnace?

3. Is it possible to produce pig iron by other means than in the blast furnace? If so, why are the other methods not used more often?

4. Draw a sketch and describe the iron blast furnace process.

5. What raw materials go into the blast furnace? Explain their function in each case. Explain the importance of the air introduced into the blast furnace?

6. State the chemical equations and explain in each instance the *indirect* reduction and the *direct* reduction reactions.

7. Name the four main slag-making constituents in the blast furnace, and explain their sources.

8. How much iron ore, coke, and limestone must be used to produce one ton of pig iron? What type of coke must be used? Why?

9. What is the most important element of control in the operation of the blast furnace?

10. Describe the acid-Bessemer process of steel-making, including the products going into the Bessemer converter and those coming from it.

11. Is it possible to regulate the composition of the steel in the Bessemer converter by stopping the "blow" at some point? Explain.

12. What are the fundamental factors that control the quality of the product coming from the Bessemer converter?

13. Because of extensive research and development in the use of an oxygen-enriched blast in the acid-Bessemer converter, what improvements in operation have resulted?

14. Define the following tems and explain: killed steel; rimmed steel; deoxidizers.

15. Which process is more important in the production of steel, the acid-open-hearth or the basic open-hearth? Why?

16. Although there are five types of charges of raw materials for the basic open-hearth furnace, there are two that are most commonly used. Name and describe them.

17. Describe the various types of ingot molds and state when and how they are used. Draw sketches of each type.

18. What would constitute the "ideal" ingot? Why?

19. Sketch the four types of killed ingots of steel and tell how they were made and the results of each.

20. Compare the deoxidizing qualities and performance of carbon with the conventional deoxidizers, such as aluminum and silicon.

21. Why has vacuum degassing, melting, and pouring of steel come into such prominence in recent years?

22. Explain the term "latent heat of fusion" in the melting of metals and tell its importance in the metallurgy of steel.

23. When metals solidify, what determines the size of the crystals formed? What is the most important factor as to grain size?

24. Upon what factors does the correct choice of melting method depend?

25. State the advantages and disadvantages of the electric furnace in the melting of metals.

26. What are some of the advantages and limitations of continuous casting of steel? Of what material are the molds made in continuous casting of steel? Why?

References

American Iron & Steel Institute, *The Basic Oxygen Process*. New York: 1960.

Burton, Malcolm S., *Applied Metallurgy for Engineers*. New York: McGraw-Hill Book Company, 1956.

Clark, Donald S., *Engineering Materials and Processes*. Scranton, Pennsylvania: International Textbook Company, 1959.

Clark, Donald S., and Wilbur R. Varney, *Physical Metallurgy for Engineers*. princeton, New Jersey: D. Van Nostrand Co., Inc., 1962.

Cresswell, S. J., *Increasing Importance of the Bessemer Process*. New York: American Iron and Steel Institute Yearbook, 1951.

Guy, Albert G., *Elements of Physical Metallurgy*. Reading, Massachusetts: Addison-Wesley Publishing Company, 1962.

McDonough, William G., *Oxygen as a Means of Increasing Bessemer Production*. New York: American Iron and Steel Institute Yearbook, 1951.

McGannon, Harold E. (ed.), *The Making, Shaping and Treating of Steel*. Pittsburgh, Pennsylvania: United States Steel Corporation, 1964.

Miller, David H., and Terrence E. Dancy, *Continuous Casting—Past Present and Future*. New York: Iron and Steel Engineer, 1963.

Sims, C. E. (ed.), *Electric Furnace Steelmaking*. New York: Interscience Publishers, 1962.

Taylor, Lyman (ed.), *Metals Handbook*, 7th and 8th ed., Metals Park, Ohio: American Society for Metals, 1948 and 1961.

Metallurgy and Production of Nonferrous Metals

9-1 Production of Nonferrous Metals—Copper and Copper Alloys

The subject of extraction of metal from their ores was discussed in Chapter 2; however, it is well in this chapter to discuss in depth the production of a few of the most important metals, including copper, aluminum, magnesium and titanium, from native ore to finished product.

Copper

Although copper in all its natural compounds comprises only about 0.010 part of the lithosphere and therefore ranks low among the elements in the earth's crust, the minerals of copper have been found on the surface in all the continents and in many of the world's islands. About two-thirds of the world's copper comes from deposits in the Cordillera of the Western United States and South America, and are in the form of what we term *porphyry copper*. These are essentially large, low-grade ore deposits mined by bulk methods and handled on a large scale. The mining of these copper ores is done either by "shaft" mining or "open-pit" mining methods. The shaft method is also referred to as the "underground" method. In open-pit mining the over-burden must be removed in order to expose the ore. Equipment for haulage, such as trucks, railroad cars, locomotives, etc., must be provided. In underground, or shaft mining, tunnels must be driven and shafts provided; in addition, haulage and hoisting equipment must also be installed.

As is the case in most copper mines, almost all non-ferrous mines have concentrating plants located near the site of the mines. In the case of larger operations, such as the Phelps-Dodge, Kennecott, Anaconda and Magma mines, we usually find complete metallurgical plants, including smelters, operating on site for the recovery of the metals.

The nature of copper ore and its copper content determines the best method of producing metallic copper from the ore. This is done, for the most part, by three different methods, as follows:

1. Ores in which the copper is present as sulfides are usually concentrated, then smelted from the molten slag and *matte*. Copper matte is about 30 per cent copper and 70 per cent waste material, so the matte is an impure metallic sulfide of copper. The next step in the smelting process is the coversion of liquid matte into metallic copper in the converters, where low-pressure air is blown through the liquid material, the oxygen in the air united with the sulfur to form sulfur dioxide gas, and the iron in the matte also oxidized and skimmed off in the form of slag formed by union with silica ore. *Blister copper* results, containing only a small amount of sulfur, this being transferred to a smaller vessel called the oxidizing furnace, in which air is blown through until all sulfur is removed. About 98 to 99 per cent metallic copper is present in blister copper, which is treated with a reducing gas (reformed mixture of natural gas and air) by blowing the gas through the molten copper, during which the carbon in the gas unites with the oxygen in the copper, purifying it. When nearly all the oxygen is removed, the copper is cast into 700-lb bars called *anodes* which are shipped to the electrolytic refinery for further refining and for the recovery of the small amount of gold and silver that is carried with the copper through the smelter. Electrolytically refined copper contains approximately 99.99 per cent pure copper and is suitable for all electrical applications.

2. The second method of obtaining copper from its ores is used when copper is present in the ores in the form of oxides, or when copper is present as native or nearly pure copper. In either case, these may be smelted in the blast furnace or open-hearth type smelter, then fire-refined and, in some cases, electro-refined.

3. The third method applies to the low grades of oxidized ores, such as are found in Arizona and Utah. Such ores are usually leached with sulfuric acid solutions and then concentrated and classified, and the concentrates of approximately 90 per cent copper are ready for the smelter. From this point on the process follows that is described in (1) for the copper sulfides.

In all cases where the copper is smelted in the reverberatory furnace, gases from the furnace pass through a pair of boilers which make supplemental steam for use in the power house. All gases pass through a Cottrell Plant, where valuable copper-rich dust is recovered before the gases pass to the chimney, which is usually from 360 to 450 ft high, measuring 15 to 20 ft in diameter at the top.

The Kennecott Copper Company recently announced a 35-million-dollar expenditure to install new facilities for a modified leaching vat system using sulfuric acid made from exhaust smoke, thereby increasing their production at Ray Mines Division by 24,000 tons of copper annually. Smoke from the stacks at Hayden, Arizona will be converted to sulfuric acid at the rate of 750 tons per day. This acid will be used to refine copper silicate ore from Kennecott's nearby deposit east of Mineral Creek. As was stated in Chapter 2, the rocks of the earth's crust are classified as igneous, metamorphic, and sedimentary; however, the igneous rocks are undoubtedly the basis of all terrestrial matter. In other words, the composition of the crust as a whole will not be much different from the composition of the igneous rocks. Amounts of the various elements present in the earth's crust have been estimated by geochemists by calculating the weighted averages of the compositions of many samples of the elements in igneous rocks, as given in Table 2–1, Chapter 2.

Element	Per Cent	Element	Per Cent
Oxygen	46.59	Zirconium	0.026
Silicon	27.72	Nickel	0.020
Aluminum	8.13	Vandium	0.017
Iron	5.01	COPPER	0.010
Calcium	3.63	Uranium	0.008
Sodium	2.85	Tungsten	0.005
Potassium	2.60	Zinc	0.004
Magnesium	2.09	Lead	0.002
Titanium	0.63	Thorium	0.002
Manganese	0.10	Cobalt	0.001
		Beryllium	0.001

(Above figures taken from F.W. Clarke and H.S. Washington, "Composition of the Earth's Crust", U.S. Geological Survey Professional Paper 127, 1924)

As may be observed from the figures above, the percentage of the elements including copper in the earth's crust are very low for the most part, so that mass production and economical methods must be used in extracting these elements from their ores. The lower grade oxidized ores of copper are usually leached with sulfuric acid solutions and then electrodeposited in an electrolyte onto a pure copper plate. Several types of copper are produced, depending on the source from which they were obtained and upon the method used. These include *cathode copper, electrolytic tough-pitch* (ETP) copper, and *oxygen-free high-conductivity* (OFHC) copper. As the name implies, cathode copper is produced from the cathodes obtained in the electrorefining of the copper, and has a purity of 99.9 per cent and upward, and an oxygen content of approximately 0.05 per cent or less. The two principal sources for metal to be converted to tough-pitch copper that has been fire-refined and deoxidized are the cathode copper and secondary copper with an oxygen content of 0.03 to 0.05 per cent. *Oxygen-free high-conductivity* (OFHC) copper is produced by fire-refining in an atmosphere that is reducing in nature.

Copper has many properties that are significant and important in commercial use, the most important being its high electrical and thermal conductivity. It is also a metal with good corrosion resistance, easy to machine and fabricate, and still has desirable strength when alloyed with other metals, such as tin, zinc, lead, and nickel. Copper is second highest in the scale of electrical and thermal conductivity, being excelled only by silver. Oxygen-free high-conductivity copper is used extensively in the production of electronic tubes because of its characteristic of making perfect seals in conjunction with glass. When alloyed with about 0.06 per cent tellurium, *free-cutting* copper is obtained, with superior machining properties desirable in the manufacture of welding tips, bolts, switching gears, and other precision electrical components.

The more common elements alloyed with copper are zinc, lead, tin, nickel, aluminum and silicon, although beryllium, arsenic, iron, silver, manganese, and cadmium are also used in certain applications. By far the most important alloying element for copper is zinc, which is the base for brass and also an essential additive for the bronzes and other alloys, as shown in Table 9–1.

TABLE 9–1.   Some Important Copper-Zinc Alloys*

Common Name and Composition in Per cent	Condition	Tensile Strength psi	Yield Strength psi	Elong. in 2 in. (%)	Some Uses
Gilding Metal (95% Cu, 5% Zn)	0.035 mm G.S.	35,000	11,000	45	Coins, emblems, fuse caps, and jewelery
	1/4 hard	42,000	32,000	25	
	Hard	56,000	50,000	5	
	Spring	64,000	58,000	4	
Commercial Bronze (90% Cu, 10% Zn)	0.035 mm G.S.	38,000	12,000	45	Screen cloth, marine hardware primer, caps
	1/4 hard	45,000	35,000	25	
	Hard	61,000	54,000	5	
	Spring	72,000	62,000	3	
Red Brass (85% Cu, 15% Zn)	0.035 mm G.S.	41,000	14,000	46	Electrical sockets, condenser tubes, architectural trim
	1/4 hard	50,000	39,000	25	
	Hard	70,000	57,000	5	
	Spring	84,000	63,000	3	
Cartridge Brass (70% Cu, 30% Zn)	0.035 mm G.S.	49,000	17,000	57	Lamp fixtures, springs, radiator cores
	1/4 hard	54,000	40,000	43	
	Hard	76,000	63,000	8	
	Extra spring	99,000	65,000	3	
Yellow Brass (65% Cu, 40% Zn)	Annealed	49,000	17,000	57	Architectural grillwork, etc.
	1/4 hard	54,000	40,000	43	
	Hard	74,000	60,000	8	
	Spring	91,000	62,000	3	
Muntz Metal (60% Cu, 40% Zn)	Annealed	54,000	21,000	45	Large nuts and bolts, condenser tubes, arch. trim
	1/2 hard	70,000	50,000	10	
Naval Brass (60% Cu, 39-1/4% Zn, 3/4% Sn)	Soft. ann. rod	57,000	25,000	47	Condenser plates, welding rods, marine hardware
	Rod 1/4 hard	69,000	46,000	27	
	Rod 1/2 hard	75,000	53,000	20	
Manganese Bronze (58.5% Cu, 39% Zn, 1% Sn, 0.1% Mn)	Rod soft ann.	65,000	30,000	33	Pump rods, welding rods, valve stems
	Rod 1/4 hard	77,000	45,000	23	
	Rod 1/2 hard	84,000	60,000	19	
Aluminum brass (76% Cu, 22% Zn, 2% Al)	Tube 0.025 mm G.S.	60,000	27,000	55	Condenser tubes, etc.

*From American Society for Metals (ASM) Metals Handbook, 1948 edition.

As will be observed from a study of Table 9–1, brasses are made up principally of copper and zinc, some of these alloys also containing other elements, such as tin, lead and aluminum, depending upon the color, strength, machinability, corrosion resistance and ductility desired. In Fig. 9–1 is the portion of the copper-zinc equilibrium diagram which is used mainly with respect to the commercial alloys shown in Table 9–1. Just as with other alloys, the mechanical properties of alloys in the copper-zinc system are closely related to the phase diagram of the system. Both the tensile strength and ductility of this system increase with the higher content of zinc, up to approximately 35 per cent. When the beta solid solution begins to appear, an increase in the strength, with a lowering in ductility, is seen. Very few alloys containing more than 40 per cent zinc are of much importance commercially, for the reason that beta and gamma solid solutions are not ductile like the alpha solid solution. The alloys in this system, containing only alpha solid solution, can be hot or cold worked with ease; however, alloys with both alpha and beta solid solutions do not lend themselves to any considerable amount of cold working without danger of rupture. As a result, these alloys must be hot worked. It is possible to hot roll, forge, and extrude very easily the copper-zinc system alloys that contain mostly beta solid solution; however, when the gamma solid solution is present, it is difficult to hot or cold work the alloy, so that these alloys must be used in the form of castings when required.

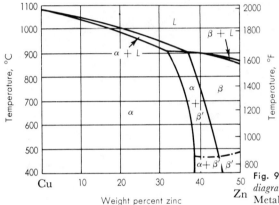

Fig. 9-1.   *Copper-rich portion of the Cu-Zn equilibrium diagram. (By permission of American Society for Metals, Metals Handbook.)*

It will be noted in Table 9–1 that *tin* is the principal addition used in most bronzes, most of our commercial alloys being within the alpha range of the copper-tin equilibrium diagram, as shown in Fig. 9–2. Copper-tin alloys possess very fine properties so far as strength, wear-resistance, and corrosion-resistance in salt water environment is concerned. The alloys in this system that are most useful from an engineering standpoint are those with less than 20 per cent tin, although other elements are often added to give the best properties for certain applications. At room temperature the solubility of tin in copper is somewhat restricted, as noted in the equilibrium diagram shown in Fig. 9–2.

A convenient range of compositions of the bronzes, so far as content of tin and copper are concerned, are as follows:

1. Alloys with up to 8 per cent tin are used mainly for cold-worked applications (sheets, wire and coins).
2. Alloys with from 8 to 12 per cent tin are used mainly for gears, bearings, marine hardware, etc.
3. Bearings are made largely from the 12 to 20 per cent tin-copper alloy.
4. Bells are the principal product made from copper-tin alloys with from 20 to 25 per cent tin, alloys in this group being very hard and extremely brittle, compared to the others listed above.

Aluminum increases substantially the mechanical properties, as well as the corrosion resistance, of copper alloys. This is particularly true at elevated temperatures; how-

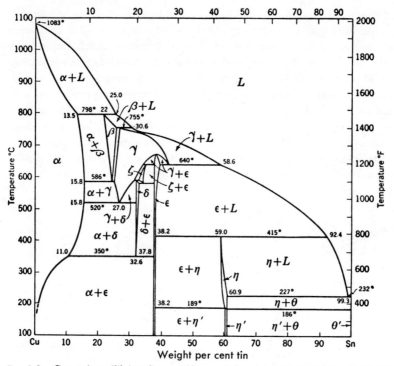

Fig. 9-2. *Copper-tin equilibrium diagram.* (*By permission of American Society for Metals*, Metals Handbook.)

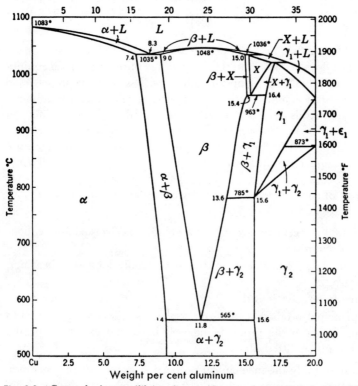

Fig. 9-3. *Copper-aluminum equilibrium diagram* (*Courtesy of American Society for Metals*, Metals Handbook.)

ever, because of the rapid oxidation of the aluminum, it is difficult to cast copper-aluminum alloys, most of these alloys being utilized in the form of rods, sheets, and sections as well as for gears used in heavy machinery, pump parts, electrical contacts, etc. Shown in Fig. 9-3 is an equilibrium diagram of the copper-aluminum system; alloys in this system usually have about 10 to 12 per cent aluminum and about 5 per cent iron, with smaller amounts of tin present. Although the alpha phase alloys may be hot or cold worked, they are difficult to machine to any extent.

As will be noted in Fig. 9–3, the maximum solubility of aluminum in the alpha solid solution is about 9.5 per cent at 1060F, the beta phase undergoing a eutectoid reaction at this temperature where $\beta > 2 + \gamma_2$ with the formation of an alloy $(\alpha + \gamma_2)$. Iron, up to 5 per cent, increases the strength and hardness of the aluminum bronze, in addition to supplying the hardness that is coupled with refinement of the grains. Up to about 5 per cent, nickel has the same effect as iron, but smaller amounts are required. Silicon, up to 2 per cent, will improve the machinability while manganese increases the soundness in castings as well as the tensile strength. A substantial tonnage of aluminum bronzes in the heat-treated condition is used for the production of gears, propeller hubs, bearings, various pump parts, and for forming and drawing dies, primarily because of their high wear and corrosion resistance.

Beryllium bronzes are in demand for parts that must have good formability in the soft condition, along with high fatigue and yield strengths and resistance to creep in the hardened condition, as in the case of important springs. Firing pins, dies, non-sparking tools, and other hard parts required to wear well when used with hardened steel, are other applications where beryllium bronzes are used to advantage. An equilibrium diagram for the copper-rich portion is shown in Fig. 9–4. As may be seen here, the solubility of beryllium in the alpha solid solution decreases from 2.2 per cent at 1588F to less than 0.25 per cent at room temperature. Such a change in solubility is always an indication that it is possible to age harden such alloys. The best mechanical properties of an alloy in this series occur in alloys

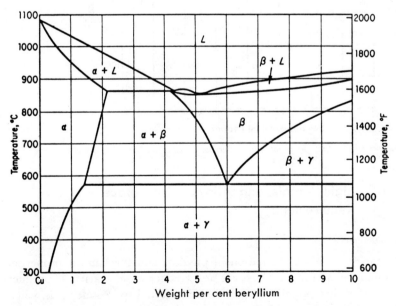

Fig. 9-4. *Copper-rich portion of copper-beryllium alloy system. (By permission of American Society for Metals, Metals Handbook.)*

containing approximately 2.00 per cent beryllium, in which case would be used a heat treating cycle of solution-annealing at 1450F, water quench, cold work, and then age hardening at 600F. The use of too high an aging temperature causes coarsening of the grains, as always occurs with over-aging. Beryllium oxidizes very readily and its oxide is poisonous, so extreme care must be used in handling molten copper-beryllium alloys.

Another alloy that should properly be classified under the precious metals of gold-silver-platinum is included here, inasmuch as it is an alloy of *silver-copper-zinc* which we usually refer to as the silver solders, or silver brazing, alloys. Often these alloys also contain cadmium and tin in addition to silver, copper, and zinc. In the popular joining operation of brazing, the physical mechanism of bounding that takes place is very similar to that found in soft soldering, the only difference being that it occurs at room temperature in the case of soldering and at elevated temperatures in brazing. Melting does not take place in the metal being joined; the bond results from the interfacial penetration of the brazing alloy used. These alloys have considerable use in industry because of their low melting temperatures and their ability to flow freely into the joint, making them useful in the joining of both ferrous and nonferrous metals with exceptionally high-quality joints. Brazing alloys of copper-silver-zinc (silver solders or silver brazing alloys) can be produced by properly varying the components that have melting points from 1150 to 1550F.

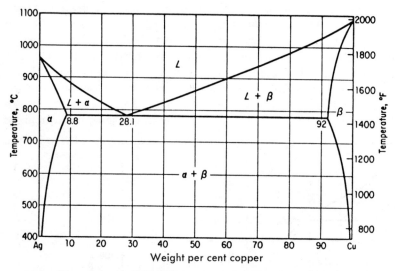

Fig. 9-5. *Silver-copper alloy system. (By permission of American Society for Metals,* Metals Handbook.)

9-2 Light Metals and Alloys—Outerspace Requirements

Aluminum

Because of their unusual combination of physical and mechanical properties, wrought aluminum and aluminum alloys are preferred for a wide variety of products and applications. This is especially true in the aircraft and spacecraft fields, where many exacting requirements are being met by aluminum, a metal with many outstanding properties, including light weight, excellent corrosion resistance, good strength, high conductivity, ease of fabrication, and in situations where a combination of these properties may be put to useful advantage. Undoubtedly the most useful property of aluminum is its light weight, the density of aluminum and aluminum alloys being only about one-third that of steel. As a result of this, high-strength, heat-treatable aluminum alloys have strength-to-weight ratios exceeding those of many steels and most nonferrous metals and alloys.

TABLE 9–2. Mechanical Properties of Typical Wrought Aluminum Alloys.

Alloy	Tensile Strength (lb/in.²)	Yield Strength (offset = 0.2%) (lb/in.²)	Elongation % in 2 in. Sheet Spec. $\frac{1}{16}$ in. Thick	Elongation % in 2 in. Round Spec. $\frac{1}{2}$ in. Dia.	Brinell Hardness (500-kg. Load 10-mm Ball)	Shear Strength (lb/in.²)	Endurance Limit* (lb/in.²)
EC-O	12,000	4,000	Wire approx. 23% in 10 in.		—	8,000	—
EC-H19	27,000	24,000	Wire approx. 1-$\frac{1}{2}$% in 10 in.		—	15,000	7,000
2EC-T6	32,000	29,000	—	19	—	—	—
2EC-T64	17,000	9,000	—	24	—	—	—
1060-O	10,000	4,000	43	—	19	7,000	3,000
1060-H18	19,000	18,000	6	—	35	11,000	6,500
1100-O	13,000	5,000	35	45	23	9,000	5,000
1100-H18	24,000	22,000	5	15	44	13,000	9,000
2011-T3	55,000	43,000	—	15	95	32,000	18,000
2011-T6	57,000	39,000	—	17	97	34,000	18,000
2011-T8	59,000	45,000	—	12	100	35,000	18,000
2014-O	27,000	14,000	—	18	45	18,000	13,000
2014-T4	62,000	42,000	—	20	105	38,000	20,000
2014-T6	70,000	60,000	—	13	135	42,000	18,000
2017-O	26,000	10,000	—	22	45	18,000	13,000
2017-T4	62,000	40,000	—	22	105	38,000	18,000
2018-T61	61,000	46,000	—	12	120	39,000	17,000
2024-O	27,000	11,000	20	22	47	18,000	13,000
2024-T3	70,000	50,000	18	—	120	41,000	20,000
2024-T36	72,000	57,000	13	—	130	42,000	18,000
2024-T4	68,000	47,000	20	19	120	41,000	20,000
2024-T81	70,000	65,000	6	—	128	43,000	18,000
2024-T86	75,000	71,000	6	—	135	45,000	18,000
2025-T6	58,000	37,000	—	19	110	35,000	18,000
2117-T4	43,000	24,000	—	27	70	28,000	14,000
2218-T72	48,000	37,000	—	11	95	30,000	—
3003-O	16,000	6,000	30	40	28	11,000	7,000
3003-H18	29,000	27,000	4	10	55	16,000	10,000
3004-O	26,000	10,000	20	25	45	16,000	14,000
3004-H38	41,000	36,000	5	6	77	21,000	16,000
4032-T6	55,000	46,000	—	9	120	38,000	16,000
5005-O	18,000	6,000	30	—	28	11,000	—
5005-H18	29,000	28,000	4	—	—	16,000	—
5005-H32	20,000	17,000	11	—	36	14,000	—
5005-H38	29,000	27,000	5	—	51	16,000	—
5050-O	21,000	8,000	24	—	36	15,000	12,000
5050-H38	32,000	29,000	6	—	63	20,000	14,000
5052-O	28,000	13,000	25	30	47	18,000	16,000
5052-H38	42,000	37,000	7	8	77	24,000	20,000

Table 9–2.

Alloy	Tensile Strength (lb/in.²)	Yield Strength (offset = 0.2%) (lb/in.²)	Elongation % in 2 in.		Brinell Hardness (500-kg. Load 10-mm Ball)	Shear Strength (lb/in.²)	Endurance Limit* (lb/in.²)
			Sheet Spec. $\frac{1}{16}$ in. Thick	Round Spec. $\frac{1}{2}$ in. Dia.			
5056-O	42,000	22,000	—	35	65	26,000	20,000
5056-H38	60,000	50,000	—	15	100	32,000	22,000
5083-O	42,000	21,000	22	—	—	25,000	—
5083-H113	46,000	33,000	16	—	—	—	23,000
5086-O	38,000	17,000	22	—	—	23,000	—
5086-H34	47,000	37,000	10	—	—	27,000	—
5086-H112	39,000	19,000	14	—	—	—	—
5154-O	35,000	17,000	27	—	58	22,000	17,000
5154-H38	48,000	39,000	10	—	87	28,000	21,000
5154-H112	35,000	17,000	25	—	63	—	17,000
5254-O	35,000	17,000	27	—	58	22,000	17,000
5254-H38	48,000	39,000	10	—	80	28,000	21,000
5254-H112	35,000	17,000	25	—	63	—	17,000
5357-O	19,000	7,000	25	—	32	12,000	—
5357-H38	32,000	30,000	6	—	55	18,000	—
5454-O	36,000	17,000	22	—	62	23,000	—
5454-H34	44,000	35,000	10	—	81	26,000	—
5454-H112	36,000	18,000	18	—	62	23,000	—
5454-H311	38,000	26,000	14	—	70	23,000	—
5456-O	45,000	23,000	24	—	—	—	—
5456-H321	51,000	37,000	16	—	90	30,000	—
5456-H112	45,000	24,000	22	—	—	—	—
5456-H311	47,000	33,000	18	—	—	—	—
5652-O	28,000	13,000	25	30	47	18,000	16,000

(Courtesy of *Materials in Design Engineering*, "Materials Selector Issue" of Mid-October 1965.)

Aluminum's electrical conductivity is second only to copper on an equal volume basis, but it is more than twice that of copper on an equal weight basis. Also, by virtue of its naturally formed protective oxide film, aluminum resists corrosion in many atmospheric and chemical environments. Its good formability and machinability make complex parts relatively easy to fabricate. Aluminum is also non-toxic, has a high degree of reflectivity, and possesses non-magnetic and non-sparking properties—all important in many applications and particularly so in outer-space vehicles.

Typical specifications for various types of aluminum and aluminum alloys are given in Table 9–2.

9-3 Types and Forms of Aluminum

Alloy Designations

The most common designations for wrought aluminum and aluminum alloys follow the four-digit index system adopted by the Aluminum Association in 1954 and approved by the American Standards Association (ASA H35.1) in 1957.

As indicated below, the first digit indicates the alloy group. The second digit designates alloy modifications or impurity limits. The last two digits identify the alloys or indicate aluminum purity.

Aluminum–99.00% minimum: 1XXX
Aluminum alloys grouped by major alloying elements:
    Copper 2XXX
    Manganese 3XXX
    Silicon 4XXX
    Magnesium 5XXX
    Magnesium and Silicon 6XXX
    Zinc 7XXX
    Other elements 8XXX
Unused series: 9XXX

Aluminum. In the 1XXX series (minimum aluminum content of 99.00 per cent), the last two digits indicate the minimum aluminum percentage in hundredths. The second digit designates modification in impurity limits. For example, if the second digit is zero, this indicates that there is no special control on individual impurities; integers 1 to 9, assigned consecutively, indicate special control of one or more impurities.

Aluminum alloys. In the 2XXX to 8XXX series, the last two digits identify the different alloys in the series; as new alloys become available commercially, they are assigned consecutively, beginning with XX01. The second digit in the alloy designation indicates alloy modifications. If this digit is zero, it indicates the original alloy; integers 1 to 9, assigned consecutively, indicate alloy modifications.

Experimental alloys. During development, a new alloy is identified by a serial number assigned by the developer. Once the alloy is available for commercial evaluation, the serial number is discontinued, and the alloy is designated in accordance with the above four-digit index system, but indicated with the prefix X. The prefix is discontinued when the alloy becomes standard.

General Alloy Characteristics

Typical properties, grade, and condition at various temperatures for the major types of aluminum and aluminum alloys are shown in Table 9–2. The higher strength aluminum alloys, which also contain copper in addition to zinc and magnesium, are somewhat limited because of their poor weldability. Although the addition of copper provides increased strength, it also impairs weldability and corrosion resistance. To improve weldability and corrosion resistance, new alloys have been developed which either do not contain copper or in which the copper content is substantially reduced. Alloy 7039 is a notable example, for although the strength of 7039 is less than that of the copper-bearing alloys, it does provide a good combination of strength, weldability and corrosion resistance.

Alclad alloys. Aluminum alloy sheets, plates, tubes, and wire may be clad with high purity aluminum or aluminum alloys to improve corrosion resistance. In this case, the alloys are identified by preceding the designation of the core alloy with the designation *alclad*; for example, *alclad* 2024–0 sheet. Sheet and plate may be clad on one or both sides. The strength of the cladding material is usually less than that of the core alloy. Consequently, the strength of the *alclad* metal is slightly less than that of unclad materials, in proportion to the amount of cladding applied.

TABLE 9–3. Typical Properties of Wrought Aluminum Alloys at Various Temperatures.

Grade and Condn	Temp, F	Ult Str, psi	Yld Str[a], psi	Elong[b], %	Grade and Condn	Temp, F	Ult Str, psi	Yld Str[a], psi	Elong[b], %	Grade and Condn	Temp, F	Ult Str, psi	Yld Str[a], psi	Elong[b], %
1100-0	-320	24,000	6000	56	2117-T4	-320	56,000	33,000	30	5083-0	-320	63,000	22,500	36
	-112	15,000	5000	49		-112	45,000	25,000	29		-112	51,000	20,000	31
	75	13,000	5000	45		75	43,000	24,000	27		75	42,000	21,000	22
	212	11,000	5000	45		212	36,000	21,000	16		212	44,000	22,000	33
	300	8500	4500	55		300	30,000	17,000	20		300	30,000	19,000	50
	400	6000	3500	65		400	16,000	12,000	35		400	23,000	17,000	62
1100-H18	-320	35,000	26,000	28	2218-T61	-320	73,000	53,500	20	5086-0	-423	77,000	23,000	40
	-112	26,000	23,000	16		-112	61,000	44,000	17		-320	56,000	22,000	60
	75	24,000	22,000	15		75	59,000	44,000	13		75	38,000	17,000	30
	212	22,000	18,000	15		212	57,000	46,000	15		212	37,000	17,000	37
	300	18,000	14,000	20		300	40,000	34,000	18		400	22,000	16,000	60
	400	6000	3500	65		400	18,000	12,000	34		500	17,000	11,000	85
2011-T3	-320	73,500	56,000	26	2219-T62	-320	78,000	52,000	14	5086-H34	-423	95,500	47,000	30
	-112	57,500	47,500	17		-112	65,000	44,000	12		-320	65,500	41,000	24
	75	55,000	43,000	15		75	61,000	42,000	11		75	47,000	37,000	10
	212	47,000	34,000	16		300	44,000	30,000	15		200	45,000	33,000	14
	300	28,000	19,000	25		400	33,000	24,000	18		400	28,000	21,000	34
	400	16,000	11,000	35		500	27,000	20,000	18		500	18,000	13,000	62
2014-T4	-320	79,000	55,000	20	2219-T81	-320	86,000	63,000	13	5154-H38	-423	93,500	54,000	35
	-112	64,000	44,000	22		-112	73,000	56,000	12		-320	67,000	52,000	24
	75	62,000	42,000	20		75	70,000	53,000	11		75	48,000	39,000	14
	300	46,000	33,000	—		300	48,000	38,000	15		212	45,000	36,000	17
	400	18,000	12,000	—		400	34,000	29,000	16		400	23,000	15,000	35
	500	11,000	8500	—		500	28,000	23,000	16		500	16,000	9000	70
2014-T6	-320	84,000	69,000	14	2618-T61	-320	73,000	53,500	14	5456-0	-320	63,000	27,000	30
	-112	74,000	63,000	13		-112	61,000	44,000	17		-112	46,000	23,000	26
	75	70,000	60,000	13		75	59,000	44,000	13		75	45,000	23,000	20
	212	63,000	56,000	14		300	50,000	46,000	14		212	43,000	22,000	30
	300	40,000	35,000	15		400	31,000	26,000	25		400	23,000	17,000	60
	400	16,000	13,000	35		500	14,000	9000	52		500	17,000	11,000	85
2017-T4	-320	78,500	51,500	28	3003-H18	-320	41,000	33,000	23	6061-T6	-320	60,000	47,000	22
	-112	64,000	41,000	26		-112	32,000	29,000	11		-112	49,000	42,000	18
	75	62,000	40,000	22		75	29,000	27,000	10		75	45,000	40,000	17
	212	56,000	37,000	18		212	26,000	21,000	10		212	42,000	38,000	18
	300	40,000	30,000	16		300	23,000	16,000	11		300	34,000	31,000	20
	400	16,000	13,000	35		400	14,000	9000	18		400	19,000	15,000	28
2018-T61	-320	72,000	51,000	12	3004-0	-320	42,000	13,000	38	6063-T42	-320	34,000	16,000	44
	-112	64,000	47,000	12		-112	28,000	11,000	30		-112	26,000	15,000	36
	75	61,000	46,000	12		75	26,000	10,000	25		75	22,000	13,000	33
	212	56,000	43,000	12		212	26,000	10,000	25		212	22,000	14,000	18
	300	45,000	40,000	12		300	22,000	10,000	35		300	21,000	15,000	20
	400	19,000	13,000	25		400	14,000	9500	55		400	9000	6500	40
2024-T3	-320	85,000	62,000	18	3004-H38	-320	58,000	43,000	20	6063-T6	-320	47,000	36,000	24
	-112	75,000	52,000	17		-112	44,000	38,000	10		-112	38,000	33,000	20
	75	70,000	50,000	17		75	41,000	36,000	6		75	35,000	31,000	18
	212	66,000	48,000	16		212	40,000	36,000	7		212	31,000	28,000	15
	300	55,000	50,000	11		300	31,000	27,000	15		300	21,000	20,000	20
	400	29,000	22,000	23		400	22,000	15,000	30		400	9000	6500	40
2024-T6	-320	83,000	68,000	11	4032-T6	-320	66,000	48,000	11	7075-T6	-423	113,000	105,000	6
	-112	72,000	60,000	10		-112	58,000	46,000	10		-320	100,000	91,000	14
	75	69,000	57,000	10		75	55,000	46,000	9		75	83,000	73,000	11
	212	65,000	55,000	10		212	50,000	44,000	9		212	74,000	68,000	12
	300	45,000	36,000	17		300	37,000	33,000	9		300	30,000	26,000	30
	400	27,000	20,000	27		400	13,000	9000	30		400	18,000	16,000	45
2024-T81	-320	85,000	77,000	8	5050-0	-320	37,000	9500	46	7075-T73	-320	94,000	78,000	15
	-112	75,000	68,000	7		-112	24,000	8500	38		75	73,000	63,000	13
	75	70,000	65,000	7		75	21,000	8000	24		212	64,000	59,000	15
	212	66,000	61,000	8		212	21,000	8000	28		300	31,000	27,000	30
	300	55,000	50,000	11		300	19,000	8000	38		400	16,000	13,000	55
	400	29,000	22,000	23		400	14,000	7500	58		500	11,000	9000	65
2024-T86	-320	91,000	86,000	5	5050-H38	-320	50,000	38,500	26	7079-T6	-423	115,000	95,500	16
	-112	80,000	77,000	5		-112	38,000	32,000	18		-320	92,000	80,000	12
	75	75,000	71,000	5		75	32,000	29,000	6		75	78,000	68,000	14
	300	55,000	51,000	11		212	31,000	29,000	15		300	33,000	28,000	37
	400	20,000	16,000	28		400	14,000	8500	60		400	16,000	13,000	60
2025-T6	75	58,000	37,000	19	5052-0	-320	44,000	16,000	45	7178-T6	-423	123,000	111,000	8
	212	52,000	35,000	18		75	28,000	13,000	30		-320	107,000	100,000	9
	300	36,000	29,000	18		212	28,000	13,000	37		75	88,000	78,000	10
	400	19,000	14,000	35		400	18,000	11,000	60		300	32,000	29,000	36

(Courtesy of *Alcoa Aluminum Handbook*, Aluminum Company of America, and *The Aluminum Data Book* of Reynolds Metals Company.)

Temper Designations

Aluminum and aluminum alloys fall into two general categories, depending on their response to heat treatment. Alloys in the 3000 and 5000 series, which owe their strength to the hardening effects of manganese and magnesium, respectively, cannot be strengthened by heat treatment. They are commonly called the *non-heat-treatable alloys*. However, these alloys can be strengthened by cold working, and

they are available in various strain hardened conditions. When alloys having appreciable magnesium content are used in the strain hardened conditions, they are usually
given a final elevated temperature treatment in order to stabilize their properties.

Alloys in the 2000, 6000, and 7000 series are characterized by substantial
additions of copper, magnesium, and zinc respectively, in combination or with small
percentages of other elements. Since these elements show increasing solubility in
aluminum at elevated temperatures, the alloys can be strengthened by thermal
treatment. Therefore, these alloys are known as the *heat-treatable alloys*. Although
some alloys in the 4000 series are heat-treatable, most of these alloys are used mainly
for brazing sheet and welding wire.

The standard temper designation system established by the Aluminum Association, which has also been approved by the American Standards Association (ASA
35.1), consists of denoting the basic temper by a letter, and modifications of the
temper by one or more digits following the letter. A complete list of symbols and the
conditions which they describe follows:

–F–   As fabricated. Temper produced by normal manufacturing operations. No control exercised over the temper of the alloy, and no guarantee of mechanical properties.

–O–   Annealed, recrystallized. The softest temper of aluminum and aluminum alloys.

–H–   Strain hardened. Temper produced by cold working with or without supplementary thermal treatments to obtain partial softening.

–H1–   Strain hardened only. Temper produced by cold working without supplementary thermal treatments. The digit following this designation indicates the degree of strain hardening.

–H2–   Strain hardened and partially annealed. Temper produced by cold working more than the desired amount, followed by partial annealing to the desired strength level. –H2– temper, for alloys which age-soften at room temperature, has approximately the same ultimate strength as the corresponding –H3– temper. For other alloys, the –H2– temper has roughly the same ultimate strength as the corresponding –H1– temper, but slightly greater elongation. The digit following this designation indicates residual amount of strain hardening remaining after partial annealing.

–H3–   Strain hardened and stabilized. Temper produced by cold working followed by low temperature treatment to stabilize mechanical properties. This temper pertains only to magnesium-bearing alloys which age-soften at room temperature unless stabilized. The digit following this designation indicates residual amount of strain hardening remaining after stabilizing.

–H111–   Strain hardened. Temper produced by cold working to less than amount required to obtain a controlled –H11– temper.

–H112–   Strain hardened. Temper produced by cold working without special control over the amount of strain hardening or thermal treatment, but where mechanical property limits or mechanical property testing are required.

–H311– Strain hardened. Temper produced by cold working to less than the amount required for a controlled –H31– temper. In addition to the above, many other three digit –H– temper designations are used for specifying patterned or embossed sheet fabricated from annealed and two digit –H– temper material.

–W– Solution heat treated. An unstable temper applicable only to alloys that age harden at room temperature (natural aging) after solution heat treatment. This designation is specified only when the period of natural aging is specified (e.g., –W– 1/2 hour).

–T– Thermally treated to produce stable tempers other than –F–, –O–, or –H–, with or without supplementary strain hardening. The –T– designation is always followed by numbers 1 to 10 to indicate the specific treatments, as follows:

–T1– Partially solution heat treated and naturally aged to a substantially stable condition. Temper produced by a partial solution heat treatment resulting from an elevated temperature, rapid cool fabrication process, such as extrusion.

–T2– Applicable to cast products only.

–T3– Solution heat treated and cold worked. Temper produced by cold working after solution heat treatment to improve strength, or where subsequent cold working in flattening or straightening is recognized in applicable specifications.

–T4– Solution heat treated and naturally aged to a substantially stable condition. Applies to alloys not cold worked after solution treatment, or where the effect of cold working in flattening or straightening may not be recognized in applicable specifications.

–T5– Partially solution heat treated and artificially aged. Temper produced by artificial aging to improve mechanical properties or dimensional stability after an elevated temperature, rapid cool fabrication process, such as extrusion.

–T6– Solution heat treated and artificially aged. Temper produced by artificial aging after solution heat treatment without cold working, or where the effect of cold working in flattening or straightening may not be recognized in applicable specifications.

–T7– Solution heat treated and stabilized. Temper produced by a stabilizing thermal treatment after solution heat treatment, to control special characteristics such as growth, distortion or residual stresses.

–T8– Solution heat treated, cold worked and artificially aged. Temper produced by solution heat treatment and artificial aging, with intermediate cold working to improve strength, or where intermediate cold working in flattening or straightening is recognized in applicable specifications.

–T9– Solution heat treated, artificially aged, and cold worked. Temper produced by cold working after solution treatment and artificial aging to improve strength.

–T10– Partially solution heat treated, artificially aged and cold worked. Temper produced by artificially aging and cold working after an elevated temperature, rapid cool fabrication process, such as extrusion. The period of natural aging that may occur between or after the treatments for tempers –T1– to –T10– is controlled when it is metallurgically important to do so. Additional digits may be added to designations –T1 to –T10 to show variations in treatment which significantly alter characteristics of the alloys. These may be arbitrarily assigned and registered with The Aluminum Association to indicate specific treatments or mechanical property limits. For example, the following digits have been assigned for stress-relieved tempers:

–TX51–   Stress relieved by stretching. Temper produced by stress relieving after solution heat treatment, stretching to permanent sets of 1.5 to 3 per cent for plate and to 1 to 3 per cent for rod, bar, tuning, and shapes. Temper applies directly to plate and rolled or cold-finished rod and bar, which receive no further straightening after stretching. It also applies to extruded rod, bar, tubing, and shapes when designated as follows: –TX510– for mill forms receiving no further straightening after stretching, and –TX511– for mill forms that may receive minor straightening after stretching, to meet standard tolerances.

–TX52–   Stress relieved by compression. Temper produced by stress relieving after solution heat treatment, compressing to a permanent nominal set of 2.5 per cent.

–T53–   Stress relieved by thermal treatment.
          The following designations apply to alloys heat treated by the user (4032–T62 and 6101–T62 are exceptions):

–T42–   Solution heat treated by the user. Temper is produced by solution heat treatment where the mechanical properties attained are different from those of the –T4–temper.

–T62–   Solution heat treated and artificially aged by the user. The temper is produced by solution heat treatment and artificial aging where the mechanical properties attained are different from those of the T6–temper.

Fig. 9–6. *Apollo 15 liftoff from Pad A, Launch Complex 39, Kennedy Space Center, Florida on July 26, 1971, at 9:34 a.m. The huge, 363-foot tall Apollo 15 is on a lunar landing mission. Aboard the spacecraft were Astronauts David R. Scott, commander; Alfred M. Worden, command module pilot; and James B. Irwin, lunar module pilot. (Courtesy National Aeronautics and Space Administration, Lyndon B. Johnson Space Center —Christopher C. Kraft, Jr., Director, and Mr. Robert L. Johnston, Chief, Materials Technology Branch).*

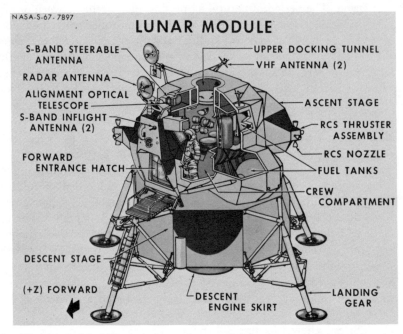

Fig. 9–7. *The lunar module (LM), the first manned spacecraft designed to operate exclusively in a space environment, was required to accomplish the lunar-landing phase of the Apollo Program. The LM was designed with emphasis on a minimum-weight structure. A typical area in which considerable weight saving was accomplished was in the reduction of structural joints. This reduction was accomplished by machining large structural members instead of machining a number of smaller members and joining them by fasteners.*

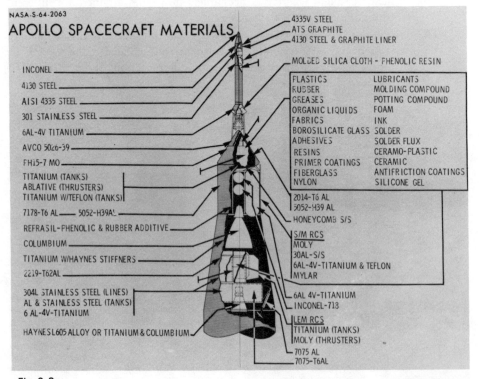

Fig. 9–8.

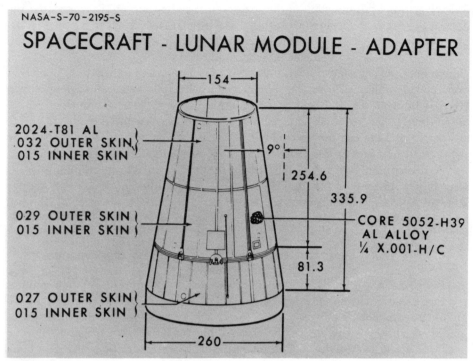

Fig. 9–9.

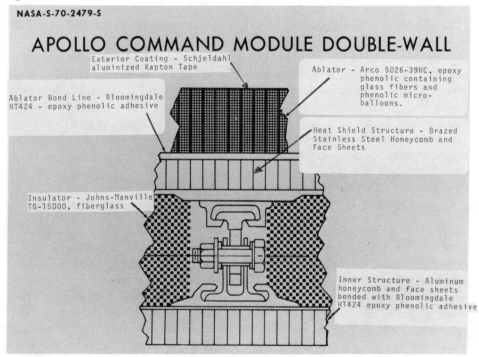

Fig. 9–10.

(Photos on pages 198 and 199 courtesy of National Aeronautics and Space Administration, Lyndon B. Johnson Space Center—Christopher C. Kraft, Jr., Director, and Mr. Robert L. Johnston, Chief, Materials Technology Branch).

Referring to the cabin section of the spacecraft shown in Fig. 9–10, we see that the sides of the cabin are covered with shingles of beaded René 41 (0.16 in. thick). The composition of René 41 is as follows: 53 per cent nickel, 19 per cent chromium, 11 per cent cobalt, 9.75 per cent molybdenum, 3.15 per cent titanium, 1.6 per cent aluminum, 0.09 per cent carbon, 0.005 per cent boron, and less than 2.75 per cent iron. The aluminum used in the spacecraft was 7075–T6 and the magnesium was HK–31. Both the Stage I and Stage II tanks of the Gemini IV launch vehicle are made of 2014–T6 aluminum. Although stainless steels and refractory materials are used in the Project, they are not in significant amounts, because of the specific requirements governing the entire spacecraft throughout the flights.

All photographs and other information on the Gemini IV mission and vehicles were kindly furnished the author by National Aeronautics and Space Administration, through the good offices of Dr. Robert C. Seamans, Jr., Director of Manned Space Craft Center, and his assistant, Dr. George E. Mueller.

9-4 Electrical and Thermal Properties of Aluminum

The electrical conductivity of aluminum is second only to copper among common conductor materials, as stated previously. For example, the conductivity of EC aluminum is about 62 per cent IACS in all temper conditions. Other high purity grades are almost as conductive, including alloys 5005, 6063, 6101, and 6201.

The electrical resistivity of aluminum and its alloys ranges from about 17 ohms per cir mil ft, for high purity grades, to 20 to 38 ohms per cir mil ft for other alloys. The thermal conductivity in Btu/hr/sq ft /°F/ft ranges from a high of about 135 for high purity aluminum grades to a low of about 67 for several 5000 and 7000 series alloys.

Aluminum also has excellent corrosion resistance in many environments, its good performance being due to the formation of a protective, tightly adherent, invisible coating of oxide film which developes in air, oxygen or oxidizing media. This film is generally stable in solutions having a pH between 4.5 and 8.5; however, because the film is soluble in certain strong alkaline or acid solutions, aluminum can be severely attacked in these media. Only those higher strength aluminum alloys that precipitate seperate phases in the microstructure are susceptible to stress corrosion.

Age-Hardening of Alloys

In the case of aluminum alloys, two basic types of heat treatment can be used:

1. Solutionizing and precipitation
2. Annealing.

In the first, the alloy is heated from 900 to 1000F in an electric or gas furnace or salt bath, then quenched in air, oil, or hot water. After quenching, the alloys slowly harden and increase in strength, if they are held at room temperature. This is what is termed *age-hardening;* its effects are most pronounced in the first few days after quenching, but still appear at a slower rate for several weeks. In casting alloys of Al and Cu, the age-hardening is complete in three months. Aging of this type is accelerated at higher temperatures, but in such cases it is termed *artificial aging* or precipitation hardening. Careful control in the treatment of the alloys for precipitation (PH) hardening is required, due to the fact that there is a very close range within which the homogeneous solid solution is possible. If the alloy is heated too high, an embrittlement and possible burning and fusion is likely to result. On the other hand, if heated at too low a temperature, a complete separation of a part of the second phase in the grain boundaries is most likely to follow, making it impossible to achieve maximum hardening. Therefore, the alloy is best given what is termed a *solution treatment*, allowing just the correct amount of time for complete homogenization to take place, at the correct temperature. This will vary from 10 or 15 minutes up to several days.

In addition to the Al-Cu alloys we can also precipitation-harden low carbon steel alloys, where the carbon content runs from 0.04 to 0.06 per cent and more especially in the stainless steels, where the analysis is in the range of 17 to 18 per cent chromium, 7 to 8 per cent nickel, about 1.20 per cent aluminum, and 0.07 per cent carbon. Such stainless steels are termed 17–7 PH or 18–8 PH steels, depending on the percent of chromium and nickel contents in the steels.

More will be discussed on this entire subject of annealing and recrystallization in the next chapter. Age-hardening and precipitation-hardening were discussed at some length in Chapter 6 of the text.

Fig. 9-12. *Prior to forging a 3,000-lb closed die forging, the dies used in the forging operations are placed in preheating furnaces for 24 hours to bring them to the required temperature. Here is one of the die-blocks, weighing 30 tons, being carried by a 200-ton crane. (Aluminum Company of America.)*

Fig. 9-13. *This aircraft forging is being removed from the dies of the 50,000-ton press at the USAF Heavy Press Plant operated by Aluminum Company of America.*

9-5 Aluminum Production

Aluminum is produced from *bauxite*, which is a mixture of the hydroxides of aluminum, $Al_2O_3 \cdot 3H_2O$ and $Al_2O_3 \cdot H_2O$, together with impurities with which it is contaminated, such as oxides of iron, titanium and silicon. Bauxite is produced by the weathering and change of aluminum silicate rocks and is found in widely distributed sections

Fig. 9-14. *A battery of solution-treating furnaces used to heat treat heavy press forgings to achieve optimum physical properties at USAF Heavy Press Plant at Cleveland, Ohio, operated by Aluminum Company of America. A quenching bath is located beneath the hearth of the furnace.*

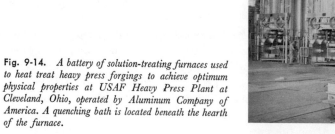

Fig. 9-15. *Forged aluminum automobile wheels for Cadillac Eldorado, produced on an 8,000-ton press at Aluminum Company of America's Cleveland (Ohio) Works.*

Fig. 9-16. *Lightweight, high-strength lateral beams of aluminum alloy, for this nation's newest fighter plane, to be used in the landing gear of the Air Force/Navy F-111 (formerly TFX) supersonic jetcraft built by General Dynamics, Ft. Worth.*

of the world, usually in tropical and semitropical regions, where there has been an accelerated weathering process. The principal sources of bauxite at present are in the United States, British Guiana, France, Hungary, Italy, Russia, Yugoslavia, and Surinam. As may be seen, bauxite is not a rare ore; however, its principal value lies in the high costs of transportation of the refined concentrates for further electrolytic processing and chemical refinement for purification into a useable product. For the production of aluminum, bauxites usually contain 50 to 65 per cent alumina, so that four pounds of bauxite ore is necessary in order to produce one pound of aluminum. Geologists tell us that there is sufficient bauxite known in the world today to supply all the needed aluminum for the next five hundred years, at the present rate of consumption.

Refining Methods

Any impurities in the bauxite, such as iron, silicon or titanium, are reduced along with the alumina in the electrolytic reduction of aluminum oxide. For this reason, alumina is first of all refined, removing these impurities, so it is best to start with raw materials of highest purity; this includes not only the alumina, but also the carbon electrodes and the fused electrolyte used in the process. The process used almost universally for the purification of bauxite is the Bayer process, in which the bauxite is treated with caustic soda under pressure, and the alumina is dissolved out as a solution of sodium aluminate by a digestion process. The residue, known as "red mud," contains the oxides of iron, silicon, and titanium, and is subsequently separated by settling and filtration. In the case of the aluminum hydrate, it is separated from the solution by seeding and precipitation and, by a calcination process, is converted to the oxide of aluminum, Al_2O_3.

Based on the discovery of Charles M. Hall in 1886 that molten cryolite dissolves alumina, and that aluminum can be separated continuously from the molten solution at about 1000C by electrolysis, the important electrolytic reduction process for aluminum came into being. This electrolytic reduction takes place in large cells consisting of a steel shell lined with carbon, forming an inner cavity, and it is in this cavity that the electrolyte of cryolite is held. Immersed in the electrolyte, the carbon electrodes or anodes introduce the current by means of which the metallic aluminum is separated electrolytically, and also provide the heat necessary to keep the bath molten. Deposited onto the bottom of the cell, molten aluminum is removed from time to time as it collects. The primary aluminum produced in this manner is about 99.90 per cent pure, depending largely upon the skill and care with which the raw materials have been prepared and the reduction process executed. In the Hoopes electrolytic refining process, aluminum of purity as high as 99.99 per cent can be produced. In this process the aluminum is dissolved electrolytically from a molten aluminum-copper alloy and deposited in a layer of pure aluminum, acting as the cathode, and floating on the molten electrolyte that separates the anode from the cathode layers. In this process, the production of one pound of aluminum requires approximately 10 kwhr of electrical energy, so it may be seen that low-cost electric power is essential for the economical commercial production of aluminum.

Although there are many important alloys of aluminum, as shown in Table 9–2, the aluminum alloy used throughout the Gemini V spacecraft (which completed 121 orbits of the earth after breaking ten space records) was aluminum alloy 7075–T6 and it was found to be highly satisfactory. In both the Stage I and Stage II tanks of

TABLE 9–4. Average Composition of Wrought Aluminum Alloys*

Alloy	Cu	Si	Fe	Mn	Mg	Zn	Cr	Ni	Other
EC	Maximum impurities 0.40%								
2EC	0.05	0.4	0.3	0.01	0.6	0.05	0.01	—	
1050	0.05	0.25	0.4	0.05	0.05	0.05	—	—	Ti 0.03
1060	0.05	0.25	0.35	0.03	0.03	0.05	—	—	Ti 0.03
1100	0.2	Si + Fe =	1.0	0.05	—	0.10	—	—	
1130	0.2	Si + Fe =	0.7	—	—	—	—	—	
1175	0.1	Si + Fe =	0.15	—	—	—	—	—	
1260	0.04	Si + Fe =	0.40	—	0.01	—	—	—	
2011	5.5	0.4	0.7	—	—	0.3	—	—	Pb 0.4 Bi 0.4
2014	4.4	0.9	1.0	0.8	0.5	0.25	0.10	—	Ti 0.15
2017	4.0	0.8	1.0	0.7	0.5	0.25	0.10	—	
2018	4.0	0.9	1.0	0.2	0.7	0.25	0.10	2.0	
2024	4.5	0.5	0.5	0.5	1.5	0.25	0.10	—	
2025	4.5	0.8	1.0	0.8	0.05	0.25	0.10	—	Ti 0.15
2117	2.6	0.8	1.0	0.2	0.3	0.25	0.10	—	
2218	4.0	0.9	1.0	0.2	1.5	0.25	0.10	2.0	—
2618	1.3	0.25	1.1	—	1.5	—	—	1.0	Ti 0.07
3003	0.2	0.6	0.7	1.2	—	0.10	—	—	
3004	0.25	0.3	0.7	1.2	1.0	0.25	—	—	
4032	0.9	12.2	1.0	—	1.0	0.25	0.10	0.9	
4043	0.3	5.0	0.8	0.05	0.05	0.10	—	—	Ti 0.20
4343	0.25	7.5	0.8	0.10	—	0.20	—	—	
5005	0.2	0.4	0.7	0.2	0.8	0.25	0.10	—	
5050	0.2	0.4	0.7	0.1	1.4	0.25	0.10	—	
5052	0.1	Si + Fe =	0.45	0.1	2.5	0.10	0.25	—	
5056	0.1	0.3	0.4	0.12	5.0	0.10	0.12	—	
5083	0.1	0.4	0.4	0.6	4.5	0.25	0.15	—	Ti 0.15
5086	0.1	0.4	0.5	0.5	4.0	0.25	0.15	—	Ti 0.15
5154	0.1	Si + Fe =	0.45	0.1	3.5	0.20	0.25	—	Ti 0.20
5254	0.05	Si + Fe =	0.45	0.01	3.5	0.20	0.25	—	Ti 0.05
5356	0.1	Si + Fe =	0.50	0.12	5.0	0.10	0.12	—	Ti 0.15
5357	0.07	0.12	0.17	0.32	1.0	—	—	—	
5454	0.1	Si + Fe =	0.40	0.75	2.7	0.25	0.12	—	Ti 0.20
5456	0.2	Si + Fe =	0.40	0.75	5.0	0.25	0.12	—	Ti 0.20
5554	0.1	Si + Fe =	0.40	0.75	2.7	0.25	0.12	—	Ti 0.12
5556	0.1	Si + Fe =	0.40	0.75	5.0	0.25	0.12	—	Ti 0.12
5652	0.04	Si + Fe =	0.40	0.01	2.5	0.10	0.25	—	
6053	0.1	0.6	0.35	—	1.2	0.10	0.25	—	
6061	0.27	0.6	0.7	0.15	1.0	0.25	0.25	—	Ti 0.15
6062	0.27	0.6	0.7	0.15	1.0	0.25	0.09	—	Ti 0.15
6063	0.1	0.4	0.35	0.10	0.67	0.10	0.10	—	Ti 0.10
6151	0.35	0.9	1.0	0.20	0.62	0.25	0.25	—	Ti 0.15
6253	0.1	0.6	0.5	—	0.25	2.0	0.25	—	
6463	0.2	0.4	0.15	0.05	0.67	—	—	—	
6951	0.27	0.3	0.8	0.10	0.6	0.20	—	—	
7072	0.1	Si + Fe =	0.7	0.10	0.10	1.0	—	—	
7075	1.6	0.5	0.7	0.30	2.5	5.6	0.3	—	Ti 0.20
7076	0.65	0.4	0.6	0.5	1.6	7.5	—	—	Ti 0.20
7079	0.6	0.3	0.4	0.2	3.3	4.3	0.17	—	Ti 0.10
7178	2.0	0.5	0.7	0.3	2.7	6.8	0.3	—	Ti 0.20
7277	1.2	0.5	0.7	—	2.0	4.0	0.25	—	Ti 0.10

* From *Materials in Design Engineering*, by permission of Editor, H. R. Clauser. Published by Reinhold Publishing Corp. New York.

the Gemini launch vehicle, aluminum alloys 2014–T6 was used. The nominal analyses of the two alloys used so successfully are as follows:

Alloy	Cu	Si	Fe	Mn	Mg	Zn	Cr	Ni	Other
7075	1.6%	0.5	0.7	0.30	2.5	5.60	0.30	—	Ti 0.20
2014	4.4	0.9	1.0	0.80	0.5	0.25	0.10	—	Ti 0.15

The designation "T6" indicates that the alloy has been heat treated in some manner, and in this case a T6 alloy means that it has been subjected to a solution heat treatment, followed by artificial aging. Other heat treated alloy temper designations were given in paragraph 9.3 of this chapter.

Fig. 9–17. *The United States Air Force's second proto-type B-1 strategic Bomber scheduled to fly for the first time in spring of 1976, complete with offensive avionics sys-tem. Much faster penetration speed, lower penetration altitude, greater hardness to the effects of a nuclear blast and greatly reduced radar image than the current B-52, the B-1, while only two-thirds the size of the B-52, is designed to carry nearly twice the payload. (Courtesy Air Force Systems Command, Aeronautical System Div., Wright-Patterson AFB, Ohio, Captain Fred Morgan).*

The *temper of an aluminum alloy* is one of the major factors governing strength, hardness and ductility, as well as other mechanical and physical properties. Some aluminum alloys are hardened and strengthened by cold working or strain harden-ing, accomplished by cold rolling, drawing, stretching, or coining. Other aluminum alloys are heat treatable, and their properties can be improved appreciably by appropriate thermal treatments.

Annealling of work-hardened aluminum alloys is accomplished by heating to a temperature at which recrystallization will occur. The temperature depends upon the alloy and is chosen so that recrystallization is virtually instantaneous. Annealing of material that has been heat treated requires heating to a slightly higher tempera-ture, followed by slow cooling, in order to obtain maximum softening.

Solution heat treatment, a hardening and strengthening process, consists of heating the metal to a high temperature, holding it at temperature to effect solution of the hardening constituents, and then quenching it very rapidly. As the name implies, this type treament dissolves the soluble alloying constituents and disperses them uniformly in the matrix. Subsequent rapid cooling by quenching does not allow time for them to precipitate, in accordance with the changes in solubility at lower temper-atures.

Age hardening of the aluminum after solution treatment results in an increase in the strength and hardness of heat-treatable aluminum alloys by precipitation of some of the hardening constituents as submicroscopic particles dispersed throughout the solid solution matrix. In some aluminum alloys, this process takes place naturally when the material is allowed to stand for several days at room temper-

TABLE 9–5. Typical Properties and Applications of Wrought Aluminum and Aluminum Alloys*

Grade	Nominal Composition, %	Forms[b]	Corrosion Resistance	Machin-ability	Weld-ability[d]	Strength (max), psi[e]	Strength (ann), psi[f]	Typical Applications
EC	99.45Al min	STEPBW	A, A	D, C	A, A	27,000	10,000	Electrical conductors
1100	99.00Al min	STEBWFO	A, A	D, C	A, A	24,000	13,000	Sheet metal work; spun ware
1130	99.30Al min	S	A, A	D, C	A, A	26,000	12,000	Reflector sheet
1145	99.45Al min	SO	A, A	D, C	A, A	28,000	12,000	Foil, light sheet metal work
1345	99.45Al min	WB	A, A	D, C	A, A	28,000	12,000	Nonelectrical wire applications
1060	99.60Al min	STW	—	—	—	20,000	10,000	Chemical equipment, railroad cars
2011	5.5Cu-0.5Bi-0.5Pb	BW	C, C	A, A	D, D	60,000	—	Screw machine products
2014	0.8Si-4.4Cu-0.8Mn-0.4Mg	STEBF	C, C	B, B	B, C	70,000	27,000	Truck frames, aircraft structures
2017	4.0Cu-0.5Mn-0.5Mg	BW	C	B	B, C	62,000	26,000	Screw machine products
2117	2.5Cu-0.3Mg	WB	C	C	B, C	43,000	—	Rivets and redraw rod
2018	4.0Cu-0.6Mg-2.0Ni	F	C	B	B, C	61,000	—	Aircraft engine cylinders, pistons
2218	4.0Cu-1.5Mg-2.0Ni	F	C	B	B, C	48,000	—	Jet engine impellers and rings
2618	2.3Cu-1.6Mg-1.0Ni-1.1Fe	F	C	B	B, C	64,000	—	Aircraft engines
2219	6.3Cu-0.3Mn-0.10V-0.15Zr	SEF	B	B	A	70,000	25,000	High temp structures, weldments
2024	4.5Cu-0.6Mn-1.5Mg	STPEBW	C, C	B, B	B, B	75,000	27,000	Aircraft structures, truck wheels, screw machine products
2025	0.8Si-4.5Cu-0.8Mn	F	C, D	B, B	B, B	58,000	25,000	Forgings, aircraft propellers
3003	1.2Mn	All forms	A, A	D, C	A, A	30,000	16,000	Cooking utensils, chemical equipment, pressure vessels, sheet metal work
3004	1.2Mn-1.0Mg	S	A, A	D, C	A, A	41,000	26,000	Sheet metal work, storage tanks
4032	12.2Si-0.9Cu-1.1Mg-0.9Ni	F	C, D	D, C	B, C	55,000	—	Pistons
4043	5.0Si	W	—	—	—	—	—	Welding wire
4343	7.5Si	SW	—	—	—	—	—	Brazing sheet and wire
5005	0.8Mg	SWO	A, A	D, C	A, A	30,000	18,000	Appliances, utensils, conductors
5050	1.4Mg	STPO	A, A	D, C	A, A	32,000	21,000	Builders' hardware, appliances
5052	2.5Mg-0.25Cr	STBWPO	A, A	D, C	A, A	42,000	28,000	Sheet metal work, hydraulics, appliances
5252	2.5Mg-0.25Cr	S	A, A	D, C	A, A	39,000	28,000	Automobile trim
5652	2.5Mg-0.25Cr	STBW	A, A	D, C	A, A	42,000	28,000	Welded structures, pressure vessels
5154	3.5Mg-0.25Cr	STPEBW	A, A	D, C	A, A	48,000	35,000	Welded structures, storage tanks, pressure vessels, salt water service
5254	3.5Mg-0.25Cr	SW	A, A	D, C	A, A	48,000	35,000	Tank cars, pressure vessels
5454	0.8Mn-2.7Mg-0.10Cr	STPEB	A, A	D, C	A, A	44,000	36,000	Welded structures, pressure vessels, marine service
5056	0.1Mn-5.2Mg-0.10Cr	BW	A, C	D, C	A, A	63,000	42,000	Cable sheathing, rivets, wire screen
5356	0.1Mn-5.0Mg-0.10Cr	W	—	—	—	—	—	Welding wire
5456	0.8Mn-5.1Mg-0.10Cr	SEP	A, B	D, C	A	56,000	45,000	High strength welded structures, storage tanks, pressure vessels, marine applications
5657	0.8Mg (+0.10Cu, alloy 5757)	S	A, A	D, C	A, A	32,000	19,000	Anodized auto and appliance trim
5083	0.7Mn-4.5Mg-0.15Cr	SEBF	A, C	D, C	A, B	52,000	42,000	Unfired, welded pressure vessels, marine ser-
5086	0.5Mn-4.0Mg-0.15Cr	SETP	A, C	D, C	A, B	50,000	38,000	vice, auto and aircraft parts, cryogenic applications, drilling rigs, transportation equipment, missile components
6101	0.5Si-0.6Mg	TPEB	A, B	B, C	A, B	32,000	14,000	High strength bus conductors
6011	0.9Si-0.6Cu-0.9Mg-1.5Zn	S	—	—	—	—	—	Moderate strength products
6151	1.0Si-0.7Mg-0.25Cr	F	A, B	C	A, B	48,000	—	Moderate strength forgings for machine and auto parts
6053	0.7Si-1.3Mg-0.25Cr	BW	A, B	C	B, C	42,000	16,000	Wire and rod for rivets
6061	0.6Si-0.25Cu-1.0Mg-0.25Cr	STPEBWF	A, A	B, C	A, A	45,000	18,000	Heavy duty corrosion resistant structures, truck and marine parts, railroad cars, furniture, pipelines
6262	0.6Si-0.25Cu-1.0Mg-0.09Cr-0.6Pb-0.6Bi	WB	A, A	A, A	B, B	58,000	—	Screw machine products
6063	0.4Si-0.7Mg	TPE	A, A	D, C	A, A	42,000	13,000	Railings, furniture, architectural extrusions
6463	0.4Si-0.7Mg	E	A, A	D, C	A, A	35,000	22,000	Architectural and trim extrusions
6066	1.3Si-1.0Cu-0.9Mn-1.1Mg	TPEBF	B, C	D; B	A, A	57,000	22,000	Welded structures
7001	2.1Cu-3.0Mg-0.30Cr-7.4Zn	TEB	C	B	D	98,000	32,000	High strength structures
7039	0.2Mn-2.7Mg-0.20Cr-4.0Zn	S	A, C	B	A	60,000	32,000	Cryogenic and missile welded structures
7072	1.0Zn	S	A, A	D, C	A, A	74,000	13,000	Fin stock
7075	1.6Cu-2.5Mg-0.30Cr-5.6Zn	STEBWF	C	B	D	83,000	33,000	Aircraft and other structures, keys
7076	0.6Cu-0.5Mn-1.6Mg-7.5Zn	F	C	B	D	70,000	—	High strength forgings
7178	2.0Cu-2.7Mg-0.30Cr-6.8Zn	STEP	C	B	D	88,000	33,000	Aircraft and other structural uses
7079	0.6Cu-0.2Mn-3.3Mg-0.20Cr-4.3Zn	EFS	C	B	D	78,000	32,000	Structural parts for aircraft

[a]From "*Standards for Aluminum Mill Products*," The Aluminum Association, New York, '64. [b]B = bar or rod, E = extrusions, F = forging stock, O = foil, P = pipe, S = sheet or plate, T = tube, W = wire. [c]Relative ratings in decreasing order of merit—A, B, C, D; where applicable, ratings for both annealed and hardest tempers are given (for example: A, C). [d]A = generally weldable, B = weldable with special techniques for specific applications, C = limited weldability, D = not weldable. Ratings are given for arc welding; gas welding and brazeability ratings are the same or differ by only one rating, except for most of the 2000 and 7000 series alloys. [e]Typical maximum tensile strength for fully work hardened condition or heat treated to highest strength level. [f]Typical annealed tensile strength.

* From *Materials in Design Engineering* by permission of Editor, H. R. Clauser; published by Reinhold Publishing Corp., New York.

ature. Other alloys, however, will not age-harden sufficiently at ordinary temperatures but will require an artificial aging treatment at an elevated temperature to produce maximum strength and hardness. Shown in Fig. 9–18 is the equilibrium diagram for the aluminum–copper system. Here we find that the solubility of copper in aluminum decreases from 5.65 per cent at 1018F (548C) to less than 0.25 per cent at room temperature. Furthermore, a eutectic is formed at 33 per cent copper as noted. Aluminum–copper alloys of greatest value to industry are those with copper content less than 10 per cent. As noted on the tables herein, the mechanical properties of both the wrought 4 per cent copper and cast 8 per cent copper alloys are improved substantially by precipitation of the theta phase ($CuAl_2$) from the solid solution. Copper increases the mechanical properties at elevated temperatures, as do almost all other alloying elements with high melting points. The corrosion resistance of aluminum alloys is lessened by copper; in fact, in some environments and under certain conditions, copper has been found to make aluminum-copper alloys susceptible to intergranular corrosion. In such cases, cladding with pure aluminum or with some corrosion-resistant alloy has been found to retard or prevent intergranular corrosion.

One of the normal impurities in aluminum is *silicon*, found in percentages of from 0.15 to 0.40 per cent in virgin aluminum. As a rule, it is found combined with iron, which is another normal impurity of aluminum forming intermetallic com-

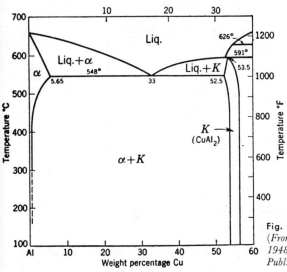

(In general, Aluminum Grade 2219 is highly weldable and is being used successfully in the aerospace industry and in the so-called space shuttle programs. However, diffusion is a problem, and welding must be done under very specific time and temperature restrictions to insure adequate service life.)

Fig. 9-18. *Aluminum-copper equilibrium diagram. (From American Society for Metals Handbook, 1948 edition, by permission of Allen G. Gray; Published by ASM, Metals Park, Ohio.)*

pounds which have very little effect on the properties of the aluminum. In order to improve the fluidity of aluminum alloys, silicon is often added in percentages up to 30 per cent. As will be noted in Fig. 9–19, the eutectic alloy formed at 11.6 per cent silicon has a high degree of fluidity in the molten state. Aluminum alloys with 3 per cent or more of silicon are readily cast into molds of any desired shape, and when more than 12 per cent silicon is present, the wear-resistance of the resulting alloy is substantially improved because of the formation of primary silicon crystals with high hardness characteristics. So far as corrosion-resistance is concerned, silicon does not have much effect; however, it does reduce machinability and workability of the alloy.

Up to about 10 per cent, *zinc* may be added to aluminum; however, it is usually associated with other elements, such as copper, silicon, or magnesium. Fig. 9–20 shows the aluminum-zinc equilibrium diagram, wherein it will be observed that zinc dissolves into solid aluminum to a considerable extent. The improvement of the

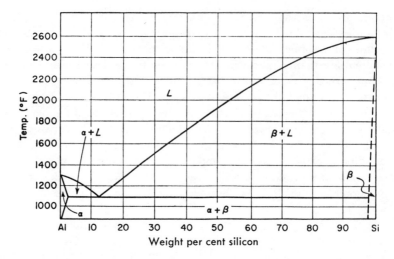

Fig. 9-19. *Aluminum-silicon equilibrium diagram.* (*From American Society for Metals* Handbook, *1948 edition, by permission of Allen G. Gray; Published by ASM, Metals Park, Ohio.*)

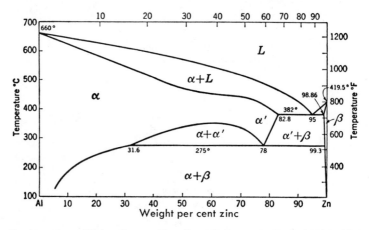

Fig. 9-20. *Aluminum-zinc equilibrium diagram.* (*From American Society for Metals*, Metals Handbook, *1948 Edition, by permission of Allen G. Gray A.S.M., Metals Park, Ohio.*)

properties of such alloys through age-hardening is rather limited. Age-hardening is possible when magnesium is present, through the formation of $MgZn_2$, $MgZn$, and $AlMgZn$, permitting the formation of the aluminum alloys with the highest mechanical properties, as shown in Table 9–5. The corrosion resistance of aluminum alloys is reduced by the addition of zinc, and just as in the case of copper additions, some zinc additives to aluminum have been known to make the alloy susceptible to intergranular and stress corrosion. The melting point is lowered by the addition of zinc, making the alloy more fluid in the molten state, endowing such alloys of aluminum-zinc with very good castability. There is always the danger, however, of making the aluminum-zinc alloys hot-short because of excessive zinc additions.

    Shown in Fig. 9–21 is the equilibrium diagram of the *aluminum-magnesium* system of alloys. These alloys are the lightest in weight of all the conventional aluminum-base alloys and they offer a maximum resistance to atmospheric, salt water, and alkaline corrosion when there is a minimum amount of impurities present. *Magnesium* goes into solid solution with aluminum in substantial amounts, thereby increasing the strength of these alloys. Alloys with magnesium on the high side are age-hardenable; however, there is not sufficient increase in most properties to justify their use as commercial alloys in the market. Magnesium has a maximum solubility of 14.9 per cent at 845F (452C), dropping to less than 2 per cent at room temperature.

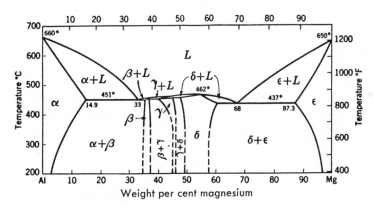

Fig. 9-21. *Aluminum-magnesium equilibrium diagram.* (*From American Society for Metals,* Metals Handbook, *1948 edition, by permission of Allen G. Gray, A.S.M., Metals Park, Ohio.*)

9-6 Magnesium

Today the most economical method of producing magnesium is by electrolysis of fused magnesium chloride obtained at lowest cost from sea water, brines, and dolomite (calcium magnesium carbonate). The impurities normally found in commercial magnesium are aluminum, silicon, magnesium oxide, and iron, all present in very small amounts so that the normal purity of primary magnesium will run from 99.6 per cent up to 99.9 per cent.

Of all structural metals, magnesium has the highest stiffness-to-weight ratio. The modulus of elasticity for magnesium is 6.5 million lb/sq in.; for aluminum, 10 million, and for steel 29 million. This is why magnesium is used extensively for floor beams in airplanes; for radar horns and reflectors where low inertia and stiffness are required. It is also necessary for such important applications as the extruded magnesium alloy stringers and skin in the adapter module housing the fuel cell, retro rockets, orbital maneuvering system fuel, and life support oxygen storage in the Gemini V spacecraft, several pictures of which are shown in this text. The particular alloy used for this purpose in the spacecraft was the HK–31 alloy with T6 temper, described in the discussion of aluminum above.

Inasmuch as magnesium is hexagonal close-packed, it is difficult to form in this condition, so that when formability is desired, the lattice is transformed into body-centered cubic; in this conformation it can be readily formed by the addition of small quantities of lithium to the melt. Any deep forming operations on magnesium must be done at elevated temperatures, as embrittlement sets in when magnesium alloys are worked cold.

The more common elements used as alloying additives are aluminum, zinc, and manganese, with aluminum the most desirable, since it dissolves readily in magnesium and hardens it appreciably, increasing its strength, hardness and castability. From 3 to 10 per cent aluminum added to magnesium is customary; however, any amount in excess of 10 per cent will embrittle the resulting alloy. Age-hardening is possible where the aluminum content is from 6 to 8 per cent. The rate of diffusion of aluminum however, in magnesium is so low that so homogenization of alloys requires a considerable length of time, during which grain growth would ensue in the wrought products.

Zinc, along with aluminum, is also used as an alloying element, with magnesium-base alloys in amounts up to 3 per cent as an aid to resistance to salt water corrosion as well as to offset the detrimental effects of iron and copper impurities. Any excess amount of zinc in the alloy will result in brittleness and porosity, caused by the formation of the hard compound $MgZn_2$.

Corrosion resistance can also be improved in magnesium-base alloys with the addition of manganese, providing that aluminum or aluminum and zinc are both present. For maximum welding characteristics a binary alloy of magnesium, with 1.30 per cent manganese, is desirable; this alloy is readily hot worked, but with a loss of strength properties. Iron is not readily miscible in magnesium, so it does not often exceed 0.10 per cent in the molten state; however, even small amounts of iron in the alloy substantially curtail its corrosion resistance, because of the wide difference between magnesium and iron so far as their electrotyic potential is concerned.

Fig. 9–22 illustrates the magnesium-rich end of the magnesium-aluminum equilibrium diagram; it will be observed that the solubility of aluminum in magnesium decreases from about 820F (439C) to 2.3 per cent at room temperature. At 32.2 per cent aluminum we find the formation of a eutectic, and at approximately 45 per cent aluminum we find the formation of the beta solid solution.

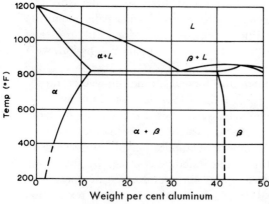

Weight per cent aluminum

Fig. 9-22. *The magnesium-rich end of magnesium-aluminum equilibrium diagram.*

It is possible to improve substantially the physical properties of the magnesium-aluminum casting alloys by precipitation of this beta phase out of the supersaturated alpha phase solid solution. Even though it is true that the better and more useful alloys of the magnesium-aluminum system contain under 10 per cent aluminum, considerable improvement in properties have been effected by adding zinc and manganese in sparing amounts. Just as in the case of aluminum alloys, magnesium alloys are usually classified as casting or wrought alloys.

Fig. 9-23. *Typical magnesium forgings made at Alcoa plants. (Courtesy of Aluminum Company of America.)*

9-7 Titanium

The element titanium was discovered in 1763 by an English clergyman, William Gregor, an amateur chemist with an inquiring mind. In the black sands of Cornwall he discovered a new element which attracted little scientific interest at the time. A few years later, an Austrian, Klaproth, extracted the same element from the ore known as *rutile*, a mineral consisting of titanium dioxide (TiO_2)—a reddish-brown colored substance with a metallic luster. The same mineral is found in the ore known as ilmenite, in the Ural mountains of Northwest Asia. *Ilmenite* is $TiFeO_3$, a compound of titanium and iron in the oxide form. Although titanium minerals are known to exist in many parts of the world, only a few of the deposits are being worked successfully, the more important ones in India, from beach sands, and in the United States, in the Adirondack mountains of New York state, and in Florida.

The basic process used for the production of titanium was developed many years ago by Dr. Wilhelm Kroll of Luxembourg. The Kroll patent was taken over by the United States during World War II and experimentation was continued by the U.S. Bureau of Mines. In 1946 the Bureau announced the operation of the first pilot plant producing titanium metal by the Kroll process. In 1949, on an experimental basis, the National Lead Company started out with a capacity of 100 pounds per day (less than 20 tons per year). Today production has reached over 40,000 tons per year, and, with the ever-increasing demand for the light-weight metal, it will exceed this figure before long.

The first step in the extraction of titanium from its ore is to chlorinate a TiO_2 and carbon mixture to titanium tetrachloride, which is then reacted with magnesium metal in a heat-resistant steel vessel at red-heat, under an inert gas blanket, to prevent oxidation. The resulting products are spongy titanium, known as titanium sponge, and magnesium chloride, $MgCl_2$, the latter drained out of the reaction chamber as a liquid. Chlorine and magnesium are recovered from the molten $MgCl_2$ in electrolytic cells.

The subsequent melting of the titanium sponge into massive ingots takes place, with the complete exclusion of oxygen and nitrogen, under inert argon or in a vacuum. Melting may be accomplished in a number of ways; however the Titanium Metals Corporation uses large consumable electrodes in its furnaces, and double-melting techniques for maximum purity have been adopted by most titanium producers today. In general, the ingots are cast individually, but experimental work is being done on continuous casting of ingots.

Titanium is a silver-grey metal, classified as one of the so-called light metals, being 60 per cent heavier than aluminum but only 56 per cent as heavy as alloy steel. Titanium-base alloys are very strong and in addition very ductile, easily drawn or hammered down to thin sections. It has a low specific gravity (4.5), a high corrosion resistance to acids, and a high strength to weight ratio, especially at elevated temperatures. Because of its affinity for oxygen, titanium was slow in being adopted by industry. Today, however, it has been found to have many properties that are helpful in the design of aircraft, pressure vessels, etc., where light weight, yet high strength, are required. Although titanium's value as a container vessel for liquid metals has only partially been explored to date, early experimentation shows excellent long-time resistance to gallium at 752F. Titanium has good resistance to attack by magnesium up to 1382F, and also shows excellent resistance to attack by tin at temperatures up to 932F.

Although only in its infancy, titanium already has many applications and countless potential uses in the future. Using titanium in jet engine parts, a saving of over 1000 pounds has been made possible in the weight of each engine. There are also many other military and domestic uses in industry for titanium, including with the current commercial use of electron-beam welding techniques, that permit the joining of metals not only to similar but also to dissimilar metals, with little if any oxidation and heat-affected zone such as plagues fabricators of metal products with all other types of welding processes. We will undoubtedly see an even

Fig. 9-24. *Underseas research-type vehicle developed by the U.S. Navy Marine Engineering Laboratory. (Courtesy of* Journal of Metals, *345 East 47th St ., New York City.)*

broader use of titanium than in prior years. For example, the U.S. Navy has just announced an extensive program in research investigations to develop construction materials for vehicles to be used in future hydrospace missions. One of the most promising materials being considered is titanium. In fact, initial studies established titanium as a leading candidate and served to justify extension of the program to cover several problem areas that remain before titanium can be used as a pressure-hull material. At the present time it appears that Ti-8Al-2Cb-1Ta is the best alloy for this particular application. Another alloy with promise for heavy plates to be used in deep-dividing undersea vehicles is 6.9 Al-7.7 Zr-0.5 Mo in weight per cent. To date several investigators of these materials, (titanium, in particular) have determined that a number of titanium alloys can develop levels of strength and toughness exceeding the minimum specified requirements for a titanium hull material. With electron beam welding now a reality, it should put titanium in the forefront in the race, along with aluminum, magnesium, and certain stainless steels.

9-8 The U.S. Navy Titanium Program

Deep-Diving Vehicles

A significant statement made by I.R. Lane, Jr., an engineer with the U.S. Navy Marine Engineering Laboratory, Annapolis, Md., included the following remarks; "The principal factor governing operation in deep-water environment is the development of vehicles for the operation. Development of vehicles is, in turn, dependent on availability of suitable construction materials to withstand the adverse conditions under which the vehicles must operate." Shown in Fig. 9–24 is one of the research-type vehicles built to determine the feasability of its construction. The titanium alloy used in this vehicle was Ti-6Al-4V, which is expected to develop a minumum yield strength of 120,000 psi.

9-9 Outerspace and Oceanspace Potentials for the Future

Although we have heard more about the thrilling outerspace missions of the Mercury, Saturn, and Gemini spacecrafts during recent years, the tremendous potentials of oceanspace explorations are equally as important. In fact, those who are vitally interested in, and working in the field of, oceanography state that in this area lies the greatest future, and they document their reasons for these statements. It is, of course, a fact that mineral resources, whether they come from the 29 per cent of the earth's dry land surface, or from the 71 per cent that is covered with water, are one of the basic ingredients of industrial power and are of vital concern to every nation around the world. The rapidly increasing demands for minerals, accompanied by a world-wide population explosion, and efforts to raise standards of living, make the existing sources of supply of some minerals most inadequate. Known domestic reserves of many important minerals and metals in the United States have been so depleted that we are almost entirely dependent on imports to meet current needs. The extent of our dependency on foreign sources, and the seriousness of our position, was starkly illustrated during World War II when the

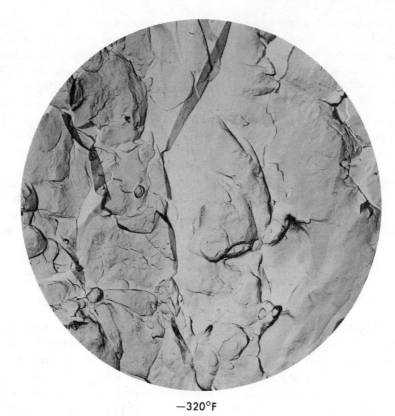

−320°F

Fig. 9-25. *A photomicrograph of Ti-6A1-4V low interstitial solid solution alloy of titanium, proved to have desirable properties for structural applications for both aerospace and oceanspace vehicles. This electron microscope fractograph shows a dimpled rupture of a fractured surface generated at −320F. This was taken at 4,000 diameters. (Courtesy of* Journal of Metals.)

United States had to rely on imports to supply at least three dozen strategic minerals. Undoubtedly the most favorable long-term solution to the problem is to exploit the mineral resource potential of the oceans, which ultimately could be a source of needed raw materials for the United States and other nations as well. The sea is an immense storehouse of many elements for which this country now depends in varying degrees on foreign sources. Included among the most important of these are manganese, nickel, copper, and cobalt from deep-sea nodules; fluorine and phosphate from phosphorite nodules; iron, tin, titanium, columbium, tantalum, chromium, tungsten, platinum, gold, silver, zirconium, hafnium, thorium, and rare earth elements from heavy mineral sands; iodine from organic matter, and barium from the barite concentrations. Sea-water, sometimes called "chemical soup," contains a great wealth of dissolved minerals, but, at this time must be considered a low-grade source of important elements. It holds enormous reserves, but not in a highly concentrated form, as is the case with sea-floor minerals.

The volume of the oceans is about 330 million cubic miles, of which 95.5 per cent is water and 4.5 per cent dissolved mineral matter. It is estimated that the oceans contain more than 50 quadrillion metric tons of dissolved minerals, including virtually all the natural chemical elements known to man. Conservatively,

212°F

Fig. 9-26. *Another electron microscope fractograph of the low interstitial Ti-6A1-4V alloy fracture surface with fracture surface in this case generated at 212F. This photomicrograph was taken at 4,000 diameters to show every detail and contrast.* (*Courtesy of* Journal of Metals *and the U.S. Navy Marine Engineering Laboratory.*)

the oceans hold 15 billion tons of manganese, 10 billion tons of gold, 7 trillion tons of boron, and 0.5 billion tons of silver. They also hold organic chemicals emanating from biological processes of sea plants and animals.

It is certain that a vast frontier with great potential for the future exists under the ocean. In his editorial, "Critical Point," appearing in a recent issue of *Metal Progress*, editor Allen G. Gray* stated, in part, as follows: "One estimate is that one and a half trillion tons of manganese, nickel, and copper nodules lie on the floor of the Pacific ocean. This is just one example of the rich harvest we might expect if we develop the engineering capability to deal with the hostile environment at the bottom of the seas. That the continental shelves are rich in oil, gas, sulfur and 'phosphorite' —a source of important phosphate fertilizer—is well known."

Dr. Milner B. Schaefer, chairman of the Committee on Oceanography of the National Academy of Sciences, National Research Council, predicts that, "despite our limited knowledge of the oceanspace frontier, hydrospace activities will return $6 billion annually to the national economy within 15 years. Many companies believe that oceanspace holds greater potential value than does outerspace."

---

* *Metal Progress* is published by American Society for Metals, Metals Park, Ohio.

Only time will evaluate the truth of these significant statements; however, it is a certainty that metallurgy and engineering in general will play an important part in the exploration and development of both outer space and oceanspace. Those who are identified with these disciplines are the privileged ones who will accept the challenges of tomorrow.

9-10   The Ocean: Mining's Newest Frontier

The drawings shown on the following pages were furnished by *Engineering and Mining Journal* and were made by their engineers with the exception of the drawing showing a hydraulic dredging system controlled from the surface, which was done by Frank Pennock of the *Oakland Tribune.* Undoubtedly the most urgent need today in this direction lies in establishment of new centers of undersea mineral technology, where specialized engineering and metallurgical knowledge can be developed and applied to problems in the marine environment. Such knowledge, techniques, and methods should be used as a new tool in exploration for and exploitation of marine mineral resources. Government, industry, and technology must combine forces and talents in one effort in this important mission.

Fig. 9-27.   *One concept of vehicles for exploitation of the ocean floor as conceived by IIT Research Institute, Chicago, Illinois, in cooperation with William S. Pellini, Superintendent of the metallurgy division at the U.S. Naval Research Laboratory, Washington, D.C. (From* Metals Review, ASM, *August 1965.) For the fabrication of hulls for such vehicles, it is essential to have structural density and pressure resistance, as they are critically related to the strength-to-density ratio of the materials used for them. Conventionally, the structural density of the hull is expressed in terms of percent of buoyancy (hull fraction) used up by hull weight. Within limits, the thickness of any material used for hulls may be increased to attain greater depths, but this increases the hull fraction, so that it is essential that we concentrate on developing materials with high strength-to-density ratios.*

9-11   Sea Floor Mining

Future methods for mining consolidated or hardrock deposits may include shaft sinking from submersible or stationary prefabricated structures on the sea floor. They may also include the use of nuclear explosives or other unique systems for sinking the shaft. Considerable engineering research will be required to adapt these systems to large-scale operations. However, ocean mining offers some advantages over land mining. It represents an entirely new concept, so operations can be fully automated with design of new machines and equipment free from the traditions of current mining industry. A good number of sea floor minerals in unconsolidated form may be mined without removal of overburden, without use of explosives, and without need for expensive drilling programs and high costs for ore breakage. Such mining systems would have a high degree of mobility and could be designed as multi-purpose units, movable from one area to another depending on current prices and market demands. Sea transportation would be more economical than land transportation. If recovered materials are processed at sea, the gangue or waste product can be readily disposed of on site.

Although mining the deep-sea floor is speculative and little tested to date, several companies are seriously considering the mining of deep-sea manganese nodules, nickel, cobalt, titanium and vanadium. It has been estimated that a sea-floor mining operation large enough to supply our total domestic production of

Fig. 9-28. *Airlift dredge for suction mining of sea floor is equipped with self-propelled floats to support column of depth, in this concept. (Drawing by Frank Pennock of the* Oakland Tribune.)

nickel would also yield about 300 per cent of our annual consumption of manganese, 200 per cent of the cobalt, 1500 per cent of the titanium, and 300 per cent of the vanadium we use. This is highly important, inasmuch as reserves of certain metals contained in sea floor deposits of manganese nodules amount to 50 to 5,000 times the commercial reserves on land, and many deposits are comparable in metal concentration to ores now mined on land.

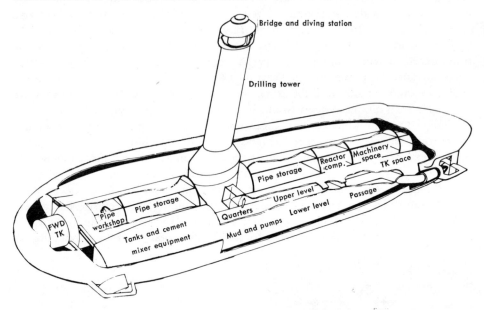

Fig. 9-29. *Submersible drill rig for grid sampling is nuclear-powered, in this concept of basic design. Unit would have ability for extended life support and would figure in probing of three-dimensional ore below sea floor. (Courtesy of* Metals Review, *August 1965. American Society for Matals, publisher; Allen Gray, ed.)*

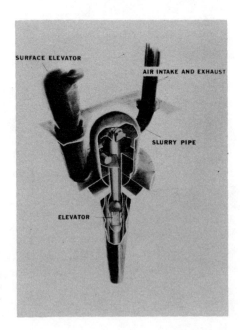

Fig. 9-30. *Mining below sea floor. This concept incorporates a sealed underwater shaft, work structure, ocean-floor-to-surface elevator, special air intake-exhaust system, and floor-to-surface slurry pipe for ore. (Courtesy of* Metals Review, *August 1965. American Society for Metals, publisher; Allen Gray, ed.)*

Fig. 9-31. *Underground mining from deep sea floor in this system makes use of work structure, living quarters, bulk processing and handling equipment, and submersible transport vehicles for logistics and ore. Small manned submersibles would be used for exchange of workers. (Courtesy of* Metals Review, *August 1965. American Society for Metals, publisher; Allen Gray, ed.)*

9-12 Mining on the Moon

At a recent meeting of the Oak Ridge Chapter of the American Society for Metals it was revealed by an authority on the subject that the prospects of obtaining economic mineral recovery from the moon are practically nil. This view was based on the best educated guesses as to the nature of the surface and atmosphere of the moon, derived from various scientific observations, including those supplied by the Ranger and Lunic probes. Since the density of the lunar atmosphere is 10^{-13} to 10^{-16} of the earth's, it follows that there is no water on the moon. The absence of water means the absence of sedementary deposits, where most of the accessible mineral wealth of the earth is concentrated.

The surface of the moon is covered with porous rock thought to be predominantly silicates. The great Maria configuration may well be large lava flows. Obviously, since there is no water on the moon, there are no fossil fuel deposits, so the possibility of anything of value lying around on the moon's surface is remote. It follows that mining and refining operations on the moon would have to be supplied with water or other solvents, as well as fuels designed for vacuum operation in the moon's temperature range (from about $-175°C$ of the lunar night to $100°C$ of the lunar day) from the earth. Although it is true that lunar explorations are valueless, from a mining viewpoint, they are fascinating, since a study of the moon's barren waste lands may tell us what our earth was like at its birth. (Extracted from *Metals Review*, June, 1966.)

9-13 New Supersonic Transport 2000

A photo of the new Lockheed-California Company's 2000 supersonic transport, which is to be capable of cruising at 1800 mph is shown in Fig. 9–32, This picture shows the nose of the plane in the "up" position as it will be in regular flight. Fig. 9–33 is a photo of the same SST plane with the nose lowered 15 degrees from normal supersonic cruise position to provide the pilot excellent vision for takeoff, holding and landing. The 2000 will weigh 275 tons and will carry 266 passengers from Phoenix, Arizona, to New York City in 90 minutes. The plane is designed to fly 13 miles above the earth and will have a price tag of around 30 million dollars.

Fig. 9-32. Lockheed-California's *SST 2000 with needle-like nose in the "up" position, as it will cruise at over 1800 mph.*

Fig. 9-33. *The SST 2000* Lockheed-California *plane with nose lowered 15 degrees to permit better visibility for pilot on take-off, holding, and landing of the craft. The fuselage is made up of 95 per cent titanium alloys.*

Fig. 9-34. *Another engineering and metallurgical achievement, the YF-12A is also 95 per cent titanium alloys in structures, and is capable of speeds in excess of 1800 mph, the fastest interceptor plane in the world. (Courtesy of* Lockheed-California.)

Shown in Fig. 9–34 is the YF–12A, also built by Lockheed-California Company, Burbank, California, which is the world's most advanced interceptor. Also capable of speeds of 1800 mph like the 2000, it is a product of titanium technology pioneered by Lockheed-Burbank, with a structure that is 95 per cent titanium. Both of these aircraft are of the fixed, double-delta wing configuration which have proven themselves to be highly satisfactory in every way.

These aircraft are examples of engineering achievement and represent several break-throughs in metallurgy, as it is one thing to design and make models of such craft and another to incorporate metals, and alloys into them, so that they will function "life-safe" at three times the speed of sound and under varying environmental conditions with maximum reliability and performance.

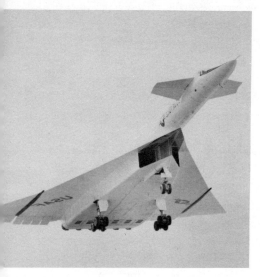

Fig. 9-35. *The XB-70 airplane, built by North American Rockwell Corp., is capable of a speed of Mach 3 (2000 mph); it is 185 feet long; weighs more than 500,000 lb, including fuel. The XB-70 is built of stainless steel honeycomb (the first time this steel had ever been used in an airplane); the entire forward section is built of titanium. (Courtesy of North Ameri— can Rockwell Corp., Los Angeles Division.)*

QUESTIONS

1. Where are copper and all its natural compounds found in greatest abundance?

2. Define "porphry copper ore." How is it processed?

3. State the two most common methods of mining copper, and give the advantages of each.

4. Describe the three different methods of producing copper from ore.

5. Solve the following typical problem in copper metallurgy: how many pounds of copper are there in a ton of ore containing 7 per cent copper glance (calcocite, which is Cu_2S)?

6. State the more common alloying elements used with copper and name the most important one, together with the reason for its importance.

7. Which of the copper-tin alloys are more important? Why?

8. For what purpose is aluminum added to copper to form the copper-aluminum alloys?

9. What content of beryllium with copper makes the best alloy so far as mechanical properties are concerned? Name some applications of copper-beryllium bronzes.

10. Which one of the copper-base alloys is used in soldering or brazing? Why is it used?

11. Why are wrought aluminum and aluminum alloys specified for aircraft and spacecraft applications?

12. Explain the four-digit system of designating wrought aluminum and aluminum alloys, grouping them according to the major alloying elements present.

13. Although the addition of copper to aluminum-base alloys provides increased strength, does it also improve weldability and corrosion resistance? Explain.

14. Discuss the term and use of *alclad* alloys.

15. So far as their response to heat treatment is concerned, into what two categories do aluminum and aluminum alloys fall? Be specific.

16. Explain the standard temper designation system for aluminum alloys.

17. Discuss the electrical conductivity and electrical resistivity of aluminum as compared to these properties in copper.

18. Which of the aluminum alloys are susceptible to stress corrosion? Why?

19. Trace the production and refinement of aluminum from ore to finished commercial products.

20. Which aluminum alloys were found to be most useful in the Gemini V mission? Why?

21. What system is used to designate the heat treatment of aluminum alloys? What does the designation T5 imply?

22. What is one of the major factors in controlling strength, hardness, and ductility, as well as other mechanical and physical properties, of an aluminum alloy?

23. Describe the most economical method of producing magnesium.

24. Inasmuch as magnesium is hexagonal close-packed in microstructure and therefore difficult to form in this condition, how is it possible to make products of the metal requiring drawing and forming?

25. What is the most desirable alloying element used with magnesium? Why?

26. In what specific way is the Kroll process different from iron smelting? Who was Kroll?

27. Compare the economics for present day use of aluminum, titanium, and stainless steel in spacecraft and oceancraft vehicles.

28. Which of the titanium alloys seem most promising for future hydrospace missions? Why?

29. Why is considerable attention being given today to explorations of oceanspace, so far as metallurgy and the other sciences are concerned?

30. State your own personal concepts of oceanspace exploration and mining vehicles, with improvements over those described in this chapter, giving your reasons for your concepts. Use sketches.

References

Aluminum Handbook, Kent Van Horn (ed). Pittsburgh, Pennsylvania: Aluminum Company of America, 1959—1962.

Brooks, Carson, "*Aluminum Alloys for Pressure Hulls*," *Metals Engineering Quarterly*, American Society for Metals, Metals Park, Ohio.

Clark, Donald S., *Engineering Materials and Processes*. Scranton, Pennsylvania: International Textbook Co., 1959.

Everhart, John L., Tech. Ed, "Aluminum Alloy Castings," *Materials in Design Engineering*, New York: Reinhold Publishing Co., 1958.

Gray, Allen G., Ed, "Oceanspace: New Challenge to Materials," *Metals Progress*. American Society for Metals, Metals Park, Ohio, 1965.

Hull, Daniel R., *Casting of Brass and Bronze*, American Society for Metals, Metals Park, Ohio, 1950.

Marczoch, Sigrid, "Ocean Engineering," *American Engineer*, November 1965.

Minkler, Ward W., "The Future of Titanium in Everyday Use," *Metals Progress*, American Society for Metals, Metals Park, Ohio, Nov. 1964,

Noda, Toshio, "Titanium from Slag in Japan," American Institute of Mining, Metallurgical and Petroleum Engineers, February 1964.

Ramsdell, J. D., and E. D. Hull, *Properties of Titanium-Vanadium-Cobalt Alloys*. Washington, D.C.: Bureau of Mines Bulletin 5591, 1960.

Raynor, Geoffrey V., *The Physical Metallurgy of Magnesium and its Alloys*. London: Pergamon Press, 1959.

Symposium on Titanium, Philadelphia, Pa: American Society for Testing and Materials, 1957.

Heat Treatment
of Steel

10-1 Heat Treatment and Designation of Phases

In general, it may be stated that *heat treatment* is a combination of timed heating and cooling operations, applied to a metal or alloy in the solid state in such a way as to produce certain desired properties. The plastic working of metals (both hot and cold working) were discussed in Chapter 5; however, when a metal or alloy is heated for the sole purpose of hot working, the process does not come within the meaning of heat treatment, as it will be discussed in this chapter. In Chapter 7, in the discussion of annealing of cast irons, and in Chapter 9 (where the treatment of nonferrous metals' heat treatment, annealing and tempering was discussed), no mention was made of heat treatment of other metals and alloys.

In this chapter, a discussion of heat treating steel will be developed to bring out the changes that take place in the properties of steel, and how these properties are directly related to the alterations that take place in the structure of steel, during and subsequent to, various types of heat treatment. Steel is highly important in industry, not only because of its low cost and availability, but even more so because of the relative ease with which its properties may be altered by correctly and accurately controlling the ways in which steel is heated and cooled.

Although the iron-iron carbide equilibrium diagram is basic to the study of steels as well as cast irons, it is significant that steels are more than mere alloys of iron and iron-carbide; the properties of steels are altered, not only by proper heat treatment and hot working, but also by the addition of alloying elements. By means of heat treating, some of the characteristics of steel may be enhanced; a great deal of the versatility of steel comes from the fact that its properties can be controlled and changed by means of some type of heat treatment. If a steel is to be formed into an intricate shape, it can be made soft and ductile by heat treatment; however, if, on the other hand, it is to resist wear, it can be heat treated to a very hard, wear-resisting condition as required by the product's end use.

The science of heat treatment involves factors and mechanisms that are related to the control of the constitution of steel by heating and cooling, and the relationships between the constitution and the properties of steel. Many of these constitutional changes can be observed by making microstructural studies and metallographic investigations, which have been greatly enhanced by the discovery of the electron microscope, permitting us to make photomicrographs at thousands of diameters.

Although most plain carbon steels also contain manganese, silicon, phosphors, sulfur, oxygen, traces of nitrogen hydrogen, and other chemical elements, the two constituents of steel, (the amount and distribution of which primarily control its properties), are iron (*ferrite*) and iron carbide (*cementite*). The other elements mentioned may, to a certain extent change its constitution in regard to ferrite and cementite, the cementite is always the predominating influence in steel. This is substantially true even in the case of medium-alloy steels, which may also contain considerable precentages of nickel, chromium, molybdenum, vanadium, or titanium. The properties of such steels are still dependent primarily upon the distribution and amount of their two constituents, ferrite and cementite. The important effect of the alloying elements is to assist in the distribution and control of these elements, although the properties may well be modified by solution of the alloying element in the ferrite, or by its combination with the carbide phase.

The metallographic name for iron in steel is *ferrite*, and its microstructural appearance in the low-carbon steel in which it is the predominant constituent is shown in Fig. 10–1. Here the ferrite is seen as polyhedral grains, as distinguished by the etching out of the grain boundaries with a reagent of dilute solution of nitric acid in ethyl alcohol (Nital). Fig. 10–2 shows the appearance of ferrite in steel that was cooled very slowly. Here it shows up as a white or light-etched network surrounding bodies of *pearlite*, which is another common metallographic constituent in steel, made up of thin plates of ferrite and carbide, and known as lamellar aggragates. These lamellae are often very thin and can be resolved only under a high-power microscope and with the employment of the best techniques of the metallurgist. The electron microscope has helped a great deal in observing and distinguishing these pearlite plates. The ferrite in pure iron-carbon alloys consists of iron with a trace of carbon in solution; however, in steels it may also contain considerable amounts of alloying elements, including manganese, silicon, or nickel.

Carbon frequently occurs in steel as the iron-carbide known as *cementite*, the proportions of iron and carbon corresponding to the chemical formula Fe_3C. Thus, cementite consists of 6.67 per cent carbon and 93.33 per cent iron. It is very hard and brittle; in fact, it is the hardest constituent of plain carbon steel, capable of scratching glass and feldspar, but not quartz. Fig. 10–3 shows the metallographic appearance of cementite in the grain-boundaries of a slowly cooled, relatively high carbon steel. Here the cementite appears as a brilliant white network around the pearlite colonies, or as needles interspersed with pearlite. Shown in Fig. 10–4 is the metallographic appearance of cementite in a steel which has been heated to a temperature just below that at which austenite forms. Such heating causes the cementite to coalesce into spheroidal particles which are observed here in a matrix of ferrite. This form of cementite is termed *spheroidized cementite*, with the entire structure known as *spheroidite*.

One of the important high-temperature phases in steel is *austenite*, a homogeneous phase consisting of a solid solution of carbon in gamma form of iron. *Austenite* is formed when steel is heated to the relatively high temperature of more than 1450F (788C), with the limiting temperatures for the formation of austenite varying with composition. In Fig. 10–5 is photomicrograph of a small sample of alloy steel which has been cooled very rapidly from the temperature range at which austenite is stable. This steel is high enough in alloy content to permit the retention of the austenitic structure at room temperature. The atomic structure of austenite is the same as that of gamma iron, face-centered cubic, the atomic spacing varying with the carbon content of the steel.

With the cooling of a plain carbon steel of approximately 0.80 per cent carbon at a slow rate of cooling from the temperature range at which the austenite is stable, we find the formation of pearlite, with a microstructure as illustrated in Fig. 10–6. As a rule it is similar in characteristics to a eutectic structure; however, since it is formed from a solid solution instead of from a liquid phase, it is known as a *eutectoid* structure. The iron-iron carbide equilibrium diagram shown in Fig. 10–8 is a portion of the iron-iron carbide equilibrium diagram shown in Fig. 7–2, but is shown here for convenience in discussing the steel portion of this important phase equilibrium diagram. Considering a steel with 0.30 per cent carbon that starts to cool at temperature *a*, in this Fig. 10–8, solidification begins with the first formation of crystals consisting of delta solid solution. As cooling continues, the delta solid solution continues to form down to temperature *b* where an alloy is formed containing 50 per cent delta solid solution and 50 per cent liquid metal. (The transformation diagram for this reaction was shown in Fig. 7–3.)

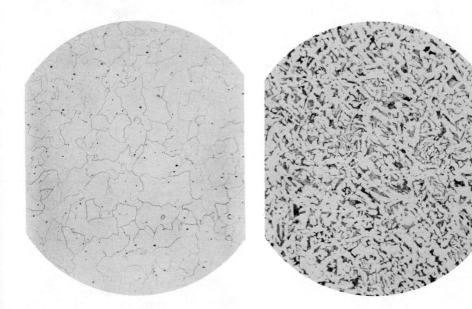

Fig. 10-1. *The microstructure of ferrite in steel heated to 1750 F and then furnace cooled. Magnification of 50X. (Courtesy of United States Steel Corporation.)*

Fig. 10-2. *Microstructure of slowly cooled hypoeutectoid steel showing ferrite and pearlite. Magnification of 50X. (Courtesy of U. S. Steel Corporation.)*

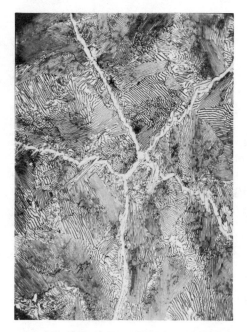

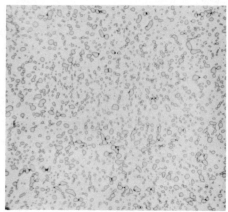

Fig. 10-3. *Microstructure of a slowly cooled high-carbon steel, showing pearlite, with cementite in the grain boundaries. Magnification of 500X. (Courtesy of United States Steel Corporation.)*

Fig. 10-4. *Micrograph showing an excellent example of spheroidized cementite in a matrix of ferrite. Magnification of 500X (Courtesy of United States Steel Corporation.)*

Fig. 10-5. *Microstructure of austenite in an alloy steel cooled from a temperature range where austenite is stable. Magnification of 250X. (Courtesy of United States Steel Corporation.)*

Fig. 10-6. *Microstructure of pearlite in a plain carbon steel, with carbon in approximately 0.80 per cent. Magnification of 500X (Courtesy of United States Steel Corporation.)*

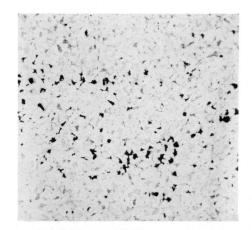

Fig. 10-7. *Micrograph showing graphite particles in a low-carbon, steel wherein the graphite has become a constituent of the steel, which has been subjected to prolonged heating at a temperature below that at which austenite is formed. Magnification of 50X. (Courtesy of United States Steel Corporation.)*

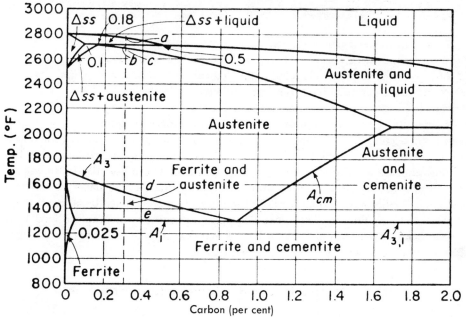

Fig. 10-8. *A portion of the iron and iron carbide equilibrium diagram.*

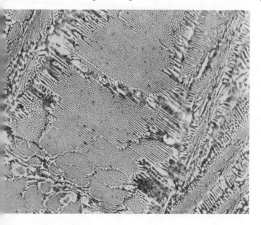

Fig. 10-9. *Microstructure of ledeburite. This is the metallographic term for the iron-iron carbide eutectic, containing 4.27 per cent carbon. Magnification 75X. (Courtesy of United States Steel Corporation.)*

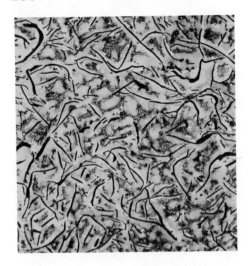

Fig. 10-10.   *Micrograph of gray cast iron revealing graphite flakes. Magnification of 50X. (Courtesy of United States Steel Corporation.)*

At the iron-iron carbide eutectic, containing 4.27 per cent carbon, there is a constituent known as *ledeburite*, found in iron-carbon alloys containing in excess of 2.01 per cent carbon. Therefore, it is logical to find a dividing line between steels and cast irons at 2.00 per cent carbon. Fig. 10–9 shows a photomicrograph of ledeburite in cast iron containing 4.27 per cent carbon.

Cementite (Fe_3C), being unstable over certain ranges of compositions and temperatures, decomposes into iron and graphite, so that in most slowly-cooled cast irons, graphite is an equilibrium constituent at room temperature. The metallographic appearance of graphite in gray cast iron is shown in Fig. 10–10, the microstructure in this case showing the graphite to be in the form of flakes rather than nodules or spheroids. Under certain conditions, graphite may be a constituent of steels, and in Fig. 10–7 the metallographic appearance of graphite in a low-carbon steel which has undergone prolonged heating at a temperature below that at which austenite is formed is shown.

10-2   Mechanical and Microstructural Properties of Steel

As was stated previously, the properties of steel depend a great deal upon its constitution, so it follows that the properties vary with the temperature at which austenite transforms, in accordance with corresponding changes in microstructure. Under equilibrium conditions, that is, with very slow cooling, austenite transforms to pearlite when it is cooled below the A_1 critical temperature. When it is more rapidly cooled, however, this transformation is depressed and does not occur until a lower temperature is reached; the faster the cooling rate, the lower the temperature at which transformation occurs. Furthermore, the nature of the ferrite-carbide aggregate formed when the austenite transforms, varies markedly with the temperature of transformation, and the properties are found to vary correspondingly. It may be seen, therefore, that heat treatment involves a controlled supercooling of austenite, and that in order to take full advantage of the wide range of structures and properties which this permits, a knowledge of the transformation behavior of austenite and the properties of the resulting aggregates is essential.

It has been observed from the previous discussion that iron-carbon alloys, and therefore all grades of steel, consist of a solid solution of carbon or of the carbide of iron, Fe_3C, in gamma iron above the critical range. This is known as *austenite*. When it is sufficiently cooled, slowly, through the critical range, such solid solutions are transformed into aggregates of *pearlite* and *ferrite* in hypoeutectoid steels and into *pearlite* and *cementite* in hypereutectoid steels. The steels are then in their

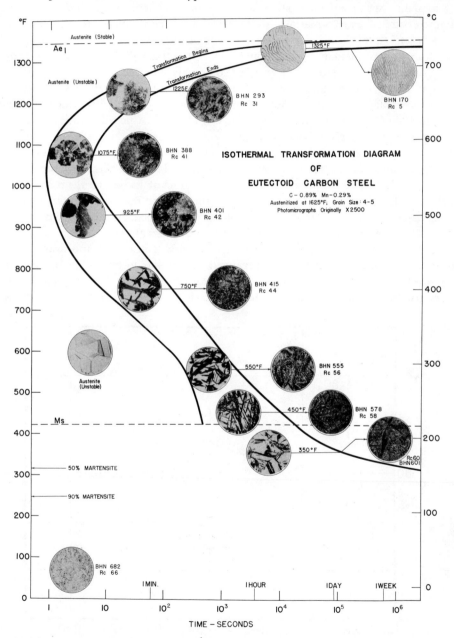

Fig. 10-11. *Isothermal transformation diagram for a plain carbon eutectoid steel, showing the hardness values and microstructures characteristic of transformation at various temperature levels. (Courtesy of United States Steel Corporation.)*

pearlitic condition, which is the stable condition at room temperature. They possess the maximum softness and ductility, and minimum strength, consistent with their composition, unless the steel is subjected to a spheroidizing treatment, as will be described later. In this case, the ductility is further increased. If steel is present in the hardened steel structure, tempering may bring about the isothermal conversion of austenite to bainite. Fig. 10–11 shows an *isothermal transformation* diagram for a plain carbon eutectoid steel, with the microstructures and hardness values characteristic of transformations at the various temperature levels. This diagram has a "nose" that will be observed for that temperature of most rapid transformation, which for this particular steel is about 1000F. It will also be noted that the transformation rate at temperatures near A_1 is exceedingly slow and that it is also relatively slow at lower temperature ranges. This series of photomicrographs was taken originally at 2500 diameters. Transformation over the temperature range of about 1300 to 1000F (in carbon and low-alloy steels) results in a pearlitic microstructure; in fact, the characteristic lamellar appearance of these structures will be observed in the photomicrographs shown in Fig. 10–11. It will also be observed that as the transformation rate and temperature decreases, the lamellae become more closely spaced, so that, as transformed at 1000F, it is difficult to resolve them by means of the metallurgical microscope. By means of the electron microscope, with its much greater resolving power, far superior resolution is obtained. As the lamellar spacing becomes smaller, it will be noted that the hardness values are seen to become greater.

The transformation to bainite, a structure with a feathery appearance consisting of ferrite and cementite not arranged in lamellar form, will be observed in Fig. 10–11 as taking place over the temperature of about 1000 to 450F. The microstructure of bainite differs considerably from that of pearlite in that it is

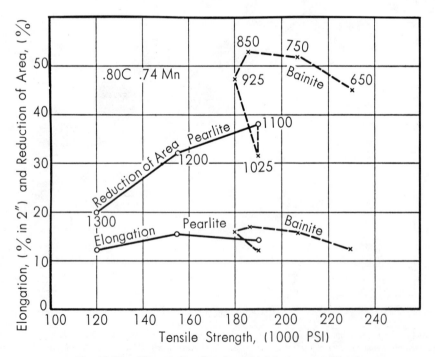

Fig. 10-12. *The properties of pearlite and bainite in a eutectoid steel.*

acicular (needle-like) in nature. Here again, the hardness increases as the transformation temperature decreases, although the bainite that forms at the highest possible temperature is many times softer than pearlite formed at an even higher temperature.

The *transformation to martensite* of this eutectoid steel occurs below 450F and differs markedly from the transformation to either pearlite or bainite in that it is not dependent on time, but occurs almost instantly during cooling. Furthermore, the percentage of transformation is dependent only on the temperature to which it is cooled. Therefore, in this steel the transformation to martensite will start on cooling to 450F, which we designate M_s temperature, and will be about 50 per cent complete when the temperature reaches about 300F. It will be essentially completed at a temperature of about 200F, which is designated the M_f temperature. Here again we see an acicular microstructure of martensite, the hardest of all transformation products of austenite. At times and under certain conditions it is possible to form a little martensite at, perhaps, 425F and then to cause bainite to form isothermally shortly afterward.

Fig. 10–12 illustrates the properties of pearlite and bainite in a eutectoid steel and, as may be seen here, in a given steel bainitic microstructures will generally be found to be both harder and tougher than pearlite, although the hardness will be lower than that of martensite. The coarse-grained steels coarsen gradually and consistently as the temperature is increased, while the fine-grained steels coarsen only slightly, if at all, until a certain temperature is reached, above which an abrupt coarsening occurs. This temperature is known as the *coarsening temperature*. Table 10–1 shows the general effects of the austenite grain size in heat treated products.

TABLE 10–1. Trends in Heat-Treated Products

Property	Coarse-Grain Austenite	Fine-Grain Austenite
Hardenability	Deeper hardening	Shallower Hardening
Toughness	Less tough	Tougher
Distortion	More Distortion	Less Distortion
Quench Cracking	More Prevalent	Less Prevalent
Internal Stress	Higher	Lower

10-3 Steel Tempering

When particular mechanical properties are desired, the method used most often is to quench the steel in a suitable medium from just above the Ac_3 temperature and to follow this operation with a tempering quench at the correct temperature. It is customary to quench in water steels containing less than 0.35 per cent carbon, to quench in oil or water those containing from 0.35 to 0.55 per cent carbon, and to quench in oil those plain carbon steels containing in excess of 0.55 per cent carbon. One of the important changes in mechanical properties of steel may be obtained by means of *tempering*, which is the process of heating a hardened steel to any temperature below the lower critical (A_1) temperature in the case of a steel with less than 0.83 per cent carbon, and the $A_{1,3}$ where the carbon is in excess of 0.83 per cent, then cooling the steel at a desired rate. The purpose of tempering is to reduce hardness and to relieve the internal stresses of a quenched steel, thereby affording greater ductility than is possible with a high-hardness steel that has been quenched. Where retained austenite, when cooling from its austenitic condition to room temperature, actually assumes a pearlitic structure —that is, if its transformation is complete —its heat treatment would be of relatively little importance and it would be impossible to produce the remarkable and widely different properties which sharply distinguish the iron-carbon alloys from other metals and alloys, and place them near the top in industrial metals and in a class by themselves.

The formation of austenite is relatively simple. In the as-rolled or as-forged condition, steel consists almost invariably of ferrite and carbide, in mixtures that vary widely depending on the composition of the steel, the finishing temperatures, and the cooling conditions. All of these structures can be converted to austenite by heating the steel above the critical temperature, this being known as the *austenitizing* temperature. An important fact in this regard is that the more homogeneous the structure of an austenitized steel, the more completely lamellar will be the structure of the annealed steel. Conversely, the more heterogeneous the structure of the austenitized steel, the more completely spheroidal will be the annealed structure.

Grain size and properties are closely related, the coarseness of the ferritic and pearlitic "grains" in the cooled steel reflecting the grain size of the austenite prior to its transformation, and the properties of the product are profoundly influenced by its grain size. Austenitic grain growth may be inhibited by undissolved carbides or by a suitable distribution of nonmetallic inclusions. Steels of this type are commonly referred to as *fine-grained steels*, while steels which are free from these grain-growth inhibitors are known as coarse-grained steels.

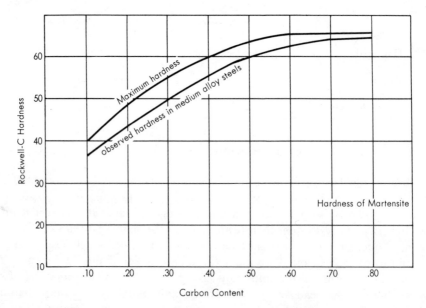

Fig. 10-13. *The effect of carbon content on hardness of martensite. (Courtesy of United States Steel Corporation, The Making, Shaping and Treating of Steel, 1965.)*

10-4   Tempered Martensite

The hardest and most brittle of the microstructures obtainable in a given steel is that of martensite. Fig. 10–13 is a graph showing the hardness of martensite as a function of carbon content. The hardness of martensite at any given carbon content will vary somewhat with the rate of cooling; the maximum hardness values shown in Fig. 10–13 were attained by rapid cooling, whereas the lower readings were of average hardness values, as might be expected. Although for certain purposes it is desirable to obtain the high hardness values of martensite, for wear resistance, the principal importance of the martensitic structure is its use as a starting material for *tempered* martensitic structures, which in the latter condition have definitely superior properties. An important correlation exists in the constant relationship between hardness, tensile strength, yield strength, elongation, and reduction of area of quenched and tempered low-alloy steels, regardless of composition. This is true provided that the steel is quenched to a fully martensitic structure prior to tempering, and provided that and the tensile strength

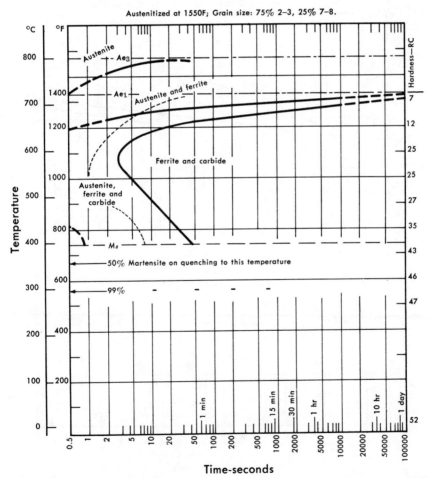

Fig. 10-14.   *Isothermal transformation diagram for a 0.35 per cent carbon, 0.37 per cent manganese, plain carbon steel. (Courtesy of United States Steel Corporation.)*

does not exceed 200,000 lb/in.^{2} A fully martensitic structure is too brittle for most applications, so tempering is used to soften and toughen the steel. This tempering consists of reheating the martensitic structure at temperatures somewhat above room temperature, bringing about a movement toward equilibrium, and the rejection of the resulting excess solute. As the precipitation occurs, the solvent lattice undergoes rearrangement and reaches the equilibrium structure. The precipitation of excess solute also continues with the formation of an intermediate phase, such as is found in the process of age-hardening. As will be observed in Fig. 10–13 the hardness of martensite increases markedly with carbon content up to 0.60 per cent, but from then on only slightly with higher carbon contents. The tempering of martensite relieves the quenching strains and, even more important, replaces the highly distorted phase with an aggregate of very fine ferrite and carbide. As a result the hardness decreases, but the resistance to impact increases.

The effect of carbon content on transformation rates for a plain carbon steel with 0.35 per cent carbon is shown in Fig. 10–14. Compare this with the trans-

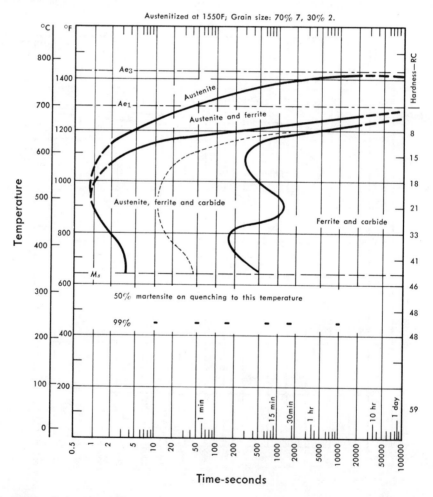

Fig. 10-15. *Isothermal transformation diagram for a 0.35 per cent carbon, 1.85 per cent manganese steel. (Courtesy of United States Steel Corporation.)*

formation curve shown in Fig. 10–11 for the eutectoid steel, with 0.89 per cent carbon. The effect of lowering the carbon content will be observed to have shifted the lines of the diagram to the left, showing a more rapid transformation rate. Another difference in this diagram from that of the eutectoid steel is that the transformation of pearlite is preceded by a precipitation of ferrite, and the diagram, as a result, shows a line designating the time for the initiation of this ferrite precipitation at the temperature levels wherein this separation precedes the formation of pearlite.

Shown in Fig. 10–15 is an isothermal transformation diagram for a 0.35 per cent carbon steel with 1.85 per cent manganese content. When we compare this with Fig. 10–14 (the lower manganese steel), it will be noted that the entire curve has been displaced to the right; that is, transformation at all temperatures starts later and is completed more slowly. This is characteristic of the effect of alloys in solution in austenite; in general it may be said that increased alloy content delays the start of transformation and increases the time for its completion.

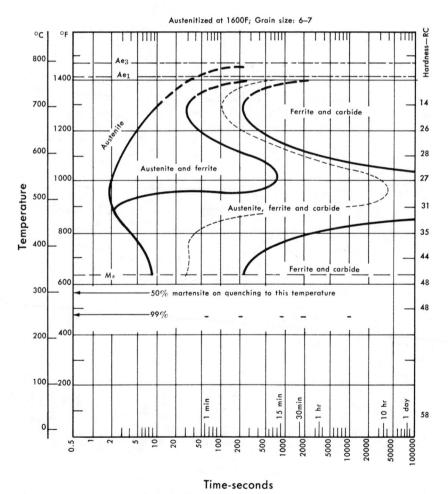

Fig. 10-16. *Isothermal transformation diagram for a 0.33 per cent carbon, 0.45 per cent manganese, 1.97 per cent chromium steel. (Courtesy of United States Steel Corporation.)*

10-5   Effect of Alloying Elements on Isothermal Transformations

As has been stated, alloy additions usually tend to delay the start of transformation and to increase the time for its completion; however, the addition of alloys differs a great deal in both the magnitude and the nature of their effects, depending on the alloy involved. Fig. 10–16 shows the isothermal transformation diagram for a 0.33 per cent carbon, 0.45 per cent manganese, 1.97 per cent chromium steel. It will be seen by comparing this with that of the plain carbon steel in Fig. 10–14, that the effect of the chromium has been not only to move the curve to the right, but also to change the actual shape of the curve. Here the time for beginning of transformation in the pearlite region has been greatly increased, while that for the beginning of the bainite region has been only moderately increased. So we see that this diagram has two "noses" (or time minima), one in the temperature region of transformation to pearlite, and the other in the bainite region.

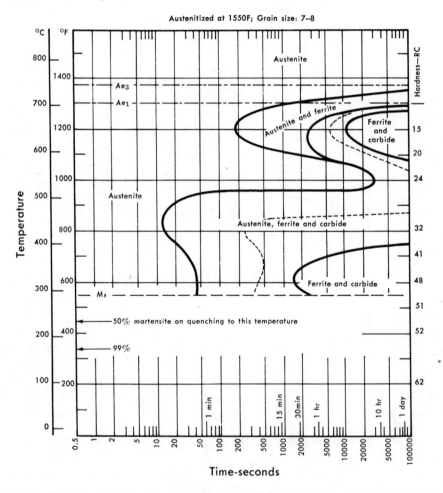

Fig. 10-17. *An isothermal transformation diagram for an SAE 4340 steel with 0.42 per cent carbon, 0.78 per cent manganese, 1.79 per cent nickel, 0.80 per cent chromium, and 0.33 per cent molybdenum. (Courtesy United States Steel Corporation.)*

Fig. 10–17 is an isothermal transformation diagram for a more complex alloy steel—an SAE 4340 steel containing 0.42 per cent carbon, 0.78 per cent manganese, 1.79 per cent nickel, 0.80 per cent chromium, and 0.33 per cent molybdenum. It will be seen that the effect of the addition of only moderate amounts of these alloys has been to displace the curve even farther to the right than it was in the case of the 1.97 per cent chromium steel, shown in Fig. 10–16. This is one of the effects of alloys; relatively small amounts of several alloying elements are more effective in decreasing transformation rates than are larger amounts of a single alloy. In other words, they are more retarding than if they were merely additive, as we might expect. It may be seen from the foregoing discussion of the effects of alloying elements on transformation behavior that the general effect of increasing alloy content is to delay both the start and completion of transformation and, furthermore, that the effect of alloy additions is cumulative. It is also a fact that the effects of alloying elements differ greatly both in magnitude and in specific effects on transformation in different temperature regions, so that it is difficult to predict precisely the effect of any given alloy combination.

10-6   Hardenability of Steel

One of the most important attributes, if not the most important, especially to the heat treater, is the capacity of steel for hardening, usually referred to as its *hardenability*. This quality has a twofold significance since it is first of all important not only in relation to the attainment of a high degree of hardness or strength by means of heat treatment to the desired microstructure, but also by reason of its ability to attain a high degree of toughness using certain heat treatments. This is usually attained with the tempered martensite or lower bainite microstructures. In fact, perhaps the toughness is the most important attribute, since the attainment of a certain level of high strength may have little importance unless it is accompanied by enough toughness to do the job required of the steel under service conditions.

The term hardenability refers to the *depth of hardening* or the size of the piece which can be hardened under a specified set of cooling conditions, and not the maximum hardness that can be achieved in a given steel. As stated previously, maximum hardness is dependent almost entirely upon carbon content (Fig. 10–13), while the depth of hardening, or hardenability is, in general, far more dependent upon alloy content and grain size in the austenite than upon carbon content. A material that has a higher hardenability, (more susceptible to hardening by quenching), is said to harden more uniformly throughout the test piece than one that has a lower hardenability. Hardenability is a function of the isothermal transformation diagrams in that a steel that has a low critical rate of cooling will be found to harden to a greater depth on quenching than a steel with a higher cooling rate. An understanding of hardenability has made it possible, during periods of critical shortages of certain strategic alloying elements, to substitute a steel with a hardenability curve very much like that of the alloy steel, and to come up with a steel that is satisfactory in every respect.

Coarsening the austenitic grain structure of a steel can make the steel take a deeper hardening, due to the fact that such treatment will move the isothermal transformation curve to the right, and thereby to longer times. The grain size produced by austenitizing a steel is determined by the microstructure of the steel prior to heat treatment, the chemical composition of the steel, the austenitizing temperature, and the time it is held at the austenitizing temperature.

The changes that take place in a steel as it is heated through the critical range indicate that just below the lower critical temperature the microstructure of the steel consists of *ferrite* and *carbide phases* in the carbon steels, the carbide phase in the form of *cementite*. When the steel contains carbide-forming elements (molybdenum, vanadium, tungsten, titanium, columbium, or chromium), the carbide phase contains iron, carbon, and the alloying elements. The austenite begins to form at the lower critical temperature, with austenite nuclei appearing at the interface of the ferrite and carbide phases. Originally the austenite grain size is very small, but as the temperature is raised the austenite grains begin to grow.

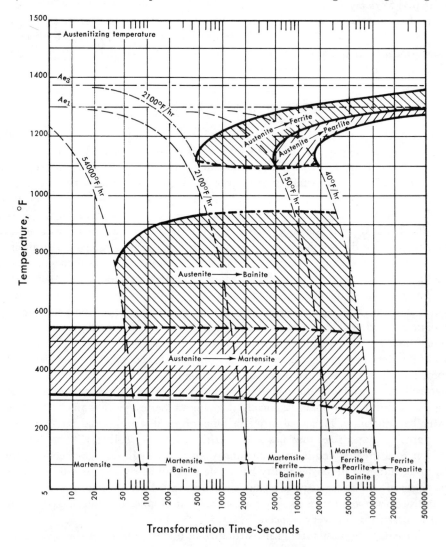

Fig. 10-18.   *Continuous-cooling transformation diagram for an SAE 4340 type steel, with cooling curves superimposed to show the manner in which transformation behavior during such continuous cooling controls the final microstructure of the steel. (Courtesy of United States Steel Corporation.)*

Forming out of ferrite and carbide the grains continue to grow until their boundaries meet, any further growth being limited by the presence of neighboring grains. After the austenite grains touch, some may continue to grow by absorbing their neighbors, but the ultimate size will depend substantially upon the temperature, and also upon the size of the grains at the time of contacting the neighboring grains.

In aluminum-containing steels (killed steels), austenitic grain growth is seriously retarded because of the temperature elevation at the time rapid grain growth starts in the steel. The addition of from one to two pounds of aluminum to a ton of steel as an oxidizer has a marked effect on grain growth, due to the formation of aluminum nitride and aluminum oxide, presumably in the form of submicroscopic inclusions distributed throughout the steel.

Steels in which austenitic grain growth has been retarded are referred to as *inherently fine-grained steels.* If such steel is heated, no appreciable grain growth is observed until a specific temperature, known as the *coarsening temperature,* is attained. At this temperature and above it, grain growth begins abruptly and the austenite quickly attains a *coarse grain size.*

10-7   Relationship of Hardenability to Transformation Rates

As has been stated previously, the hardness of steel increases as the transformation temperature decreases. It is also well to keep in mind that the lower-temperature transformation products, such as lower bainite and martensite, when tempered, exhibit superior properties of ductility and toughness at a specific strength level. Therefore, in order to attain the superior properties of these low-temperature transformation products, prior transformation at a higher temperature to softer consistency must, so far as possible, be prevented. In other words, the steel must be cooled through these high temperature transformation ranges at a rapid enough rate so that transformation does not take place, even at the "nose" of the transformation diagram. Such a rate, which will just permit transformation to martensite without any prior transformation at a higher temperature, is known as the *critical cooling rate* for martensite. This is one method of expressing hardenability and it can be readily determined from the continuous cooling diagram. Shown in Fig. 10–18 is a steel of the SAE 4340 type, in which the critical cooling rate for martensite is 54,000F per hour or 15F per second.

10-8   Measurement of Hardenability

The critical cooling rate can be used to express hardenability; however, it has the disadvantage that, in practice, cooling rates are not usually constant but vary during the cooling cycle. This is especially true of liquid quenching, when the cooling rate is always slower as the temperature of the cooling medium is approached, and it is also substantially affected by the presence of a vapor phase in the earlier part of the quenching cycle. It is also true that hardenability refers to *depth of hardening,* and not to hardness of the metal involved. Thus, in order to facilitate the application of hardenability measurements to actual practice, it is customary to express hardenability in terms of the depth of hardening in a standardized quench. The condition of quenching used in this expression is a hypothetical one, in which the surface of the piece is assumed to come instantly to the temperature of the quenching medium. This condition is known as an *ideal quench,* and the diameter of a round bar which will quench just to the desired micro-structure, or corresponding hardness value at the center in an ideal quench, is known as the *ideal diameter,* and is identified by the symbol D_1. Inasmuch as the cooling rate relationships between the ideal quench and other quench conditions are known, hardenability values in terms of ideal diameter of the bar can be used to predict the size of round which will harden in any quench, the characteristics of which are known; or, similarly, if the diameter which will harden just to the center in a standardized quench is known, these data can be converted into the ideal diameter value used to express hardenability.

10-9   Cylinder Series Method

The most direct method of measuring hardenability in terms of ideal diameter is by quenching a series of cylinders. In this method a series of bar sizes are quenched under identical conditions, the bars preferably having a length at least four times the diameter. The bars are next sectioned, etched, and cross-section hardness readings taken. The depth of hardening of each of the bars is determined by the point at which the etching characteristics change, corresponding to a microstruc-ture of 50 per cent martensite, or by the corresponding hardness value. The micro-structure of 50 per cent martensite is often used as the criterion of hardenability because of the ease with which it may be located. The diameter of the bar in this series which hardens just to the center is identified and is known as the *critical diameter* (D) for the series of cylinders used. As stated, this critical diameter value can be translated into the fundamental terms of ideal diameter (D_1), by charts such as those shown in Fig. 10–19 and Fig. 10–20. However, in order to make this conver-

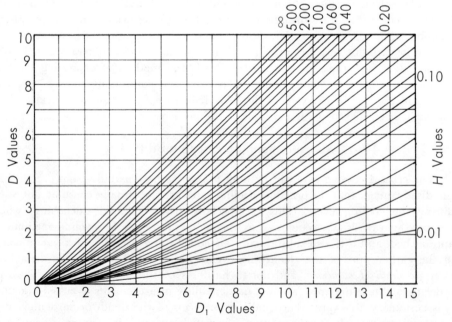

Fig. 10-19.   *Relationships among ideal diameter, critical diameter, and severity of quench. (Courtesy of United States Steel Corporation.)*

sion, it is necessary to evaluate the factor expressing the *severity of quench* (termed the *H* factor). Typical value of this *H* coefficient are shown in Table 10–2.

TABLE 10–2. Typical Values of the *H* Coefficient Designating the Severity of Quench (*H* Value).

Agitation	Oil	Water	Brine
None	0.25–0.30	0.9–1.0	2.0
Mild	0.30–0.35	1.0–1.1	2.0–2.2
Moderate	0.35–0.40	1.2–1.3	
Good	0.40–0.50	1.4–1.5	
Strong	0.50–0.80	1.6–2.0	
Violent	0.80–1.1	4.0	5.0

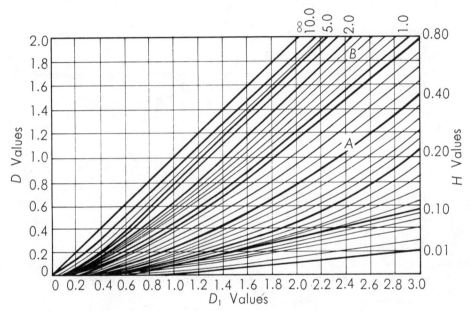

Fig. 10-20. *An enlargement of the portion of Fig. 10–19 for D values between 0 and 2.1 and D₁ values from 0 to 3.0. (Courtesy of United States Steel Corporation.)*

10-10 Jominy End-Quench Method of Test

Even though the cylinder series of tests is the most direct method of measuring hardenability, having many advantages, the *end-quench* method developed by W. E. Jominy and A. L. Boegehold is the hardenability test which is now in greater use and is generally accepted everywhere. In this procedure a cylindrical test specimen 1 in. in diameter and 4 in. long is heated to the desired hardening temperature and then quenched in a fixture by a stream of water impinging upon one end only, as shown in Fig. 10–21. The test bar is then ground on two opposite sides to a depth of 0.015 in. below the surface and hardness readings taken at 1/16-in. intervals along the length of the specimen. The hardenability is expressed as a curve, illustrating hardness versus distance from the quenched end of the specimen. A typical end-quench hardenability curve is shown in Fig. 10–22. Both the American

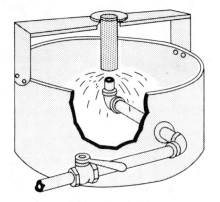

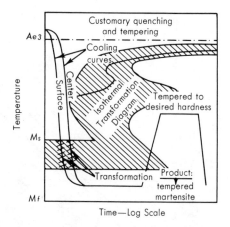

Fig. 10-21. *Quenching fixture for Jominy end-quench test. (Courtesy of United States Steel Corporation.)*

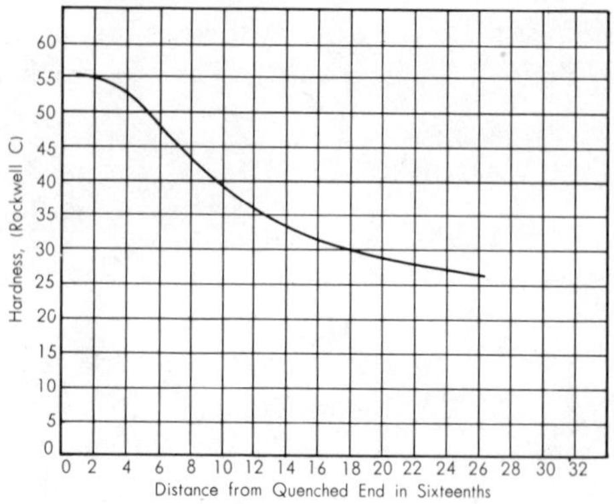

Fig. 10-22. *Typical end-quench hardenability curve. (Courtesy of United States Steel Corporation.)*

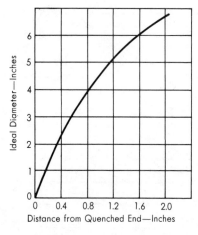

Fig. 10-23. *Curve for converting distance from the quenched end, corresponding to the desired microstructure (or hardness) in the end-quench test to hardenability values, in terms of ideal diameter. (Courtesy of United States Steel Corporation.)*

Fig. 10-24. *Transformation diagram for quenching and tempering. (Courtesy of United States Steel Corporation.)*

Society for Testing Materials and the Society of Automotive Engineers have established standard procedures for performing the Jominy hardenability test, and students are referred to the publications of these societies for more detailed testing procedures.

One of the advantages of the Jominy test is that it furnishes a method of applying a continuous series of varying cooling rates to a single specimen, and since these rates are known, the results can be converted to hardenability values in terms of ideal diameter Fig. 10–23 shows the curve used for this conversion. The distance along the end-quench bar to the desired microstructure, or corresponding hardness value, is noted and the ideal diameter corresponding to this distance is read from the curve. It is a simple matter then to convert this ideal diameter value into terms of bar size which can be hardened under any given quenching conditions, using the methods described above.

10-11   Quenching and Tempering

Quenching and tempering is the heat treatment most commonly used to obtain desirable properties in tempered martensite, this is usually the final heat treatment used to achieve optimum properties. In Fig. 10–24 this method is shown illustrating in diagrammatic form a continuous cooling from the austenitizing temperature through the martensite transformation temperature range, at a rate rapid enough to prevent any transformation at temperatures above the M_s temperature; this is followed by tempering to the desired hardness or strength level wanted.

The material must first be heated to a temperature at which austenite will form, this actual austenitizing temperature being such that all the carbides are in solution, so that full advantage may be taken of the hardenability effects of the alloying elements. In some cases, however, particularly in tool steels, it may be desirable to leave some undissolved carbides. The temperature, however, should not be so high as to cause pronounced grain-growth. The work should, therefore, be held at the austenitizing temperature just long enough to dissolve the carbides, but not long enough to bring about excessive grain-growth.

A heating rate that is too high may set up stresses, particularly if irregular sections are involved. A rule of thumb for a heating rate is one hour per inch of section, which has been found to be satisfactory by heat treaters. In some cases, however, a more rapid heating rate may be used, but in such instances the advisability of the practice must usually be determined by trial and error. Flame hardening, in which rapid heating is achieved by the actual impingement of a high-temperature flame on the surface of the piece being heated, is based on the fact that the heating rate is a function of the difference in temperature between the piece and the heating medium, at a temperature well over the desired austenitizing temperature, then removing the piece when this temperature is reached. Temperature control is obviously uncertain in treatments of this nature, as well as in continuous furnace practice, where the temperature of the furnace is kept well above the desired temperature and the passage of the work through the furnace is so timed that the work will reach the desired temperature at the terminal end of the furnace. Such rapid heating practices are the exception, however; the more common and safe practice is the relatively slow but uniform heating to the austenitizing temperature, followed by a holding period at that temperature long enough to insure that the piece is at a uniform temperature throughout the workpiece.

Caution must be taken against excessive *oxidation* and *scaling*, which may also result in *decarburization*, both usually undesirable in the heat treating of steel. Scaling means a loss of actual metal, with a consequent marring of the surface and the possible prevention of the rapid extraction of heat in the quenching operation. Excessive decarburization results in a soft surface and it may seriously affect the fatigue strength and life of the metal. These processes do not necessarily go together; for this reason, a slightly oxidizing atmosphere is often desirable when freedom from decarburization is essential. Since time and temperature are the two elements that determine the amount of scaling of the workpiece, austenitizing temperatures and times should be as low as is consistent with the principles given herein, to curtail the amount of scaling. One sure way to reduce scaling is to introduce 4 per cent or more of carbon monoxide into the furnace atmosphere.

Where it is mandatory to have complete freedom from scaling or decarburization, it is often essential to heat the work in a muffle furnace containing reducing gases (carbon monoxide or methane and hydrogen mixtures); to pack in cast-iron chips or in a mixture of charcoal and sodium carbonate; or to heat in neutral salt or lead baths. All of these methods have their limitations and disadvantages and special precautions must be taken to ensure their successful employment. At times the compositions of the gases used in controlled atmospheres in the furnace may vary with the temperature and composition of the steel being heat treated, and must be carefully balanced so that neither carburization or decarburization take place. Packing mixtures, such as charcoal and sodium carbonate, may also lead to carburization at the higher temperatures, so that special precaution must be taken. Caution must be taken in the use of salt or lead baths, as they may become contaminated with oxides through contact with the atmosphere, and thus accelerate decarburization of the piece.

10-12 Martempering

The transformation to martensite during rapid cooling through the martensite temperature range, with the accompanying sharp temperature gradient, results in high stresses in the workpiece. As a result of this a modified quenching procedure, known as *martempering*, is helpful in lowering these stresses after quenching. In Fig. 10–25 this method is diagrammatically shown. It is ordinarily carried out by quenching the piece in a molten-salt bath at a temperature just above the M_s temperature, holding it in this bath long enough to permit the piece to reach the temperature throughout, and then air-cooling to room temperature. Transformation to martensite then takes place during the relatively slow air-cooling, and, inasmuch as the temperature gradient characteristic of the conventional quench is not present, the stresses set up by the transformation are much lower than in conventional quenching and tempering. In addition to the lower stresses much greater freedom from distortion is also achieved and the likelihood of cracking is reduced. After martempering, the workpiece is usually tempered to the desired strength level. Martempering is used in the heat treatment

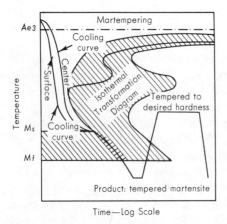

Fig. 10-25. *Transformation diagram for martempering. (Courtesy of United States Steel Corporation.)*

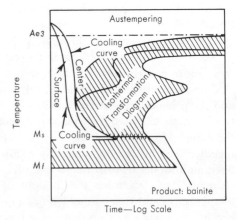

Fig. 10-26. *Schematic transformation diagram for austempering (Courtesy of United States Steel Corporation.)*

of tools, bearing dies, etc., where difficulty was formerly encountered with quench-cracking, or distortion, when the usual heat treating by conventional quenching and tempering were used.

10-13 Austempering

As previously stated, the properties of lower bainite are usually similar in strength and are somewhat superior in ductility to those of tempered martensite. In order to overcome this, an isothermal heat treatment to lower bainite in order to obtain optimum strength and ductility has been developed; this heat treatment is known as *austempering*.

The austempering treatment is illustrated diagrammatically in Fig. 10-26. It involves quenching to the desired temperature in the lower bainite range, usually in molten salt, and holding at this temperature until transformation is complete. Customarily it is best to hold for twice as long as indicated by the isothermal transformation diagram, to ensure complete transformation of the segregated areas. The piece may be quenched or air-cooled to room temperature after transformation is complete and may be tempered to a lower hardness level if desired.

Just as in every other heat treatment procedure, austempering has its advantages and disadvantages. It has one advantage, which is considerable, over conventional quenching and tempering, in that the bainite transformation takes place isothermally at a relatively high temperature resulting in very low, transformation stresses, with a resultant absolute minimum of distortion and a practically complete freedom from quench-cracking in the workpiece. On the other hand, austempering has the same disadvantage as martempering, because of the slower cooling rates of the molten baths (salt), as compared to the usual water or oil quenches required by a higher hardenability steel that is required to prevent high temperature transformation during the cooling down to the bainite temperature.

In addition to these higher hardenability features are longer times for complete transformation to bainite; austempering may take considerably more time than martempering or conventional quenching and tempering methods. This hardenability limitation may be overcome to a degree by the introduction of a prequench in water or oil to a temperature just below the M_s temperature in order that some of the martensite transformation occurs prior to the final holding at the bainite transformation. The final product of this is a mixture of tempered martensite and bainite; steel with this microstructure has very good properties for many applications.

Because of this hardenability limitation, austempering has found its widest application in the heat treatment of plain high carbon steels in small section sizes, such as sheet, strip, and wire products. It is also presently being used for the heat treatment of alloy steels and cast iron applications in which it is important to hold distortion down to a minimum.

10-14 Normalizing and Annealing

Normalizing is a term referring to the heating, or rather reheating, of steel to about 100F (40C) above its critical temperature, (Ac_3), and then cooling in air.

The two main purposes of normalizing are, first, to refine the grain size and, second, to obtain a carbide size and distribution more favorable for carbide solution, on subsequent heat treatment, than the "as-rolled" structure was prior to this treatment. The as-rolled grain size depends upon the finishing temperature during the rolling operation, and this obviously is subject to wide variations; therefore, there is a corresponding wide variation in the grain size of the as-rolled products. As the name implies, the normalizing process or operation serves to refine a coarse grain size resulting from a high finishing temperature, and to ensure a uniform, relatively fine-grained microstructure.

Machining is made much easier and more effective by normalizing in a hypoeutectoid steel consisting substantially of ferrite and coarse pearlite; such a steel is easier to machine if the ferrite and cementite are more evenly and finely distributed. Steel in the soft condition is apt to tear in the machining operation, so the normalizing of such a steel brings about a slight increase in hardness and, consequently, a more brittle chip, thereby improving its machinability. In alloy steels, especially if they have been slow-cooled after rolling, the carbides in the as-rolled condition tend to be rather large in size and are therefore difficult to dissolve on later austenitizing treatments. In such cases, normalizing ensures a more uniform and a finer carbide particle size facilitating subsequent heat treatment to a more uniform final product. Although, as stated, it is the usual practice to normalize from 100 to 150F above the upper critical temperature, for some alloy steels containing carbides soluble only with difficulty, considerably higher temperatures are often used to ensure carbide solution. Any heating, generally, should be slow enough to ensure uniform temperatures and low thermal stresses. Normalizing is now very often carried out in continuous furnaces; in fact, this method is especially well adapted to strip and sheet steel because it may be heated quickly. It is also used for normalizing plates and bars of long lengths. Any type of furnace is suitable for the normalizing process, just so long it will ensure uniform heating and the accurate control of temperatures.

10-15   Annealing

The term *annealing* refers to any heating and cooling operation that is usually utilized for the softening of steel or iron. The main purposes of *annealing* are to relieve cooling stresses induced by cold or hot working, and to soften the steel to improve its ability to be more easily machined or formed, subsequently. At times it involves only a subcritical heating to relieve stresses, to recrystallize cold-worked material, or to spheroidize the carbides; in other cases it may involve heating above the critical temperature, with subsequent transformation to pearlite or directly to a spheroidized structure when cooled.

Full Anneal

As stated previously, the most desirable microstructure for ease in machining of low or medium-carbon steels is coarse pearlite. The usual heat treatment employed to develop such a microstructure is a *full anneal*, as shown in Fig. 10–27. Full anneal consists of austenitizing at a relatively high temperature to obtain full carbide solution, followed by slow cooling; a resulting transformation takes place entirely in the high temperature end of the pearlite range. Although this is a simple heat

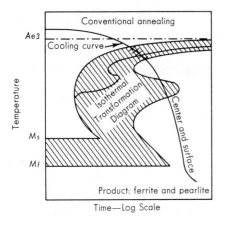

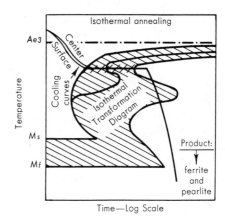

Fig. 10-27. *A transformation diagram for full annealing of steel.*

Fig. 10-28. *Schematic transformation diagram for isothermal annealing.*

treatment, it is very useful and is reliable for most steels; however, it has the disadvantage of being time-consuming, since it involves a slow cooling over the entire temperature range, from the austinitizing temperature to a temperature below that at which the transformation is culminated.

10-16   Isothermal Annealing

The annealing process used to produce coarse pearlite, can be accomplished isothermally by cooling the work to the correct temperature for transformation to coarse pearlite, and holding is at this temperature until the transformation is complete; this is similar to the procedure previously described for austempering. Isothermal annealing is illustrated diagramatically in Fig. 10–28. This type of isothermal annealing saves a great deal of time for the heat treater over the conventional method of full annealing previously mentioned and described in Fig. 10–27. Inasmuch as neither the time from the austenitizing temperature to the transformation temperature, or from the transformation temperature to room temperature, are of much importance and, in fact, are not critical, these times may be accelerated as much as is practical or, in fact, as much as is desired.

Isothermal annealing is used frequently where fullest advantage may be taken of rapid cooling to the transformation temperature, and from this temperature down to room temperature. Therefore this method of annealing is found to be most desirable for small parts which can be handled in the salt bath conveniently, or in lead baths, as we can effect substantial savings in time for the annealing, over the conventional slow cooling in the furnace. The isothermal anneal is also adapted to continuous heat treatment, continuous annealing by this method being known as *cycle annealing*. This is generally carried out in a furnace that has been especially designed for the purpose, with an air-blast chamber made a part of it in order to permit rapid cooling from the high-heat stages for austenitizing to the lower temperature stages where transformation to pearlite takes place. In batch annealing large loads of work, where the rate of cooling from the outside to the center of the load may be so slow as to preclude any rapid cooling to transformation temperature, this method of annealing is not recommended, as it is not economically feasible.

The conventional full-annealing method usually offers better assurance of the desired microstructure and properties, in such applications.

10-17 Process or Recrystallization Annealing

When materials have been cold worked, they become too hardened for optimum machinability, particularly in the higher carbon steels. Machinability is accomplished by heating the metal to a temperature at which new, strain-free crystals are formed and replacing the crystals that are distorted by the cold working operation, resulting in a softer steel. Inasmuch as grain size is affected mainly by three factors, percentage of cold work, temperature of anneal, and time, it is obvious that these factors are interrelated and therefore must be controlled in order to obtain the required grain size.

The best example of process or recrystallization annealing is the box annealing of cold-rolled low carbon sheet steel; this annealing is carried out at temperatures of from 1100 to 1300F. The heating and holding at temperature usually takes about 24 hours, after which the load is slowly cooled in the box. Approximately 40 to 42 hours are necessary for the entire process.

10-18 Stress Relief Annealing

This method of annealing is used to release the residual stresses that are often present in metallic materials for various reasons. These include, for example, cold forming, grinding of heavy castings, uneven cooling of castings (such as from uneven quenching), stresses set up in welds, and other sources of residual stresses. Often the release of these stresses brings about undesirable dimensional changes. In the case of metals under heavy load, residual stresses may accentuate the load stresses and result in failures. Such failures may be brought on, in part, by substantial acceleration of corrosion, known as stress corrosion, leading to abnormally early failure of the metal. Stress relief annealing is very beneficial in all such cases, releasing the residual stresses without changing the structure or dimensions of the parts, since the recrystallization temperature is above that at which this stress relief annealing is carried out. Providing that the combination of time and temperature of stress relief annealing do not bring about recrystallization, we may ignore both time and temperature in this method.

10-19 Spheroidize Annealing

Inasmuch as coarse pearlite microstructures are too hard for machining steels containing higher carbon, it is best to anneal such steels in order to convert the carbides present into round, spheroidal particles, instead of thin plates, such as we get in pearlite structures. We do this by tempering the as-rolled, slow-cooled, or normalized materials at a temperature just below the lower critical temperature; this method is termed "subcritical annealing." It may take longer holding times for full spheroidization of the carbides to take place at such a subcritical temperature, so this method is rather slow, but it is still one of the more simple heat treatments used in industry and in many cases is more convenient than annealing above the critical temperature.

The annealing procedures just described for producing pearlite can, with some modifications, be adapted to other operations for producing spheroidized micro-structures. For example, if free carbide remains after the austenitizing treatment, transformation (in the temperature range at which coarse pearlite would ordinarily form) will continue to spheroidize rather than form into pearlitic plate structures. Therefore, heat treatment to form spheroidized microstructures can be accomplished in a manner similar to that used to form pearlite, except that in the former we use lower austenitizing temperatures. So it is apparent that spheroidize annealing may involve a slow cooling similar to full-annealing treatment to produce pearlite, or it may call for an isothermal treatment similar to the isothermal annealing whereby pearlite is formed. It is customary to use an austenitizing temperature of not over 100F above the lower-critical temperature for the supercritical annealing process, when spheroidized microstructures are required.

10-20 Heat Treating Furnaces

Heat treating furnaces may be classified into two general categories, batch and continuous, and there are many different types in each group. The simplest furnaces are the direct-fired batch type, with manual controls. Installations for large production lines are more elaborate and are usually continuous furnaces, with automatic programming controls. In some cases controls are included in the furnace for controlling the atmosphere in the working chamber, in order to obtain the desired surface condition. In general, the most common heat treatments performed in furnaces are annealing, normalizing, hardening, spheroidizing, temper-ing, carburizing, and stress relieving. As a rule heat treating furnaces are not designed for temperatures higher than 2000F and, in general, they operate at from 800F to 1600F. Insulation is important in maintaining uniform temperatures and least expense, and the furnaces are built tight to prevent infiltration of air or loss of special atmospheres.

For handling batch loads of material to be heat treated, quenched, and tempered, quench tanks and cranes should be located so that there is a minimum of time expended in transporting material from the furnace to the quenching medium. Furnaces should also be so arranged as to have a second furnace available for taking material after quenching for such additional treatment as may be required. As a rule, three furnaces are used in operations of this type, two for heating and one for tempering the work.

10-21 Methods of Applying Heat

The type of treatment and the nature of the material to be processed dictate method of heat application. The usual heat-transfer laws govern the flow of heat to the metal in heat treatment, just as they do in other furnaces. The surface of the material absorbs the heat transmitted to it by either radiation or convection, or both, and this heat is transferred through the body of the material by conduc-tion. The transfer of heat by convection is more important and indeed more significant in heat treating furnaces than it is in furnaces operated at a higher temperature level.

The two main sources of heat are gaseous fuel and electric power, although in some cases fuel oil has been substituted for gas, either because of a shortage of the latter or for other economic reasons. Although heat treating furnaces may be either directly or indirectly heated, direct firing is more commonly used. This method permits the products of combustion to circulate about the material to be heated. Open burners used in the direct firing method may be installed in the furnace proper or outside the work-heating chamber in the path of an external circulating fan, to circulate large volumes of hot gases throughout the furnace. The only limiting factor to the temperatures we can obtain by such a method is the material of which the fan is constructed, as this is, of course, a critical factor.

Fig. 10–29 is an illustration of one of several batch-type furnaces, this one being the car-bottom furnace, which consists of a furnace shell equipped with burners or heating units, with the hearth built upon a separate car which runs in and out of the furnace shell to charge and unload the furnace. The doors of the furnace are of the vertically lifting type, full width of the furnace, and are operated either hydraulically or electrically. Car-bottom furnaces have been constructed to process charges only a few tons in size to several hundred tons, and are used for the heat treatment of axles, bars, heavy plates, castings, and many miscellaneous shapes. Some car-bottom furnaces are known as elevator-furnaces in which case the car is rolled under the furnace shell and then raised into the furnace by means of a motor-driven lifting mechanism. The furnace shown in Fig. 10–29 is one in which the shell is lowered over the car and is used to provide a more complete sand or water seal than is possible with conventional car-bottom furnaces. Other batch-type furnaces for heat treating are box furnaces, bell-type, pit furnaces, and salt- or lead-bath furnaces, each of them dependent on the nature of the work to be treated, its volume, sources of economical fuels available, etc.

Fig. 10-29. *Car-bottom furnace with charge of mixed sizes of steel bars, supported above hearth by cast-alloy fixtures, ready to be rolled under bell-type furnace body which will then be lowered over the charge. The toothed rack above the floor at lower left is driven by a pinion to move the car. (Courtesy of Surface Combustion Corporation.)*

10-22 Continuous Furnaces

Continuons furnaces are designed with or without auxiliary equipment for atmosphere control, heat being applied either by direct or indirect firing, or electrically. They are especially adapted to zone heating and cooling. A furnace of this type is shown in Fig. 10–30; this is a rotary-hearth furnace used for heating pieces that are to be handled individually, such as gears, shells, cylinders, billets, etc., where they are to be fixture-quenched or handled individually for scale-free hardening without decarburization, for normalizing or drawing. This type of furnace is also used for heating smaller parts loaded in lightweight trays and for pack-carburizing. In this furnace charging and discharging are both accomplished

Fig. 10-30. *Rotary-hearth furnace for heat treatment of steel. Hearth is rotated by a chain and sprocket drive seen in the foreground. (Courtesy of United States Steel and Surface Combustion Corporation.)*

at the same work station. Rotary-hearth furnaces are designed in a wide variety of sizes, to heat from just a few hundred pounds up to 60 tons per hour.

Another type of continuous heat treating furnace is the *roller-hearth* type, used for high production (Fig. 10–31). This is particularly suited for uniform treatment of large quantities of the same material as in the bright annealing of tubes, stampings, drawn parts, etc., and for normalizing, annealing, hardening, and tempering steel bars. It is also used extensively for annealing malleable irons, small steel and iron castings, and forgings. It is also useful in normalizing flatrolled products. The roller-hearth furnace is constructed as a single furnace, or a line of furnaces, for zone heating and cooling and, at times, such furnaces have an intermediate section with a tank for quenching.

Fig. 10-31. *A continuous-type heat treating furnace in which the material treated is carried through the furnace on belt conveyors made of high strength alloy material suitable for high temperature.*

Conveyor-type furnaces are similar to roller-hearth furnaces, except that in this case belt conveyors are used to carry materials through the furnace. They are particularly adapted for accurately heat treating small pieces which would not ride properly on the roller-hearth. The production rate, or heating cycle, of the continuous conveyor-type furnace is controlled by both the temperature setting desired and the speed of the conveyor. The belt conveyors are made of an alloy material sufficiently strong at high temperature to carry the load and are resistant to heat, corrosion, oxidation, and abrasion.

10-23 Surface Treatment and Case Hardening of Metals

Frequently it is desirable to have a steel part which is very hard and wear-resistant on its outer surface, but tough and comparatively soft at the interior. Often a part is machined to the desirable shape in the soft, ductile condition and, after machining, the outer surface is hardened by one of several methods: carburizing, nitriding, cyaniding, or by means of induction or flame hardening. All of these processes come under the general heading of surface treatment, which is more generally referred to as *case hardening*.

Low carbon steels (0.10 to 0.25 per cent carbon) are designated as carburizing steels and are used for many carburized parts. However, the choice of steel within this group is determined largely by the core properties desired for the particular application. For example, the lower alloys and combinations of them, such as AISI 4023, with about 0.25 per cent Mo, 0.80 per cent Mn, and 0.20 to 0.25 per cent C; AISI 4118 steel, with 0.50 to 0.70 per cent Cr, 0.08 to 0.15 per cent Mo, and 0.18 to 0.23 per cent C; and AISI 5015 steel, with 0.30 to 0.40 per cent Cr and 0.15 to 0.20 per cent C, are all used for better core-toughness properties since they are superior for casehardening AISI C1018 (the nonsulfurized basic open-hearth and acid-Bessemer carbon steel), or AISI C1117 (resulfurized basic open-hearth and acid-Bessemer carbon steel). The AISI 4023, 4118, and 5015 steels also have the advantage of being hardenable in oil, in moderate sections, so that they can be heat treated with less distortion than on those types of steel which require water quench after heat-treatment. The higher alloy carburizing steels, such as:

AISI 3120   Ni 1.25 per cent, Cr 0.65 per cent
AISI 3310   Ni 3.50 per cent, Cr 1.55 per cent
AISI 4320   Ni 1.80 per cent, Cr 0.50–0.80 per cent, Mo 0.25 per cent
AISI 4620   Ni 1.55 percent to 1.88 per cent, Mo 0.20–0.25 per cent
AISI 4815   Ni 3.50 per cent, Mo 0.25 per cent
AISI 5120   Cr 0.80 per cent–1.05 per cent
AISI 6120   Cr 0.80–0.95 per cent, Vd 0.10–0.15 per cent min.
AISI 8620   Ni 0.55 per cent, Cr 0.50–0.65 per cent, Mo 0.20 per cent
AISI 9310   Ni 3.25 per cent, Cr 1.20 per cent, Mo 0.12 per cent

are all used for superior case and core properties.

When iron or lower carbon steel is heated in contact with carbonaceous material, either gaseous or solid, a shell or case containing Fe_3C is formed at the surface which grows thicker as heating is continued. It should be pointed out that nickel in steel actually retards case hardening by itself, but with Cr and Mo present the detrimental effect is overcome. (Ni is needed for better core toughness as may be observed in the case of the higher alloy steels mentioned above.) The earliest form of steel was made this way by treating wrought iron, and the same principle applies in case hardening, except that the temperature in the latter is lower (only 850 to 950C) and the time required much less. In the case of armor-plate for ships, tanks, and guns, a Cr-Ni steel is specified, while for ball-bearings a Ni-Mo steel is used.

Often surfaces to be carburized are machined, and then those portions that are not to be case hardened are either copper-plated or covered with a protective enamel or wash, and the pieces are then packed in iron, steel, or special alloy boxes containing the carburizing mixture. Heat is applied up to 850 to 900C for a predetermined time, depending on the thickness of case desired, and the pieces are then removed from the furnace. In some plants the case-hardened pieces are quenched directly from the carburizing treatment, rendering a high-carbon "case" which is very hard, while the low-carbon core remains comparatively soft. This results in a wear-resistant exterior combined with an interior possessing great toughness, as is needed for gears, camshafts, etc.

Carburizing, as a rule, is carried out by packing the steel in boxes with carbonaceous solids, well sealed to exclude the atmosphere, and heating to about 1700F for a period of time depending on the depth of case desired. This is known as *pack carburizing* or *solid carburizing*. The carbonaceous material used in this process is usually a mixture of charcoal, barium, calcium, and sodium carbonates. The box is sealed to prevent oxidation and to obtain the maximum benefit of carbon monoxide gas (CO) generated within the box. At the temperature to which the materials in the box are heated, which is above the A_{c3} temperature, the austenite absorbs the carbon from the CO, the penetration ranging from 1/32 in. to 3/32 in., thereby giving an outer case of high carbon steel where desired. In this connection, it should be remembered that the steel does not absorb carbon from the solid carbonaceous material, the mechanism of absorption being such that a little oxygen is trapped in the sealed box, and this oxygen burns to CO in an excess of carbon and it is from this CO gas that the austenite receives its carbon content. After robbing the CO of its C, the freed oxygen unites with more C and carries it over to the Fe. Oxygen is thus the carrier of the carbon, and it is obvious that the CO gas is an effective carburizer. Natural gas is also effective as a surface hardening carburizer.

The chemical equation for the action of the energizer is as follows:

$$BaCO_3 \longrightarrow BaO + CO_2, \quad \text{then} \quad CO_2 + C \longrightarrow 2CO$$

Then CO carburizes the steel as follows:

$$3Fe + 2CO \longrightarrow Fe_3C + CO_2$$

Where it is essential or advisable to speed up the reaction, the temperature may be elevated to 1750 to 1800F. More careful control is essential for the higher temperatures in order to assure uniform case results. In the case of the higher-nickel alloy steels, lower temperatures of from 1625 to 1650F are used, these lower temperatures having the added advantage of keeping warpage to a minimum.

For best case hardening, the carbon content at the surface usually should not be over 1.15 per cent, and the gradation toward the core will be more uniform. Control of gradation can be made to a considerable extent by controlling the composition of the carburizing compound; for example, by reducing the amount of the energizer and increasing the charcoal (or coke) content, the carbon content at the surface will be lowered. It is a general rule that the maximum carbon content at the surface of the steel will increase with decreases in carburizing temperatures, primarily because of the low diffusion rate of the carbon at the lower temperature.

10-24 Liquid Carburizing

Parts to be carburized are immersed into a molten salt bath containing about 30 per cent sodium cyanide at 1600F for from one-half to one hour periods to effect a light hard case of 0.010 in., which will also be a hard case suitable for many years of wear resistance. The case is a mixture of carbides and nitrides, and its relatively high hardness reflects, to a considerable extent, the presence of iron nitride.

The cyaniding process is now largely being replaced by liquid carburizing in activated baths which use a floating slag of calcium cyanide as the active agent, producing deeper cases which are lower in nitrogen and higher in carbon than the ones produced with the simple sodium-cyanide bath. An activated bath has a composition of about the following:

Calcium Cyanamide	$CaCN_2$	2 to 5 per cent
Calcium Cyanide	$Ca(CN)_2$	43 to 48 per cent
Sodium Chloride	NaCL	30 to 35 per cent
Calcium Oxide	CaO	14 to 16 per cent
Carbon	C	4 to 5 per cent

Fig. 10–32 is a graph of comparative case depths as a function of time and temperature in activated and cyanide baths. In general, the cases obtained with activated baths range from 0.70 to 1.00 per cent carbon with approximately 0.2 per cent nitrogen, concentrated mainly at the surface of the steel parts being processed.

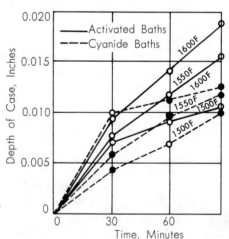

Fig. 10-32. *Comparative case depths as a function of time and temperature in activated and cyanide baths. (Courtesy of American Society for Metals.)*

10-25 Gas Carburizing

For purposes of *gas carburizing* the gases most commonly used are natural gas, "manfuactured" gas, and certain propanes. Infrequently, butane is also used, but when it is used, it should be the normal butane and not isobutane. When they are available with a high degree of purity, natural gas and propane are preferred, the best propane being derived from natural gas rather than from peroleum, due to the fact that propane obtained from petroleum as a by-product in oil refining often contains excessive amounts of ethylene, propylene, and other unsaturated hydrocarbons that break down quickly to oily soot or even to coke.

In order to be assured of uniform carburizing, it is essential that complete and adequate circulation of the furnace gases is provided. Inasmuch as hydrocarbon gases provide large quantities of available carbon, relatively small flows of gases are required. The circulation resulting from just the flow of gas alone is not sufficient, as a rule, to effect uniform carburizing of the load. It is essential in such cases that the furnace have a high-volume fan to force circulation of the gases to all parts of the work load. A common practice is to use an endothermic gas or a purified exothermic gas as a carrier and to enrich it with one of the hydrocarbon gases. The ratio of carrier gas to hydrocarbon gas varies substantially in industry, but is usually in the range of 8 to 1, to about 30 to 1, the ratio used depending on the types of carrier and hydrocarbon gases, the furnace size and condition, the amount of circulation, and the amount of work surface being treated. Parts being carburized are placed in contact with gases rich in CO (such as methane CH_4 and other hydrocarbon gases) and at temperatrues of 1600 to 1800F for best results. Great care must be used in controlling the composition of the carburizing gas used.

Carburizing gives a deeper case than any other method. Quenching from 1700F may produce both a core and a case with coarse-grained structures so that two reheatings and a quenching to refine the grains in both the case and core may be necessary, one just above the A_3 of the low carbon core and the other just above the A_3 of the high carbon case. Many fine-grained steels are quenched directly from the carburizing operation. A photomicrograph of a carburized case would reveal that:

1. There is a gradation carbon content in the steel—high at the surface and much lower at the core.
2. There is gradual tapering off of the carbon toward the interior, identified as light-colored ferrite grains where low carbon exists, then, as the carbon increases, the proportion of pearlite increases up to a point where it is 100 per cent.
3. From this point on, toward the surface, particularly at the exterior surface, we see the microstructure of cementite (Fe_3C).

10-26   Heat Treatment of Carburized Parts

Because carburized parts have a high-carbon case and a low-carbon core, the correct heat treatment temperature for the case will be one that is too low for the core, and vice versa. It is therefore desirable to use a double heat treatment to obtain the optimum properties of both case and core. The work is first heated to above the critical temperature corresponding to low-carbon core, and suitably cooled to refine its microstructure. Then it is reheated to just above the critical temperature of the case and quenched, in order to harden the case to *martensite.* When the carburizing temperature is not too high, refining the core may not be too imperative and, after cooling from the carburizing temperature, a single reheating and quench from above the critical temperature of the case is sufficient. Although quenching directly from the carburizing temperature is sometimes done, the operation must be carefully controlled to minimize undue warpage.

10-27 Measuring the Case Depths of Metals

In the measurement of case depths of metals of primary importance is the "effective case depth," the perpendicular distance from the surface of the hardened case to the farthest point at which the specified level of hardness is maintained. Unless otherwise specified, the hardness criterion for case hardened steel is Rockwell C50. The "total case depth" is the distance measured perpendicularly from the surface to a point where no chemical or physical changes or variations are distinguishable. There are several methods for measuring the case depth, including the following:

1. Chemical method—by taking drillings at various depths of the case and running chemical analysis of the carbon content, either by the wet chemical method or by means of the carbon analyzer, the combustion method, or use of the Quantovac instrument.

2. Mechanical method—by taking hardness readings on a transverse section of a polished area on the case, the core prepared by one of several methods shown below:

(a) case core
     This method is best for light and medium cases.
(b) case core
     This is best for medium and heavy cases.
(c) case core
     Taper-ground specimen for light and medium cases.
(d) Step-grind method—used for medium and heavy cases.

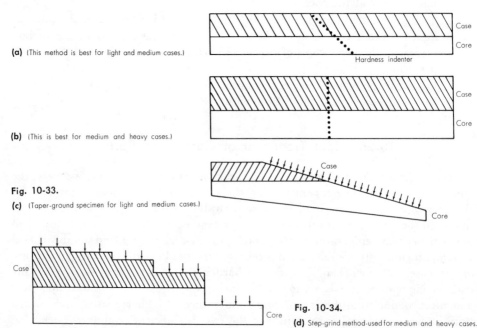

(a) (This method is best for light and medium cases.)

Hardness indenter
Case
Core

(b) (This is best for medium and heavy cases.)

Case
Core

Fig. 10-33.

(c) (Taper-ground specimen for light and medium cases.)

Case
Core

Case
Core

Fig. 10-34.

(d) Step-grind method-used for medium and heavy cases.

It is essential that we control the depth of case in steels, and this is accomplished in various ways, depending on the method used in applying the case. For example, in induction hardening of steel we can determine and control the depth of case using the following methods (in applicable controlling control *minimum* case depths):

1. Varying the coil design
2. Varying the power input
3. Controlling the electrical frequency and the time of heating
4. Selecting and controlling the method and time of quenching

To control the maximum case depths we can:

1. Control the carbon content of the metal
2. Control the temperature of the metal during case-hardening

10-28   Nitriding of Steel Parts

This is a nitrogen case-hardening process, subjecting machined and preferably heat treated parts to the action of a nitrogenous medium, commonly ammonia gas, under conditions wherein the surface hardness is imparted to the material without the necessity of any further treatment. Retention of hardness at elevated temperatures, wear resistance, and resistance to certain types of corrosion are other properties that *nitriding* imparts to steel parts. Experimentation has shown that chromium and aluminum are desirable components in steels for nitriding, and compositions especially adapted for nitriding have been developed, a typical composition being as follows:

Carbon	0.20 to 0.30 per cent
Manganese	0.40 to 0.60 per cent
Aluminum	0.90 to 1.40 per cent
Chromium	0.90 to 1.40 per cent
Molybdenum	0.15 to 0.25 per cent

The nitriding process consists, as a rule, of subjecting the parts to the action of ammonia gas at temperatures ranging from 930 to 1220F. The range most commonly used is 950 to 1000F. The case produced by nitriding is usually light, a case depth of 0.010 to 0.015 in. being produced in about 48 hrs at 975F. However, the surface hardness is very high (800 to 1200 on the Vickers scale and 64 to 78 on the Rockwell C scale). It has been found that this hardness is retained even after reheating the work to temperatures up to 900F.

The nitriding process was developed by Dr. H. Fry, of the Krupp Works in Germany, prior to World War 1. He found that steel having a varying carbon content, aluminum of 1 per cent, 1.50 per cent chrominum, and 0.20 per cent molybdenum, could be nitrided at such low temperatures that they did not need any further heat treatment after exposure to ammonia gas. One of the main advantages of the nitriding process is that steel parts can be heat treated applied prior to the case-hardening operations. Some of the nitrogen from the ammonia gas which becomes disassociated from the ammonia combines with the alloying elements in the steel to form complex nitrides, which are finely dispersed in the case.

Nitriding has three distinct advantages over other forms of case-hardening, as follows:

1. The process does not require as high a temperature (500–550C or 900 to 1100F), so that not only can warping be avoided, but it is also unnecessary

to quench the parts. (There is only a slight growth in the dimensions of the parts, about 0.002 in. for a case of about 0.030 in. thick.)

2. Alloy steels or steel of higher carbon content may be used, since no heat treatment is necessary.

3. The resulting nitrided case is not only harder, but is also so resistant to corrosion that there are instances where nitrided parts have replaced stainless steel.

10-29   Flame and Induction Hardening of Steel

This method consists of heating just the surface of the steel and then quenching it. It is a much simpler method for case hardening, as it can be applied directly to only the areas to be hardened. Steel hardened by this method must contain sufficient carbon to be hardenable. Although the heating may be done with a flame, the more practical method is to use induction heating, such as in the "Tocco" process. This method is excellent for mass production of such parts as automobile crankshafts, containing carbon up to 0.40 to 0.60 per cent. Cast irons with carbons of 2.50 per cent can also be induction hardened successfully.

The greatest advantage of induction hardening is that heat can be localized by means of induction coils, and also that it can be done very quickly—in fact, in a matter of seconds. Specially-prepared induction blocks are shaped around the surface to be hardened, and a high frequency current of from 1,000 to 15,000,000 cycles per second is applied. The voltage is comparatively low and the amperage quite high. Most of the heating is done by eddy currents, although magnetic hysteresis is also helpful. It is known, of course, that alternating current magnetizes steel—first in one direction, then in another polarity—sixty times per second, so any residual magnetism results in heat and a waste of energy. This is what is known as "magnetic hysteresis." So, in the induction hardening of steel there is a situation where two wasters of energy, eddy currents and magnetic hysteresis, are put to work in the case hardening of steel by the induction method.

The principal disadvantage of induction hardening is that each type and configuration of piece so treated requires its own fixtures and conductors; of course, this also applies to flame hardening of steel parts. With carburizing and nitriding, a wide variety and quantity of pieces can be treated together at a lower cost, unless conditions, such as the induction hardening of crankshafts for automobiles, on a mass production basis, warrant it.

QUESTIONS

1. What is meant by the term "heat treating" of metals?

2. Is the heat treatment of alloys the sole means of altering the properties of steels? If not, what other means are available?

3. What two principal constituents of steel primarily control its properties?

4. What is the metallographic name for iron in steel?

5. Explain the difference between ferrite in pure iron-carbon alloys, with only a trace of carbon in solution, and ferrite in steels.

6. Define the term "cementite" as found in steels.

7. What is meant by the term "spheroidized cementite"? Where is it found?

8. Define the important high-temperature phase in steel consisting of a solid solution of carbon in gamma iron. What is its atomic structure?

9. Name and describe the iron-iron carbide eutectic containing 4.27 per cent carbon. Is this found in low and medium carbon steels also?

10. Into what three classifications can the microstructures of the transformation of austenite be divided? Is there also a fourth classification to be considered? If so, what is it?

11. Explain the method used to obtain special mechanical properties in a steel.

12. Draw the isothermal transformation diagram of eutectoid carbon steel, and explain in detail the relationship between hardness values and microstructures of the transformation at different temperature levels.

13. Show by means of a series of graphs the properties of pearlite and bainite in a eutectoid steel.

14. What is the most brittle and the hardest of the microstructures obtainable in a given steel? Using a graph show the relationship between hardness and carbon content. What effect, if any, is brought about by the rate of cooling the steel? Explain.

15. Compare the isothermal transformation diagrams for steels with 0.35 per cent carbon and 0.37 per cent manganese, and another for steel with 0.35 per cent carbon and 1.85 per cent mangnese. Draw the diagrams for each steel.

16. What is the difference between the hardness of a steel and the hardenability of the steel? Why is the hardenability of steel so important to the heat treater?

17. Explain the relationship between hardenability and transformation rates, employing a transformation diagram to illustrate.

18. By means of a transformation diagram describe and explain the quenching and tempering of a steel in order to produce its optimum properties.

19. Of what special importance are the temperature to which a steel is heated and the rate at which the temperature is attained? What factors are of greatest importance in the heating, quenching, and tempering of tool steels?

20. Draw a transformation diagram and explain fully the modified quenching procedure called *martempering*. Is this process of significant importance to treaters of tool steels? Why?

21. Explain fully the austempering treatment of steel, and state some of its advantages and disadvantages.

22. Define and fully explain the processes called *normalizing* and *annealing*. What do we mean by *full anneal*?

23. What is the process used to produce coarse pearlite in steel?

24. Explain the meaning of, and the procedures for *process-* or *recrystallization annealing*. Where is it found to be most useful in industry?

25. Stress-relief annealing is one of the most important and yet one of the most neglected procedures in the steel and iron industries. Explain what this consists of and why it is of major importance.

26. What is meant by *stress-corrosion*, and why is it important to steel manufacturers and users?

27. Because coarse pearlite microstructures in steel are often difficult to machine, especially those with higher carbon contents, it is essential to give them special treatment. What is such treatment called, and how is it accomplished?

28. Into what two categories can heat treating furnaces be classified? Explain each of them fully.

29. In heat treating metals, what primarily dictates the type of treatment and the method of applying heat?

30. Is there any difference between the continuous disc-roller-hearth type of normalizing furnace and the conveyor-type furnace? If so, what is the difference?

31. What is the purpose of case hardening steels? What processes fall into this general classification of surface treatment?

32. In flame hardening steels, what controls the minimum and maximum depths of case that can be achieved?

33. Compare the metallurgical processes and results of *induction hardening* and *flame hardening*.

34. Describe liquid carburizing as it is done today and explain its function and its advantages over the cyaniding process formerly used.

35. In gas carburizing how can uniform carburizing be assured?

36. Explain and sketch the several methods for measuring the case depths of metals.

37. The quenched end of a Jominy bar of steel has a hardness value of 44 R_c. Calculate the carbon content of this steel.

38. What will be the hardness of the quenched end of an AISI 4620 steel on the Rockwell scale?

39. Given a 2.5 in. round AISI 1040 steel quenched in agitated oil, calculate its hardness at a point 1 in. below the surface of the round and explain your answer.

40. Explain why water quenching should be more severe than oil quenching.

References

American Society for Testing and Materials, ASTM Standards, Part I, E19–46, Philadelphia, Pa: *Standard Classification of Austenitic Grain Size in Steels.*

Atlas of Isothermal Transformation Diagrams (1951) *and Supplement* (1953), Pittsburgh, Pennsylvania: United States Steel Corporation.

Barrett, Charles S., *Structure of Metals.* New York: McGraw-Hill Book Company, 1952.

Clark, Donald S., and Wilbur R. Varney, *Physical Metallurgy for Engineers.* Princeton, New Jersey: D. Van Nostrand Co., Inc., 1962.

Grossman, M. A., *Principles of Heat Treatment.* American Society for Metals, Metals Park, Ohio, 1953.

Elements of Hardenability. American Society for Metals: Metals Park, Ohio, 1956.

McGannon, Harold E., (Ed)., *The Making, Shaping and Treating of Steel.* 8th ed., Pittsburgh, Pennsylvania: United States Steel Corporation, 1964.

Alloys and Alloying Elements in Steel

11-1 Effects of Alloying Elements in Steel

The principal function of alloying elements in steel is the improvement of its properties. A high percentage of some elements is used for this purpose in order to obtain increased corrosion-resistance, as in the case of stainless and heat-resisting steels. In other cases, alloying elements are added to steel sparingly in order to impart greater strength and corrosion-resistance to low-carbon steels in the as-rolled condition for use in welded structures as will be discussed in this chapter. Alloying elements are also added to resist abrasion, as in the case of tool steels discussed in Chapter 16. In other applications alloying elements are added to steels in order to enhance their electrical and magnetic characteristics.

In general, it may be said that alloying elements are added to steels in order to accomplish the following purposes:

1. To improve the mechanical properties of the steel by improving its microstructure.
2. To improve the resistance of the steel to corrosion and oxidation.
3. To develop such special properties as:
   a) magnetic and electrical characteristics
   b) high strength at high temperatures
   c) steels that are austenitic at room temperature. The rate at which austenite decomposes to ferrite and cementite can be controlled by means of added alloying elements.
4. To stabilize the iron-carbide in steel by adding chromium, vanadium, titanium, manganese, tungsten, or molybdenum in varying amounts, depending on the end use of the product.
5. To promote graphitization by the addition of silicon, aluminum, or copper.

In most metal systems, both solid solutions and compounds are formed by the addition of alloying elements to steel. The solid solution is usually formed with the iron in the steel while the compound is usually in the form of carbides. The carbide particles, in addition to increasing wear resistance, because of their hardness, may also prevent grain coarsening when the steel is subjected to a heat treatment in the austenite range of temperatures.

The exact identification of steels becomes difficult without making a chemical analysis; however, all steels may be classified in accordance with their (1) method of manufacture, (2) form and use, (3) composition, and (4) quality. A brief description of these four identifying media follows.

11-2 Method of Manufacture

There are five distinctly different methods for manufacturing steel in the United States, as listed below in the order of decreasing tonnage produced during the past ten years.

(a) Basic open-hearth process
(b) Electric furnace process
(c) Basic oxygen process
(d) Acid-Bessemer process
(e) Acid open-hearth process

A discussion of the classification of killed and rimmed steel, both of which are results of the basic open-hearth method, was given in Chapter 8, the killed steels being those that have been completely deoxidized in the process of refining, and the rimmed steels the ones that have been only partially deoxidized when poured into ingot molds at the steel mill. The basic open-hearth process produces, by far, the largest tonnage of steel; during the past five years, the tonnage produced by the direct oxygen process has been increasing substantially.

The mechanism by which alloying elements affect the microstructure through various types of heat treatment was discussed in the previous chapter. In general, alloying elements decrease the rates of transformation of austenite at subcritical temperatures, thereby facilitating the attainment of low-temperature transformation to martensite or lower bainite (when these are the end products desired), without any prior transformation to unwanted higher-temperature products. This function of the alloying elements can be evaluated and expressed in terms of *hardenability* discussed as in paragraph 10–6, Chapter 10 and, in more detail, in paragraph 11–7 of this chapter. Alloying elements thus control the microstructure through their effect on hardenability, and this effect is by far their most important function in steel.

The most important alloying element used with steel is carbon, and there are very few steels which do not contain significant amounts of carbon. Increasing the carbon content in steels produces an increase in the amount of carbides; and since carbides are hard, they increase wear resistance, decrease machinability, and increase the hardness of the alloy only slightly at the expense of ductility. The largest tonnage of alloy steels contain from 0.25 to 0.55 per cent carbon and even less where the steel is to be used for carburized parts in the end product. Where such carburized parts are to be produced in the automotive and aircraft industries, they are usually quenched and tempered to impart the high strength and toughness specified in the design.

In the manufacture of alloy steels the alloying elements accomplish certain purposes, including the following:

1. To increase the fineness of the austenitic grain size, aluminum, silicon, or manganese are added, all of these elements acting as deoxidizers.
2. To improve machinability of the steel, sulfur is added in small amounts of from 0.10 to 0.30 per cent, in which case sulfur acts as a hardener and as what is termed a "chip breaker" during machining.
3. For corrosion-resistance, chromium, nickel and copper are added.

11-3   Forms and Uses of Steel

In classifying steel according to its form and use, the form may be either in the cast or wrought condition, depending on the end use. As was seen in Chapter 8, steel products may have their origin in semifinished form, either as a steel casting or as a wrought configuration, such as billets, bars, sheet, plate, or forging. Certain steels are classified according to the end use for which they are intended; these include boiler, flange and firebox steel, case-hardening steel, deep-drawing steel, electrical steel, heat-resistant and corrosion-resistant steel, free-cutting steel, forging steel, machinery steel, tool steel, and several others, all steels that are used commercially.

11-4   Composition or Grade of Steel

This refers to the type of steel involved, such as plain carbon, alloy steel, tool steel, etc. Steels with carbon present are termed plain carbon steel when the properties are mainly the result of the presence of carbon. This does not mean that other elements, such as silicon, manganese, phosphorous, and sulfur may not be present also; they usually are in small amounts. However, they do not appreciably control or change the mechanical properties of the steel. The following classification of plain carbon steels is useful in industry according to the amount of carbon present:

(a)   Low-carbon steel contains from 0.10 to 0.30 per cent carbon
(b)   Medium-carbon steel contains from 0.30 to 0.85 per cent carbon
(c)   High-carbon steel contains from 0.85 to 1.40 per cent carbon

Steels containing other elements in appreciable amounts used, for the purpose of altering the mechanical properties of the steel, are termed *alloy steels*.

Several, organizations such as the American Iron and Steel Institute, the American Society for Testing Materials, the Society of Automotive Engineers, and others, have prepared specifications for carbon and alloy steels, including, in many instances, the mechanical properties, dimensional tolerances, standards of quality, methods of manufacture, and limits of composition, so far as elemental content are concerned. For example, the Society of Automotive Engineers (SAE) established as far back as 1911 code designations for machinery steels, setting up the analysis limitations without respect to the quality of the steel, designating primarily the type of steel and its approximate carbon content. For example, in the classification 1XXX the first digit indicates that it is a plain carbon steel. The second digit points out any modification of the class; for instance, a 10XX series is one including plain carbon steels. On the other hand the 11XX series include steels which contain appreciable amounts of sulfur and are more commonly classified as *free-cutting steels*. The last two digits indicate the average content of carbon, .01 indicating that 0.01 per cent of carbon is present and .40 referring to the fact that there is an average of .40 per cent carbon in the steel. AISI 1040 steel indicates that the steel is in the plain carbon series and that it contains an average of 0.40 per cent carbon, that is, it contains from 0.38 to 0.42 per cent carbon.

11-5 Composition of Carbon and Alloy Steel Grades

Still another classification of steel established by The American Iron and Steel Institute in 1941 incorporated a letter prefix into the number in order to identify the melting method used in the manufacture of the steel, as follows:

A as a prefix means the steel is basic open-hearth—alloy

B as a prefix means the steel is acid-Bessemer—carbon

C as a prefix means the steel is basic open-hearth—carbon

D as a prefix means the steel is acid open-hearth—carbon

E as a prefix means the steel is electric furnace

Thus an AISI C1030 steel indicates that it was manufactured by the basic open-hearth method and that it contains an average of 0.30 per cent carbon. When no prefix is given in the classification of an AISI steel, the implication is that the steel is essentially an open-hearth type.

Alloying elements may be added to steel with the charge in the steel-making furnace, or in the molten bath near the end of the finishing period, or in the ladle prior to being poured into ingots, or even directly into the molds themselves. The matter of when to make the addition is determined by the effect of the additive on the molten steel temperature, the ease with which specific additions go into solution, the susceptibility of the addition agent to oxidation, and the formation and elimination of reaction products in the process.

Consideration must be given to the relative affinity of alloying elements for oxygen, as compared to the affinity of iron for oxygen, as these are important in the economical production of alloy steels. By way of example, copper, molybdenum, or nickel may be added to the charge or during the working of the steel, as they are entirely recovered. On the other hand, chromium and manganese should be added late in the heat, due to the fact that they are easily oxidized, so that all or part of them should be added in the ladle prior to pouring the steel. In open-hearth practice, readily oxidized elements, including aluminum, boron, titanium, vanadium, and zirconium are usually added in the ladle to reduce the loss due to their oxidation.

Because of the fact that undue chilling of the bath is detrimental, it is often best to preheat the ferroalloy. In cases where large amounts are added entirely to the bath, time must be allowed for the molten steel to be reheated to the desired temperature prior to tapping. The ferroalloy additions may be split between the furnace and the ladle, and in cases where excessive chilling of the metal in the ladle must be avoided, the lesser alloy additions in the furnace must be accepted. Where large additions are made that are apt to cause a chilling effect, in order to minimize or eliminate the need for preheating, some addition-alloys, such as ferromanganese and ferrochromium can be procured mixed with chemical reagents that will provide exothermic reactions, thereby permitting the addition of these agents without undue chilling of the steel. The agents to be added to the bath should be lump size, of about 5 or 6 in. in diameter, in order to penetrate the slag more easily. In the case of ladle additions, on the other hand, it is best to have the alloy additions about 2 in. in size to assure their quick solution.

11-6   Effect of Alloying Elements in Low-alloy Steels

The two phases commonly present in low-alloy steels are the *ferrite* and *carbide*. The alloying elements previously discussed distribute themselves between these two phases in somewhat the following manner:

(a) In the ferrite phases—silicon, aluminum, copper, nickel, cobalt, zirconium and phosphorus.

(b) In the carbide phases—manganese, chromium, molybdenum, tantalum, vanadium, columbium, and titanium.

These alloying elements have the following effects on steel and effect these purposes:

Nickel in amounts of from 30 to 50 per cent reduces the thermal expansion and magnetic permeability of alloys, while from at 1 to 5 per cent it increases the hardenability. Nickel also has the characteristic of graphitizing and producing a corrosion-resistant, tough steel alloy. In addition, it slows down the austenite-to-pearlite transformation.

Cobalt improves the high-temperature properties of steel. It also is added to high-speed, heat-resistant steels, tending to decrease hardenability in steel.

Chromium provides effective corrosion and oxidation resistance. In addition, it improves the wear-resistance of steels and increases its hardenability.

Aluminum is usually added to produce completely deoxidized, killed steel. It also increases steel's resistance to oxidation.

Manganese in amounts of from 0.30 to 1.50 per cent is a good deoxidizer, while in higher amounts it increases the hardenability of the steel.

Molybdenum (also titanium, niobium, and vanadium) increases the wear-resistance and strength of steel at high temperatures. It also increases its hardenability.

Copper is used mainly to improve corrosion-resistance, for it dissolves only in the ferrite and does not form carbides. Copper also improves the machinability of steel.

Lead is seldom added to steels, as it is practically immiscible with iron and steel in both the liquid and solid states. In small amounts, however like copper, it improves the machinability of steel.

Sulfur improves the machinability of steel in amounts of from 0.10 to 0.30 per cent, together with 0.60 to 1.50 per cent manganese, by means of the formation of manganese sulfide. It has a tendency to make steel hot and cold-short in heat treatment.

Phosphorus is used to increase the corrosion-resistance of steel in some structural grades, when in the presence of small amounts of copper. The percentage of phosphorus is usually held down to 0.04 per cent maximum and, in this small amount, is negligible in effect.

Silicon dissolves mainly in the ferrite and it has a substantial strengthening effect.

In amounts up to 0.20 to 0.50 per cent, silicon is used as a deoxidizer, and in higher amounts it is used to improve the steel's resistance to oxidation.

Combining two metals in an alloying operation produces different behavior, according to the metals involved. The simplest behaviors occur in either of the following combinations:

1. When the pairs of metals are completely immiscibile in both the liquid and solid states or
2. When the two metals are completely miscible in both the liquid and solid states.

Two metals that are completely immiscible in the liquid state, that is, where each is insoluble in the other, form two layers, like oil and water, in both the liquid and solid states. Naturally, such combinations are not of much interest in the present context, but the characteristics of mutual insolubility may have a practical value if one of the metals can be distributed throughout the other in the manner of an emulsion. This occurs in the combination of iron and lead, which do not form an alloy; however, the lead in such a mixture will be present as an assemblage of small particles. Because of the greater atomic weight of the lead atoms, the atoms are less penetrable by X rays than the iron matrix atoms, and so are readily distinguishable. As stated before, lead is added to iron and steel primarily to improve its machinability.

11-7   Hardenability and the Effects of Alloying Elements on Hardenability

Hardenability measurements of a series of steels in which a single alloying element is the only variable, are used as a means of quantitatively evaluating the effects of alloys on the grain size or the hardenability of steels. Fig. 11–1 is an illustration of

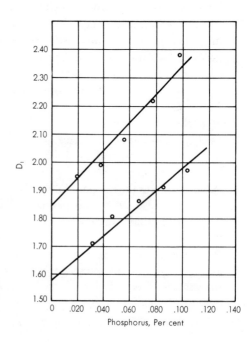

Fig. 11-1. *Hardenability as a function of phosphorus content in two series of steels.* (*Courtesy of* Metals Handbook, *American Society for Metals, Metals Park, Ohio.*)

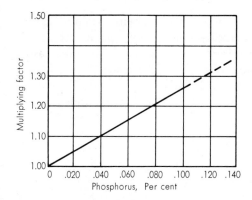

Fig. 11-2. *Multiplying factors for phosphorus. As shown, the effects of the alloys on grain size or hardenability may be quantitatively evaluated by hardenability measurements on a series of steels in which a single alloying element, in this case phosphorus, is the only variable. (Courtesy of* Metals Handbook, American Society for Metals, Metals Park, Ohio.)

one method of quantitatively evaluating the effects of alloys on grain size or hardenability, showing the hardenability of two series of steels in terms of ideal diameter for a microstructure of 50 per cent martensite. The series here illustrated was made by adding phosphorous to successive ingots, so that in each series the composition was constant except for the amount of phosphorus. As shown in Fig. 11–1, hardenability increases regularly as the phosphorus content is increased. It is also obvious that the rate of increase is more rapid for the steel with the higher base hardenability. To arrive at a numerical evaluation of the effect of phosphorous on hardenability, the hardenability of the steel with phosphorus content should be divided by the base hardenability of the steel containing no phosphorus. It is this value that expresses the effect of the element (phosphorus, in this illustration) on hardenability, called the *multiplying factor*. The multiplying factors for phosphorus, shown in Fig. 11–1, are plotted in Fig. 11–2, wherein it may be seen that a steel with 0.020 per cent phosphorus has 1.05 times the hardenability of a steel with no phosphorus, and that a steel with 0.100 per cent phosphorus has approximately one and one-quarter times the base hardenability. Knowing this fact, we can determine the effect of increasing the phosphorus content from 0.020 to 0.100 per cent by multiplying the hardenability of the 0.020 per cent phosphorus steel by 1.27/1.05, or 1.21.

Certain experimenters, including M. A. Grossmann, and E. C. Bain, found that the cumulative effects of alloying elements on hardenability could be determined by multiplying the base hardenability of the iron-carbon alloy progressively by the multiplying factors for the elements involved. Fig. 11–3 is a chart that permits us to calculate the hardenability, in terms of 50 per cent martensite microstructures, of a given alloy combination. The principle of the multiplying factor is important not

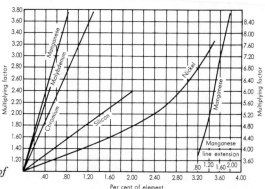

Fig. 11-3. *Multiplying factors for a number of alloying elements. (American Iron and Steel Institute.)*

only as a means of predicting the hardenability of a steel from its composition, but, just as significant, as an indication that, as a rule, the addition of comparatively small amounts of several alloying elements is more important and effective in increasing hardenability than a relatively large amount of only a single element. This principle was used effectively during World War II in the development of substitute compositions making the greatest use of the hardenability effects of alloying elements more readily available to us.

Series Designation	Types
10xx	Nonresulphurized basic open hearth and acid bessemer carbon steel grades
11xx	Resulphurized basic open hearth and acid bessemer carbon steel grades
12xx	Rephosphorized and resulphurized basic open hearth carbon steel grades
13xx	Manganese 1.75 per cent
23xx	Nickel 3.50 per cent
25xx	Nickel 5.00 per cent
31xx	Nickel 1.25 per cent—Chromium 0.65 per cent
33xx	Nickel 3.50 per cent—Chromium 1.55 per cent
40xx	Molybdenum 0.25 per cent
41xx	Chromium 0.50 or 0.95 per cent—Molybdenum 0.12 or 0.20 per cent
43xx	Nickel 1.80 per cent—Chromium 0.50 or 0.80 per cent—Molybdenum 0.25 per cent
46xx	Nickel 1.55 or 1.80 per cent—Molybdenum 0.2 or 0.25 per cent
47xx	Nickel 1.05 per cent—Chromium 0.45 per cent —Molybdenum 0.20 per cent
48xx	Nickel 3.50 per cent—Molybdenum 0.25 per cent
50xx	Chromium 0.28 or 0.40 per cent
51xx	Chromium 0.80, 0.90, 0.95, 1.00 or 1.05 per cent
5xxxx	Carbon 1.00 per cent—Chromium 0.50, 1.00 or 1.45 per cent
61xx	Chromium 0.80 or 0.95 per cent—Vanadium 0.1 per cent or 0.15 per cent min.
86xx	Nickel 0.55 per cent—Chromium 0.50 or 0.65 per cent—Molybdenum 0.20 per cent
87xx	Nickel 0.55 per cent—Chromium 0.50 per cent —Molybdenum 0.25 per cent
92xx	Manganese 0.85 per cent—Silicon 2.00 per cent
93xx	Nickel 3.25 per cent—Chromium 1.20 per cent —Molybdenum 0.12 per cent
98xx	Nickel 1.00 per cent—Chromium 0.80 per cent —Molybdenum 0.25 per cent
TS	denotes Tentative Standard Steel, as in TS 41 and others.
B	denotes Boron Steel, as in 46B12 and others.
BV	denotes Boron Vanadium Steel, as in TS 43BV and TS 43BV14.

Fig. 11-4. *Basic numerals for designating various types of AISI steels, including plain-carbon steels.* (*Courtesy of* Metals Handbook, *American Society for Metals, Metals Park, Ohio.*)

11-8   AISI Low Alloy Steels

In Appendix C, at the end of this book, will be found the composition ranges of alloy steels most commonly used for heat-treated parts, these steels identified by a numerical index system that describes, in a measure, the composition. The type of steel is indicated by the first digit, as stated previously; "1" indicates a carbon steel, "2" indicates a nickel steel, and "3" indicates a nickel-chromium steel. The second number, in the case of the simple alloy steels, usually indicates the percentage of the predominating alloying element. In general, the last two or three digits indicate the average carbon content in "points," or hundredths of a per cent. For example, AISI 2340 indicates a nickel steel of approximately 3 per cent nickel (3.25 to 3.75 per cent) and 0.40 per cent carbon (0.35 to 0.45 per cent). Shown in Fig. 11–4 are the basic numerals for various types of AISI steels, including plain carbon steels. This list is valuable to the metallurgist and engineer in selecting the type of steel to be used in structures, etc., as it is a standardization and simplification of thousands of alloy-steel compositions. Inasmuch as many of these steels were developed for specific applications and have proven themselves, a considerable degree of standardization has resulted that has been helpful to the industry.

11-9   AISI Low Alloy Steels—Their Applications

The low-carbon steels (0.10 to 0.25 per cent carbon) are termed carburizing steels, used almost entirely in carburized parts. The choice of a steel within this group, however, is determined largely by the core properties required for a specific application. The lower alloy combinations, such as 4118, 4023, and 5015, have the advantage of being hardenable in oil in moderate sections, and can therefore be heat treated with less resulting distortion than the types requiring quenching in water. Steels the three here mentioned, and others like them, are also used when better core properties for specific applications are desired. Where superior machinability is desired, the higher manganese and sulfur steels are used. A few typical applications of low-alloy steels of the carburizing grades are the production of wrist pins, cam shafts, clutch fingers, and similar automotive parts, where high strength and superior core properties are not required.

TABLE 11–1.   Composition of Some High Temperature Alloys*

Alloy ↓	Form[b]	C	Mn	Si	Cr	Ni	Co	Mo	W	Cb[c]	Ti	Al	Fe	Other
IRON-BASE														
A-286	W	0.05	1.35	0.95	15.50	26.0	—	1.25	—	—	1.95	0.20	Bal	V 0.30
D-979	W	0.05	0.50	0.50	15.0	45.0	—	3.75	3.75	—	3.0	1.0	Bal	B 0.01
Discaloy	W	0.04	0.9	0.8	13.5	26.0	—	2.75	—	—	1.75	0.07	Bal	—
Incoloy 901	W	0.05	0.50	0.35	13.0	40.0	—	6.0	—	—	2.50	0.20	Bal	B 0.03
N-155, Multimet	W, C	0.10	1.50	0.70	20.75	19.85	19.50	2.95	2.35	1.15	—	—	Bal	—
Refractaloy 26	W	0.03	0.8	1.0	18.0	38.0	20.0	3.2	—	—	2.6	0.2	Bal	—
Refractaloy 70	W	0.04	?.0	0.3	20.0	21.0	30.0	8.0	4.2	—	—	—	Bal	—
S-590	W	0.4	1.5	0.6	20.0	20.0	20.0	4.0	4.0	4.0	—	—	Bal	—
Unitemp 212	W	0.08	0.05	0.05	16.0	25.0	—	—	—	0.50	4.0	0.15	Bal	B 0.06, Zr 0.05
V-57	W	0.06	0.25	0.55	14.75	25.50	—	1.25	—	—	3.0	0.25	Bal	B 0.008, V 0.30
W545	W	0.05	1.50	0.40	13.5	26.0	—	1.50	—	—	2.85	0.20	Bal	B 0.08
16–25 6	W	0.08	1.35	0.70	16.25	25.5	—	6.0	—	—	—	—	Bal	N 0.15
19 9DL	W	0.30	1.10	0.60	19.0	9.0	—	1.25	1.20	0.40	0.30	—	Bal	—

Table 11-1 (Continued)

NICKEL-BASE

Cosmoloy F	C	0.04d	0.10d	0.10d	15.0	Bal	—	3.8	2.2	—	3.4	4.7	0.20d	B 0.08, Zr 0.07
GMR 235	C	0.15	0.25d	0.60d	15.5	Bal	—	5.25	--	—	2.0	3.0	10	B 0.06
Hastelloy B	W, C	0.05d	1.0d	1.0d	1.0d	Bal	2.50d	28.0	..	—	—	—	5.5	V 0.4d
Hastelloy C	W, C	0.08d	1.0d	1.0d	15.5	Bal	2.50d	16.0	3.75	—	—	—	5.5	V 0.35d
Hastelloy X	W, C	0.10	1.0d	1.0d	22	Bal	1.5	9.0	0.6	—	—	—	18.5	—
Inconel 700	W	0.13	0.08	0.25	15.0	46.0	29.0	3.0	—	—	2.20	3.20	0.80	—
Inconel 702	W	0.04	0.10	0.25	15.50	79.0	—	—	—	—	—	3.0	0.50	--
Inconel 713C	C	0.12	0.15	0.40	13.0	Bal	—	4.50	—	2.25	0.60	6.0	1.0	—
Inconel X	W	0.04	0.70	0.30	15.0	73.0	—	—	--	0.90	2.50	0.90	7.0	—
M 252	W	0.10	1.0	0.70	19	54	10	10	—	—	2.5	0.75	2.0	B 0.0005
Nicrotung	C	0.10	..	—	12.0	Bal	10.0	--	8.0	—	4.0	4.0	..	B 0.05, Zr 0.05
René 41	W, C	0.12	0.1	0.5	19.0	Bal	11.0	10.0	--	—	3.1	1.5	—	—
Udimet 500	W	0.15d	0.75	0.75	17.5	Bal	16.5	4.0	--	—	3.0	2.75	4.0d	B 0.008d
Udimet 700	W	0.15d	—	—	15.0	Bal	17.5	5.0	--	—	3.5	4.25	1.0	B 0.10d
Waspaloy	W	0.05	0.50d	0.75d	19.50	Bal	13.5	4.25	--	—	3.0	1.25	2.0d	B 0.005, Zr 0.06
1753	W	0.24	0.05	0.10	16.25	50.0	7.20	1.60	8.40	—	3.15	1.90	9.50	B 0.008, Zr 0.06

COBALT-BASE

HS-21	C	0.25	1.0d	1.0d	27.0	2.75	Bal	5.5	..	—	—	—	2.0d	B 0.007
HS-25, 1-602	W	0.10	1.5	1.0d	20.0	10.0	Bal	--	15.0	—	—	—	3.0d	—
Nivco	W	0.02	0.35	0.15	—	22.5	Bal	--	--	—	1.8	0.22	1.0	Zr 1.1
3-816	W	0.38	1.32	0.56	20.0	20.0	Bal	4.0	4.20	3.7	—	—	5.0d	—
V-36	W	0.30	0.90	0.40	25.0	20.0	Bal	4.0	2.3	2.0	—	—	2.0	—
X-40, HS-31	C	0.50	1.0d	1.0d	25.5	10.5	Bal	—	7.5	—	—	—	2.0	—

REFRACTORY

Chromium (pure)	W	--	...	—	Bal	—	—	—	—	—	—	—	—	—
Cr-1 Ti	W	—	—	—	Bal	—	—	—	—	—	1.0	—	—	—
Columbium (pure)	W	..	—	—	—	—	—	—	Bal	—	—	—	—	—
Cb-10 Ti-10 Mo	W	.	—	—	—	—	10	—	Bal	10	—	—	—	—
Cb-15 W-5 Mo-1 Zr	W	.	—	—	—	—	5	15	Bal	—	—	—	—	Zr 1
Molybdenum (pure)	W	—	—	—	—	—	—	Bal	—	—	—	—	—	—
Mo-0.5 Ti	W	0.026	—	—	—	—	—	Bal	--	—	0.47	—	—	—
Mo-0.5 Ti-0.07 Zr	W	0.017	—	—	—	—	—	Bal	—	—	0.46	—	—	Zr 0.074
Tantalum (pure)	W	—	—	—	—	—	—	—	—	—	—	—	—	Ta Bal
Ta 90-W 10	W	...	—	—	—	—	—	—	10	—	—	—	—	Ta 90
Tungsten (pure)	W	...	—	—	—	—	—	Bal	—	—	—	—	—	—

* Compositions vary with different manufacturers. b_W = wrought; C = cast. Where both forms are available, composition given is for wrought form. (Courtesy of *Materials in Design Engineering*, published by Reinhold Publishing Corporation, New York, N.Y.,

11-10   Nickel Steels in Low-Alloy Series

Nickel was one of the first elements alloyed with iron and carbon in steel, its principle advantage being in the higher tensile strength attainable without substantial reduction in elongation and in area of specimen. Inasmuch as critical temperatures are lowered with the addition of nickel, it is possible to use lower heat treating temperatures, effecting savings in the cost of production and affording other advantages. In addition, nickel steels in the low-alloy series have good "as-normalized" mechanical properties. Nickel, in moderate amounts, also decreases the critical cooling rate, so that a slower quench is possible in obtaining hardness values similar to those of plain carbon steels.

The low-alloy steels are sometimes referred to as pearlitic steels, since their microstructures are similar to those of plain carbon steels. The classification of alloy-steels is usually based on the amount of the alloying element present, and the steels are identified as follows:

Steels with less than 10 per cent alloying element—low alloy
Steels with more than 10 per cent alloying element—high alloy

TABLE 11-2. Composition Ranges of Some Representative High-strength Low-Alloy Steels. (*United States Steel Corporation.*)

Brand	Chemical Composition (Per Cent)								
	C	Mn	P	S (max.)	Si	Cu	Ni	Cr	Other
COR-TEN*	0.12 max.	0.20–0.50	0.07–0.15	0.05	0.25–0.75	0.25–0.55	0.65 max.	0.30–1.25	—
COR-TEN**	0.10–0.19	0.90–1.25	0.04 max.	0.05	0.15–0.30	0.25–0.40	—	0.40–0.65	V: 0.02–0.10
TRI-TEN	0.22 max.	1.25 max.	0.04 max.	0.05	0.30 max.	0.20 min.	—	—	V: 0.02 min.
MAN-TEN	0.28 max.	1.10–1.60	0.04 max.	0.05	0.30 max.	0.20 min.	—	—	—
EX-TEN 50***	0.22 max.	1.25 max.	0.04 max.	0.05	—	—	—	—	Cb or V: 0.01 min.
GLX-50-W	0.20 max.	1.00 max.	0.04 max.	0.05	0.10 max.	—	—	—	Cb: 0.20 min.
Dynalloy	0.15 max.	0.60–1.00	0.05–0.10	0.05	0.30 max.	0.30–0.60	0.40–0.70	—	Mo: 0.05–0.15
Mayari "R"	0.12 max.	0.50–1.00	0.12 max.	0.05	0.20–0.90	0.50 max.	1.00 max.	0.40–1.00	Zr: 0.10 max.
NAX High Tensile	0.18 max.	0.50–0.90	0.04 max.	0.05	0.60–0.90	—	—	0.40–0.70	Mo: 0.20 max., Zr: 0.03–0.13
Yoloy "E" HSX	0.18 max.	0.90 max.	0.08 max.	0.05	—	0.20–0.50	0.40–1.00	0.20–0.35	—
Jalten #1	0.15 max.	1.30 max.	0.04 max.	0.05	0.10 max.	0.30 min.	—	—	V: 0.035–0.065
Yoloy "E" ACR	0.10 max.	0.60 max.	0.05 max.	0.05	—	0.25–0.50	0.60 max.	0.35 max.	—

* 1/2-inch and under in thickness.
** Over 1/2-inch in thickness.
*** In addition to EX-TEN 50 steel (50,000 lb. per sq. in. minimum yield point), EX-TEN steels are also available with minimum yield points of 45,000, 55,000, 60,000, and 65,000 lb. per sq. in.

Included in the high alloy series are the alloy tool steels, to be discussed in Chapter 16, as well as corrosion and wear-resistant steels. In the latter groups the microstructures are usually austenitic or ferritic, rendered stable at room temperature because of the higher amounts of alloys involved.

11-11   Low-Alloy Manganese Steels

Normal amounts of residual manganese, ranging from 0.25 to 1.65 per cent, are found in the plain carbon and free-machining steels of the 10XX and 11XX series. Strength may be increased by the addition of up to 1.9 per cent manganese in the as-rolled condition, rendering a steel with substantially greater strength and ductility when heat treated. Another group of steels in the intermediate manganese 1300 series renders high tensile strength ductility and is superior to plain carbon steels with the same carbon content, costing far less for the alloying element concerned. These 1300 series steels, in the intermediate manganese group, are used extensively in making forged parts because of their highly satisfactory mechanical properties when normalized. In steels containing more than 0.60 per cent manganese, *temper brittleness* is encountered; however, this can be removed by reheating the steel to the tempering temperature, followed by quenching. Brittleness of this type is probably due to the formation of either martensite or bainite from the retained austenite. *Temper brittleness* results when certain steels are held within, or are cooled slowly through, a certain range of temperature below the transformation range. The brittleness shows up in notched-bar impact tests at room temperature or at lower temperatures. Temper brittleness in alloy steels is another example of discontinuous increase in plasticity on tempering, and is discernible as a loss of toughness on slow cooling after tempering at temperatures of 1100F or above, or on tempering in the temperature range of approximately 850 to 1100F. Freedom from temper brittleness in an alloy steel is obtained by quenching the steel from a tempering temperature of 1150F; the steel is found to be very tough, as revealed by notched-bar impact tests.

Decided brittleness is encountered in steels containing from 2 to 10 per cent manganese; however, if the manganese content is increased to between 10 and 14 per cent in steels with 1.0 to 1.25 per cent carbon, a tough and wear-resistant steel is obtained with proper heat treatment and quenching; this product is known as Hadfield's austenitic manganese steel. This is one of the first important alloy steels produced on a commercial basis and it has been found to be highly desirable, as it is resistant to impact-abrasion, overcoming as it does, the tendency for work-hardening to take place by means of the continual impact and abrasion of the part in certain applications. Where abrasion takes place without impact, rapid wear results. As a consequence, this material is found to be most applicable in power-shovel teeth, rock-crusher jaws, buckets for dredges, etc., and is singular in its superior mechanical properties for such applications.

11-12   Low-Alloy Chromium Steels

Substantially improved hardenability, strength, and wear-resistance are obtained by the addition of chromium to plain carbon steels; however, temper-brittleness is likely unless extra care is taken to cool rapidly when the parts are tempered in the range of 1050 to 1250F. Steels in the 50XX series with low chromium content of between 0.20 and 0.29 per cent amplify the action of the carbon present and are low-cost as well. Steels containing some chromium in the very low-carbon series are especially adaptable for carburizing and result in a hard, wear-resistant surface; however they are not as tough as the nickel steels in the 23XX series previously discussed. Tools and dieblocks used in drop forging, requiring sharp cutting edges, are sometimes fabricated from the plain chromium-carbon steels; however, they are not as satisfactory for these applications as the nickel-chromium steels to be discussed next, for the reason that they do not have the toughness that such parts often require. Air-hardening, and subsequent cracking, is sometimes produced in steels with higher chromium content, so that considerable care must be taken to cool such steels properly after rolling and forging in order to minimize or eliminate such cracking.

Just as is true of the carburizing steels, the lower-alloy higher-carbon steels, including plain chromium (5130 and 5150), are used for applications involving relatively small sections, but which are subject to severe service conditions, or in larger sections, which may not necessitate optimum properties. In applications such as these, advantage is taken of the weight saving derived from the use of higher strength steels. A few typical uses for such steels are high-strength bolts, automotive axles, automotive steering parts, and small machinery axles and shafts. Another popular use for these low-alloy chromium steels is in the manufacture of balls and races or rollers of antifriction bearings, the steel used more than others being grade 52100, containing from 0.95 to 1.23 per cent carbon and from 1.30 to 1.62 per cent chromium. In addition to its high strength properties, it is also superior in wear-resistance.

11-13   Low-Alloy Nickel-Chromium Steel

Nickel-chromium steel in the 31XX series, particularly lower alloy nickel-chromium like 3120, with 1.25 per cent nickel and 0.65 per cent chromium, is customarily used for automotive gears, UNIVERSAL joints, small tools, connecting rods, highly stressed pins, etc. Plain carbon steels are greatly enhanced by the addition of nickel, which increases their ductility and toughness, and by the addition of chromium in combination, giving the resulting steel superior strength, surface hardness, and ability to be hardened in depth. Although these steels also have inherent temper brittleness, it is controlled by the proper ratio of nickel to chromium, as previously stated. The 33XX series of nickel-chromium steels, containing 3.5 per cent nickel and 1.55 per cent chromium, are used where deeper drawing and severe carburizing requirements are essential, as in the fabrication of heavy-duty rear axles and transmission gears, and similar parts. In Chapter 13 a full discussion of steels with over 3.5 per cent nickel content and 1.5 per cent chromium, will be given, as these steels in the corrosion and scale-resistant group are also important for their particular properties and applications.

11-14   Low-Alloy Molybdenum Steels

Molybdenum is one of several elements, along with tungsten, vanadium, tin, columbium, phosphorus, aluminum, and titanium, which decrease the "size" of the austenite field, these elements being referred to as *ferrite-formers*. In relatively small amounts, molybdenum has a considerable effect in the improvement of properties of carbon steels, especially when added in combination with manganese, nickel, and chromium. Even molybdenum itself, when added to carbon steels, will enhance their properties considerably. In any of the molybdenum steels, the amount of molybdenum will range from 0.12 to 0.65 per cent, depending upon the end use of the steel. In general, molybdenum is added to carbon steels for the following reasons:

1. Improvement of creep-resistance at higher temperatures because of the stability of the carbides formed.
2. Substantial reduction of temper brittleness.
3. Better machinability with even higher hardness values.
4. Improved hardenability, especially when chromium is also added.
5. Decided improvement in ductility and toughness for a given elastic limit.
6. The carbides present inhibit grain boundary sliding.

Two disadvantages in molybdenum steels are that they require higher tempering temperatures in order to develop mechanical properties on a par with carbon steels, and secondly, that they require a considerably longer holding period for heating at quenching or normalizing temperatures, in order to ensure complete solution of the molybdenum-iron carbide. These two factors are actually not disadvantages, as the improvement in properties of plain carbon steel either with molybdenum alone added, or in combination with other elements, far outweighs the precautions that must be taken in the control of the above-mentioned. temperatures

11-15   Nickel-Chromium-Molybdenum Low-Alloy Steels

Low-alloy steels with these three important elements added make up the nickel-chromium, molybdenum steels, sometimes referred to as the triple-alloy steels. These have been developed primarily by experimenters investigating the hardenability of steel, this being the most important factor in the use of alloying elements in AISI Alloy Steels. In fact, the selection of the correct alloy steel for use in given applications is based largely on its hardenability. Engineers with the American Society of Automotive Engineers and the American Iron and Steel Institute set up maximum and minimum end-quench hardenability curves that they have termed *hardenability bands*, for most of the alloy steels in this series. These hardenability limits or bands are based on data collected from hundreds of heats of each grade of steel, and this information permits steels to be marketed on the basis of the important hardenability property. Steels that are sold on this basis are referred to as "H" steels. Fig. 11–5 shows a typical hardenability band for a 4140H steel, while Fig. 11–6 is a chart showing minimum hardenability limits for 4140H, 4340H, 5140H, 8640H, and 9840H steels, illustrating a comparison of the minimum hardenabilities of steels with varying alloy content, but the same carbon content.

For application purposes, the minimum hardenability values for a given steel are usually the most important, so we therefore show the minimum hardenability limits for the "H" steels in Fig. 11–6. Shown in Fig. 11–7 is another comparison of the minimum hardenability limits for a group of steels of varying content. The steels in Fig. 11–7 are in the nickel-chromium-molybdenum series AISI8600. This figure also indicates the effect on the minimum hardenability limit of the increasing carbon content in the AISI8600 series of steels.

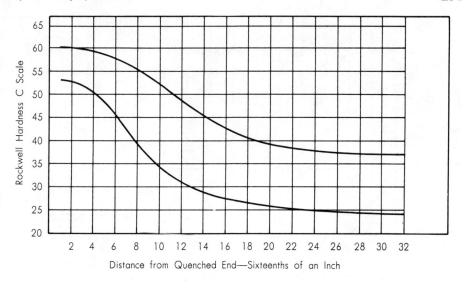

Fig. 11-5. *Typical hardenability band for 4140H steel. (See Chapter 10, paragraph 10.10, for an explanation of Jominy end-quench test.) (Reprinted, by permission, from* The Making, Shaping, and Treating of Steel, *United States Steel Corporation, 1964.)*

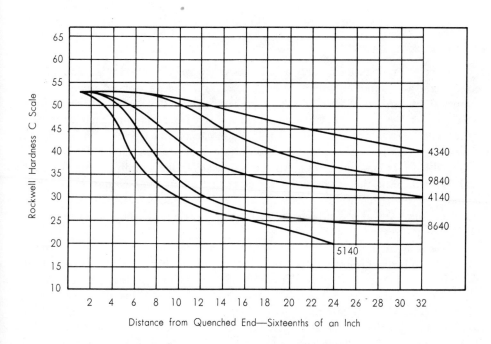

Fig. 11-6. *Minimum hardenability limits for 4140H ,4340H, 5140H, 8640H, and 9840H, comparing minimum hardenabilities for steels of different alloy content but with the same carbon content. (Reprinted, by permission, from* The Making, Shaping and Treating of Steel, *United States Steel Corporation, 1964.)*

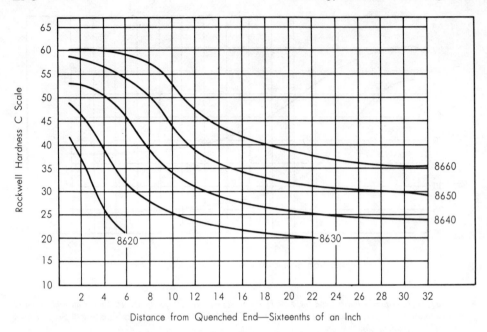

Fig. 11-7. *Minimum hardenability limits for a group of the 8600 (nickel-chromium-molybdenum) series, showing the increase in minimum hardenability with increasing carbon content.* (*Reprinted, by permission, from* The Making, Shaping and Treating of Steel, *United States Steel Corporation, 1964.*)

11-16   Low-Carbon Quenched and Tempered Constructional Alloy Steel

For many applications, such as in pressure vessels, earth-moving and mining equipment, and major members of large steel structures, a class of quenched and tempered low-carbon constructional alloy steels has been developed. These steels are referred to as *low-carbon martensites*, to set them apart from constructional alloy steels with higher carbon content, which develop high-carbon martensite when quenched. They have a relatively high strength, and minimum yield strengths, of 100,000 lb per sq in., with good toughness at temperatures as low as $-50F$, in addition to weldability, with welded joints that show full joint efficiency when the welding is done with suitable low-hydrogen welding rods. As a rule these steels are used in plate form.; however, they are also available in sheets, bars, structural shapes, forgings, and in some semi-finished products.

These constructional alloy steels are all low-carbon, with carbon content ranging from 0.10 to 0.20, this low content being an important factor in the toughness and weldability of the steels. The hardenability of each of these steels is such that transformation on water quenching, in sizes within the specified thickness range, occurs predominantly at low temperatures, lowering the bainite or martensite structure. The additive alloying elements used to give this requisite hardenability have been selected to give a product at as low a cost as possible, commensurate with the desired properties of the end product. The very significant hardenability effect of only a small percentage of boron is found in some of these steels, all alloying elements and hardenability characteristics being varied in line with the size of the section in which the steel is to be used. As a result, in many instances, a distinct advantage may be taken of the higher strength and superior toughness of these alloy steels, at a lower cast than that for the plain carbon steels, which might previously have been used with heavier sections, but with lower strengths. Small additions of carbide-forming elements, such as vanadium or titanium, are used in these steels to permit retention of high strength after tempering or stress-relieving at relatively high temperatures. (Chemical composition and mechanical properties of these structural steels can be obtained by referring to *American Society for Metals* Handbook, Vol. 1, 8th Ed., or to other steel handbooks of a similar nature.)

11-17 Maraging Steels

A new family of high nickel martensitic steels which are strengthened by precipitation-hardening are called the "maraging" steels. These steels are available in three groups, based on nickel content, and they have a yield strength range of from 200,000 to 300,000 lb per sq in. One of the significant properties of these steels is that the martensite has a low carbon content (less than 0.03 per cent), and is therefore relatively soft and formable, which is unusual for martensite in even so-called low-carbon steels. As a consequence, these steels can be easily formed prior to being strengthened by subsequent precipitation-hardening.

The maraging steels have unique combinations of properties not available in the low or even medium-alloy steels previously discussed. In end products they offer useful yield strengths up to 300,000 lb per sq in. and at the same time have a high degree of toughness and impact energy.

Engineers using maraging steels have found many other advantages, including the following:

1. A simple heat treating procedure is possible
2. Through-hardening is available without quenching
3. Excellent formability after solution-treatment
4. Excellent machinability—comparable to that of AISI 4340 (at equal levels of hardness values)
5. Little distortion during the maraging (or precipitation-hardening) treatment
6. Little or no decarburization after heat treatment
7. Weldability is very good.

In general, iron-carbon martensite is hard and brittle in the as-quenched condition and becomes softer and more ductile only after tempering. Carbon-free-iron-nickel-martensite, on the other hand, is relatively soft and ductile, but becomes hard, strong, and tough after aging. Therefore the maraging steels can be fabricated while they are in a comparatively ductile martensitic condition and later strengthened by a simple aging treatment. The first the iron-nickel martensitic alloy contained about 0.01 per cent of carbon, with either 20 or 25 per cent of nickel and 1.5 to 2.5 per cent of aluminum and titanium. Later an 18 per cent nickel steel, containing cobalt, molybdenum, and titanium was developed, and still more recently a series of 12 per cent nickel steels, containing chromium and molybdenum, was introduced. Fig. 11–8 shows the chemical composition and mechanical properties of the 18 per cent, 20 per cent, and 25 per cent nickel steels. As shown on the chart in Fig. 11–8, the 18 per cent nickel maraging steel contains from about 7 to 9–1/2 per cent cobalt, 3 to 5 per cent molybdenum and 0.1 to 0.8 per cent titanium. By proper adjustment of these percentages, yield strengths in the range of 200,000 to 300,000 lb per sq in. can be obtained. Inasmuch as molybdenum has an adverse effect on toughness, more cobalt rather than molybdenum is used to attain the highest strength levels.

Steel	Ni	Ti	Al	Co	Mo	Cb	Treatment	Cold Work, %	Direction	Yld Str (0.2% Offset), 1000 psi	Ten Str, 1000 psi	Elong, %	Notch Ten Str, 1000 psi
18 Ni 200 Grade[b]	17-19	0.15-0.25	0.05-0.15	8-9	3-3.5	—	Marage 900 F	0	L	203	209	11	321
									T	208	212	11	323
250 Grade	17-19	0.3-0.5	0.05-0.15	7-8	4.6-5.1	—	Marage 900 F	0	L	252	262	4.5	263
								50	L	290	292	2.5	261
300 Grade	18-19	0.5-0.8	0.05-0.15	8.5-9.5	4.6-5.2	—	Marage 900 F	0	L	309	310	2.5	275
Cast Grade	16-17.5	0.15-0.45	0.05-0.15	9.5-11	4.4-4.9	—	Marage 900 F	0		225-250	240-260	5-11	313-354
20 Ni	19-20	1.3-1.6	0.15-0.30	—	—	0.3-0.5	Refrig[e] + marage 850 F	0	L	256	264	6	271
									T	260	269	4.5	260
								50	L	264	273	4.2	211
									T	264	281	3.3	161
							Refrig[e] + marage 900 F	0	L	244	256	4.5	256
									T	246	257	3.5	248
								50	L	273	281	4	180
									T	279	293	3.7	256
25 Ni	25-26	1.3-1.6	0.15-0.30	—	—	0.3-0.5	Ausage[f] + refrig[e] + marage 800 F	0	L	225	245	9	209
									T	226	248	8	—
								25*	L	254	268	4	211
									T	261	278	4	205
								75*	T	288	300	3	134
							Ausage[f] + refrig[e] + marage 850 F	0	L	258	272	4.5	150
									T	262	284	4.5	—
								50*	L	262	273	4	228
									T	272	273	2	224

*Plus (in %): B, 0.003 added; Zr, 0.02 added; Cu, 0.05 added; C, 0.03 max; Mn, 0.1 max; Si, 0.10 max; P, 0.01 max; S, 0.01 max. [b]Data for 1-in. thk plate. [c]All material annealed at 1500 F except cast grade which was homogenized at 2100 F for 4 hr. [d]K_t >12.
*At −100 F for 16 hr. [f]At 1300 F for 4 hr. [g]In all cases, cold work eliminates need for ausage.

Fig. 11-8. Maraging Steels. (Courtesy of *Materials in Design Engineering* published by Reinhold Publishing Corporation, New York.)

Heat treatment of the maraging steels is very simple; they are annealed for one hour at 1500F, air cooled to room temperature, and then aged at about 900F for 3 hours. To obtain different strength levels, the aging treatment can be varied from the one described above. Inasmuch as the 18 per cent nickel alloy transforms to martensite during air cooling from 1500F, it can be maraged immediately after hot rolling eliminating the annealing step, although this step is usually included to ensure uniformity of starting the desired microstructure. It is believed that strengthening the 18 per cent nickel maraging steels during aging is achieved mainly by the precipitation of extremely fine particles of the intermetallic compounds Ni_3Mo and Ni_3Ti on dislocation lattice sites.

In addition to the 18 per cent, 20 per cent, and 25 per cent nickel maraging steels, another series of these steels is represented by the 12 per cent Ni-Cr-Mo series. Steels in this series, after solution annealing and aging, develop yield strengths of from 150,000 to 200,000 lb per sq in. and are identified by nickel contents of from 10 to 12 per cent, chromium from 3 to 5 per cent, molybdenum of about 3 per cent, and amounts of titanium and aluminum properly adjusted to develop yield strengths in this range.

The 12 per cent series of maraging steels (12 per cent nickel content) usually show notch-toughness considerably higher than that obtained in alloy steels quenched and tempered to the strength levels indicated above.

11-18   High Temperature Metals

Continuing demands for high stresses and maximum efficiency in present and future designs have brought about an expanding spectrum of materials with yield strengths above the 175,000 psi level. Not only is this true for materials at room temperatures, but it has become more imperative than ever that we have structural metals that will meet high strength requirements at temperatures from 1200 to 2500F and even higher. The subject of high-strength, heat-resistant metals and alloys is of major importance to every metallurgist and engineer in the design of structural members built to conquer space and to extend the range of rockets, missiles, and aircraft, as well as for the spacecraft of today and tomorrow. Designs must be found for power plants that consume fuel at high temperatures, and metals to do the job must keep pace with design. This is particularly true for the leading edges of airframes subject to intense aerodynamic heating. Other fields being explored along these lines include nuclear power, commercial aircraft, automotive engines, chemical processing, and steam power plants. In many instances high temperature applications involve essentially non-structural materials, such as furnace liners, ablative skins, and thermal insulations.

11-19   Essential Properties in Heat-Resistant Metals and Alloys

In the important matter of correct selection of materials for given applications, stress-temperature parameters are of primary inportance in most metals. Revolving around these parameters are other properties, also directly related to service conditions, such as short-time tensile strength and the ability to resist oxidation at high temperatures. Finally, factors other than service conditions must be considered, including response of the metals to strengthening treatments, the forms in which the materials can be produced, and the methods by which they can be formed and joined.

All of the properties of a metal are affected by the great sensitivity of high temperature materials to the interrelated factors of composition, and the way in which they have been processed. In producing these materials, the procedures used, composition, traces and impurities, the degree of cold working, and the heat treatments and aging procedures used, all have very important effects. In fact, they determine relative strength levels for different types of loading at certain temperatures; furthermore, they affect structural stability by shifting critical temperature ranges (such as transformation and recrystallization ranges), discussed in Chapter 5.

One of the critical factors which affect both fabricability and service operation is *structural stability.* Because of the high degree of mobility of atoms at elevated temperatures, few alloys are stable for very long. By way of example, age-hardened materials may over-age, work-hardened materials may anneal, and alloys containing many different elements may form entirely new phases and lose strength or, in some cases, become brittle. Other alloys may become hot-short or brittle in certain temperature ranges. These characteristics usually limit the effectiveness of strengthening treatments because such treatments cannot always be performed in the most advantageous temperature range.

Important parameters to every property of materials are temperature and time. In fact the threefold factors of temperature-time-stress are the so-called "long-time" properties—creep and stress-rupture strength—that are usually accepted as criteria for high temperature service of a material. The term "long-time," of course, is given here in quotes since such a term is relative today. For example, service during which high stress levels and extreme temperatures are encountered for a few hours, minutes, or even seconds, in some cases, is, in terms of materials deformation and stability, recognized to be long-time service in such applications.

Load-bearing structures for service at atmospheric temperature are designed on the basis of yield strength, in most cases. In other cases, they are designed on the basis of tensile strength, both the yield strength and tensile strength determined at room temperature by means of the tension test method. In service at ordinary temperatures, with a design stress determined in this manner, metal behaves in an elastic manner; that is, the structure undergoes an elastic deformation immediately upon the application of the load, and no further deformation takes place with time. When the load is removed, the structure returns to its original dimensions.

At elevated temperatures the behavior of metal is found to be different; a structure designed according to the principles used for atmospheric temperature service continues to deform with time after load application, even though the data used in the design may have been based on tension tests at the temperature under consideration. This deformation with time is called *creep*, since at the design stresses at which it is first recognized, it takes place at a relatively slow rate. When *creep* was first investigated 30 or 40 years ago, it was logical for the experimenters or designers to decrease the stress to a point low enough so that creep did not take place. In this, however, it was discovered that the lower the creep stress, the greater the sensitivity of the measuring apparatus; low stresses would have to be used to eliminate the possibility of creep that could be measured. In fact the required stresses were so low, and the section size large so correspondingly, that the application of metals to service at high temperatures was considerably retarded. As a result, a new and more rational technique of design was developed and is now used by most engineers and designers, This technique recognizes the existence of creep and is concerned, not with an attempt to avoid it, but rather with limiting it to tolerable values within the expected life of the structural parts.

Rate of creep depends upon the stress placed on the material and also upon the temperature and history of the material. For these reasons, the creep-testing laboratory has as its function: the determination of the dependence of creep upon these variables of stress, temperature, and history of the material under consideration. At elevated temperatures, fractures are generally intercrystalline rather than transcrystalline at room temperature, resulting from the mechanical action of slip, such as found in ductile metals. The type of fracture that takes place is influenced by temperature and also by the rate of strain. The temperature, or range of temperatures, at which grain boundaries become weaker than the grains themselves, is known as the *equicohesive temperature* of a metal or alloy.

Other service requirements for materials may be classified as mechanical, thermal, and environmental, and these may be considered individually or in combination. Many combinations of mechanical loads are imposed on today's airframes and power plant components, and such applications necessitate a knowledge of such properties as short-time tensile strength, elongation, impact strength, ductility, fatigue strength, shear strength, notch-impact and notch-tensile strengths, bearing strength, and modulus of elasticity.

There are also thermal mechanical properties, such as thermal shock and thermal fatigue, both of which are of great importance, although inadequate data are available for their effect on most materials. Thermal failures result from sudden, intermittent, or widely fluctuating temperatures. Structures with high strength-weight ratios are increasingly important for most applications at high temperatures. In airborne vehicles the penalty exacted by one extra pound of structural weight multiplies because of the extra fuel and power needed. This, in turn, adds weight and requires added lifting potential. Considering the fact that it takes one ton of thrust to lift and place a single pound of material in space at a distance of 300 miles, it can be appreciated that it is imperative to keep the weight of aerospace structures down to a minimum, and the strengths extremely high—high enough to fill the requirement plus an adequate safety factor.

Still another matter which must be given consideration is the fact materials which satisfy strength and other service requirements at elevated service temperatures may have limitations that cause serious problems at other temperatures. For example, some alloys that *maintain* their strength levels at high temperatures do not necessarily possess high strength, per se, in relation to other materials at lower temperatures. Some alloys that operate at service-required temperatures for a time have lower strengths at lower temperatures than they did prior to service. Also, some alloys adequate for service-stresses at elevated temperatures often lack ductility at room temperature.

11-20   Physical Thermal Properties

Physical thermal properties, such as the coefficient of thermal expansion, thermal conductivity, emissivity, and melting point, are other important design factors that must be met in considering elevated temperature service. Thermal stresses resulting from differential expansion of parts subjected to different temperatures, or the differential expansion at a joint between metals having different coefficients of expansion, can produce 50 per cent or more of the total load applied to a part. There are many cases of failure on record that resulted from differential thermal expansion. Although it is true that a low coefficient of expansion is usually desirable, it is equally important, in the case of joints of dissimilar metals, that an *equivalent* coefficient of thermal expansion, either high or low, be utilized by the design engineer.

The property of *emissivity* has only recently been seriously considered by power plant engineers; however, it is extremely important that combustion chambers have an inside surface with as low an emissivity factor as possible, in order to reflect the maximum radiated heat from combustion gases. A ramjet engine, on the other hand, with a combustion chamber open to the sky, should have an emissivity factor that is as high as possible, in order to radiate maximum heat from the wall to the sky. The factor of emissivity can result in a difference of hundreds of degrees in operating wall temperatures.

The melting points of alloys have a direct relationship to their maximum service temperatures. Present structural materials, that are in general capable of unprotected operation at temperatures above 1500F have melting points below 2700F.

So far as the third service requirement—environmental—is concerned, the major properties to consider are resistance to scaling, oxidation, and chemical corrosion. The problem is complex, however, for although oxidation generally leads to low strength, some metals actually lose strength or ductility due to the fact that they have been protected from oxidation by coatings or reducing atmospheres. This situation is caused by internal oxidation's actually strengthening some metals around intercrystalline cracks, and, in other instances, solid solution alloying may occur with oxygen from the atmosphere.

The nature of the environment and temperature determine the kind of reaction that takes place. Inasmuch as protective coatings seem to afford the best hope in this area, the properties of castings may actually be of greater importance, in the end, than the properties of the structural materials themselves.

11-21   Tests for Determining High Temperature Properties of Metals

During the past 40 years a great deal of work has been done to develop tests for the evaluation of alloys for high temperature service. In the early days different laboratories obtained different results from identical tests, many of these discrepancies being due to test procedures used, and not the alloy being tested. Now most laboratories follows a standard test procedure and are therefore able to check with each other closely and with American Society for Testing Materials standards (ASTM).

Tests made on materials are, for the most part, made for the purpose of establishing reproducibility, so they cannot be considered as being fundamental. The main purpose of these tests is to determine accurately that the material in question meets some specification which may be empirically related to a certain application. Very few laboratory tests have been designed that will reproduce actual conditions in service. As an example, all laboratory tests for evaluating types of strength (tensile, yield, creep, rupture time, relaxation) are based on uniaxial tensile stresses, whereas, in service, very seldom are stresses all in a single direction. It should also be understood that all tests and their results are statistically distributed. In other words, there is no such thing as a true tensile strength, a true creep strength, or an exact rupture strength; instead, there is a range of values one may expect to find in making duplicate tests. This is why the so-called factor of safety is introduced according to which the reported strength values obtained are divided by a realistic number, such as 4 or 5, for purposes of design calculations in order to be on the safe side.

The tests that are in most common use today for determining high temperature properties of materials are as follows:

1. STRUCTURAL-STABILITY TESTS
   Tensile
   Impact (Charpy and Izod)
   Hardness (Brinell, Rockwell, Vickers, etc.)
   Ductility in rupture
   Metallographic examinations
2. SURFACE-STABILITY TESTS
   Corrosion
   Metallographic
   Impact

3. LOAD-CARRYING ABILITY TESTS
   Tensile
   Creep
   Rupture
   Creep-Rupture
   Relaxation
4. FATIGUE TESTS
5. IMPACT TESTS
6. THERMAL EXPANSION TESTS
7. HOT WORKABILITY TESTS
8. HOT HARDNESS TESTS

Several years ago a joint committee, made up of members of American Society for Testing Materials (ASTM) and American Society of Mechanical Engineers (ASME), developed a standard procedure for conducting all of these high temperature tests, the official name of the group being the Joint ASTM-ASME Committee on the Effect of Temperature on the Properties of Metals. The standard procedure they established covers selection of materials, test specimen dimensions, apparatus used, procedures to be followed, and the recording and reporting of data. Since these standard procedures were set up, there has been a high degree of uniformity and agreemen of results of tests among different laboratories testing the same material.

Basically, the laboratory equipment required for most of the physical tests at elevated temperatures mentioned above is the same as that used at room temperature, except for the following:

1. A furnace must be inserted between the heads of the machine, in order to heat the specimen to, and maintain it at, the desired temperature.
2. A temperature controller and, preferably, a temperature recorder, must be provided for maintaining the temperature within the required limits.
3. In case the elastic properties are to be determined, a high temperature extensometer must be used for determining the strain or deformation resulting from the applied load.

In the case of surface-stability tests dealing with corrosion at high temperatures, there is increasing concern with aerospace and outerspace developments during the past few years. Although this subject will be covered in more detail in Chapter 15, it should be stated here that corrosion occurs in various chemical solutions, in air, from exhaust fumes, steam, etc. With the new and increasingly more severe corrosive conditions in our complex civilization, the effects of corrosion on residual mechanical properties is an important aspect of this problem, at room, elevated, and subnormal temperatures.

To determine *hot hardness values* for metals at elevated temperatures, a conventional Rockwell hardness testing unit is used after being modified by adding a furnace, for heating the specimen, and water-cooling jackets at the ends to prevent the heat from damaging the testing equipment. Also, a protective atmosphere of either dry nitrogen or argon gas is maintained around the specimen to prevent corrosion. The formation of oxide scale would obviously invalidate the hardness reading. As far as the specimens themselves are concerned, they are the same size and are prepared in the same manner as those for tests at room temperature.

Although, as previously stated, it is impossible to reproduce exactly in the laboratory the conditions found in service, laboratory tests are, nevertheless, of great importance in the selection of the correct materials to be used in structures, as well as in determining the cause or causes of failure of metals when in service. More will be discussed on the subject of service failures and fractures of metals in the field, in Chapter 17.

11-22   Selection of Alloys for Specific High Temperature Applications

Ever since the phenomenon of creep was first observed about 35 years ago, a large amount of data on high temperature metals and alloys has been collected. It is apparent from a study of these findings that different alloys are capable of rendering satisfactory service in certain applications; in fact, it has been found that many different alloys will do a commendable job. So the problem of here we can select the best and most suitable alloy for the specific application we have in mind is to be selected.

Several factors are involved in the selection of alloys for varying applications among them:

1. Expected life of the product
2. Temperature and stress to which it will be subjected
3. Corrosion characteristics of the alloy
4. Uniformity of temperature to which it is subjected
5. How often it is inspected
6. How much deformation is allowable, if any
7. Hazards involved in case of failure
8. Availability and cost of the alloy

It will be observed from these criteria that three of them, (temperature and stress, permissible deformation, and resistance to corrosion), are physical properties of the alloy. Expected life, uniformity of temperature, frequency of inspection, and hazards involved, are dependent on operating environment and conditions. Also, it will be recognized that all of the above factors except the last two are more or less dependent on the others. For example, the expected life may vary from less than one hour to over 35 years, and this has a direct bearing on the amount of allowable stress and maximum temperature at which the alloy is required to operate. The degree of corrosion expected will also influence the choice of both the type of alloy to be used and the section size of the part involved.

The expected service life of the product has an important influence on the alloy chosen to be used. For example, in considering steels to be used as tubular members in thermal cracking stills in petroleum plants, some companies have standardized, selecting expensive high-alloy steels, such as the 18–8 (18 per cent chromium—8 per cent nickel) type, which have an expected life for economical operation of at least 70,000 hours, or about 8 years, and in some cases over 120,000 hours, or 14 years. Other petroleum companies, using the same type of equipment and processing the same type of oils, adopt the less expensive, low-alloy chromium-molybdenum steels and expect to make partial replacements after 3 or 4 years perhaps replacing all the tubes in question within 5 or 6 years. Both of these practices have merit; in the first case, using high-alloy 18–8 steel, investment at the outset is considerably greater and the loss of tubes through faulty operation or mechanical abuse is much more serious. It is also true that because of technological developments, with changing practices, equipment may be obsolete in a few years. This is virtually true now, as the old style thermal cracking units are replaced in many plants by catalytic cracking units. A distinct advantage, of course, of the more expensive equipment in the pipes is the important fact that it is possible to get more continuous operation with a minimum of downtime for repairs—and this is most desirable.

Determining the correct alloy to use, so far as service life is concerned, becomes a problem in economics; just how long do we really want the product or alloy to last, all things considered? The temperature to be considered in the computations of structural design in any given application, is the temperature of the metal parts, and not necessarily that of the material or product being heated. It is important that we keep the two separate in our thinking, as they are not interchangeable; for example, in the tubes used for heating fluids or gases, the temperature of the metal parts must be higher than the material temperature we are processing; otherwise it would be impossible to achieve the proper heating required. In such problems, the amount of temperature difference will depend on such factors, such as the rate of heat input, the nature of the alloy, the cleanliness of the metal surfaces. The temperature difference between the metal and the material being heated through the walls of tubes is, in general, about 50 to 100F; however, if the metal surfaces between the tubes and the material heated are not kept clean, this differential obviously is much greater.

Although corrosion will be discussed more fully in Chapter 15, it is important to note here that when severe corrosion is anticipated, an alloy with high corrosion-resistance should be selected. In this connection, when severe corrosion is expected, it is the part of wisdom to design the cross-sectional areas with greater thickness, so that corrosion losses can be tolerated without causing an overstressed condition. On the other hand, if heat is passed through the alloy, any increase in wall thickness will result in less efficient heat transfer, and, consequently, higher metal temperature. It would follow that this results in higher rates of corrosion, thicker layers of scale, and a further lowering of thermal efficiency. Scale formation must, in all such operations, be kept to a minimum, especially where prolonged service life is desired. The best and most effective alloying elements for high temperature corrosion-resistance are chromium, silicon, and aluminum. In some applications, however, where the formation of a certain amount of scale is desirable, such as in the case of alloys used as piercing plugs in making seamless tubes, and in mandrels in many hot-working operations where a metal-to-metal contact is made, this scale formation may be not only tolerated but desired. Actually, the relative corrosion-resistance of alloys cannot be adequately evaluated in the laboratory; the best industrial evaluation is accomplished by the use of corrosion test specimens installed in commercial units and, through trial-and-error, determining the best alloy for the job in question. Until the appearance of jet aircraft, the major application of high temperature alloys for airplanes was in engine exhaust valves; however, despite the alloy used, premature failures often occurred. Subsequently, the valves were made hollow and filled with metallic sodium. Inasmuch as sodium has high thermal conductivity, the valve head temperature was considerably reduced. The seating face of the valve, and the tappet, were metal-sprayed with stellite to increase hardness and resistance to wear, so the use of sodium and stellite increased the life of the valves appreciably.

Although the same alloys were used in the first aircraft jet engines as in the turbo supercharger, these have been replaced with age-hardenable alloys such as A286 (15 per cent chromium—26 per cent nickel—1-1/4 per cent molybdenum and 2.0 per cent titanium). The S816 blades were replaced by a nickel-base alloy such as M252 (20 per cent chromium—54 per cent nickel—10 per cent cobalt—10 per cent molybdenum—2-1/2 per cent titanium, and 3/4 per cent aluminum.) There is a great demand for alloys with much higher strengths than that of A286 and M252, and progress is being made along this line, as shown in Table 11–1, which lists the compositions of high temperature alloys in the iron-base, nickel-base, cobalt-base and refractory categories. Among these, Rene 41, which is available in both wrought and cast form, shows great promise, due partially to the fact that it has high purity, being vacuum melted and refined.

A list of the refractory alloys, with melting points above 3400F are as follows:

Tungsten	6170F
Rhenium	5740
Tantalum	5425
Osmium	4900
Molybdenum	4760
Ruthenium	4500
Iridium	4449
Columbium	4380
Rhodium	3571
Chromium	3430
Vanadium	3150
Hafnium	3100

A great deal of research and development is being done as these refractory metals and their alloys seem to hold the most promise for applications requiring strength above 2000F. The metals which are the object of most attention are tungsten, tantalum, molybdenum, columbium, and chromium. All of those materials have about the same strengths at the same homologous temperatures (i.e., the same per cent of melting point).

The refractory metals are, as a rule, produced in the form of a powder (sponge) which is consolidated prior to further processing by one of three methods: powder metallurgy, employing hydrostatic pressure and elevated temperature, by which method large ingots are produced; arc-casting, which produces molybdenum alloys as well as some of the so-called "super-alloys;" and electron beam melting, this method developed for obtaining high purity, and somewhat limited in alloying ability, but advantageous in the production of columbium, tantalum, and their alloys.

Although, as a group, refractory metals do show high strength properties over a wide range of temperatures above 1600F, their properties at room and inter-mediate temperatures are considerably lower than those of the super-alloys. Columbium and tantalum have better low-temperature ductility than the others listed above. In addition to their warm-working property, the elevated temperature strength of the refractory metals may be improved by alloying them to obtain solid solutions, interstitial solutions, and dispersions of insoluble compounds.

One of the adverse properties of refractory metals is their characteristic of extremely low resistance to high-temperature oxidation. This disadvantage has been overcome to a degree by alloying; however, considerably more work is being done to overcome this tendency. At present it is necessary to rely on coatings on the refractory metals; however, many of the coatings themselves are still in the research and development stage with investigation of cladding with nickel-base alloys, deposition of silicon by means of the vapor-phase, and applying coatings with compositions of ceramics possessing similar thermal-expansion characteristics. By improving the oxidation resistance, and increasing the hardness of the molybdenum base alloys by the addition of 0.50 per cent titanium, great promise is held for overcoming the oxidation difficulty.

At the present time, with research in arc-cast ductile tungsten going on, it is possible to produce forgeable tungsten ingots on a small scale, thereby achieving a break-through with this highest-melting-point metal which holds great promise for future high-temperature applications of tungsten for structural members.

Tantalum-base alloys, containing 17 per cent tantalum along with some tungsten and molybdenum, produced by the vacuum induction melting furnace method, had been found to have superior properties for current requirements for high-temperature, high-tensile strengths, such as are used in the Apollo project—America's project to land a man on the moon. It has been found that, in general, the wrought alloys have superior strength characteristics at 1250F although they are also generally sensitive to variations in finishing temperatures; however, with proper control in heat treatment this sensitivity can be held to a minimum.

11-23 Alloy Tool Steels

The main functions of the alloying elements in tool steels are increasing hardenability, forming hard, wear-resisting alloy carbides, and increasing resistance to softening when tempered. These attributes are usually attained by high carbon and alloy content. Alloy tool steels may be classified roughly according to the extent of the utilization of these three functions. The three classifications, on this basis, are

1. *Comparatively low-alloy tool steels.* Higher hardenability than afforded by plain carbon, so that they may be hardened in heavier sections or with less drastic quenches, resulting in less distortion.
2. *Intermediate-alloy tool steels.* Usually containing such elements as tungsten, molybdenum, or vanadium to form hard, wear-resisting carbides. These are used in the manufacture of fast-finishing tools, in which the retention of a smooth cutting edge is of major importance.
3. *High-speed tool steels.* Containing sizeable amounts of carbide-forming elements which serve a dual role, that of providing wear-resisting carbides, and promoting secondary hardening, thereby increasing resistance to softening at elevated temperatures during tempering.

Some typical compositions of these three classes of tool steels are shown in Table 11–3. Detailed information on types of tool steels, their composition, heat treatment, and applications may be found in the eighth edition of *Metals Handbook* (1961) of the American Society for Metals, and also in an excellent book, *Tool Steels*, by Gill, Rose, Roberts, Johnstin, and George, published by the American Society for Metals, Metals Park, Ohio.

TABLE 11–3. Composition of Some Tool Steels (Per Cent)

Class	Type	C	Mn	Si	Ni	Cr	Mo	W	V	Co
1	Non-Deforming ...	0.90	1.60	...	......	....	....	......	...	...
1	Chromium	0.90–1.10	0.25	0.25	......	1.0–2.0	....	......	...	...
1	Chromium-Vanadium	0.50–1.10	0.25	0.25	......	0.75–1.50	....	......	0.20	...
1	Chromium-Nickel .	0.40–0.75	0.40	0.25	1.0–2.0	0.75–2.25	....	......	...	...
1	Chromium-Molybdenum ...	0.40–0.75	0.40	0.25	......	0.75–1.50	0.20–0.50	......	...	...
1	Nickel-Chromium-Molybdenum ...	0.40–0.75	0.40	0.25	1.0–2.0	0.75–1.50	0.20–0.50	......	...	...
2	Tungsten Finishing	1.35	0.25	0.25	......	....	....	3.0–4.0	...	...
2	Tungsten Finishing	1.35	0.25	0.25	......	0.50–1.00	....	3.0–4.0	...	...
2	Tungsten Finishing	1.35	0.25	0.25	......	....	0.50–1.00	3.0–4.0	...	...
2	Tungsten Chisel...	0.50	0.25	0.25	......	1.50	....	2.10	0.25	...
3	18-4-1 High Speed.	0.50–0.80	0.25	0.25	......	4.00	....	18.00	1.00	...
3	18-4-3 High Speed.	0.95	0.25	0.25	......	4.00	....	18.00	3.00	...
3	Tungsten Cobalt ..	0.75	0.25	0.25	......	4.00	....	18.00	1.00	5.00
3	Molybdenum High Speed..........	0.75	0.25	0.25	......	4.00	8.50	1.50	1.00	...
3	Tungsten-Molybdenum High Speed.....	0.80	0.25	0.25	......	4.00	4.75	5.75	1.50	...

(Courtesy of United States Steel Corporation, Pittsburgh, Pennsylvania.)

There are hundreds of varieties of tool steels, in addition to those shown in Table 11–3, required by the diverse uses in various applications. The compositions and types of tool steels available for even a single application would constitute a list too long for this text. Handbooks on tool steels list most of the best but, obviously, not all of them. It is obvious, however, that high-speed tool steels are used for applications requiring long life at relatively high operating temperatures, such as are used for heavy cuts or for high-speed machining operations. The intermediate-alloy tool steels are used for finishing operations requiring extreme wear-resistance, where ability to retain a smooth cutting edge on light cuts is of paramount importance. The first classification of tool steels is, as above noted, the general purpose variety, choice of which is based primarily on size of section, distortion permissible, intricacy of design, and the toughness and hardness requirements of the application in which they are to be used. All of these are, to a considerable extent, functions of the hardenability of the steels. In applications where a low "movement" (required change of dimension in hardening), the higher hardenability steels are used, inasmuch as relatively slow oil or even air quenches are used. Such steels as these are also designed to be capable of hardening from relatively low quenching temperatures, which also tend to reduce distortion and the danger of quench cracking. Higher carbon steels within this class are used for applications requiring high resistance to wear or abrasion; the lower carbon steels are used in applications where resistance to shock, impact, and vibration are major considerations.

11-24   Heat Treatment of Alloy Tool Steels

The general principles of heat treatment as described in Chapter 10 obviously apply also to the heat treatment of alloy tool steels. Alloy tool steels are, in general, high carbon, and many of them are also relatively high-alloy steels, so that the heat treatment of these grades necessarily involves special precautions to eliminate or reduce distortion, cracking, and decarburization. In order to minimize thermal stress, the heating operation must be conducted at a slow rate, and, furthermore, relatively low austenitizing temperatures are usually maintained to keep distortion and cracking to a minimum. The heating operation is usually carried out in two steps, the first a preliminary preheat to an intermediate temperature prior to the second stage of heating to final temperatures. It is also customary to use controlled atmospheres, to pack the steel in cast-iron chips, or to heat it in neutral liquid baths, in order to keep to a minimum any decarburization, very harmful in tool steels. In the case of alloy-tool steels, because of their sensitivity to cracking and distortion, relatively mild quenches are commonly used in the heat-treating process. In fact, in some cases, many of them are of high enough hardenability characteristics to permit quenching them in air.

Inasmuch as residual stresses are high in high-carbon tool steels after quenching, the stress-relieving function of the tempering operation is of major importance. Therefore, tempering to relieve these stresses, and to toughen the steels, is an important part of the heat-treating operation and it should immediately follow the quenching operation. Since high hardness is usually desired, tempering temperature are usually rather low (250 to 450F). However, in such cases as die applications, where resistance to shock and impact is of major importance, higher tempering temperatures may be used. Because of phase changes that occur at a temperature range of 500 to 600F, tempering within this range should be avoided, as the formation of martensite begins in this range.

High-speed steels, typified by the 18 per cent tungsten, 4 per cent chromium, 1 per cent vanadium composition, differ from the lower alloy tool steels in that they have a higher percentage of carbide-forming elements, and also in that the secondary hardening effects of these elements are much more fully realized. They also provide a high resistance to softening at higher temperatures. A special heat treatment for these steels is required, in order that their outstanding properties may be fully realized. In general, this procedure consists of heating the steel to a high temperature (2150 to 2400F) in order to achieve solution of a substantial percentage of the alloy carbides, then quenching to room temperature, at which stage a large amount of austenite is retained; this is followed by tempering at 1000 to 1150F and again cooling to room temperature. All of the carbides are precipitated during the tempering operation, resulting in a marked secondary hardening and in a reduction of alloy content in the retained austenite (which is then transformed to martensite when cooled to room temperature). This results in still greater hardness; in fact, it is often desirable to temper a second time in order to temper the martensite formed on cooling from the original tempering operation.

Excessive grain growth and decarburization are obviously undesirable, and in order to prevent or to minimize them, the steels are held at the high temperature of quenching for only a few minutes prior to actual quenching. It is customary to preheat these steels to between 1400 and 1600F before they are transferred to the high-heat furnace, in order to eliminate the severe thermal shock that would occur if the cold tool steel were placed in the high-temperature furnace, and also to minimize possibility of decarburization by curtailing the time of exposure to high temperature.

Quenching is accomplished either in air, oil, or liquid baths; however, the air quench has the disadvantage forming a tightly adherent scale to the steel during the cooling period. Oil quenching facilitates the removal of this scale; however, it also tends to bring about higher internal stresses. By removing parts from the oil at the flash point, however, these higher stresses may be held to a minimum, so that the tools will be air cooled through the temperature range in which the transition to martensite takes place. Another method of quenching is used a great deal to ensure low quenching stresses; this one consists of quenching in a liquid bath at 1000F, holding until equalized, cooling in air to a temperature of from 200 to 300F, and then tempering rapidly in the usual manner. Intricate tools may be handled in this way and hardened without undue distortion and cracking, prevalent with some other techniques.

11-25 Availability of Tool Steels

Although about 16 grades of tool steels are carried in stock in most tool steel warehousing areas, at least 30 grades can be obtained from stock in certain areas or from the principal warehouses of producers of the steel. So far as popularity is concerned, the molybdenum-bearing types presently make up about 85 per cent of all high-speed steels produced. This was at first the result of the shortage of tungsten during World War II and the Korean war. However, during the 1950 to 1952 period its use was further accentuated by sharp increases in the price of tungsten, reaching a differential of 50 cents per pound between tungsten- and molybdenum-bearing high speed tool steels. Applying, as it did, to 20,000 tons of high-speed steel per year, the increased cost it amounted to more than $20 million per year—a sizeable factor, from an economic standpoint, in the selection of tool steel.

There has also been a noticeable trend toward greater use of vanadium-bearing high-speed steels, because of their better wear-resistance and longer tool life, brought about by the harder vanadium carbides.

11-26 Cost of Tool Steels

Tool steels as a rule are sold on a per pound basis, the practice in the industry being to add the costs of fabricating to a base price for any specific size, shape, condition, or quantity. The costs of fabricating are known as extras, and are defined in the following manner:

Base price reflects the cost of raw materials and expenses incurred in melting and refining to the required chemical composition, as well as the yield of useable tool steel.

Added to the base price of the steel are extras for:
> Quantity, annealing, heat treating, size, rough-turning, rough-machining, grinding, cold drawing, centerless grinding, cutting and wastage, shape extras, forging extras, and perhaps a few more when, as, and where they are applicable.

Although some of the above considerations may seem to be in the realm of economics rather than metallurgy, it still behooves the metallurgist and other engineers, who are buying or using tool steels, to be fully acquainted with the costs of these steels as well as their availability in considering the design of tools for various applications.

QUESTIONS

1. What is the main reason for adding alloying elements to steel?

2. Give some of the other reasons for adding alloying elements to steel.

3. What is the most important alloying element in steel? Why?

4. How may all steels be classified, in general?

5. List the several methods of manufacturing steel in the United States.

6. By which method is the largest tonnage of steel produced?

7. How may steels be classified according to their end use?

8. Plain carbon steels may be classified into what three categories?

9. Are other elements also present in carbon steels? If so, for what purpose?

10. Define the term "alloy steels."

11. Explain the current method of classifying steels, as developed by the American Society for Testing Materials, the American Iron and Steel Institute, and the Society of Automotive Engineers.

12. In addition to the designations asked for in the preceding question, how are steels designated to indentify the manner in which they were melted in their manufacture?

13. How are alloying elements added to steel, when, and in what form?

14. Name the two phases that are most commonly present in low-alloy steels, and indicate how the elements distribute themselves in these phases.

15. Discuss the purposes and effects of various alloying elements when added to steel.

16. Different effects are produced in an alloying procedure with the combining of two metals; however, the simplest effects occur in what types of combinations?

17. How may we quantitatively evaluate the effects of alloys on grain size and hardenability in steels? Make a diagram to illustrate.

18. Explain the "multiplying factor" as used in the consideration of hardenability of steels. What were the findings of Grossman, Bain, and others, concerning the cumulative effects of alloying elements on hardenability?

19. Explain what is meant by the term "low alloy steels," and state why the listing of these steels as shown in Appendix C is valuable to the metallurgist and engineer.

20. What other term is applied to low-alloy steels? Explain.

21. Discuss the low-alloy nickel steels and the low-alloy manganese steels, so far as their composition, properties, and value to industry are concerned.

22. How may the temper-brittleness of low-alloy nickel-chromium steels be controlled?

23. Which of the alloying elements in low-alloy steels control the size of the austenite field? What are they called?

24. For what basic reasons do we add molybdenum to carbon steels?

25. To what group of low-alloy steels do we assign the term "triple-alloy" steels? Why are they important?

26. In what carbon range do the constructional alloy steels fall? Why?

27. Explain in some detail the term "maraging steels," and discuss their advantages over other steels, and their special properties.

28. Discuss the increasing requirements for high-temperature, high-tensile steels, and show how they are being met.

29. Power plant engineers are concerning themselves with the property "emissivity" of metals and alloys. Explain fully.

30. Why did different laboratories obtain different results in testing for high temperature properties of metals, years ago? How have these discrepancies been resolved?

31. How are the hot hardness values for metals at elevated temperatures determined? Is it possible to reproduce exactly in the laboratory conditions found in the field?

32. What are the several factors involved in the selection of alloys for various service applications? Which of these are in the category of physical properties?

33. Discuss the production and processing of most refractory metals and alloys. Is there any difference in their properties at elevated and room temperatures?

34. What is meant by the term "super-alloys"? Do they excel in their resistance to oxidation? Explain.

35. Into what three classifications may tool steels be divided? Discuss the purposes and qualifications of each class.

36. In general, what can be said regarding the heat treatment of tool steels of the alloy type?

37. What must the metallurgist and engineer know concerning the availability, cost, and pricing of tool steels? Why is this important?

References

Austin, James B., *Trends in the Metallurgy of Low-Alloy, High-Yield Strength Steels*. Philadelphia, Pennsylvania: American Society for Testing and Materials, 1963 Gillett Memorial Lecture.

Bain, Edgard, and Harold W. Paxton, *Functions of the Alloying Elements in Steel*. Metals Park, Ohio: American Society for Metals, 1961.

Clark, Donald S., *Engineering Materials and Processes*. Scranton, Pennsylvania: International Textbook Co. 1959.

Varney, W. R., *Physical Metallurgy for Engineers*. Princeton, New Jersey: D. Van Nostrand Co., Inc., 1952.

McGannon, Harold E., (Ed), *The Making, Shaping and Treating of Steels*. Pittsburgh, Pennsylvania: United States Steel Corporation, 1964.

Taylor, Lyman, (Ed.), *Metals Handbook*, 8th ed., 1964, Metals Park, Ohio: American Society for Metals.

Equipment and Techniques Used in Metallurgical Investigations

12-1 Macroscopic Examination of Metals

Often investigations of metals and alloys are made by the usual chemical and metallographic methods; however, in many instances they do not give a true picture of the entire piece being examined. This is due to the fact that, while metals are, for the most part, somewhat homogeneous in nature, they do have many inhomogeneities in them. In other words, they are heterogeneous. Such inhomogeneities are best observed by etching the piece of metal and then examining it with the naked eye, without the use of the metallurgical microscope. In certain cases the nature and severity of the heterogeneous portions of the metal may be observed advantageously.

The macroscopic examination is accomplished at a low magnification of less than 10 diameters using magnifying glass. Macroetching and the subsequent examination of the etched specimens are often employed as a method of control in the fabrication of both steel and nonferrous metals and alloys. For example, by macroetching selected samples at different stages in the forming process, defective material can be detected quickly in the early stages of operations. As a result, real savings can be effected by stopping operations if defects are found. Although the preparations and etching (macro) are not difficult, at times it is difficult properly to interpret what is revealed in the macro-inspection procedure. This ability requires considerable skill and experience; however, both of the these factors pay off in the ultimate value of the tests.

Macroscopic examinations of metal parts are made for the following reasons:

1. To examine fractures and to determine how and why they occurred. (More will be discussed on this subject in Chapter 14.)
2. To determine the amount and nature of crystalline heterogeneity.
3. To look for chemical heterogeneity because of impurities in the metal or alloy, and to localize segregation of certain chemical constituents. (At times these segregations are brought about intentionally, as when we introduce carbon into the surface of steel during case carburizing of steel.) In other instances the segregations are unintentional, such as in the case of sulfur, phosphorus, or chromium segregating in cast steels.
4. To look for cracks, gas pockets, and forging flow-lines.

TABLE 12–1. Etching Solutions for Revealing Macrostructure of Aluminum Alloys

Solution	Concentration		Specific Use
Sodium hydroxide	NaOH ....10 g		General-purpose macro-etch for clean-
	Water ....90 ml		ing surfaces, revealing unsoundness, cracks and gross defects.
Aqua Regia —HF	HCl (conc)	75 ml	For revealing grain structure of certain
	HNO_3 (conc)	25 ml	types of castings and alloys.
	HF (48%)	5 ml	
Hydrofluoric Acid	HF (48%) ......10 ml		General purpose macro-etch for reveal-
	Water ....90 ml		ing structure of high silicon alloy castings and forgings.
Sulfuric Acid	H_2SO_4 ....10 ml		Shows blow-holes, porosity, pipe, and
	Water ....90 ml		inclusion in steel
Hydrochloric Acid	HCl ....50 ml		Shows blow holes, porosity, pipe, and
	Water ....50 ml		inclusions in steel
Hydrochloric Acid	HCL (conc)	100%	Detects fatigue, service, hardening and grinding cracks.
Nital	HNO_3 .... 5%		Shows depth of penetrtaion of hard-
	Ethanol 95%		ness of heat treated samples.

Many other etching solutions are used for macro-etching, and for a complete list of them the student is referred to *Metals Handbook*, published by American Society for Metals, and to George Kehl's book, *Principles of Metallographic Laboratory Practice* (McGraw-Hill Book Company).

Of all the many etching reagents for macro-etching steel specimens, the one used more often than any others is a solution of one part commercial hydrochloric acid and one part water, the advantage of this solution being that it can be heated with little or no change in concentration. Due to the fact that fumes from this solution are corrosive, the work should be done under a hood. A temperature of 160F is recommended, for at this temperature the reaction of etching is vigorous and the solution does not evaporate too rapidly.

Obviously, interpretation of the results of macro-etching is important, for the results obtained are of great value if they are correctly interpreted. Surface seams,

internal cracks, and pipe are readily recognized; however, it is incorrect interpretation of evidence of segregation and dendritic structures, as revealed by deep
etching, that affords the greatest possibility for expensive errors and needless rejection
of material. For example, every pit does not indicate an inclusion, since pitting may
also result from acid attack around carbide particles. With interpretation of macroetched specimens, the following conditions may be determined accurately by a
skilled metallurgist:

1. *Cracks from etching* are caused by improper tempering of the hardened or
   otherwise highly stressed steels prior to macro-etching for otherwise sound
   steel may crack in the etching solution, leading to false conclusions.
2. *Grinding cracks.* Here again, although such cracks are usually easy to distinguish,
   hardened pieces should be softened by tempering prior to hot etching.
3. *Surface cracks,* as revealed by deep etching, usually follow an irregular path
   and may result from incorrect handling during the heating, forging, or rolling
   processes or cooling from the finishing temperature.
4. *Seams* in rolled material are of varying depths and usually extend in a straight
   path parallel to the direction of rolling.
5. *Center porosity,* if due to actual discontinuity within the metal, is probably
   more accurately classified as "pipe." Usually, however, the porosity is not
   visible until the specimen is etched, so the term "porosity" is generally
   restricted to segregations that are partially torn open during hot-rolling or
   forging.
6. *Unsound steel,* identified by numerous blow-holes and nonmetallic inclusions
   visible as the result of deep etch, usually means that both gases and oxides
   were distributed throughout the steel at the time the steel was in the casting
   state.
7. *Nonmetallic inclusions and metallic segregates.* The former usually appear as pits
   and must not be confused with pits that result from the etching out of metallic
   segregates. Segregations are revealed in the severity of the acid attack on
   affected areas.
8. *Internal cracks,* sometimes called "*flakes,*" "*cooling cracks,*" or "*thermal cracks,*"
   can be detected by the macro-etch test and identified by a fracture test
   of a hardened specimen in which the cracks are revealed as brightly crystalline spots.
9. *Flow-lines,* although not necessarily indicative of defective steel, depending on
   whether they are parallel or perpendicular to the direction of applied stresses,
   can be revealed by macro-etching, in which a longitudinal section will show
   more or less well-defined flow-lines resulting from elongation of structural
   constituents. When it is difficult to develop flow-lines on a particular piece
   of steel, the etched surface may be painted with India ink. Then, when the
   ink dries, the surface may be rubbed lightly with a fine abrasive cloth, resulting
   in the removal of the ink from the high portions of the surface and leaving the
   "valleys" darkened, thereby providing the contrast needed to show up the
   flow-lines in the material.
       The tensile strength of the material is, in general, greater in the direction
   of flow, while the shear strength is greater in a direction perpendicular to the
   flow direction. Information about the nature and direction of flow-lines in

metals is of great significance to engineers and designers enabling them to capitalize on the best properties of the materials in question.

12-2   Microscopic Examination of Metals

For microscopic examination, it is usually necessary to cut specimens to a size that will be convenient for polishing. Obviously, such specimens should be cut with a hacksaw and at no time should any other method, such as use of a cutting torch, be used for such extraction, as this would alter the microstructure of the specimen and render the results of the tests invalid. To be of value, metallographic specimens, just as is true of any other type of testing or sampling material, must be truly representative of the parent metal from which it is extracted, both in composition and physical condition.

Ordinarily, the purpose of the investigation, and the shape and condition of the material, indicate the position from which the specimen should be cut, but there are several general rules that are followed for best results:

1. If the purpose of the examination is to find the cause of failure of the part in question, the specimen should be taken from an area close to the point where failure occurred. Another specimen should be taken from an area remote from the point of failure, in order to make an accurate comparison of the sound metal with that of the portion which failed.

2. In the case of rolled or forged materials, both transverse and longitudinal test specimens should be examined. This is important both for studying non-metallic inclusions (metalloids) and the structure itself. If the material has been cold worked, the specimen should be taken in the direction of the working operation.

3. In the testing of wrought iron, or wrought and heat treated materials, it is advisable to use specimens that will include a portion of the outer skin, so that decarburization and other surface conditions may be studied.

4. In case segregations in the metal are suspected, several specimens from different points should be extracted and studied.

In cutting the specimen, whether with a hacksaw or a bandsaw, heating and "dragging" the metal at the cut surface must be avoided. Heating hardened steel particularly must be avoided, as it is likely to be tempered, so in such cases it is best to cut the specimen with a cut-off wheel operating under a flow of water. In extracting specimens of soft material that are apt to "drag," a saw lubricated blade should be used. For ease in handling, the specimen should be from 3/8 in. to 1 in. in diameter or square and less than this in thickness. Smaller samples are too difficult to handle and almost impossible to polish without rounding the edges. Larger specimens are difficult to finish properly without scratching and dislodging nonmetallic inclusions.

It is not always possible to get samples of exactly the right size for testing, such as is true in the case of sheet metal, wire, and other parts that are too small in cross-section to handle with ease. Such specimens should be mounted in clamps, or a pack can be made by binding a number of pieces of the sheet or wire together using fine wire or machine screws. The pack should be clamped tightly in order to minimize capillary retention and subsequent exudation of solutions from crevices. The specimens are then mounted in either Bakelite or one of the transparent or semi-transparent plastics, care being taken to avoid a mounting material that will cause galvanic attack during etching, or is severely attacked during the etching procedure. The procedure best followed for the preparation of specimens for microscopic examination is:

1. The specimen may be drawn over a long-angle lathe file to render a plane surface and to remove any distorted metal from the sawing operation.
2. It is then rubbed on a 180-grain Aloxite paper to remove file marks, and then successively rubbed with long strokes on No. 0 through 000 metallographic emery cloth papers, exercising care to keep the specimen absolutely flat in order to prevent rounding of the corners and edges.
3. The specimen is then polished, on a rotating disc polisher, with successive cloths (billiard cloth, kitten-ear broadcloth, etc.), using water with levigated alumina or a similar abrasive in suspension on the polishing cloth. This operation is most efficient at a polishing speed of from 250 to 300 rpm. A final polishing should be done, using a suspension from which all coarse particles have settled, to avoid the possibility of scratches on the surface.
4. Final polishing is accomplished on a rotating disc covered with finer kitten-ear broadcloth or "Gamal" cloth, and operated at a speed of 150 to 200 rpm, using heavy magnesium oxide powder or some other suitable polishing medium to produce a scratch-free surface on the specimen. The surface must be free of scratches in order to eliminate the possibility of mistaking such scratches for metallic defects or grain boundaries under the microscope.
5. After the scratch-free surface has been prepared, the specimen should not be allowed to dry but must be washed thoroughly in a stream of water, preferably warm tap water, and then dried by blowing the excess water from the surface with a hand-blower. Specimens will retain their finish indefinitely providing that they are kept in a desiccator or some other container where dust and dirt from the atmosphere will not collect on their surfaces.

12-3 Etching Solutions for Metallographic Microscopic Examination

There are many etching reagents available for use on both ferrous and non-ferrous materials, a complete list of which may be found in the *Metals Handbook* of the American Society for Metals, as well as in Kehl's book on metallographic procedures, referred to in paragraph 12-1. In general, the etching reagent must be one that will best suit the chemical composition and physical condition of the metal being tested. Etching is accomplished by one of two methods, immersion or swabbing, the latter method accomplished with a dilute solution of hydrofluoric acid (or sodium hydroxide in the case of aluminum alloys) agent having been found to give a uniform result by removing surface flow and outlining constituent particles. Experience has shown that both the temperature of the specimen and of the etching reagent, and the concentration of the reagent and the time etching, must be controlled for best results.

The principal reason for etching specimens prior to observing them under the microscope is to produce a contrast in the phases, by eroding or etching away the grain boundaries of the specimens, and also to remove the disturbed (cold-worked) layer of material on the surface. The specimen should not be etched more than is absolutely necessary or it will become over-etched, necessitating polishing over again. Determining the correct degree of etching, and the proper contrast in phases, comes largely from experience. Applying the etching reagents to the metal specimen reveals the structural details, by the process of "unbuilding" the structure from the surface downward. This method of showing the metallurgical structure is possible only because of the various constituents in a multi-phase alloy, or the section planes of differently oriented grains in a pure metal, or in a single-phase alloy have different rates of solution in the usual etching reagents. It is also significant that the structure in a single-phase alloy is developed because of the different rates of dissolving the constituents with the usual etching reagents. Not only are structural details obtained by the preferential dissolution, but, at times, certain phases are selectively discolored or stained. The mechanism of etching multi-phase alloys (like pearlite) is actually electrochemical in nature and is based on the difference in potential between the structural components when the specimen is brought into contact with the etching reagent. The phase at the higher potential is anodic (electro-positive) to the other, and therefore tends to go into solution readily during normal etching. Since the cathodic (electro-negative) phase is at a lower potential, it is not affected very much during etching. Because of this difference in potential, not found in the case of pure metals, duplex alloys etch faster than either pure metals or single phase alloys.

In general, reagents suitable for etching metallographic specimens are composed of organic and inorganic acids, alkalies of various kinds, and other complex substances in solution with some appropriate solvent, such as water, alcohol, glycerine, glycol $(C_2H_4(OH)_2)$ a dihydroxyl alcohol, ethyl alcohol (C_2H_5OH), methyl alcohol (CH_3OH), or mixtures of these solvents.

The activity and general behavior of these etchants are associated with one of the following characteristics:

1. The hydrogen ion concentration of the etchant
2. The hydroxyl ion concentration of the etchant
3. The ability of the reagent (etchant) to stain preferentially one or more of the structural components, such as in the case where Picral (picric acid in alcohol) is used to etch iron and steel.

In order to select and use the correct reagent for etching metals, we should know the composition of the specimen to be etched and something about its structural phases. For example, an etchant composed of ammonium hydroxide and hydrogen peroxide is ideal for copper and alpha brass, but is completely unsuitable for etching iron and steel and other ferrous alloys. Furthermore, this same reagent, although good for etching copper and single-phase brass alloys, is not as suitable as others for etching the multi-phase brass alloys, such as the alpha-beta brasses.

Specimens are etched in order to study the specimen, subsequently, under the microscope and later, perhaps, with the metallograph, to determine its constitution and microstructure as revealed by these instruments. This is accomplished by the corrosion or etching away of the grain boundaries of the metal, these boundaries being the first to etch away, since they are the weaker portion of the structure, having been formed by the interlacing of the ends of the branches of the treelike dendrites at the time freezing occurred from molten metal.

12-4   The Microscope for Metallurgical Studies

Upon the completion of mounting, polishing, and etching, the specimen is examined by microscope, as shown in Fig. 12–2 since it is generally impossible to resolve the structural variation of metals and alloys with the unaided eye. The microscope is used in order to examine in finer detail, by means of greater resolution of the specimen. As shown in Figs. 12–1 and 12–3, the metallurgical microscope differs from the biological microscope in that opaque metals must be viewed by reflected light instead of transmitted light. This means that the specimen is, of necessity, lighted by means of a vertical illuminator, and this characteristic of the metallurgical microscope differentiates it from the biological microscope. Details of the various components of the metallurgical microscope are shown in Fig. 12–1 in which the location and purpose of the optics are revealed.

The human eye has a lens at the pupil which brings images to a focus on the retina at the back of the eyeball. The normal eye is unable to bring into focus objects closer than about 10 in., or 25 cm. The ability to discern fine detail in an object is called *resolving power*. This can be quantitatively expressed as the closest distance between

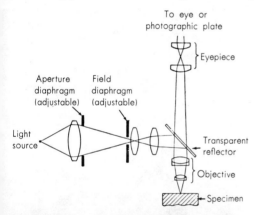

Fig. 12-1.   *Sketch of optics of metallurgical microscope.*

Fig. 12-2.   *A metallurgical microscope for individual use in the laboratory. (Courtesy of Bausch & Lomb, Rochester, New York.)*

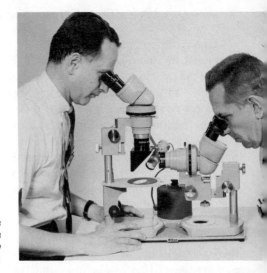

Fig. 12-3. *A stereoscopic zoom microscope with which instructor and student can view the same part or specimen at the same time and at the same magnification. (Courtesy of Nikon Instrument Division, Garden City, New York.)*

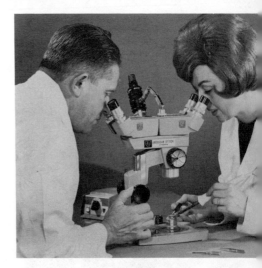

Fig. 12-4. *A dual-observation cycloptic microscope by means of which both the instructor and student can view the same specimen at the same time and magnification. (Courtesy of American Optical Co. Buffalo, New York.)*

two objects, such as ruled lines on a sheet of paper, which can be distinguished one from the other. The focal length of a lens depends on the index of refraction of the material from which the lens is made. This index of refraction, in turn, varies with the wavelength of the light that is used. Therefore, all colors cannot be brought into focus at the same distance, because of the difference in wavelengths. This explains why we sometimes see rainbow hues along the edges of the specimen when we are using white light for viewing an object. This effect is called *chromatic aberration*. The chromatic aberration can be overcome by using light as nearly as possible of a single wavelength. This is best obtained by passing the light through a filter, green being the best color for this purpose. Chromatic aberration can also be offset or overcome by combining several positive and negative lens elements with different indices of refraction.

Another important term in microscopy is *numerical aperture* (*N.A.*), this being the quantitative measure of the light-gathering power of an objective. In order to determine the N.A. the following equation is used:

$$N.\ A. = n \sin \mu$$

where n equals the index of refraction of the medium between the lens and the specimen being viewed, and μ equals one-half the solid angle of the vertex of the intercepted light cone. For air, the index of refraction (n) is 1. For other media n is greater than one, and, specifically, for oil, such as cedar oil (often for oil-immersion lenses), n equals 1.50. In this procedure a drop of cedar oil is applied to the specimen, the microscope is adjusted downward until it contacts the oil, then it is brought back up for focusing on the object, at which time the oil will cling to both the specimen and the objective lens, because of surface tension. The N.A. value is usually engraved on the side of the objective lens; for air this value is slightly less than 1, the highest value for air being 0.95 for N.A. Manufacturers of microscopes have oil immersion lenses available in where N.A. equals 1.40.

The equation for determining the resolving power of an objective lens (the distance separating the finest details which can be discerned) is the following:

$$\text{Resolving Power} = \lambda/2\text{N.A.}$$

where λ equals wavelength of the light that is used in the microscope. This equation indicates the resolving power improves as we shorten the wave-length of light used. In other words, it has been determined that short wavelength ultraviolet light possesses superior resolving power to visible light; however, the image cannot be seen because of difficulties in focusing. Green light, with a wave-length of $5,300\,\text{Å}$ (0.00053 mm), is usually used. In order to take full advantage of the resolving power of an objective lens, the eyepiece should magnify the finest detail resolvable, to at least 0.11 mm.; in fact, a magnification of several times this amount results in a picture that is more easily examined. Any further magnification is useless, as it enlarges the detail but leaves it blurred and difficult to resolve. A simple rule-of-thumb statement is that the highest *useful magnification* is approximately one thousand times the N.A.

12-5. The Metallograph and Photomicrography

Fig. 12–5 is a metallograph like those used for research and in industry. This is actually a metallurgical microscope, with a high-power source of light such as carbon arc or, preferably, an electric lamp of high intensity. The entire instrument is mounted on delicate springs in order to render it as free from vibration as possible, making it easier to take photomicrographs of high quality and to do so quickly. The lenses in the metallograph must be kept clean and all lens openings should be covered with the dust-covers provided with the instrument, in order to keep the entire optical system free from dust. In fact, for best results, the metallograph should be used in a room that is as free from dust and vibration as possible. The correct combinations of eyepieces, objective lenses, and openings for the aperatures are usually supplied by the manufacturer of the instrument, and tabulated in an accompanying set of directions. Although the photographic equipment formerly used as a part of the metallograph was the conventional photographic film plates used by commercial photographers, there has been a trend toward the quicker, Polaroid-type camera with which, with the correct film, lighting, and timing, photomicrographs may be had within a few seconds of time, eliminating the necessity for a darkroom and developing time. It is still the opinion of some metallurgists, however, that the glass-plates and slower developing times produce better, clearer photomicrographs than the quicker Polaroid-type camera and film.

The main purpose of the metallograph and the photomicrographs produced with it is to provide a picture of the microstructure of the metal, both for purposes of comparison and for later reference. Satisfactory photomicrographs may be produced on the metallograph with magnifications up to 2,500 or 3,000 diameters. Much higher magnifications are possible with the *electron microscope* and photographic attachments, going as high as 36,000 diameters, which may be increased to 200,000 diameters using accessory lenses. The greater magnification possible with the electron microscope is due to the tremendous advances that have been made in resolving power. This is because, under certain conditions, high-velocity electrons act much like short wavelength light. Inasmuch as the electron beam has a wavelength nearly 100,000 times smaller than the wavelength of visible light, the resolving power of the electron beam is tremendously increased, producing high magnification.

Since specimens of metals are obviously opaque to an electron beam, it becomes necessary to prepare a thin replica of the specimen by polishing it and then etching it in the usual manner, after which it is placed on a hot-plate with a small pellet of special-type plastic placed on the etched surface. The plastic flows with the rise in temperature, and then pressure is applied to ensure intimate contact between the etched surface and the plastic material. The replica now imbedded with the microstructure from the etched specimen is then cooled and peeled off carefully for further observation in the electron microscope. One of the refinements developed to improve the contrast in the structure is the application of a thin coat of carbon or tungsten, by means of evaporation, onto the replica at an angle from one side or the other. Due to the fact that this replica is understandably fragile, it is usually supported on a disc made of very fine copper mesh screen. This disc is then placed over the apera-

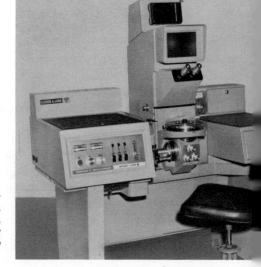

Fig. 12-5. *A Research II metallograph for high-precision materials research, incorporating bright-field, dark-field, polarized light, sensitive tint, phase contrast, and oblique illumination with high-power stereoviewing capability. (Courtesy of Bausch & Lomb, Rochester, New York.)*

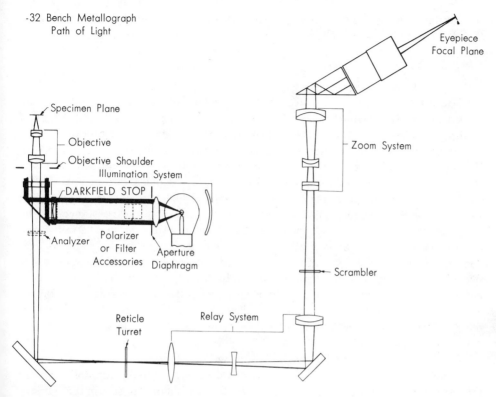

-32 Bench Metallograph
Path of Light

Eyepiece
Focal Plane

Specimen Plane

Objective

Objective Shoulder
Illumination System

DARKFIELD STOP

Zoom System

Analyzer   Polarizer
or Filter   Aperture
Accessories   Diaphragm

Scrambler

Reticle
Turret   Relay System

Fig. 12-6. *Exploded view of bench-type metallograph showing its various component parts and the light-path. (Courtesy of Bausch and Lomb, Rochester, New York.)*

Fig. 12-7. *An RCA Type EMU-4 Electron Microscope complete with accessory Image Intensification equipment. (Courtesy of Radio Corporation of America, Broadcast & Communications Products Div.)*

ture in the specimen holder, which, in turn, is then incorporated into the column of the electron microscope itself.

12-6   Tensile Test

The two methods of mechanical testing by which it is possible to maintain the strains uniformly distributed throughout the specimen over a considerable range of strains, are the *tension test* and the *compression test*. Ductile materials do not fracture in compression, except through the action of parasitic tensile stresses developed in the surface or skin after "barreling" has commenced. Tests for ductility are best accomplished by the tensile testing machine, such as the one shown in Fig. 12–12.

The tensile testing machine consists essentially of two components: (1) a device for straining the specimen, and (2) a means of measuring the resistance of the specimen to such straining. Often it is desirable to construct the stress-strain curve for the specimen undergoing tests, so a third device is then necessary, a strain-gage, commonly known as an extensometer, designed to measure the strain over only that portion of the specimen in which strain is substantially uniform. The final over-all elongation is obtained by means of the extensometer after the necking-down begins and the strain applied becomes more localized. Fig. 12–10 is a sketch of a standard test specimen for the tensile test, such specimens made strictly in accordance with ASTM (American Society for Testing Materials) specifications and standards.

The tensile testing machine shown here is one by which the specimen is strained hydraulically; however, there are also mechanical screw-type devices for straining the test specimen. In the hydraulic type of machine, when the pressure in the cylinder is used to indicate the load on the specimen, it is important that accurate aligning devices be used, in order to prevent misalignment of the piston in the cylinder, or frictional errors will result. The rate of motion of the moving crosshead can easily be varied over a wide range with the hydraulic machines, while this is more difficult with the mechanical type.

For measuring the loads applied, devices are usually either mechanical or hydraulic; in the latter case, the pendulum type is most popular. In order to avoid the frictional errors involved in directly measuring the pressure in the strain cylinder of the hydraulic machine, a hydraulic capsule is usually used, making the straining system and the weighing system entirely independent of each other. The force applied is indicated on a calibrated dial, as shown, and where the original cross-sectional area of the specimen is recorded, the actual stress set up with any load may be readily calculated. The extensometer measures the amount of deformation or strain over a fixed length, usually 2 in. From this, the unit strain may be obtained by dividing the measured elongation by the gauge length used.

The elongation of the specimen after fracture has occured in the tensile machine is determined by fitting the two parts of the fractured specimen together and measuring the distance between the original gauge marks. The equation for this calculation is as follows:

$$\text{Elongation (in. \%)} = \frac{L_f - L_0}{L_0} \cdot 100$$

where L_f equals final gauge length, and L_0 equals original gauge length, usually 2 in. It is imperative in calculating per cent elongation that the original gauge length be reported, inasmuch as the per cent elongation will vary according to the gauge length.

Another factor reported is that of *reduction in area,* and this is also obtained from the fractured portions of the test specimen, by measuring the minimum cross-sectional area, then using the equation:

$$\text{Reduction in Area (per cent)} = \frac{A_0 - A_f}{A_0} \cdot 100$$

where A_0 equals original cross-sectional area of specimen used, and A_f equals final cross-sectional area of the specimen.

A number of important properties may be determined by means of the tensile test, including the following:

Yield Point. Referring to the stress-strain diagram for a ductile material such as soft steel, as the load is increased on the test specimen, a stress is reached at which the material, without an increase in load, continues to deform. In the Fig. 12–8 stress-strain diagram, the stress at point Y is referred to as the *yield point.* At times there will appear an upper and lower yield point where the stress actually decreases momentarily. The yield point of metals is of major importance, since the design of structural members in machines, towers, beams, etc., is largely determined by this factor, which is relatively easy to measure.

Yield Strength. In the case of many nonferrous materials and high-carbon and alloy steels which do not have a definite yield point, the most useful strength that can be determined is the *yield strength,* which is the stress at which a material is permanently elongated a specified small amount. At this point of stress the

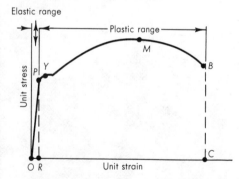

Fig. 12-8. *Stress-strain diagram for a ductile material.* (*Courtesy of* Metals Handbook, *Vol. 8, American Society for Metals, Metals Park, Ohio.*)

material shows a specified limiting deviation from the usual proportion of stress to strain. Shown in Fig. 12–9 is a stress-strain diagram for a brittle material. Such a diagram is used to determine yield strength by what is known as the "offset" method. On this diagram the specified offset OX is laid off along the strain axis. From this point a line is drawn parallel to the original slope of the stress-strain diagram. In the case shown here, XW is drawn parallel to line OP, and the intersection of XW with the stress-strain diagram, or point Y, is then located. It is the value of stress at point Y that is the desired yield strength of the material. The value of this offset is commonly used as being 0.15 to 0.20 per cent of the gauge length.

12-7 Notched-Bar Impact Tests

The notched-bar test sometimes provides triaxial stress components high enough to induce brittle failure in steels, yet no reliable method has ever been devised for

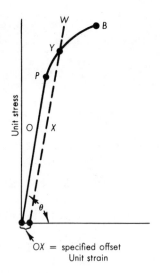

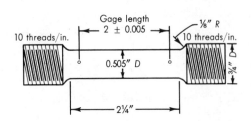

Fig. 12-9. *Stress-strain diagram for a brittle material. (Courtesy of* Metals Handbook, *Vol. 8, American Society for Metals, Metals Park, Ohio.)*

Fig. 12-10. *Standard tension test specimen (ASTM Standard). (American Society for Testing and Materials, Philadelphia, Pennsylvania.)*

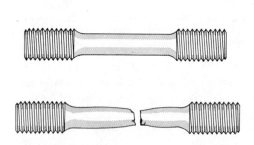

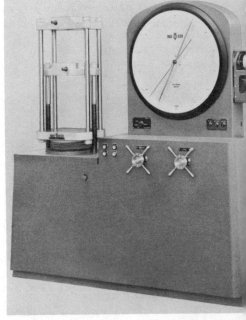

Fig. 12-11. *ASTM standard tension test specimens before and after tension test, showing necking down at point of fracture. (The Making, Shaping and Treating of Steel, published by United States Steel Corporation, 1964 edition.)*

Fig. 12-12. *Hydraulic Universal Testing Machine (60,000 lb capacity). (Tinius Olsen Testing Machine Company, Willow Grove, Pennsylvania.)*

measuring or computing the stress components in notched bars. This is due to the fact that a given geometry of notch in the test specimen does not impose the same stress system when used with different materials. Therefore, data taken from the notch-bar test are subject to limited interpretation, in that they merely indicate that a given steel is or is not brittle when tested at a certain temperature with a notch of a given form and severity of impact. In this concept, the comparison of results from one material with those from other materials can produce a useful estimate of quality and a correlation with the properties of other materials of presumably similar composition.

Actually, the impact value is the result of a simple evaluation of the notch toughness as a summation of load applied, and deformation and differentiates between different steels under certain test conditions imposed. Although the impact method is a positive method of obtaining toughness value, it must not be assumed that the results correlate entirely with shock loading. In other words, although this is a method for determining energy absorption by the test specimen, it is not a test of the impact behavior of the specimen.

There are two types of tests that may be used for impact testing, the Charpy and the Izod; however, the type of machine shown in Fig. 12–13 will perform both the Charpy and the Izod tests by simply adjusting the Change-O-Matic head of the machine. (In fact, in addition to the impact tests, the machine shown here can be used for Tension-Impact tests by means of a simple adjustment of the head.)

Shown in Fig. 12–15 are several types of test specimens designed by ASTM (American Society for Testing Materials) including exact dimensions. The Charpy test specimen, supported at both ends in the machine as a simple beam, is broken by a single blow of the pendulum, applied at the middle of the span. As a rule, the specimen breaks at the notch, the two halves fly away, and the pendulum passes in

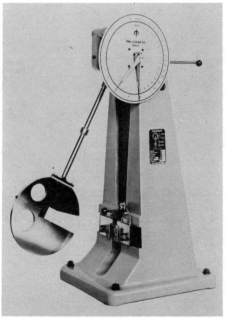

Fig. 12-13. *Impact Testing Machine with "Change-O-Matic" head for both Izod and Charpy specimens (capacities 120 ft lbs and 264 ft lbs). (Tinius Olsen Testing Machine Company Willow Grove, Pennsylvania.)*

Fig. 12-14. *Impact hardness tester, the product of Mohr and Federhaff AG of Mannheim, Germany, manufacturers of fine instruments for testing, etc. (Courtesy of Adolph I. Buehler, Inc. Evanston, Illinois, agents.)*

between the two parts of the holding anvil. The height of the fall of the pendulum, minus the height of its rise, gives the amount of energy absorption by the specimen in becoming deformed and breaking, plus friction losses and the energy of the flying pieces, normally considered to be from 1 to 2 ft lb. This instrument has a scale with a moving pointer calibrated in terms of energy, to give the "impact value" of the test specimen. One or more specimens are broken in order to determine the impact value of the metal; however, because of the several variables usually present in the specimens (quality of machining, the location and extent of nonmetallic inclusions), it is best to test at least three specimens to arrive at a significant value. In the Charpy impact test specimens, the notch at the center may be either of the *V-notch type* or the *key-hole type*, both of them as shown in Fig. 12–15.

The test specimen for the Izod notch-bar impact test is as shown here, with the notch located near one end of the bar, and it is the same type of notch as the V-notch in the Charpy type, with a 45° included angle notch as shown. In the Izod test, the specimen is held rigidly in the vise of the impact testing machine, as a cantilever beam, with the center of the notch coincident with the upper face of the jaws. With this method, one half of the test specimen is broken off, and the impact value is calculated as stated above for the Charpy impact test.

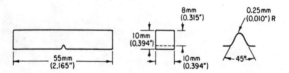

Simple-beam notched-bar specimen with key-hole notch (Charpy)

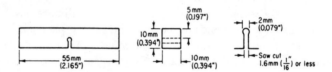

Simple-beam notched-bar specimen with V-notch (Charpy)

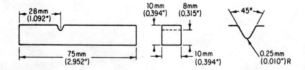

Cantilever-beam notched-bar specimen with V-notch (Izod)

Fig. 12-15. *Charpy and Izod notched-bar impact test specimens. (All made to ASTM specifications.) (Courtesy of* Metals Handbook, *1948 edition, American Society for Metals, Metals Park, Ohio.)*

12-8   Hardness Tests

As the term is commonly used in metallurgy, *hardness* is a measure of the resistance of a material to indentation, by an indenter of certain fixed geometry under a static load. Although a great deal can be learned from the hardness test, it is essential that an intelligent appraisal of a hardness number be made in the light of the composition and condition of the material at the time of testing, as well as a full understanding of the factors that influence the accuracy of the test. Fig. 12–16 shows the relationship between hardness and carbon content of martensite, wherein it is seen that by increasing the carbon content from 0.10 per cent to 0.60 per cent, the hardness of the martensite increases from 40 C to 70 C on the Rockwell C scale.

The tensile strength of heat treated carbon steel and low-alloy steel may be estimated by multiplying the BHN (Brinell Hardness Number) by 500; however, there seems to be no generally useful relationship between hardness and tensile strength for nonferrous materials. Unless all factors determining mechanical properties are known to be controlled, a hardness test is no substitute for the tensile test, and it gives no information concerning ductility.

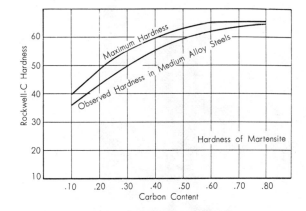

Fig. 12-16.   *The hardness of martensite as a function of carbon content.* (The Making, Shaping and Treating of Steel, *published by United States Steel Corporation, 1964 edition.*)

Hardness tests such as the Brinell, Rockwell, Vickers, and the Shore Scleroscope, along with other tests (tensile, impact, and elongation), are all so positive that they may be made the basis for specifications to determine if the materials are suitable for their application. All materials purchased either by industry or the military are tested before they are accepted, to see if they meet specifications. For specific uses such as in aircraft, oceanspace, manned space craft, etc., where they must be life-safe, very elaborate tests are made.

12-9   Brinell Hardness

This type of test is accomplished by means of a vertical hand-operated or electrically-operated hydraulic press designed to force an accurately ground steel ball of 10 mm ±0.0025 mm diameter, under a load of 3000 kg for ferrous metals or 500 kg for nonferrous metals, into the specimen to be tested. The tester is designed to press the steel ball under the proper load for a period of at least 10 sec for ferrous metals, and 30 sec for nonferrous metals. The diameter of the impression thus created is automatically measured by the tester, and this value is suitable for most applications.

Fig. 12-17. *Brinell Hardness Tester. Air-operated for standard Brinell loads of 500, 1000, 1500, 2000, and 3000 kg. (Tinius Olsen Testing Machine Company, Willow Grove, Pennsylvania.)*

However, where greater precision is desirable in the measurement of the impression made by the ball under load a micrometer-slide comparator type of Brinell microscope is employed that measures to ± 0.01 mm diameter.

The Brinell hardness number (BHN) is actually the ratio of the load in kilograms to the area of the impression in millimeters, and is expressed by the following formula:

$$\text{BHN} = \frac{P}{\frac{\pi D}{2}(D - \sqrt{D^2 - d^2})}$$

where P equals test load in kg, D equals ball diameter in millimeters, and d equals diameter of impression in millimeters. This calculation is rarely necessary for, as stated, either the Brinell tester will automatically record the BHN reading on the dial, or the tables furnished with the tester may be used to convert the observed diameter of the impression to the Brinell hardness number. Inasmuch as two loads are used in the Brinell tester (3000 kg for ferrous metals and 500 kg for nonferrous metals) and just one size of ball is used as the penetrator, this test is usually limited to fairly large-sized specimens.

12-10   Rockwell Hardness Test

This type of test is accomplished with a Rockwell tester, as shown in Fig. 12–18. This apparatus automatically elevates the specimen very slowly against the indenter until a minor load is applied, as indicated by an index hand on the dial gage. Then a major load is applied by releasing a loaded lever system; the speed of descent of the lever is controlled by an adjustable oil dashpot. When the descent of the lever is completed, the major load is removed, and with the minor load still acting, the Rockwell hardness number may be read on the dial gage. This number is based on the depth of indentation, less the elastic recovery following the removal of the major load, less the penetration caused by the minor load. Because of the reverse order of the numbers on the dial gage, a high number indicates a shallow impression produced in a hard material, and a low number in the case of a deep impression in a soft material.

In order to cover the range of hardness found in metals, it is necessary to have several Rockwell scales, each one associated with a specific combination of load and indenter. There are also two Rockwell instruments, one the normal tester for relatively thick sections, and a superficial tester for materials too thin to be tested with the normal tester. As shown in Fig. 12–20, a superficial hardness tester is manufactured by several companies; however, they each accomplish the same result, measuring the hardness of extremely thin materials.

In the Rockwell tester, the *depth* of the impression made by the indenter is used to measure the hardness rather than the *width* of the impression (area) in the case of the Brinell hardness tester. The depth of the impression is read directly from a micrometer scale which is graduated into specific units, one hardness unit corresponding to a depth of 0.002 mm. The scale is numbered from 0 to 100, and the hardness increases with the number. Since the units on the scale are, as stated, arbitrary, and there is no attempt to incorporate units such as load/area, it may be seen that a hardness of 60 Rc is not twice as hard a material as that of hardness 30 Rc. (on the Rockwell C scale). The diamond conical penetrator brale is used for hard materials with a major load of 150 kg, the angle of the cone being 120° with the point of the penetrator rounded off with a radius of 0.02 mm. Under the major load, every 0.002 mm of plastic deformation reduces the original reading of 100 on the machine after the minor load is applied by 1 unit. The readings are designated Rockwell C or Rc, the diamond conical penetrator being referred to as the C penetrator. For softer materials than those indicated by a hardness of Rc20 (BHN of 226), a hardened

Fig. 12-18. *Rockwell Hardness Tester with several indenters for various type of materials mounted in a turret-like fixture, operated by remote control. (Courtesy of American Chain & Cable Co. Wilson Division.)*

steel ball of 1/16 inch diameter is used as the penetrator, when a major load of 100 kg is used. The reading is on the B scale (R_b).

The superficial Rockwell machines used for shallow indentations on extremely thin stock (plated coatings, etc.), are only variations of the standard or normal Rockwell; however, in the case of the superficial test, a minor load of 3 kg and major loads of 15, 30, or 45 kg are employed, each division on the dial in this instance indicating a penetration of 0.001 in.

12-11   Vickers Hardness Tester

The Vickers hardness test uses a square-based, diamond pyramid indenter with an included angle of 136° between opposite faces, with loads usually ranging from 5 to 100 kg. With the Vickers machine, the specimen is elevated to within 1 mm of the indenter, and the lever-loading system is set in the starting position by means of a foot lever acting on a weight-and-cam mechanism that produces the motive power for the test. When the weight-and-cam mechanism is released, the indenter descends under the load, indents the specimen, and then returns to the starting position. Both the rate of descent of the indenter, and the time the indenter is in contact with the specimen, are controlled by an oil dashpot that is usually adjusted for a time cycle of from 10 to 20 sec. The operator is warned by a buzzer when the specimen is not supporting the full load, because it is too far from the indenter or not held rigidly enough for the size of the load applied. In the Vickers tester, the hardness number is the quotient of the load and the area of surface of the indention, the same as is true in the Brinell. Here, however, the diamond square-based penetrator produces an idention having equal diagonals, which are measured by use of a microscope.

Fig. 12-19. *Shore Scleroscope model C-2 on a clamping stand manufactured by Shore Instrument and Mfg. Co., Inc. (Courtesy Shore Instrument Company, Jamaica, New York.)*

Actually, in the case of the Vickers machine, the hardness numbers are obtained from tables or charts after the diagonals have been measured, rather than from specific calculations of the area of the surfaces of the indentations produced.

12-12   Shore Scleroscope

Another hardness tester is the Shore scleroscope; however, with this instrument, rather than measuring the indentation of penetration into a material, the height of rebound of a diamond-tipped weight which is permitted to fall on the specimen from a height of 10 in. is measured. Since hard metals have a higher resiliency, the weight will rebound to a higher distance than on softer metals. This scleroscope is one of the very useful and valuable testers and used primarily because of its portability and because the test may be made without damaging or, in many instances, without having to dissassemble the component part being tested from the main portion of the machine (Fig. 12–19). The diamond-tipped weight of the scleroscope operates

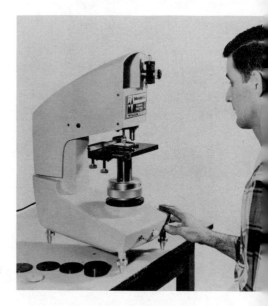

Fig. 12-20. *Tukon superficial hardness tester Model LL, manufactured by Wilson Mechanical Instrument Div. of American Chain and Cable Co., Bridgeport, Connecticut.*

within a vertical glass tube on which is inscribed a scale for measuring the height of rebound; then a dial-gage can be used for measuring and recording this height. This test is particularly useful for measuring the hardness of extremely smooth surfaces not marked by an indention. It is obvious that a rough surface will cause low readings. The accuracy of the scleroscope is not as reliable as the hardness test made by other type of testers as a rule.

12-13 Tukon Micro Hardness Test

The Tukon tester applies loads from 25 g to 50 kg and uses either the "knoop" type diamond indenter or a conventional square-based diamond pyramid indenter similar to that used in the Vickers Hardness Tester previously described. The "knoop" indenter is of pyramidal form, with an included longitudinal angle of 172° 30′ and an included transverse angle of 130° 0′. Entirely automatic, the Tukon tester is electronically controlled in a synchronous cycle. The specimen to be tested is placed on a special micrometer stage that has a two-way adjustment in a horizontal plane. The indentation is made by elevating the specimen against the indenter until it resists any further indention, at which time the electronically-operated contacts are opened, elevation of the specimen ceases, and the load remains on the specimen for a fixed period of time, after which the specimen is automatically lowered to clear the indenter and then removed to a micrometer measuring microscope. The knoop impression appears rhombic under the microscope, with a ratio of 7.11 to 1 of the long diagonal to the short diagonal. The long diagonal is measured and the knoop hardness number is then computed from the formula:

$$I = \frac{L}{A_p} = \frac{L}{l^2 C_p}$$

In this formula I equals knoop hardness number, L equals load applied in kg, A_p equals projected area (sq mm) of indentation, l equals length of long diagonal (mm), C_p equals constant for each indenter, this being supplied by the maker of the indenter. The hardness number that corresponds to a measured length "l" for a given load may be determined from a table supplied with the tester. The DPH (Diamond Pyramid Hardness) number is used when the square-based diamond pyramid indenter is used, thus calculating the required hardness number.

$$\text{DPH} = \frac{1.8544L}{d^2}$$

where L equals load applied in kg, and d equals length of diagonal (long) impression in mm.

The Tukon Hardness Tester shown in Fig. 12–20 is another instrument used for superficial hardness testing of extremely thin materials, as well as for finding the hardness of very small diameter wires, nonmetallic inclusions, etc. Brittle materials, like glass and minerals that crack or shatter under other types of indenters, can be tested with the knoop indenter and Tukon hardness tester.

Special Precautions to be Followed in Hardness Testing

1. Be sure to test the tester with test-blocks of known hardness.
2. The specimen must be flat for best results; however, round specimens may be tested by using an anvil of stage made of two round parallel bars welded to a flat stage, so that the round specimen to be tested will lie in the space between the parallel bars.
3. The specimen must be well supported.
4. The specimen must be throughly cleaned and free from scale.
5. The specimen must be thick enough so that no bulge will show up on the under side when using any of the hardness testers. The thickness usually must be at least 10 times the depth of the depression to be made by the indenter.
6. In the case of the Rockwell and Brinell testers, the steel ball cannot test materials as hard or harder than itself. The Brinell test is inaccurate for hardness readings greater than about 450.

For extremely hard materials we use either a tungsten carbide ball or the diamond-pointed indenter, and for much harder materials, like glass, minerals, etc., a knoop type, Tukon, or Kentrol superficial (micro) hardness tester, is used.

12-14   File Test for Hardness

Although it is never mentioned in specifications for materials, the file test is the simplest hardness test, being made with a common file. It is very handy in the manufacturing plant, since a fine-toothed file will not make an impression on the nitrided surface of a material being tested. A carburized and quenched surface will undoubtedly resist the file after a water-quench, but may show a scratch if the specimen has been oil-quenched. Plain carbon steels are resistant to file abrasion according to their carbon content and heat treatment. The operator rubs the surface of the specimen being tested with the sharp teeth of the file until he determines whether or not the file will "bite," that is, whether the material is what is known as "file hard." For the most part this test is limited to untempered hardened parts and is used for comparison within a given plant. It does not take the place of the more sophisticated and reliable hardness tests previously described.

12-15 Fatigue Tests

The *fatigue strength* of a material is indicated by the maximum stress that it can sustain for a specified number of cycles without failure, the stress being completely reversed within each cycle unless otherwise stated. *Fatigue resistance* of a material, then, is its favorable reaction to loads applied more than once. Fatigue strength is usually proportional to tensile strength, but this generalization does not hold in many instances, over wide ranges of tensile strengths. It is obvious that metals are not perfectly homogeneous but consist of crystals within planes of cleavage, or are slip-oriented in many directions. When enough stress has been applied, slipping takes place on planes within the individual crystalline grains. Although the slipping may not be sufficient, at first, to cause trouble, under subsequent ranges of stress sufficient to produce slip, with continued repeated slipping of sufficient magnitude, the stress ultimately causes minute cracks to form and propogate, gradually reducing the area of sound metal remaining in any cross section. In studying metal fatigue, one of the unsolved problems is the exact determination of when and how, under repeated stress, harmless slip changes to harmful slip, causing the formation of a destructive, propagating fatigue crack. It was formerly thought that metals with the jagged appearance of final fracture failed because of crystallization; however, it has since been learned that fatigue fractures start in the natural cleavage surfaces of the grains of the crystals of the metal, or along crystal boundaries, so the crystalline appearance is actually the *result* of the fracture, and not its *cause*. A thorough study of the fractured parts of a structure often will reveal the primary cause for failure under repeated loads. This subject will be covered in depth in Chapter 17, under the subject of the principles and significance of metal fractures.

In making fatigue tests, the method commonly used consists of submitting specimens of or an entire structural or machined part to cycles of a known range of load of various magnitudes, and noting the number of cycles required for fracture, or for arriving at a given specified "life" prior to fracture. The results of the test are plotted on what is called the S-N diagram, in which the maximum load or stress is plotted as the ordinate, and the number of cycles for fracture as the abscissa. The ratio of minimum stress to maximum stress during a cycle is shown on the diagram. For a cycle of partially or wholly reversed stress, the value is negative. The nature of the maximum stress should also be stated on the diagram, that is, whether it is tension, compression, or shear.

The essential parts of the machine used for making fatigue tests are (1) the drive, for applying repeated cycles of stress to the specimen; (2) a means of measuring the maximum and minimum stresses applied during a cycle; (3) a counter for indicating the number of cycles of stress applied to the specimen, and (4) a device for stopping the testing machine automatically when the specimen breaks. Fig. 12–21 shows an example of a fatigue testing machine.

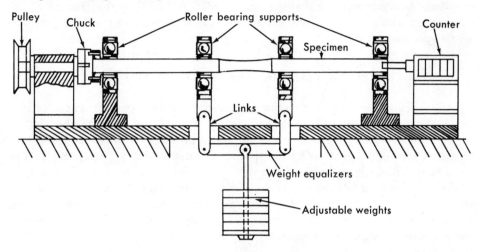

Fig. 12-21. *Rotating, simple-beam type of fatigue specimen set up for testing. Machines of this type are manufactured by the instruments division of The Budd Co., Baldwin-Hamilton, and others. (Courtesy of* Metals and Plastics *by Thomas P. Hughes, M. S., published by The Ronald Press Company, New York.)*

Another adaptation of fatigue testing machines is that used for tension-compression (push-pull), where the specimen is pushed and pulled by means of a lever which, in turn, is vibrated by the variable-throw crank and connecting rod on the machine. Still another type of fatigue testing machine is the torsion type, by mean of which the specimen is subjected to cycles of repeated torsion and is usually operated by using a variable throw crank and connecting rod arrangement, the maximum and minimum torsional moments set up being measured by the twist of a calibrated steel bar attached to one end of the specimen.

Fatigue test specimens may be classified in several ways; however, the ones most used are the following: (1) specimens designed to avoid sudden changes of form, known as "stress-raisers," that is, sharp fillets, notches, key-ways, screw-threads, holes, etc., which, of course, set up highly localized stresses and (2) specimens in which definite "stress-raisers" are formed. Tests using specimens that have no "stress-raisers" give a measure of the fatigue strength of a metal under favorable conditions; that is, the data of such tests indicate the maximum fatigue strength that can be developed in a metal. Specimens with stress-raisers are used to determine the sensitivity of a specimen to the presence of stress-raisers and are generally used in conjunction with specimens that do not have stress-raisers in them. The term most frequently used in this connection is "notch-sensitivity." All test specimens are set up in accordance with ASTM specifications and standards. It is generally advisable to make more than one fatigue test in the construction of the S-N diagram, to be sure of the results obtained. The S-N, as previously stated, means the stress vs the number of cycles, and the diagram is constructed accordingly.

The most widely used fatigue testing machine is what is known as the "R. R. Moore" type, consisting of tapered chucks on either end to hold the specimen; these chucks are rotated either by belt drive or connected motor. Two symmetrically placed loads are applied, one on either end of a fulcrum, to which known weights are hung from an equalizer bar. Then, as the specimen rotates, the weights set up cycles of completely reversed bending stress, and over the entire length there is a uniform bending moment that is equal to $Wa/2$ where W is the amount of the weight used, and a is the distance between the end of the holding chuck and the end of the specimen at each end.

12-16   Repeated Bending or Direct Flexure Test

The repeated bending or direct flexure test is another important type of fatigue test, in which the specimen is bent back and forth but is not rotated. This kind of test is especially useful in the testing of flat rolled products. It has the added advantage that surface preparation of the specimen is not necessary, permitting the test to be made on specimens which have the actual surface exposed when in service. The Krouse Testing Machine Company makes a mechanical type of machine for the flexure testing of materials. This machine introduces the load into the specimen, which is held fast at one end by means of an adjustable crank, and is known as the *direct-flexure fatigue testing machine*.

12-17   Resonant Frequency Type Direct Flexure Test

The resonant frequency type direct flexure test consists of vibrating the specimen at its fundamental frequency by an oscillating applied force. Because of the characteristics of resonant vibrations, very small forces applied at or near the resonant frequency of the specimen are capable of producing large amplitudes of vibration and correspondingly high stresses. Some testing machines of this type test make use of an oscillating magnetic field tunable to the resonant frequency of the specimen. The specimen is supported at the nodes and it vibrates as a free-free beam. Specimens of relatively large cross-section can be tested in this manner, which would require very large machines if direct mechanical loading were used. This is possible with the resonant frequency type of machine by taking advantage of resonance vibration in the specimen tested. Other resonant frequency machines make use of mechanical rather than magnetic oscillators.

12-18   Torsion Testing

In the torsion test the specimen is subjected to twisting or torsional loads much like those encountered in drive shafts, crank shafts, etc. Data obtained on the torsional strength, particularly the yield point or yield strength, are highly important to the designer of such structures. Although torsion tests are not used extensively, due to the fact that a satisfactory estimate of the yield point in torsion can be obtained from the yield point in tension, most manufacturers of automobiles, trucks, etc., test many of their components in torsion. Fig. 12–22 shows a 300,000 pound torsion testing machine at a Chevrolet plant, testing drive shafts and crank shafts. In such cases a direct measurement of the torsion properties are desirable and, in fact, are specified.

Fig. 12-22. *A torsion testing machine of 300,000 lb capacity, located at Chevrolet Motors for testing crank shafts and drive shafts. (Courtesy of The Warner & Swasey Co. Wiedman-Baldwin Division, King of Prussia, Pennsylvania.)*

Fig. 12-23. *Creep rupture-test equipment for constant-load testing up to 2200F at Applied Research Laboratory of United States Steel Research Center at Monroeville, Pennsylvania. (Courtesy of United States Steel Corporation.)*

Fig. 12-24. *Creep test microscope in position for taking measurements through window in wall of furnace. (Courtesy of United States Steel Corporation.)*

Fig. 12-25. *A battery of Universal creep testers, Type St 3-5/10, manufactured by Mohr and Federhaff AG, Mannheim, Germany. (Courtesy of Adolph I. Buehler, Inc., Evanston, Illinois, distributors.)*

Data for torsion tests are usually obtained in the form of a torque-twist curve, in which the applied torque is plotted against the angle of twist. Torsion produces a state of stress known as *pure shear*, and the shear stress at yielding can be calculated from the torque at yielding, and the dimensions of the specimen being tested. Actually, the stress varies from a maximum at the surface of the specimen, to zero at the axis. In the elastic range the variation is linear, and the maximum stress for a cylindrical specimen can be readily calculated from the following equation:

$$S = \frac{16T}{\pi d^3}$$

where S equals maximum shear stress in lb/sq in., T equals torque in inch-pounds, and d equals diameter of the specimen. In the plastic range, the calculation of the maximum shear stress is more complicated and has been developed by A. Nadai and others by studying the twisting of a cylindrical bar in the plastic range. In the elastic range, the shear strain is proportional to the shear stress, and the constant of proportionality is obtained; this is known as the *shear modulus* or *modulus of rigidity*. The shear modulus for steel is about 10,000,000 lb per sq in.

12-19   Creep Tests of Metals

The phenomenon of creep was discussed in Chapter 11 (11–19), wherein it was stated that creep is the continuing change of deformation or deflection of a stressed member, and that in regard to metals and alloys, creep is generally associated with a time rate of deformation continuing under constant load or constant stress intensities well below the yield point of the metal. It was also said to be well below the proportional and elastic limits for the specific temperature in question. The prime purpose of creep testing is, ordinarily, the determination of stress values, at temperatures involved, upon application of which the amount of deformation is limited to tolerance values over a period of time comparable to the anticipated working life of the member to be designed and manufactured.

Creep is the term given to a type of plastic flow, the continued change in dimensions that results from a particular condition of deformation; that is, under conditions of sustained stress (or load). Simple tension is not the only stress state in which the creep of metals occurs; however, by far the majority of experimental work and tests carried out utilizes simple tension as the stress state. In determination of creep, the material is subjected to prolonged constant stress or load at constant temperature, which may be either room or elevated temperatures.

In the case of creep tests of metals, the specimens are similar to those used in tension and compression tests. Where total strain of metals is of the same order of magnitude as elastic strain, magnitude of elastic strain is usually determined at each test temperature by applying load stepwise, and constructing a stress-strain diagram or, if first stage creep is too rapid for accurate measurements, by measuring elastic strain immediately upon release of the load at the end of the test.

An illustration of the three stages of creep under various stresses, but at constant temperature, is shown in Fig. 12–25A. The character of such a creep curve is affected by the stress and temperature at which the creep test is accomplished, high stresses and high temperatures increasing the minimum creep rate during secondary stage, thereby decreasing the time required for rupture of the specimen. The creep rate of a material is also governed by certain characteristics of the metal and the

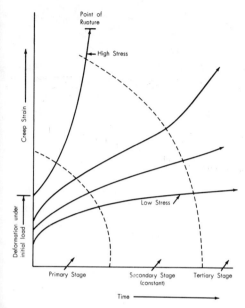

Fig.12-25A.   *The three stages of creep under various stress conditions, but at constant temperature.*

manufacturing variables inherent within the material, such as alloying elements grain size, phase transformations, etc.

Inasmuch as it is impractical to make a long-time creep test on each heat of steel or heat treatment charge intended for service at elevated temperatures, a great deal of study has been given to the development of a method of testing that will assure that a particular lot of given material has creep properties consisent with those dictated by the design requirements for the material. The principal requirements for such a test are that it can be performed within 24 hours, that it will detect questionable heats, and that the conditions of reproducibility of test results and correlation with creep data are such that mutual agreement may be reached between the purchaser and the manufacturer.

Fig. 12–23 is an illustration of a creep-rupture testing machine wherein it will be observed that it is essentially a tension-testing machine, with the mechanism for pulling the test specimen, housed in an insulated jacket, with an induction coil surrounding the specimen, and recording instruments to indicate the temperature and the tension applied to the specimen. Many high-temperature applications of metals, such as jet aircraft engines, turbosuperchargers, gas turbines, etc., require materials that will operate under extreme conditions of temperature and stress. In applications of this sort the useful life of the metal may be only several hours or up to several thousand hours. Although in many applications the permissible deformation is high or may, in fact, not be limited, in most cases the only requirement is that rupture must not occur during the life of the part in question.

In the evaluation of materials designed for relatively short-time service, stress-rupture, rather than long-time creep, tests are used. In such cases, for each temperature in question, a series of creep tests is made over a range of stresses chosen to cause rupture, over time periods varying from only a few hours to several thousand hours. The data from stress-rupture tests are usually reported as the stresses for rupture in 10, 100, and 1000 hours, along with the measurement of elongation at time of rupture.

When load is applied in the creep testing machine, some deformation takes place at once as a result of elastic strain, along with some strain of a plastic nature. There follows a time period during which the rate of creep gradually decreases; this period is termed the *primary creep stage*. The rate of creep then drops to a minimum and further deformation continues at a uniform rate for a period of time referred to as the *secondary creep stage*. Then, with relatively large amounts of deformation, the creep rate increases markedly, bringing the test specimen to the third stage, known as the *tertiary creep stage*, which is usually followed by fracture of the specimen if the test is completed. It is obvious that the stress and temperature at which the creep test is performed affect markedly the nature of the plotted graph of the creep encountered.

Since creep tests are time-consuming and costly, they are seldom carried through all three stages to final rupture. In fact, extrapolation of the secondary rate of creep has been used by engineers in the design of structural members, providing that the test has gone far enough to define the slope of the creep curve in the constant or secondary stage, sufficiently for the engineer to assume that the material will not proceed into the tertiary stage during the service life of the member. This usually requires at least 1000 hours of testing, depending upon the stress, temperature, and material involved. The extrapolated creep values are used in many ways, and especially with the knowledge that the stress that will produce 1 per cent elongation in 10,000 to 100,000 hours at a given temperature, will be within safe ranges, depending on the material in question.

12-20   Nondestructive Tests of Materials

Although nondestructive tests are such that they do not give direct and reliable measurements of the mechanical properties of metals, they are used frequently to locate defects, nonmetallic inclusions, etc., in materials which would prevent their proper performance when made a part of a machine or other structural member. There are several procedures for making nondestructive tests on materials; however, the more commonly used methods are the following:

X-Ray (Radiography)
Fluorescent-penetrant inspection
Magnetic-particle inspection (Magnaflux, Magnaglo, and Zyglo)
Ultrasonic inspection
Liquid-crystalline compound test procedure (Boeing)

12-21   Radiography

Radiography of metals is accomplished by using either X rays or gamma rays; however, several factors limit the use of gamma rays in radiography, including the important fact that gamma rays produced by radium, radon, or mesothorium all produce and emit radiation of considerably more penetrating wave-length, and consequently less contrast, than do X rays. Furthermore, the wave-length of gamma rays is somewhat characteristic of the source and cannot be regulated for contrast or variable thickness of the specimen. Gamma rays are also expensive to use and require considerable time in testing; for example, because the rental or purchase of only a small quantity of radium is feasible, exposures of 10 to 16 hours' duration would be necessary for penetrating a section of steel 2 to 6 inches thick. The use of gamma radiation does have the distinct advantage of not requiring expensive equipment, and also ease in arranging desired exposures.

X rays provide an excellent method for detecting certain discontinuities in metal by virtue of the fact that they darken the film so that regions of lower density, which readily permit penetration, appear dark on the negative, in comparison with areas of higher density, which absorb more radiation. For this reason, a cavity in metals is recorded as a darker area on the negative, whereas copper segregation in an aluminum alloy registers as a lighter area. The general appearance of the familiar discontinuities found in castings or welds is readily detected, as specimens containing variations in thickness; because of the unintentional absence of metals such a void is also more transparent, resulting in a darkening of the X-ray film. On the other hand, excess metal and inclusions more dense than the base metal appear as light regions.

The origin and identification of flaws in steel welds have been studied extensively, and it has been found that the discontinuities in the order of prevalance of occurrence are as follows:

1. Slag inclusions
2. Porosity
3. Cracks
4. Incomplete fusion between two layers of weld metal

All of these defects are less dense than steel itself, and are therefore recorded as darkened areas on the radiograph. Incomplete fusion is shown on the radiograph as a dark line of variable width parallel to the scarf; however, with this one exception the discontinuities in steel resemble those in sand castings.

In the metal industry radiography has been used principally for the inspection of welded products and castings. Examination of wrought metal, such as forged, rolled or drawn sections is limited because of the uniformly dense structure and unlikely presence of flaws large enough to be detected by the radiographic method. In other words, the commercial value of radiography depends on the nature of the material to be tested.

12-22   X-ray Diffraction

As an effective means of studying the atomic structure and spacing in crystals, as discussed in Chapter 3, in general, the most useful tools have been found to be those that make use of radiation or particles having a similar short wavelength. In crystals the separation between equally spaced parallel rows of atoms or atomic planes is in the order of a few Angstrom (Å) units. Low-voltage X rays have been found to have wavelengths of magnitudes diffracted by crystals, particularly X rays produced by tubes operated in the range of 20,000 to 50,000 volts. (These are quite different from X-ray tubes used in medical radiological laboratories, where voltages exceed 100,000.)

X rays of a given frequency, upon striking an atom within a crystal, interact with its electrons, causing them to vibrate with the same frequency as the X-ray beam. Inasmuch as the electrons become vibrating electrical charges, they are found to reradiate the X rays without a change in frequency taking place. These reflected rays bounce off the atoms in random directions, so that it can be said that the electrons of an atom "scatter" the X-ray beam. As shown in Fig. 12–26, an X-ray beam is reflected with constructive interference when the angle of incidence is equal to the angle of reflection, this being a necessary but not entirely sufficient condition for constructive interference, as set out in Bragg's Law. The rays marked x_1, x_2, and x_3 in Fig. 12–26 represent a parallel beam of X rays striking a single atomic plane, *X-Y*. As shown by the line *AA*, a wave front of this beam is indicated where all the rays are in phase with one another. Drawn perpendicular to the rays previously mentioned is line *BB*, representing the rays reflected by means of atoms in a direction in such a way that the angle of incidence equals the angle of reflection. Inasmuch as line *BB* lies at the same distance from the wave front *AA* when measured along any ray, then all points on *BB* are necessarily in phase. In other words, the path lengths of all three, x_1, x_2, and x_3 are the same between *AA* and *BB*; therefore, they are still in phase at *BB*. (For further detailed study of X-ray diffraction techniques, Bragg's Law, the rotating crystal, and the powder method, the student is referred to *Elements of X-ray Diffraction* by Dr. B.D. Cullity (Addison-Wesley Publishing Co., 1956) and to other references noted at the end of this chapter.)

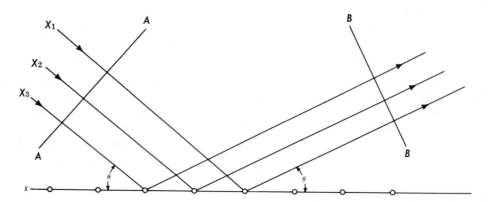

Fig. 12-26. *An X-ray beam reflected with constructive interference when the angle of incidence equals the angle of reflection.*

12-23   Fluorescent Penetrant Inspection

This is a sensitive, nondestructive method of detecting minute discontinuities open to the surface, such as cracks, shrinkage, and porosity. The procedure consists of applying fluorescent liquid penetrant, which enters the discontinuities; this is followed by removing excess penetrant from the work and, finally, by viewing by fluorescence under a near-ultraviolet radiation or black light. Indications are brilliant under intense near-ultraviolet light, lines indicating cracks and similar discontinuities, and dots indicating porosity.

The penetrant used in many plants is an oil-base, water-emulsifiable material which washes away from surfaces of all types by means of a forced spray of water. Another type of penetrant is the dry powder developer, dusted on parts after excess penetrant has been removed and the parts have been dried. Still other penetrants include a water-soluble, solvent base penetrant which is useful on ceramics.

Small parts to be inspected by means of the fluorescent penetrant are, as a rule, immersed in the penetrant and allowed to drain for a period ranging from a few seconds to about 30 minutes after which the excess penetrant is removed. Large parts may be painted or sprayed with the penetrant. In the case of welds, a local inspection may be made by applying the penetrant with a brush. After draining the parts, excess penetrant is removed by washing with forced water, or by the use of a solvent, depending on the type of penetrant used. When a developer of the colloidal suspension type is used, it may be applied to a water-washed, wet surface before drying. If dry powder developer is used, parts washed in water are dried immediately after than by heating, as a rule, although it is at times done by wiping with a cloth when a dry developer is to be used. Inspection of the parts in question under black light is carried out preferably with some exclusion of visible light. The more minute the discontinuities sought, the more darkness is required. Complete darkness for some important tests is necessary.

12-24 Magnetic Particle Inspection

This is another nondestructive testing method for detecting the presence of cracks, bursts, laps, tears, splits, seams, inclusions, segregations, laminations, shrinks, cold shuts, porosity, lack of fusion, and other discontinuities in such ferromagnetic materials as iron and steel. Discontinuities that are too fine to be seen with the unaided eye, but are open to the surface of the material, may be seen by this method. The procedure for using this process is, first, to magnetize the workpiece and then to cover it with fine magnetic particles; these two parts of the process may be accomplished simultaneously by having the magnetic particles held in suspension in a liquid that is flushed over the piece. Or the workpiece may be immersed in the suspension, or the particles may be dusted over the surface of the workpiece in the form of a powder. The presence of a discontinuity is indicated by the formation and adherence of a particle pattern on the surface of the workpiece over the discontinuity. This pattern, referred to as an "indication," takes the approximate shape of the surface projection of the discontinuity. This magnetic particle inspection is not applicable to nonferrous metals. The method just described is known as the Magnaflux process, a trade name of the Magnaflux Corporation, Chicago.

A similar inspection method, known as Magnaglo, is another variation of the Magnaflux method. In this instance the magnetic particles (fluorescent) are held in suspension in a liquid and then flowed over the work piece. Still another nondestructive method of inspection is known as the Zyglo process, a very sensitive method of detecting minute discontinuities such as shrinkage, cracks, and porosity exposed to the surface in parts that are nonmagnetic. The process in this case is quite similar to the ones previously described, except that the parts to be inspected are first immersed briefly in a liquid penetrant (fluorescent) which goes into the discontinuities. After allowing the parts to drain and removing the excess penetrant by washing with water or a solvent, depending on the type of penetrant used, the parts are then dusted with a dry powder or a powder suspended in a liquid. The dry powder or developer has the effect of drawing the penetrant from the defects in the work piece and retaining it on the surface, on top of the defect. The black light or ultraviolet lamp is then used to bring out the "pattern" or indications in the form of minute quantities of penetrant coming out of the discontinuities, the latter appearing brilliant under the intense ultraviolet or black light.

12-25   Ultrasonic Inspection

This nondestructive method of testing materials utilizing waves that are of a higher than audible frequency is also referred to as *supersonic* testing. The properties of the supersonic wave, which is elastic and of very high frequency, derive not from the fact that the waves are inaudible, but from the shortness of the wavelength. Although air transmits only one type of sound wave (longitudinal), a solid part will transmit three types of waves, providing that the wavelength is short in comparison with the smallest dimension of the part being examined. The waves of this type are of several varieties:

1. Longitudinal waves having particle displacement in the direction of propagation, with a velocity in steel of 256,000 in. per sec.
2. Shear waves having particle displacements at right angles to the direction of propagation, with a velocity in steel of 128,000 in. per sec.
3. Rayleigh waves which travel only on the surface of the part and are something like short wavelengths on water surface, except that the particle displacement of the Rayleigh waves penetrates beneath the surface for a distance approximately equal to the wavelength and with a velocity in steel of 118,000 in. per sec.

These sound waves, which have exceedingly high frequencies (up to 5,000,000 cycles per sec.) and with wavelengths as short as 1/16 in. are such that a beam of sound waves can be sent through the piece of metal being tested and the sound wave will have properties similar to those of a beam of light. Large flaws in the metal piece will cast an acoustical shadow on the face of the piece opposite the face through which the waves have entered. Small flaws in the metal can be detected by measuring the small amount of sound energy they reflect back to the point from which they originated (the sending point). The distances to the flaws, or to inaccessible faces, can be determined by measuring the scattering (attenuation) of the waves. The machine for making determinations such as these are used in many laboratories and plant inspection departments across the country.

Another piece of equipment used for detecting flaws in metal employs high-frequency current generated by a suitable electric circuit, and a searching unit in the form of a quartz crystal to send a wave train consisting of only a few waves radiated in a few millionths of a second. This equipment is known as the *supersonic reflectoscope*. It uses the principle that reflections of this train of waves coming from small flaws, or from the opposite side of the part, are seen a cathode-ray tube. These supersonic waves are interrupted wherever the solid material has a discontinuity, however thin; furthermore they are reflected from any abrupt change of density or elasticity. This equipment is used to determine and accurately locate large and small flaws in metals, including laminations in rolled plates, voids in the metal because of heavy porosity, etc. It is also useful in the inspection of the bond of welded, plated, or soldered surface; the measurement of wall thicknesses where the opposite side is inaccessible; and in the inspection of tubes of heavy and thin wall thicknesses, such as the cast aluminum "logs" produced as an interim product in the manufacture of tubing. The surface of the material inspected is oiled with a suitable oil, then touched with the searching unit (*piezoelectric crystals*) usually quartz, as stated. These piezoelectric crystals detect the supersonic waves that have been radiated and propagated, and flaws of whatever nature are thus detected. (The quartz crystals are termed piezoelectric crystals because the conversion of electrical energy to mechanical energy is termed the *piezoelectric effect.*)

12-26   Liquid Crystal Method of Detection of Metal Flaws

In the nondestructive testing laboratories of Boeing Company, a new technique for detecting flaws in metals and plastics has been developed; a liquid, which, when applied to the surface inspected, and then heated, will not only reveal the defect show it but in color. The liquid solution that does this remarkable feat is a *liquid crystal*, so named because it displays many of the properties of solid optical crystal. The liquid-crystal mixture was developed from derivatives of cholesterol, a fatty substance sometimes blamed for heart trouble.

As shown in Fig. 12–27, the liquid-crystal mixture is painted on the metal being tested, the surface is warmed and then air-cooled to a temperature of 86F. The metal surface immediately begins to blossom into color and, if the part is well-bonded and free from flaws, the color is uniform throughout the surface. Flaws or other defects, as indicated in Fig. 12–28, are detected by reason of the fact that the color in these areas is different from that of the rest of the surface as the temperature is slowly lowered.

What causes this to happen is a reflection of light from the surface of the part coated with the liquid crystal mixture in a series of planes, these planes changing their spacing instantaneously as the temperature of the part rises and falls in frac-

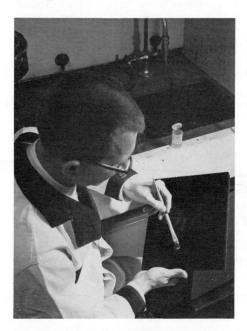

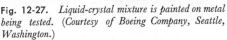

Fig. 12-27.   *Liquid-crystal mixture is painted on metal being tested. (Courtesy of Boeing Company, Seattle, Washington.)*

Fig. 12-28.   *Metal flaws show up as color spots when the metal is cooled. (Courtesy of Boeing Company, Seattle, Washington.)*

tional degrees. These temperature-triggered reflections appear as hues of color, from red, at 84F, to purple at 86F. Perfect parts, free from flaws, cool consistently, changing from purple to green to red, but flaws cool either faster or slower than the other areas, showing up as contrasting color spots.

Poor thermal insulation can be detected by reversing the technique. For example, rivets in aluminum wing-skins require a coating to prevent corrosion between the head of the rivet and the skin. Checking the quality of the rivet coating using conventional methods after insulation, is a complex undertaking. The liquid-crystal mixture makes this an easy test to perform. The rivet coating acts as a partial thermal barrier. Poor and inadequate coatings can be revealed simply by painting the rivet heads with liquid-crystal, applying a small amount of heat to the center of the rivet, and observing the color changes as the rivet becomes warm. A rivet that has been properly insulated will reach a uniform color within seconds, whereas an improperly coated rivet, in contact with the wing-skin (which acts as a heat-sink), will take much longer to turn blue in color.

The same technique is used to detect faulty connections in multilayer electronic circuit boards, coating the board with the liquid-crystal mixture, and passing a current through the circuitry. Out-of-place colors will again indicate defects. Flaws in aluminum, titanium, and columbium honey-comb sandwich combinations have been located with liquid-crystals. Dimensions of certain under-the-surface defects can also be measured.

Although liquid-crystals are not new, having been discovered in 1888, their adaption to nondestructive testing was the outcome of the work of scientists at the Boeing Company. Dr. Wayne Woodmansee and Gary Waterman, after reading an article by a Westinghouse scientist, J. L. Fergason, describing the behavior of a liquid-crystal mixture in response to small temperature changes, developed the technique for practical applications.

12-27   Pyrometry in Metallurgy

Another important tool used by the metallurgist and others responsible for the production of metals and their heat treatment is pyrometry, which deals with the measurement of temperatures higher than 950F or 500C. The basic industrial uses of pyrometry include:

> Thermoelectric
> Resistance
> Radiation
> Optical

All of these, with the exception of the optical method, can be applied to reading temperatures under 950F using certain types of equipment.

12-28   Thermoelectric Pyrometer

This method of measuring temperature is based on the principle that if two dissimilar wires are joined together at both ends, and one junction is heated, an electromotive force (emf), or voltage, is generated in the circuit. The apparatus consists of a millivoltmeter connected to two wires of different metals, with the other ends joined together and placed in a furnace. The wires in question are called a *thermocouple*, one of the wires being the positive element, and the other the negative element. Although most thermocouples are made of two elements in the form of wires as before stated, at times they are made in the form of a wire element inside a tubular element, as shown in Fig. 12–29.

Although the millivoltmeter is sometimes used with the thermoelectric pyrometer, a potentiometer is found to be more satisfactory for measuring the small voltage developed in the circuit, because the potentiometer balances the thermoelectric voltage against a similar voltage from a battery that is a part of the instrument. When the balance between these two voltages is achieved, the resistance of the circuit does not impair the reading of the instrument. The voltage from the battery is reduced by means of a resistance coil with a slide-contact. This enables the operator to calibrate the potentiometer so that a positive position of the slide-contact reveals the voltage applied in order to balance the thermocouple circuit. When standard thermocouple wire is used, it is not difficult to calibrate the instrument directly

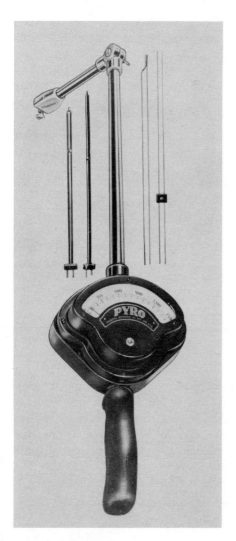

Fig. 12-29. *Thermo-electric immersion pyrometer. This is a thermocouple-type instrument, C/A calibration designed for use with nonferrous molten metals at maximum temperatures of about 2350F. (Courtesy The Pyrometer Instrument Co. Bergenfield, New Jersey.)*

Fig. 12-31. *Pyro micro-optical pyrometer used primarily as a laboratory unit with temperatures scales calibrated for blackbody conditions. (Courtesy of The Pyrometer Instrument Co.)*

Fig. 12-30. *Pyro Optical Pyrometer for general industrial use with scales calibrated for black-body conditions used for reading the spout and pouring temperature of iron, steel, monel, etc. (Photo courtesy The Pyrometer Instrument Co.)*

Fig. 12-32. *Pyro Radiation Pyrometer designed for use under blackbody conditions only. Focal distance is limited and the target (port or peephole) must be at least 2 in. in diameter. (Courtesy of The Pyrometer Instrument Co.)*

in relation to the temperature. The *calibration* of the potentiometer is accomplished by finding the millivoltage developed by the given combination of thermo-couple wires at given temperatures.

The number of metals and alloys suitable for commercial use in thermocouples is limited because, at high temperatures, such metals must be oxidation-resistant and must also be resistant to recrystallization, melting, and any contamination. Furthermore, they must develop an emf high enough to be measured without the necessity of employing delicate apparatus. These metals must also be reproducible and readily obtainable in uniformly high quality from several sources. Metals that are in common use today for thermocouples include the following combinations:

1. Platinum vs alloy with 87 per cent Pt and 13 per cent Rh
2. Platinum vs alloy with 90 per cent Pt and 10 per cent Rh

3. Chromel vs Alumel ⎫
4. Iron vs constantan ⎬ These three are the "base-metal couples"
5. Copper vs constantan ⎭

The useful life of an industrial thermocouple depends not only on the maximum temperature at which it will be used, but also on the atmospheric conditions to which it will be subjected.

The first two combinations of wires mentioned may be used up to a maximum temperature of 2800F, while the chromel-alumel will function at 2200F, iron-constantan at up to 1400F, and copper-constantan up to a maximum of 800F. Fig. 12–33 is a diagram of a simple thermoelectric pyrometer circuit which is self-explanatory. It is best to have thermocouples protected from the environment at all times, as they are readily contaminated.

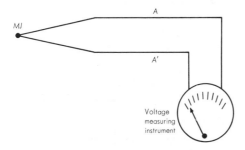

Fig. 12-33.

In Fig. 12–33 there are three junctions: the junction of the two wires inside the furnace, commonly referred to as the "hot junction," but often called the "measuring junction;" and the two junctions between the elements of the thermocouples and the copper wires connnecting them to either the millivoltmeter or a potentiometer, whichever is used—these are designated in the diagram as A and A_1. Although in the diagram there are two such junctions, the pair is usually treated as a single unit and is often referred to as the "cold junction" or, at times, the "reference junction." The thermoelectric pyrometer measures only the temperature of the hot junction of its thermocouple, so it is the necessary to know difference in temperature which exists between the junction and the object or material of which the temperature is about to be measured.

12-29   Resistance Thermometry

It this type of temperature measuring device the operation of the resistance thermometer depends on the variation with temperature of an electrical conductor. Accordingly, a high temperature coefficient of resistivity might appear of major importance. Certain of the oxides have this property, possessing at room temperature from 100,000 to 1,000,000 times that at 800F. Due to the fact, however, that the resistance of a suitably mounted material can be determined easily and accurately, it follows that a high temperature coefficient is rarely, if ever, the deciding factor in the choice of the material. It is also a desirable feature of this instrument that there is a simple and convenient relation between temperature and resistance.

Resistance thermometers, for industrial purposes, are usually made of copper, platinum, or nickel, with nickel the most satisfactory for measuring temper-

atures below 600F. Despite the fact that the resistance thermometer is very useful
in the laboratory, several precautions must be taken when it is used for industrial
work, including inspection for bad contacts in the line, a broken strand in a flexible
cable, etc., for these may be the cause of sizeable errors in results. Furthermore, the
thermometer is fragile and must be handled with extreme care; the calibration of the
instrument may be severely altered by careless handling. For temperatures above
600F, the thermoelectric pyrometer is preferable to the resistance thermometer.
The instrument most commonly used as a resistance‑measuring device is usually
a Wheatstone bridge, shown in Fig. 12–34, whose principle characteristic is that no
current will flow through the detector as long as the ratio of Resistor B/Resistor $C =$
Resistor a/Resistor b, where the resistances in B, C, a, and b are measured in ohms.

A change of resistance in any one of the four legs is indicated by a flow of
current through the detector. Since the resistance of an electrical conductor changes
with temperature, and since very small changes of resistance can be positively detected
by the Wheatstone bridge, we obtain a very fine temperature-measuring instrument
in this type of instrument. In sketch Fig. 12–34 the resistor B is usually made of
materials with a high temperature coefficient, while resistors a, b, and c are made
of practically normal coefficient materials.

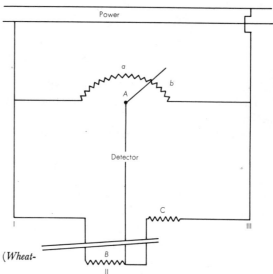

Fig. 12-34. *Resistance Temperature Detector (Wheatstone bridge).*

12-30   Radiation Pyrometry

The fundamental basis of this type of radiation pyrometry is the Stefan-Boltzmann
Law, which states:

$$W = \sigma T^4$$

where W is the total radiant flux density, termed "radiancy," σ is one of the fundamental physical constants, and T is the temperature of the body in question (absolute
temperature.)

Radiation pyrometers in general are more strongly influenced by certain bands
of wavelengths than by others; therefore their response never exactly follows this
law. These pyrometers are necessary when the temperature becomes too high to

use other types of pyrometers, or when the object being tested for temperature is too inaccessible. Since all bodies emit radiant energy with an intensity dependent upon temperature, the temperature can be determined by measuring the radiant energy. It has been found that the total radiant energy from any temperature-excited radiator increases about 4 times as fast as the temperature, while the spectral radiant energy in the red part of the spectrum increases about 18 times as fast as the temperature at 1832F and about 10 times as fast at 3632F. Therefore, it may be seen that the percentage error in measuring the temperature is much smaller than in measuring the radiant energy.

The conventional radiation pyrometer consists of (1) a blackened receiver that absorbs and is heated by incident radiation from a source of which the temperature is to be measured; (2) a housing that has a fixed aperture or apertures to limit the cone throughout which the receiver can be irradiated by the source; (3) in most cases, a lens or mirror by means of which this cone is completely filled with rays emanating from a relatively small area of the source. In order to measure the rise in temperature of the receiver, a thermocouple or thermopile is used or, in some cases, a bolometer or some other similar device that is sensitive to temperature.

When the radiation pyrometer is sighted on a blackbody at elevated temperature T_1, the receiver will be heated up quickly to temperature T_2, so that the radiant energy absorbed in unit time by the receiver, both from the blackbody and from the surrounding housing at temperature T_3, equals the energy radiated by the receiver plus that conducted away from it through the wires of the thermopile and, unless it is in a vacuum, through the air.

To determine the temperature of elevated temperatures of objects, it has been found that the temperature attained by the receiver is much lower than that of the source, and the relation between these temperatures is therefore given by the equation:

$$T_2 - T_3 = \left(\frac{X_1 T_1}{A}\right)^4$$

where T_1 is the temperature of the blackbody at high temperature, T_2 is the temperature of the receiver, T_3 is the temperature of the surrounding housing of the pyrometer, X_1 is the fraction to which the radiant energy received from the source at temperature T_1 is reduced, as a result of reflection and absorption by the lens or mirror, and A is a constant which increases when the housing temperature increases, so when T_3 rises, as by ambient temperature change, T_2 also rises, but by a smaller amount.

In the radiation pyrometer it does not require direct contact with the hot body being measured for temperature, so it follows that there is no upper range so far as the ability of the pyrometer itself to withstand extremely high temperatures, although the lower temperature limit is about 960F. An illustration of the radiation pyrometer is shown in Fig. 12–35.

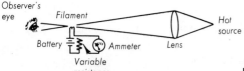

Fig. 12-35.

12-31   Optical Pyrometer

This pyrometer determines temperature by measuring the brightness of the source in a selected part of the spectrum, generally the red part, utilizing the human eye as a part of the instrument and therefore reading temperatures only above approximately 1100F. The optical pyrometer is based somewhat on the same principle as the radiation pyrometer, having the form of a telescope that is trained on the object whose temperature is to be measured. The most common type is called the *Disappearing-Filament Optical Pyrometer*, having two basic components, the telescope and the box containing the controls of the instrument. In the operation of this pyrometer, a photometric match is brought about either by varying the temperature of the filament of the pyrometer lamp or by keeping the filament at a constant temperature and varying the apparent brightness of the hot body by means of an absorbing screen. A red glass filter that transmits only a narrow band of the visible spectrum is mounted in the eyepiece of the telescope in order to make the light approximately monochromatic, which makes it easier to obtain the photometric balance needed. The red glass filters used with most optical pyrometers have an effective wavelength centering at approximately 0.65. A diagram of this type of optical pyrometer is shown in Fig. 12–35.

As a rule this type of optical pyrometer is used for measuring temperatures in the range of 1200 to 2400F for more accurate results. The element of experience and skill in the operator of the pyrometer comes into play in the making of the photometric match, so that considerable care must be used in the aspect. Another precaution is to see that any errors caused by smoke or gases between the operator and the furnace is held to a minimum or compensated for. There are, however, numerous advantages of the optical pyrometer that are also present in the radiation pyrometer, including the ability to measure not only high temperatures, but also to measure them even though somewhat inaccessible, such as in an open-hearth furnace reading.

QUESTIONS

1. Explain the technique and functions of macroexaminations of metal parts.

2. State a few of the more important etching solutions used in the study of macrostructures and give their specific used.

3. Discuss the possibilities and also the pitfalls in the interpretation of results of macroetching of specimens.

4. The skilled metallurgist with proper understanding and interpretation of macroetched specimens is able to recognize many conditions accurately and effectively. Give at least six of these conditions.

5. Are flow-lines necessarily a factor and indication of defective steels? Explain the reasons for your answer.

6. Why is it essential to use great care in the selection and extraction of specimens that are to be examined microscopically? Usually, what is the purpose of microscopic examinations?

7. It is essential that specimens for microscopic examinations be scratch-free. Why is this true? How is it accomplished?

8. What is the purpose of etching the scratch-free specimen prior to observing it under the microscope? How is the etching accomplished?

9. Basically, what can be said about etching reagents for etching metallographic specimens, so far as their composition is concerned?

10. How does the metallurgical microscope differ from the biological microscope?

11. Define the following terms: resolving power, numerical aperture, index of refraction.

12. At what spacing on the photomicrograph will be the finest resolvable detail if green light is used ($\lambda = 5,300$ Å) and if the magnification is 600 times the numerical aperture N.A.?

13. Referring to the American Society for Metals *Metals Handbook*, give a brief description of the several types of information that may be obtained by X-ray techniques.

14. Draw a sketch and describe a metallograph and relate its functions.

15. Why is it necessary to use an electron microscope in metallurgy?

16. Since metals are opaque, how can the electron microscope be used?

17. What two methods of testing can be used and still maintain the strains uniformly distributed throughout the specimen?

18. Describe the tensile testing machine, including the test specimens, etc.

19. What is an "extensometer" and what is its function?

20. Explain the procedure for determining the elongation of a tensile test specimen after fracture has occurred. Give the equation for this calculation.

21. What are some of the important properties of metals and alloys that may be determined by means of the tensile test?

22. Explain the stress-strain diagram and how it is constructed.

23. Describe the notched-bar impact tests and include sketches of the test specimens used. Is this test better than the tensile test? What is the main purpose of the notched-bar impact test?

24. There are many hardness tests that may be made on metals. Describe the following: Brinell, Rockwell, Vickers, Scleroscope and Tukon micro hardness tests.

25. Draw a graph and explain the relationship between the hardness of martensite and carbon content.

26. Explain the several precautionary measures that must be taken in all hardness tests.

27. Define the terms "fatigue strength" and "fatigue resistance" in metals. Is it possible to tell when harmless slip changes to harmful slip in studies of fatigue in metals? How?

28. Give the details of the making of fatigue tests, including the type of equipment with which they are made.

29. Is it essential to use the torsion test in order to arrive at the yield point of a material in torsion? Explain.

30. Inasmuch as the phenomenon of creep takes place over an extended period of time, is it possible to make reliable creep tests within a short period of time? Explain fully.

31. What are the various nondestructive tests of materials that may be used where it is impractical to make destructive tests, or where the latter should be supplemented with additional investigation? Explain each of them which is of a nondestructive nature.

32. Upon what does the commercial value of radiography depend? What is the X-ray particularly suited to detect in steel investigation?

33. Metal flaws are detected effectively by means of the liquid crystal method by one of the larger manufacturers of aircraft. Give the essentials of this process, and tell where it has been found to be particularly useful.

34. Explain the following heat-measuring instruments and tell when each is most useful: thermoelectric pyrometer, optical pyrometer, radiation pyrometer, resistance thermometry. Can all of these be used in the reading of temperatures under 950F? Explain.

35. What is the practical use of X-ray diffraction?

References

American Society for Testing and Materials, *Manual on Fatigue Testing*, Philadelphia, Pennsylvania, 1958.

Conway, Harry D., *Mechanics of Materials*. Englewood Cliffs, New Jersey: Prentice-Hall, Inc. 1950.

Garofalo, Frank and G. V. Smith, *Effect of Time and Temperature on Various Mechanical Properties During Strain Aging*. Metals Park, Ohio: American Society for Metals, 1955.

Garafolo, Frank, P. R. Malenock, and G. V. Smith, *Hardness of Various Steels at Elevated Temperatures*. Metals Park, Ohio: American Society for Metals, 1953.

Smith, George V., *Properties of Metals at Elevated Temperatures*. New York: McGraw-Hill Book Company, 1950.

Timoshenko, Stephen, and G. H. MacCullough, *Elements of Strength of Materials*, 3rd ed. Princeton, New Jersey: D. Van Nostrand Co., Inc., 1952.

Corrosion and
Protective Coatings

13-1 Principles and Problems of Corrosion

Corrosion of the common metals in usual environments is an electro-chemical phenomenon because it is associated with the flow of electric currents over finite distances. Electric currents related to corrosion have been detected in numerous cases, and in a limited number of instances the amount of corrosion taking place has been accounted for quantitatively by the amount of electric current which has passed between the anode and the cathode.

Awareness that corrosion is electro-chemical is important, since it helps in the development of methods of combating corrosion. For example, it is obvious that in order for electro-chemical corrosion to take place, there must be differences in potential between different areas of the corroding structure. These differences can be caused by the use of dissimilar metals or alloys in contact with one another. However, differences in potential can be caused by heterogeneities of any kind in the surface of the metal or in the environment contacting the metal. Several of the more important heterogeneities will be discussed in this chapter.

There are many ways to define this insidious phenomenon of corrosion; some metallurgists and physical chemists state the definition in terms of "free energy changes that take place," while others will hold to the electrolytic or electro-chemical terminology. A good layman's definition in terms of results rather than mechanism might express corrosion as "the degradation of a material, with resultant reduction in usefulness as far as application is concerned, because of inadvertent mechanical, chemical, or electro-chemical action or a combination thereof." This definition expresses rather simply the essential features of corrosion. First, the material is degraded from some useful product to a state of reduced usefulness. The rusting of steel structural members and the disintegration of a rivet or bolt are examples of this. Also, this definition points out that the degrading action must be inadvertent.

Many of these phenomena described as corrosive when occurring inadvertently are intentionally applied during certain processes, such as in electroplating, anodizing, chemical milling, metallographic etching, etc. To be sure, a metallographer would be eliminated if he were unable to corrode selectively his specimens to bring out their structural composition. In addition this definition indicates the manner in which the degradation might occur: mechanically, chemically or electrochemically.

According to Faraday's Law the rate of deposition or removal of a metal in an electroplating cell is dependent on the current developed. This rule also applies to the phenomena of corrosion as was found upon studying the emf series of some of the common metals and alloys in sea water.

In order to get a proper perspective on just how much is involved in the destruction of metals and products made from metals, the total approximate expenditures because of corrosion in a single year are given as follows:

> Automobile mufflers   ....$ 70 million
> Gas and oil pipe lines ....$600 million
> Organic coatings and paints................$1–1/2 billion
> Metallic coatings, galvanizing,
> cadmium, chromium etc. ....$670 million
> Corrosion-resistant alloys   ....$786 million

In other words, a total of over six billion dollars per year is expended because of corrosion, including measures employed to retard this detrimental oxidation.

There are various types and mechanisms of corrosion that should be recognized including that of electro-chemical (galvanic) action, in which one of the metals (dissimilar) coupled together forms the cathode while the other becomes the anode, which is subject to degradation. A metal in contact with water tends to dissolve with the formation of metal ions in the solution. These ions have lost their outer negatively charged valence electrons so that they become positively charged. This tendency to ionize varies with the metal; it is greater for the easily corrodible or "base" metals, such as magnesium, zinc and aluminum, than it is for the less corrodible or "noble" metals like silver, gold, and platinum. The common metals and alloys can be arranged in a series in order of their tendency to ionize when in contact with specified solutions. This series is called the "electropotential" or "electromotive force" series (emf). The series is based on hydrogen having a potential of zero and is a measure of the potentials of the elements measured in equilibrium conditions using as "zero" the potential required to liberate hydrogen from its ions when a platinum electrode covered with platinum black is immersed into an acid solution of normal hydrogen activity. Those metals that tend to go into solution more readily than hydrogen are "anodic" to hydrogen and therefore have a negative potential. Those metals with a lesser tendency than hydrogen are cathodic and have a positive potential.

Table 13–1 is a comparison of the electromotive series and solution potentials in sodium-chloride solution of the common metals and a few of the alloys. This table is often mistakenly used as if the order of metals were invariable, each metal displacing from corrosion those below it. This is often not true as is shown in the second column of the table in which the values of potential in a normal salt solution are given.

TABLE 13–1. Comparison of the Electromotive Series and Solution Potentials in Sodium-Chloride Solution of The Common Metals and a Few Alloys

Metals or Alloys	From emf Series (normal hydrogen scale)*	Potential in Volts In 1 N (5.85%) NaCl containing 0.3% H_2O_2 (0.1 N) Calomel Scale**
Magnesium, Mg	+2.37 (b)	+1.73 (a)
Aluminum, Al	+1.66 (b)	+0.85 (a)
Zinc, Zn	+0.76 (b)	+1.00 (a)
Chromium, Cr^{++}	+0.74 (b)	....
Iron, Fe^{++}	+0.44 (b)	+0.63 (a)
Cadmium, Cd	+0.40 (b)	+0.82 (a)
Cobalt, Co	+0.28 (b)	....
Nickel, Ni	+0.25 (b)	+0.07 (a)
Tin, Sn^{++}	+0.14 (b)	+0.49 (a)
Lead, Pb^{++}	+0.13 (b)	+0.55 (a)
Hydrogen, H_2	0.00	....
Copper, Cu^{++}	−0.34 (b)	+0.20 (a)
Silver, Ag	−0.80 (b)	+0.20 (a)
Gold, Au^{+++}	−1.50 (b)	....
Brass (60–40)	....	+0.28 (a)
Stainless Steel (18–8)	....	+0.15 (a)
Monel Metal	....	+0.10 (a)
Inconel	....	+0.40 (a)

*Some handbooks list the sign potential in the reverse of that shown.
** These values will vary somewhat depending on the lot of material being investigated and the surface preparation being used.
(a) Mears and Brown: "Causes of Corrosion Currents," *Industrial and Engineering Chemistry*, Vol. 33, Page 1008, Table XII. Note the sign of potential is the reverse of that shown above in Table 13-1.
(b) W. M. Latimer, *Oxidation Potentials*, Prentice-Hall, Inc., Englewood Cliffs, N.J.

From the electro-chemical series shown in Table 13–1 it might be concluded that the corrosion of zinc would be retarded by contact with aluminum, while the potential measurements in salt solution indicate that the zinc should protect aluminum. It is a fact that in sea water and in many natural waters, this protection of aluminum by zinc actually does take place. The electro-chemical series is useful since metals near the top are generally protective to those near the bottom of the table. However, when two metals differ very little in potential, i.e., they are close together in the first column of Table 13–1, it cannot be predicted which will protect the other without running actual tests in the laboratory. In many cases, the results of potential measurement in a salt solution (second column of Table 13–1) are a better guide to the ability of one metal to protect the other under natural conditions of exposure than is the electro-motive series. Numbers of factors, such as the environment to which exposed, the magnitude of the current generated, the relative area of metal exposed, the texture of metal surface, and the inherent tendency of the metal to form an insoluble protective film, very notably affect the corrosion of metals themselves or their corrosion rate when they are used as protective coatings for steel.

By referring to Table 13–1 it can be seen that if a piece of iron (Fe) is dipped into a hydrochloric acid (HCl) solution (H=Ov), there is a voltage differential of 0.44 v since Fe = − 0.44 v. If this iron (Fe) is immersed in a copper sulfate solution (Cu = −0.34) then the potential difference is 0.44 + 0.34 = 0.78 v. Thus on the voltage basis it can be concluded that corrosion of iron in $CuSO_4$ solutions is approximately twice as fast as in HCl; however, it is not actually twice as fast since there are other factors that change the resistance to the flow of electrons and therefore the rate of corrosion.

13-2 Mechanisms of Corrosion and Variables Influencing Corrosion

Corrosion occurs by the two fairly well-recognized mechanisms:

Direct chemical attack—including all types of corrosion in which there is little or no perceptible flow of current through the metal for measurable distances. (There may, however, be electro-chemical forces that are in direct chemical attack in some instances.)

Electro-chemical attack—applies to all those cases where there are areas of definite anode and cathode that are separated by finite distances resulting in the flow of current in between anode and cathode.

The following chemical reactions typify the majority of direct and electro-chemical corrosion attack:

1. Combinations of metals (Me) and non-metals (Nm) without water.

   $Me + Nm \longrightarrow MeNm$ (Ex: Hi-temp oxidation of iron or steel in dry air.)
   $2Fe + O_2 \longrightarrow 2FeO$ also $2Fe + 1\text{–}1/2\ O_2 \longrightarrow Fe_2O_3$

2. Combinations of metals with oxygen *with water*

   $Me + 1/2\ O_2 + H_2O \longrightarrow Me(OH)_2$ (Ex: Rusting of steel in ordinary atmospheres)
   $Fe + 1/2\ O_2 + H_2O \longrightarrow Fe(OH)_2$ (This decomposes to FeO or Fe_2O_3)

3. Displacement of H_2 from acids or acid solutions

   $Me + H_2SO_4 \longrightarrow MeSO_4 + H_2$ (Ex: Attack of iron by H_2SO_4 or the tarnishing of silver by H_2S in the presence of moisture.)
   $Ag + H_2S$ (moisture present) $\longrightarrow AgS + H_2$

4. Displacement of H_2 from H_2O which usually contains small amounts of dissolved inorganic substances
   $Me + 2H_2O \longrightarrow Me(OH)_2 + H_2$ (Ex: Rusting of iron in water)
   (Many times oxygen dissolves in the water and combines with the liberated H_2)

5. Displacement of one metal or the ions of another metal from the salt solution
   $Mé + H_2SO_4 \longrightarrow MéSO_4 + Me$ (Mé represents the ion of the metal)(Ex: When iron is immersed in a solution of copper sulfate, the copper will plate out on to the iron and the iron will go into solution)

Corrosion is the gradual chemical (direct) or electro-chemical attack on metal by its surroundings, in such a manner to convert the metal to oxide, salt, or some other compound, thereby losing strength, ductility and other desirable properties.

13-3   Electro-chemical Attack on a Metal
by Its Surroundings

Since electro-chemical attack involves the setting up of anode and cathode areas, separated by finite distances, it results in the flow of electric current between them. This creates an electrolytic cell of one of two types; either a *galvanic cell* type or one of the *concentration cell* types shown in Fig. 13–1.

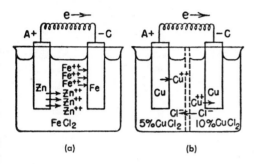

(a)   (b)

Fig. 13-1.   *Two types of electrolytic cells. (Courtesy of International Nickel Co., Inc., New York.)*

When two pieces of dissimilar metals such as iron and zinc are electrically connected and immersed in an electrolytic solution, a *galvanic cell* is set up. In Fig. 13–1 (a) the pieces of iron and zinc are immersed in an electrolytic solution of $FeCl_2$, and, of course, the more active metal, zinc, becomes the anode A which carries a positive charge, while the less active metal, iron, becomes the cathode C which carries the negative charge. The more active metal Zn tends to be attacked whereas the cathode, iron, tends to be protected. Electrons flow along the wire from the anode to the cathode. Reactions such as this occur in the case of galvanized iron sheets, the zinc galvanizing forming a sacrificial protection by retarding the corrosion of the iron beneath the zinc until all or most of the zinc has been corroded away.

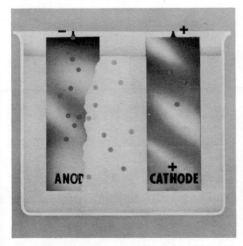

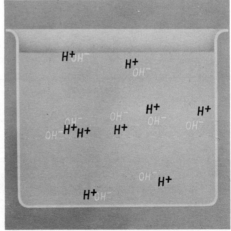

Fig. 13-2.   *The flow of electricity between anode and cathode in the corrosion of metal. (Courtesy of International Nickel Co., Inc., New York.)*

Fig. 13-3.   *The hydrogen and hydroxyl ions from the ionization of ordinary water. (Courtesy of International Nickel Co., Inc., New York.)*

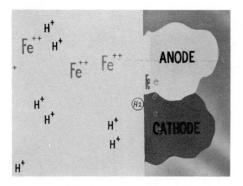 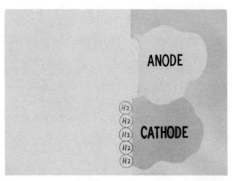

Fig. 13-4. *The formation of ions at the anode and hydrogen at the cathode in the action of a local cell. (Courtesy of International Nickel Co., Inc., New York.)*

Fig. 13-5. *The polarization of the local cathode by a film of hydrogen such as occurs in neutral electrolytes such as a salt (NaCl) solution. (Courtesy of International Nickel Co., Inc., New York.)*

13-4.   Types of Corrosion

There are several types of corrosion, which depend upon many factors, including the following:

1. *Uniform corrosion* takes place when the metal is completely homogeneous; the surface of the metal is evenly corroded and continues to dissolve, layer by layer, while at the same time remaining fairly smooth. This type of corrosion is somewhat rare since metals are seldom homogeneous enough to corrode evenly.

2. *Intergranular corrosion* occurs in alloys where there is a potential difference between the grain boundary and the center of the grain. This is one of the more common types of corrosion, and it is very serious in the Al-Cu alloys as well as in the austenitic stainless steels.

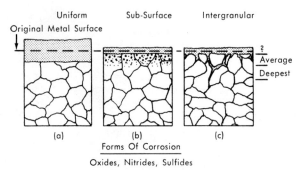

Fig. 13-6. *Schematic microstructures showing three common forms of corrosive attack. Intergranular corrosion is by far the worst as it is insidious, not showing up until failure. (Courtesy of American Society for Metals, Metals Park, Ohio.)*

3. *Pitting corrosion* is the most common type of corrosion, it occurs when heterogeneities such as inclusions, coring, and distorted zones are present in the metal. Because of the difference in potential between the different points on the surface of the alloy, some of them corrode faster to protect the remaining areas thus resulting in a pitted surface. Pit corrosion also occurs in a metal protected by an oxide film when a break or scratch in the surface film occurs. The exposed metal in such cases presents a small anode area to a large cathode area.

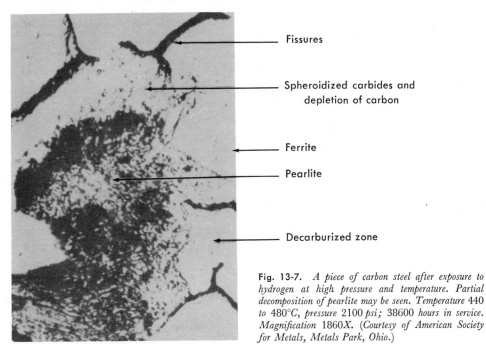

Fissures

Spheroidized carbides and
depletion of carbon

Ferrite

Pearlite

Decarburized zone

Fig. 13-7. *A piece of carbon steel after exposure to hydrogen at high pressure and temperature. Partial decomposition of pearlite may be seen. Temperature 440 to 480°C, pressure 2100 psi; 38600 hours in service. Magnification 1860X. (Courtesy of American Society for Metals, Metals Park, Ohio.)*

4. *Stress-corrosion* is the acceleration of corrosion caused by either internal or external stress; it is produced by a difference in potential between different parts of the space lattice. This type corrosion is found a great deal in cold-worked material where the distortion at the slip planes produced by the cold working causes accelerated precipitation and therefore a depletion of the solid solution of the alloy. Fig. 13–8 shows an example of this type.

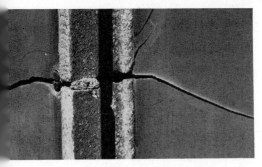

Fig. 13-8. *An example of stress-corrosion resulting in cracking induced in the metal as a result of a combination of corrosion and high tensile stresses. (Courtesy of International Nickel Co., Inc., New York.)*

5. *Galvanic corrosion* is found at the zone in which two different metals or alloys come in contact, one with the other. The severity of galvanic corrosion depends not only upon the differences of potential between the two metals or alloys, but also upon the relative surface areas of the two components of the metals. Galvanic corrosion is also affected by secondary reactions such as the formation of oxide film on the surface.

6. *Crevice-corrosion* has its origin, as the name implies, in a crevice or scratch on the surface of a metal or alloy and in many instances develops into intergranular corrosion. Where there is a sharp machine-cut into the surface of a metal, it is the likely potential for the beginning of corrosion under certain

environmental conditions. In fact, even in stainless steels a scratch on the surface will break through the usual protective coating of chromium and nickel oxides over the surface acting as a barrier to retard additional attack. A breakthrough of this protective film because of a cut or scratch will lead to crevice corrosion; however, under some conditions a new film of oxides will tend to reform in the scratch to continue its protective action. In the absence of a scratch that will often result in crevice-corrosion, the protective coating of oxides on the exposed surface of metals makes it necessary for diffusion to occur through the scale or coating for additional oxidation growth to take place.

This very troublesome type of corrosion may occur if oxygen is available at some places on the metal and is absent or used up in other localities. As a result, crevices, joints, dead spots, or the bottoms of corrosion pits are particularly susceptible to this form of attack, because even if air is present and the electrolyte is stirred, oxygen can only reach such places by slow diffusion. In a crevice or other region of imperfect mixing, where there is an insufficient supply of oxygen, only the anodic reaction takes place and the metal is corroded. Away from the crevice, where oxygen is more readily available, the cathodic reactions take place, using up electrons and forming hydroxyl ions. The presence of the latter can be determined by testing the liquid for alkali with litmus paper. Since most metal ions form insoluble compounds (hydroxides) with hydroxyl ions, a precipitate of metal hydroxide is usually formed where the products of the anodic and cathodic reactions mingle by diffusion (see Fig. 13–9 for example).

Fig. 13-9. *Severe corrosion that occurred in a crevice of a mooring pennant. This type corrosion often occurs under gaskets, washers, or in sockets as well as in crevices. (Courtesy of International Nickel Company, Inc., New York.)*

13-5   Effect of Corrosion on the Properties of Materials

In uniform corrosion there is not much change in the mechanical properties of the metal involved. When this type corrosion takes place, how much of the original load-carrying ability is left can be determined by measuring the thickness of the section involved, since its decrease in dimensions is proportional to the decrease in load-carrying ability.

TABLE 13–2.   The Effect of Corrosion on Mechanical Properties

Type of Corrosion	Loss of Weight %	Depth of Penetration %	LOSS OF PROPERTIES		
			Tensile Strength %	Yield Strength %	Elongation
Uniform	1%	1%	1%	1%	1%
Pitting	0.7%	5%	7%	5%	15%
Intergranular	0.20%	15%	25%	20%	80%
Stress	0.10%	100%	100%	100%	100%

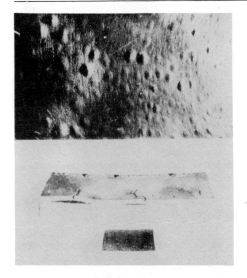

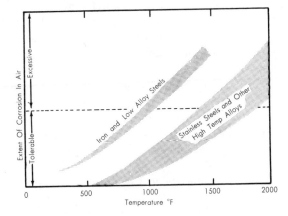

Fig. 13-10.   *An example of metal failure caused by hydrogen embrittlement. In the top of the cut is the surface of a blistered carbon steel plate and in the lower portion is a cross section cut through the same plate. (Courtesy of International Nickel Co., Inc., New York.)*

Fig. 13-11.   *A photomicrograph of almost pure nickel (99.4 per cent) showing a tough and corrosion-resistant grain structure. (Courtesy of International Nickel Co., Inc., New York.)*

Fig. 13-12.   *Graph showing extent of corrosion in air vs temperature for several materials including iron, low alloy steels and stainless steels, and other high temperature alloys. (Courtesy American Society for Metals.)*

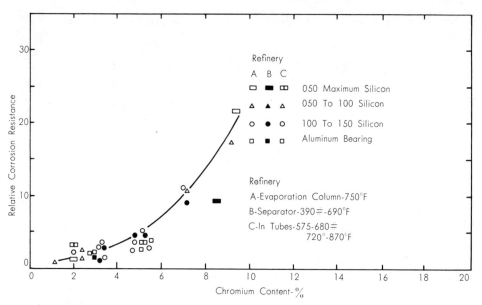

Fig. 13-13. *Corrosion test results of alloy steels taken from three different oil refineries. It will be noted that the relative corrosion resistance to hot petroleum products increases with increased chromium content although its effect in amounts below 4 per cent is not pronounced. (Courtesy American Society for Metals.)*

13-6 Hydrogen Embrittlement

Hydrogen is dissolved in molten steel from water vapor and in the solid steel when the steel is in contact with nascent hydrogen. It has a very detrimental embrittling effect, probably because of the precipitation of hydrides, causing flakes in the steel. This can be reduced substantially and practically eliminated by proper annealing of the metal. Although hydrogen may diffuse out of steel at room temperature if the section is small enough and sufficient time is allowed, tension tests on carbon steel bars will show low ductility if made soon after rolling; ductility will increase on aging at room temperature or after shorter times at elevated temperatures. This effect is, of course, more pronounced in larger sections because of the longer time required for the diffusion of hydrogen to the surface. Hydrogen contents of more than about 0.0005 per cent will produce this effect, and such contents are quite common in as-rolled steels that have been cast into ingots in the conventional manner. The content of hydrogen in steel can be reduced substantially, along with other gases, by use of the vacuum degassing process, discussed in Chapter 8, during the teeming operation. Anything in excess of about five parts per million of hydrogen (0.0005 per cent) also plays an important part in this phenomenon of *flaking* which shows up in the form of internal cracks or bursts usually occurring during the cooling from rolling or forging operations.

Fig. 13–10 shows an example of hydrogen embrittlement in a carbon steel plate.

13-7 Corrosion Fatigue

Corrosion fatigue is one type of stress corrosion. A safe endurance limit may be nonexistent if repeated stressing occurs under even mildly corrosive conditions such as exposure to ordinary tap water. In the case of fatigue failure, the strained crystals become anodic and therefore are susceptible to corrosive attack. Once a crack starts it may act as an artificial pit, and its anodic corrosion will be accelerated because of the relative area effect. This type corrosion is the combined action of corrosion and repeated stresses and is much more serious than the sum of these two factors (stress and corrosion) acting individually. The damage ratio resulting from corrosion fatigue may be expressed in the following manner to show the influence of corrosion on fatigue:

$$\text{Damage ratio} = \frac{\text{corrosion fatigue strength of the metal}}{\text{fatigue strength under normal conditions}}$$

For example, the damage ratio for salt water as a corroding medium is about 0.2 for carbon steels, 0.5 for stainless steels, 0.4 for aluminum alloys, and 1.0 for copper and most copper alloys.

D. J. McAdam, Jr., made some extensive experiments and studies of corrosion fatigue starting in 1925 and found that even under pure water, the endurance limit may be reduced far below the limit recorded in air. In fact, no definite limit for endurance limit has been found for indefinitely long life under corrosion fatigue conditions. In reporting the results in corrosion-fatigue tests, it is essential to state the limiting number of cycles used in the test and also the frequency of cycles of stress. McAdam used two terms to express the amount of damage resulting from corrosion fatigue: "total damage," meaning the percentage reduction from the endurance limit in air, and "net damage," meaning the percentage reduction from the endurance limit of metal subjected to some definite period of "stressless" corrosion to the endurance limit of specimens that have been subjected to some definite routine of corrosion fatigue. According to McAdam's data the following tentative relation is given between stress range and average rate of net damage:

$$R = CS^n$$

In this equation, R denotes the rate of net damage in percentage per day, S denotes the range of stress in lb per sq in. during a cycle, and C and n are experimental constants. C is approximately proportional to the frequency for low frequencies and nearly independent of frequency for high frequencies. Values of n will vary from 2.6 to 5.7 according to Gough and McAdams.

13-8   Dezincification

In some metals and alloys and under certain environmental conditions, localized areas may be attacked in such a manner that one or more constituents is dissolved, leaving that particular area devoid to that certain element. This is known as *dezincification*, a term that was originally applied to the removal of zinc from brasses by means of existing corrosive environment. The term now applies to any condition of corrosion in which any specific element is removed from an alloy. The dezincification of brasses results in a transformation from its usual yellow color to that of a copperred, indicating a predominance of copper and a lack of zinc, accompanied by a severe loss of strength because of this loss of zinc from the alloy.

The phenomenon of dezincification is actually the corrosion of an alloy containing zinc (usually brass) involving loss of zinc and a surface residue or deposit of one or more of the less active components (usually copper). Many of the copperzinc alloys, and in some cases aluminum-bronze and cupro-nickel, undergo this type of corrosion in the copper-zinc alloy. The initial corrosion in this type of attack is usually followed by a secondary reaction in which copper in the corrosion product is redeposited in a porous, friable, and weak mass as a residue on the surface of the metal. Corrosion of a similar nature continues beneath the primary deposit of copper, resulting in the gradual replacement of sound metal by a brittle, porous copper. This kind of action, unless it is arrested, eventually penetrates the cross-section of the metal, weakening it structurally and resulting in leakage through the porous copper layer in conduits for conducting liquids. The type of dezincification that occurs at localized areas on the metal surface is termed "plug-type dezincification." Dezincification of brasses usually occurs in contact with sea water or with fresh waters that have both a high oxygen and high carbon dioxide content. At elevated temperatures, dezincification is particularly active and destructive.

13-9   Reaction of Metals with Oxygen in Absence of Water or Moisture

The type of corrosion mentioned previously under well-recognized mechanisms of corrosion (paragraph 13-2, 1), i.e., the reaction of metals with oxygen in the absence of water or moisture, is worthy of further discussion, because the nature of the oxide that is formed is of major importance in the oxidation (corrosion) process. For example:

1. In certain instances, the oxide may be unstable, as in the case of gold oxide, and therefore oxidation does not take place.
2. In other cases, the oxide may be volatile, as in the case of molybdenum oxide, so that oxidation takes place at a constant, rather high rate.
3. At times, one or more oxides may form a layer or layers at the surface of the metal, which is the more common reaction.

When these surface oxide layers are less than about 3,000 Å, they are known as *films*; they are called *scales* when their thicknesses are greater than this value and become more easily measured. The films, being so thin, have a negligible amount of destructive effect on most metal parts; however, where sizeable amounts of wear are present, the rate of metal loss is substantially increased as a result of the removal of this thin protective film by abrasion. Thin films decrease the rate of further oxidation as a rule, and, as in the case of the thin film of oxide on aluminum, it is extremely protective in effect.

In order for any further growth to take place as a result of oxidation with a *protective oxide* formation on the surface of a metal, diffusion must occur through the scale. In some instances, the oxide scales or layers may be non-protective rather than protective, and according to the Pilling-Bedworth rule, an oxide is protective to the metal providing the oxide is at least as great as the volume of metal from which it was formed. In cases where this relationship is not true and the volume of oxide is less than this amount, the scale has been found to be not continuous and therefore ineffective in its ability to prevent oxygen from entering any exposed portion of the metal surface. Metals that have these *nonprotective* oxides have a tendency to increase in weight, W, of their scale in a linear rate fashion according to the equation:

$$W = At$$

where t is the time of exposure and A is a constant that depends on the temperature.

The rate of oxidation in those cases where the metal ionizes at the oxide-metal interface and then the metal ion, M^{++}, and the electrons diffuse through the oxide layer to the oxygen surface (the electron assisting in the formation of the oxygen ion) may be found to follow the *parabolic law:*

$$W^2 = Bt$$

where t is the time of exposure and B is a constant that depends on temperature. In the case of certain metals with protective oxides, the reaction rates diminish even more rapidly than the parabolic law indicates. As an example, under numerous conditions the oxide layer on aluminum approaches a constant thickness with the passing of time and so is governed by an *asymptotic law*. In still other cases, a *logarithmic* increase in the weight of oxide is found to exist according to the following equation:

$$W = C \log (Dt + E)$$

where C, D, and E are constants dependent on temperature. This is found in the oxidation of iron or nickel at moderate temperatures.

13-10   Protection Against Corrosion

Selection of Material. The most obvious method of preventing corrosion is to build the structure of a material which is unaffected by the conditions of service, environment, etc. This is not always feasible to do as the most inert materials may be too costly or otherwise unsuited for the product being manufactured. As a rule, the engineer must make this decision and, at times, decide upon a compromise. He cannot afford to use the most corrosion-resistant material, but instead must compromise on a material which has the lowest combined initial cost plus maintainance costs for some particular time period selected. The more knowledge the engineer has concerning the corrosion behavior of the various competitive materials under consideration for the desired service conditions, the more accurately he can select the most economical and best material to use. In this selection, the really best guide for the engineer is the previous service experience of the materials being considered. Inasmuch as small variations in service conditions can sometimes affect corrosion rates greatly, even previous service experience of the materials is not at all infallible. Despite this fact, it is still the most trustworthy criterion available to the engineer. In those situations where it is necessary to select material for equipment needed for some new process or chemical environment, there will be no previous background of experience available. In cases of this nature, the engineer must be guided by his knowledge of the behavior of various materials when used as components for similar processes or equipment in the past. Even better yet, a pilot plant or small-scale service test can be made using a material or materials in the construction that the engineer deems to be most likely to be best for the purpose intended, based on laboratory tests or information from handbooks and other published information on the subject in question.

Selection of a suitable material of construction may eliminate the necessity of using any other form of corrosion prevention; however, it is often more economical to use some material that is less corrosion-resistant but cheaper and then to employ one or even several protective measures that are available. The available protective coatings can be classified in several ways; however, based on their characteristics they may be classified as follows:

1. Anodic coatings
2. Cathodic coatings
3. Inert coatings
4. Inhibitive coatings

Coatings that show the most pronounced anodic or cathodic behavior are the metallic coatings; however, nonmetallic coatings, especially oxide or sulphide coatings will act as cathodic coatings under some conditions of exposure.

It is important to note that the same metallic coating on the same base metal can behave as an anodic coating under one set of exposure conditions and as a cathodic coating under other conditions and as an inert coating or even as an inhibitive coating under still another set of exposure conditions. For example, tin coatings on steel when exposed in sea water outdoors, in most natural water, or even to many food products in the presence of air will act in a cathodic manner to the exposed area of the steel base. When exposed to nearly air-free food products, however, tin is generally anodic to steel.

Inorganic coatings are sometimes inert, sometimes cathodic and, at times, inhibitive. Organic coatings are generally either inert or inhibitive. Either inorganic or organic coatings which contain water-soluble chromates generally act as inhibitive coatings in most natural environments. Obviously, the inhibitive value of such coatings is greatest when there is only limited opportunity for leaching of the soluble inhibiter to occur. For example, it would be expected that the inhibitive action of a coating containing a soluble chromate would be more in evidence if the coating were on the interior of a tank containing only a small amount of stagnant water than if it were on the interior of a pipe through which unrecirculated water was passing continually.

13-11 Metallic Protective Coatings

The most commonly used metallic coatings for steel include tin, zinc, terne metal (lead plus tin), nickel, chromium, cadmium, copper, aluminum, bronze, brass, silver, gold, and lead. As stated previously, a metallic coating may be either anodic or cathodic to the base metal to which it is applied. Table 13-1 gives the electro-chemical series of metals and certain alloys in the order of electrode potential referred to the standard hydrogen electrode at a temperature of 25C.

The metallic coatings may be applied to the surface of steel by several methods:

1. *Hot dip process*—where the parts to be coated are immersed in a molten bath of the metal, after thorough cleaning. Tin, zinc, terne metal, aluminum, and lead are applied commercially in this manner.

2. *Metal spraying*—may be used with most of the common metals. In this process the coating metal is usually drawn into wire and fed through a specially constructed spray gun that is operated with compressed air and a fuel gas. The gases at the nozzle are ignited, the wire is melted as it is fed into to nozzle and is projected against the surface to be coated at a speed of over 500 ft per sec. Even though the molten metal particles are cooled instantly to a temperature of about 80F, the impact causes them to adhere firmly to the

steel surface, provided it has been thoroughly cleaned, just as in the case of sand or shot blasting or even machining. This process of metal spraying is also used effectively for building up surfaces such as large drive shafts that have become worn, and also for the application of thin coatings as a pretection against serious corrosion.

3. *Metal Cementation*—a method of metal protection against corrosion in which the metals zinc, chromium, aluminum, and silicon are successfully applied by actually alloying them into the surface to be protected. This includes several procedures, depending upon the metals used, as follows:

(a) *Sherardizing* consists of thoroughly cleaning the parts to be coated (usually small parts such as bolts nuts, nails, etc.) by pickling or sandblasting, then packing them in metal drums with fine zinc dust, usually containing 5 to 8 per cent zinc oxide. The contents of the drum are heated to from 650 to 750F for several hours during which time the drums are rotated in the furnace. The resulting coating is thin and consists of intermetallic compounds of iron and zinc, ranging from an iron-rich alloy adjacent to the steel base to almost pure zinc at the surface. Very good protection against atmospheric corrosion is obtained by this method.

(b) *Chromizing* is a cementation process much like sherardizing; in this case the parts to be coated are packed in a container with a mixture of 55 parts of chromium or powdered ferrochromium and 45 parts of alumina by weight. This mixture is then heated either in a vacuum or a protective atmosphere (hydrogen is preferred) at 2370 to 2560F for three or four hours. When lesser penetration is needed, a shorter time and lower temperature may be used. Coatings by this process are generally about 0.004 inch thick and contain about 40 per cent chromium at the surface of the parts being coated.

(c) *Anodizing* is a method of coating aluminum and magnesium and their alloys, usually by the use of an electrolyte of a 3 per cent solution of chromic acid at a temperature of about 100F. In the process the voltage is raised from zero to 40 at the rate of about 8 v per min and is maintained at full voltage for 30 to 60 min; this produces a current density of about 1 to 3 amp per sq ft of surface coated. The resulting coating is very thin (0.00005 to 0.0001 in.), and its principal use has been as a base for paint on aluminum and magnesium parts. Although the usual color is grayish green, resulting from the presence of reduced (trivalent) chromium in the coating, other colors may also be obtained and are found in structural aluminum columns and beams in large buildings for exterior work as well as interiorly to simulate gold color effectively.

Anodizing capitalizes on one of the outstanding characteristics of aluminum in that it provides a high degree of protection by the thin, invisible film of aluminum oxide that is naturally formed on the surface. Oxide films of substantial thickness can also be formed by anodic treatment in certain electrolytes, usually of an acid character. Such anodic coatings are minutely porous, and during anodic treatment the current carried by the electrolyte in the pores of the metal converts the base metal into aluminum oxide. During formation, therefore, the oxide grows into the metal leaving the first-formed oxide on the surface. The oxide coating is integral with the aluminum, and this, in large part, accounts for its excellent adhesion to the base metal. Such coatings are essentially amorphous aluminum oxide, but may contain sulfate or other substances absorbed from the electrolyte.

The most widely accepted electrolyte is an aqueous solution containing about 15 to 25 per cent sulfuric acid, this electrolyte has the advantage of yielding clear transparent coatings on pure aluminum and translucent or opaque coatings on metal of lower purity such as 2S sheet (99 per cent minimum of aluminum). During anodic treatment of aluminum alloys, the behavior of alloying constituents is important in determining the characteristics of the coating. For example, certain constituents may be anodically dissolved and removed from the coating, whereas others, unattacked or partially oxidized, may remain in the coating as occlusions. Removal of constituents or inclusions from the oxide during anodic treatment may therefore affect the continuity and protective power, as well as the appearance of the coating itself.

Magnesium may also be given a protective coating by electro-chemical treatments. This may be accomplished by either acid or caustic anodizing. All acid solutions used in commercial treatments involve the use of the dichromates with additions of sulfates, fluorides, or phosphates. The baths are very similar to those used normally for direct chemical treatment. The main advantages gained by the application of current are the reduction of the duration of the treatment and lower temperatures of the bath. The main disadvantages are that the throwing power of these acid baths is often insufficient to coat complicated parts completely and also that such baths are often more expensive because of the labor involved. A typical acid anodic treatment, known as the "galvanic anodize," is a two-step procedure as follows:

Step 1. Dip parts for 5 min in an aqueous solution containing 15 to 20 per cent by weight of hydrofluoric acid maintained at room temperature.

Step 2. Anodize the magnesium at 10 amp per sq ft for 10 min in a bath operated at 50 to 60C and consisting of 30 g per l $Na_2Cr_2O_7 \cdot 2H_2O$, 30 g per l $(NH_4)_2SO_4$ and 2.5 ml per l NH_4OH (sp gr of 0.88).

Some coatings that are produced on magnesium by anodic oxidation in strongly alkaline solutions are more resistant to oxidation and corrosion in aqueous solutions than are coatings formed either chemically or electro-chemically in chromate baths. A typical caustic anodizing solution contains 25 per cent NaOH, 7 per cent diethylene glycol, and 0.2 per cent sodium oxalate. Several variations of this type composition have been proposed, but all of them essentially produce coatings that are $Mg(OH)_2$ formed in a hard, compact manner. Because of the alkaline nature of the film thus formed, the coating produced by an electro-chemical treatment on magnesium is not receptive to paint.

4. *Metal Cladding*—another effective method of coating to retard corrosion. Cladding is done with several metals including copper, aluminum, and

stainless steel. These processes give bi-metallic products, those containing steel consisting of an inner core of steel covered with a heavy layer of the cladding metal. Usually the steel core, after cleaning thoroughly, is mounted in a covered mold and heated out of contact with air to a temperature of slightly above the melting point of copper, which is then cast about it. Other methods consist of dipping the solid steel core into a bath of molten copper, or of depositing the copper onto the steel electrolytically.

Aluminum cladding is best accomplished by rolling almost any gage of steel, cleaning it thoroughly, and then either placing it between two sheets of aluminum and cold rolling, or heating the "sandwich" to between 600 and 750F and then rolling; the latter makes a superior bond between the aluminum and the steel core.

Stainless cladding may be done by any one of three methods:

(a) Electro-welding stainless steel onto carbon steel

(b) Casting the stainless steel around a solid carbon-steel slab

(c) Placing a slab of carbon steel between two plates of stainless steel and then hot rolling them together. With this method, it is best to use fluxes or metals to facilitate bonding; however, if the steels are both thoroughly cleaned before making the "sandwich," this may not be necessary. Usually a welding bead is placed around the perimeter as a further precaution against corrosion of the laminated plate structure.

5. *Vacuum Metallized Coatings*—still another method of coating metals that can be applied to almost all common metals and nonmetallic materials not only to serve as a corrosion-resistant in the case of metals, but as an improvement to appearance when used on nonmetallics. Because of their thinness, the coatings tend to provide very little in the way of corrosion resistance so that they are usually protected with a clear organic coating to resist corrosion, abrasion, and handling of the parts.

13-12   Summary of Corrosion

Controlling corrosion helps save millions of dollars every year in damaged machinery. It helps conserve our natural resources by making metals last longer. It even helps save human lives by reducing the accidents caused by the failure of parts that corrode. This is a very serious aspect of corrosion that is many times overlooked. Equally important is the fact that reducing corrosion has tremendously aided the creation of many of great industries. It has assisted old established industries to new heights of success. Many pure products considered necessities today could not be made without the virtual elimination of corrosion in their manufacturing process.

A great deal has been learned about corrosion, its causes, and its elimination or reduction, but much more must be done in research in the laboratories in order that not only the right metal be used but the right metal be used in the right way and in the right place. This is an important goal of research in corrosion. The nickel-bearing steels with nickel content of about 8 per cent and with chromium content of about 17 to 18 per cent make the most suitable corrosion-resistant alloys

(Fig. 13–17), although there are many others including monel-metal (Fig. 13–14), Ni-resist (Fig. 13–15), and Ni-Hard (Fig. 13–16) that have excellent resistance to corrosion in corrosive environments.

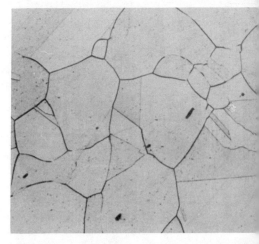

Fig. 13-14. *Monel with 67 per cent nickel, 30 per cent copper, 0.15 per cent carbon, 0.1 per cent silicon and 1.4 per cent iron.*

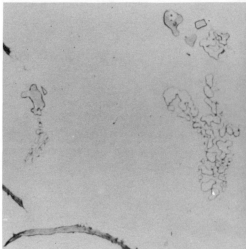

Fig. 13-15. *Ni-Resist with 30.21 per cent nickel, 2.62 per cent carbon, 1.61 per cent silicon, 0.98 per cent manganese, and 1.4 per cent chromium with the balance iron.*

Fig. 13-16. *Ni-Hard with 4.5 per cent nickel, 3.00 carbon, 2.15 per cent chromium, 0.50 per cent manganese, 0.50 per cent silicon, and balance iron.*

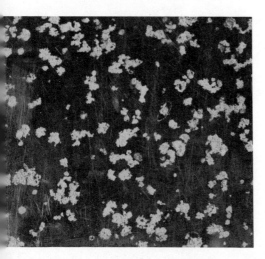

Fig. 13-17. *Pitting on the surface of an 18-8 stainless steel resulting from localized corrosion under marine organisms that became attached to the surface while the steel is immersed in sea-water. (Courtesy of International Nickel Co., Inc. New York.)*

QUESTIONS

1. Explain the basis of corrosion including some of the problems that occur in the structure and microstructure when metals corrode.

2. Define in terms of both the metallurgist and physical chemist as well as in lay terms the phenomena of corrosion.

3. Are there any instances where corrosion takes place intentionally? If so, explain such instances in detail.

4. How is the electro-motive series of metals arranged and of what use is it in industry and particularly in metallurgy?

5. Name the several types of corrosion and tell upon what factors each depends.

6. What effect do the various types of corrosion have upon the mechanical properties of metals? Be explicit.

7. How does Farraday's Law play an important part in corrosion?

8. What are some of the more important ways of protecting against corrosion?

9. In the long run, what is the safest guide for the engineer in properly selecting a material for use in corrosive environments?

10. Where there is no possibility of looking to past experience or previous background, how can the engineer and metallurgist decide on the proper materials to use under corrosive conditions?

11. How can protective coatings to prevent or retard corrosion be classified?

12. Can we be certain that the same metallic coating on the same base metal will behave the same under any and all exposure conditions? Explain the reasons for your answer citing examples.

13. What are the more commonly used metallic coatings used for protecting steel? How are they applied?

14. Define the following terms and explain each: sherardizing, chromizing, anodizing, aluminum cladding.

15. Can a high quality coating of metals and nonmetals be obtained by means of simply vacuum metallizing the surfaces in question? If so, why is it not used more frequently?

16. Name the three common forms of corrosive attack and tell which is the most detrimental and why.

17. Explain the phenomenon of hydrogen embrittlement in metals and how it affects the material. How can it be overcome?

18. Why is the problem of corrosion of metals so critically important?

References

Depaul, Donald J., *Corrosion and Wear Handbook*. New York: McGraw-Hill Book Company, 1957.

Guy, Albert G., *Physical Metallurgy for Engineers*. Reading, Massachusetts: Addison-Wesley Publishing Co., 1962.

Jastrzebski, Zkigniew D., *Nature and Properties of Engineering Materials*. New York: John Wiley & Sons, Inc., 1959.

Kubaschewski, Oswald, and B.E. Hopkins, *Oxidation of Metals and Alloys*, 2nd ed. London: Butterworth's, 1962.

Loose, William S., *Corrosion of Magnesium*. Metals Park, Ohio: American Society for Metals, 1959.

Seabright, Lawrence H. and R. J. Fabian, "The Many Faces of Corrosion," *Materials in Design Engineering*. New York: Reinhold Publishing Corp., Special Report #202, January, 1963.

Speller, Frank N., *Corrosion, Causes and Prevention*, 3rd ed. New York: McGraw-Hill Book Company, 1951.

Taylor, Lyman, (ed), *Metals Handbook*, 8th ed. Metals Park, Ohio, 1961.

Uhlig, Herbert H., *Corrosion and Corrosion Control*. New York: John Wiley & Sons, Inc., 1963.

Van Vlack, Lawrence H., *Elements of Materials Science*. Reading, Massachusetts: Addison-Wesley Publishing Company, 1959.

Metal Failure Analysis

14-1 Principles and Significance of Metal Fatigue and Failure

The basic reason for studying metal failures is to cut costs and thereby increase profits for structural parts that are used in commercial practice; however, in those instances where metal parts are components of aircraft, spacecraft etc., where the parts must be 100 percent reliable, it is essential that they must be "life-safe."

In every failure analysis there are several questions that should be asked and answered:

1. What is the material?
2. What are its physical properties?
3. What are its mechanical properties?
4. How was it produced?
5. How long was it used in service?
6. What was it designed to do in service?
7. What properties have changed?
8. What was the mechanism of failure?

Invariably a material will fail either as a result of corrosion or as the result of excessive stress—or by a combination of both of these factors. For example, mechanical failures in the petroleum and petrochemical industry are the result of several factors including abuse, manufacturing or fabricating defects, poor design, erosion, creep, fatigue, creep rupture, thermal shock, and thermal fatigue.

As was mentioned in Chapter 13, there are about 30 types of corrosion damage; however, the most common is pitting which can occur at high temperatures and also under an aqueous environment. Stress corrosion cracking, corrosion fatigue cracking, and corrosion-erosion are still other common forms which show up under aqueous conditions.

It is most desirable, if possible, to examine the part at the spot where failure occurred since in numerous cases the analyst can find an immediate solution to the problem, providing he has had adequate education, skill, and training in his work. Subsequently he may find it imperative to send the part to the laboratory for further analyses or to substantiate his opinion as to the cause or causes of failure on first on-the-site analysis. There he will have all the tools at his command including testing equipment of all types for determining the physical and mechanical properties of the parts that failed, the composition of any corrosion products, foreign matter, and base materials involved. In addition, there must be an investigation of the presence of any hidden defects as well as an analysis of the characteristics of failure.

The term "fatigue" usually means fracture caused by repeated stresses which are so low that one application of the stress apparently does nothing detrimental to the structure. Then when enough of these seemingly harmless cycles of stress are applied, they bring about a small crack which grows with continued loadings until complete fracture takes place.

Although it is true that fatigue failures can only occur by the repeated application of tension or shear stresses which tend to pull the material apart, still the application of compressive stresses alternating with stresses in tension greatly lowers the magnitude of the amount of the tension-stresses finally needed to fracture the part. Such a cycle that consists of alternating equal stresses in tension and compression is called a "fully reversed" cycle, and the endurance limits obtained by using such a cycle are the ones usually reported.

There are many methods of analyzing fractures when they occur, including hardness reading, X ray, photomicrography, chemical and ultrasonic analyses, and others, however, before the analyst gets too sophisticated and cuts up the fractured parts preparatory to polishing, mounting, etching and inspecting it under the microscope, there are certain things he can learn by a close observation and analysis of the fractured surfaces involved.

It is obvious that failures of metal parts are a costly source of information, but too often the fractured surfaces are not given the investigation and study they deserve. In order to determine the cause of failure, the surfaces of a fracture should be carefully examined, and the actual mechanism of failure determined in each instance. Information gained from examining the fractures helps correct many failures in a wide variety of parts including pressure vessels, drive shafts, tie rods, tow-bars, steel cables, bolts, etc.

Metal parts do fail—in fact, almost anything can be broken. Perhaps the metal did not perform as expected because it was not designed for the loads to which it was ultimately subjected. Or in some cases the material involved did not come up to specifications. In still other instances, failure may have occurred because of a lack of knowledge of the time, temperature, stresses or environmental conditions to which the part was subjected. In a special report for the Armed Forces, a metallurgist with one of the larger aircraft companies stated that the most troublesome and least expected failures are almost always due to brittle fracture in the metal.

When the fractured surfaces of broken parts are studied, it is found that they display markings which constitute a topographical map, so the history of events that preceded the failure can be seen. In many instances, these surfaces are easily interpreted with the unaided eye or at low magnification (20 X or less). An analyst can locate the origin of the fracture, and a more detailed study of this site will usually reveal the cause of failure. For example, the area adjacent to the origin generally has defects such as cracks, machine marks, corrosion pits, hydrogen embrittlement zones, or notches. Between the origin and the edge of the fractured surface, markings that were produced during the growth stage often can reveal much concerning the toughness of the metal. Knowledge of fracture surface characteristics assists greatly in determining whether a material or design complies with the purpose for which the part was used.

Fracture must be either transcrystalline (across the grain) or intercrystalline (along the grain boundaries), either in whole or in part. The intercrystalline fractures are easily discernible, usually being associated with relatively brittle phases precipitated either at or near the grain boundaries. Transcrystalline fracture, which presents more complexities, occurs by one of two basic mechanisms: shear or cleavage. In body-centered cubic metals of low strength, the well-known transition from ductile to brittle failure represents the change from shear to cleavage. In the case of stronger materials a similar transition apparently occurs through an alteration in the mode of shear of fracture similar to those observed in face-centered cubic materials where there is no cleavage present.

14-2 A Study of Tensile and Impact Test Specimens after Fracture

Fig. 14–1 shows a standard tensile specimen of AISI 4340 steel, tested at room temperature or slightly higher, which reveals that the fracture will contain, in addition to the origin, three distinct zones all of which are shown graphically in Fig. 14–1. As shown in the diagram, F indicates the central or fibrous zone of the fracture which is very characteristic of slow, ductile failures. The R is of the intermediate "radial" zone showing ridges which grow in relief as they radiate out to the third zone, called the "shear lip" and marked S in the diagram accompanying Fig. 14–1. Failure began here at an inclusion which was located in the bottom of the conical depression near the center. The radial markings, like spokes of a wheel, indicate rapid cracking and become larger as they project from the fibrous zone toward the "shear lip" zone. The actual zones and their sizes will vary a great deal with the temperature of testing. At cryogenic temperatures, the surface is almost entirely radial (left); however, with rising temperature, the radial zone shrinks while the shear lip and fibrous zone grows and disappears entirely at the higher temperatures. (These are shown in Fig. 14–2 with the diagram.)

Although the markings on flat tensile specimens are essentially the same as those appearing on round specimens, there are slight differences as revealed in Fig. 14–3. Here both the origin and fibrous zones are centrally located; however, the fibrous area, in this case, is elliptic in configuration rather than round. The radial marks in the intermediate zone form a pattern often referred to as "chevron" or "herringbone" marks. As a rule, these chevron markings point toward the direction of the origin of the fracture. In flat specimens, both thickness and temperature have a bearing on the zones present as well as their sizes. Increases in temperature result in larger shear lips that grow at the expense of the radial zone. When the temperature is constant, the shear lip has a critical size so that any increase in thickness of the specimen beyond this size merely increases the size of the radial area.

In round specimens such as are shown in Fig. 14–4, a circumferential notch of of sufficient sharpness alters the stress distribution very markedly. Because of the concentrations of stress, the crack begins at or near the root of the notch and propa-

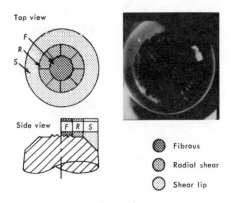

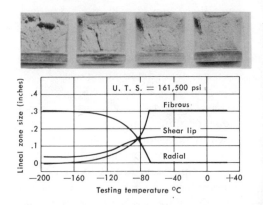

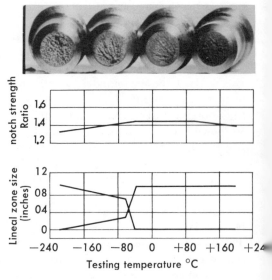

Top view

Side view

- ⬤ Fibrous
- ⬤ Radial shear
- ⬤ Shear lip

Fig. 14-1. *The three zones of fracture surfaces of tensile specimens; the fibrous zone at the center, the intermediate or radial zone, and the third zone or the shear lip.*

Fig. 14-2. *The effects of testing temperature on the presence and sizes of zones.*

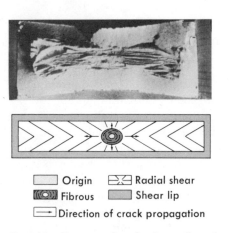

- ☐ Origin   ▭ Radial shear
- ◉ Fibrous   ☐ Shear lip
- ▭→ Direction of crack propagation

Fig. 14-3. *Fracture surface of a flat tensile specimen shows that they also have three zones as do the round specimens. However, the central fibrous zone is elliptical rather than round. Also, the radial ridges assume a "chevron" pattern pointing to the origin of failure.*

Fig. 14-4. *Failure in notched tensile bars starts at or near the root of the notch and grows inward.*

gates toward the center of the section. As a result of this, the fibrous zone surrounds the radial zone. Since the notched bar fractures internally, the shear lip is not present, and the area of final separation appears rougher than the rest of the fracture surface. Here again, notched specimens are affected by temperature just as in the case of unnotched specimens.

Fig. 14–5 shows fractures through notched test bars of AISI 4340 steel that have been heat treated, hydrogen embrittled, and stress-rupture tested. As indicated here, as the stress is raised, the fibrous area is reduced, and the radial zone becomes larger. This is in full accordance with the concepts of fracture mechanics as the stress in the elastic area is increased on specimens containing defects so that smaller "critical crack sizes," indicated by the fibrous zones, are needed to start very rapid crack growth; consequently, the radial zone increases constantly with rising stress.

Specimens submitted to Charpy V-notch tests develop the type of fracture shown in Fig. 14–6 with the crack starting at the notch and spreading out radially. The

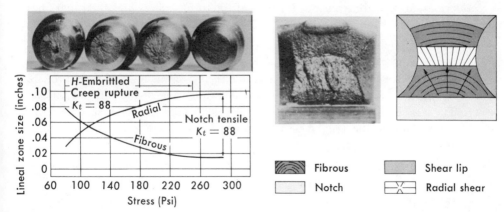

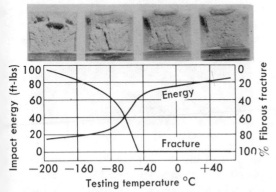

Fig. 14-5. *AISI 4340 heat treated, hydrogen embrittled, and stress-rupture tested. Fibrous area is reduced and radial zone grows larger as the stress is increased.*

Fig. 14-6. *Fracture of a Charpy V-notch specimen after impact. Note the crack starts at notch and spreads outward. Fibrous zones appear above and below the radial zone and shear lips which are at top and side.*

light portion of the surface is the radial zone with the fibrous zones above and below the radial zone, and shear lips at the top and sides of the specimen. As may be seen here, the fracture starts at a point slightly below and usually at the midwidth of the notch. Then the crack grows, spreading away from the notch and through the specimen in a semicircular manner. As a result of this, the fibrous markings are arcs or segments of circles.

Fig. 14–7 reveals the general relationship between energy and fibrosity along with curves that were obtained by plotting the linear length of the fracture zones as a function of temperature. It is possible, with data of this nature, to estimate the relative toughness of the material if the temperature at which the fracture occurred is known. It is seen here that as the temperature rises, the fibrous zone and the shear lip grow while the radial zone becomes smaller.

Fig. 14-7. *Both the photos and the diagram show how the degree of fibrosity on fracture surfaces of impact specimens are directly related to the impact strength. Here can be seen how the relative toughness of a metal can be estimated if the temperature at which failure occurred is known. As the temperature rises, the fibrous zone and shear lip grow while the radial zone becomes smaller.*

14-3   An Analysis of Failures of Metals in Service

By acquiring a knowledge of the various features of fracture surfaces, engineers, can often determine the causes of failures in service. A study of the tensile and impact test specimens previously described helps a great deal to analyze and understand why failures occurred in the field.

Information regarding various features of fracture surfaces and their markings helps in three ways:

1. The origin of the crack can be located more rapidly as well as evidence pointing out the cause of failure.
2. The fracture surface constitutes a visible record of the stages of crack growth, which becomes most important in the determination of the cause of failure.
3. The fracture zones which are present, as well as their respective sizes, qualitatively indicate the toughness of the material as it relates to the particular application involved.

Before fracture examinations are begun, several elementary precautions should be observed including the following:

1. In case the part is shattered into many pieces, all fragments should be collected, if possible, and stored in a dry atmosphere.
2. Care must be exercised to see that the fracture surfaces are well protected from chemical action, including even the secretion from the fingers.
3. Surfaces of the fracture should not be cleaned unless necessary and then, whether mechanical or chemical, cleaning should be done with gentle caution in order not to change any important conditions that should be investigated.

Fig. 14–8 shows a gun which burst on firing. This photograph was taken 50 years ago and was supposed to be only a general view to show *what* happened rather than *how* it happened; however, it is perfectly clear from this photo that fracture of the gun was of a brittle nature. The fracture surface consists mainly of radial "herring-bone" marks with very little or no fibrous zone and a complete absence of shear lip. The arrow points to the origin of failure just as the herringbone markings do, near the inside surface of the gun.

Fig. 14-8. *A 240 mm howitzer which burst on firing, in a very brittle manner. The fracture surface shows virtually no fibrous zone or shear lip, and its "herring-bone" pattern, characteristic of the radial zone, points to the fracture origin near the inside surface. (Courtesy of Metals Progress, American Society for Metals.)*

Spot where the failures originated.

The differences between the general appearances and the markings of both ductile and brittle failures are illustrated in Fig. 14–9. The ductile failure which occurred when a shell exploded within a rifle shows gross yielding, and furthermore, the longitudinal fractures show relatively large shear lips. Obviously, the gun that failed with ductile fracture is on the left in the photo; the brittle fracture on the right shows a small fibrous zone and a rather large radial zone. Conversely, the ductile fracture on the left has large fibrous and shear lip zones with bulging apparent in the gun barrel. The arrows in each case point to the spot where the failures originated. As stated previously, fracture must be either transcrystalline (across the grain) or

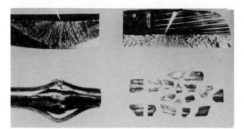

Ductile and brittle gun failures

Ductile and brittle gun failures

Fig. 14-9. *Ductile and brittle failures of two gun barrels, the ductile on the left and the brittle on the right. The latter has its characteristic fibrous zone and large radial zone, while the ductile fracture has large fibrous and shear lip zones with bulging of the barrel. (Courtesy of* Metals Progress, *American Society for Metals.)*

Fig. 14-10. *Two pressure vessels made from two steels, (H11 and AISI4340) heat treated to 180,000 yield strength. The H11 vessel on the right shattered into many pieces on hydrostatic testing while the 4340 failed in a ductile manner. (Arrows point to start of fractures in each case.) (Courtesy of* Metals Progress, *American Society for Metals.)*

intercystalline (along the grain boundaries) either in whole or in part. The first category of transcrystalline fractures may furthermore be cleavage fractures through the grains, or shear fractures through the grains. Thus, there are actually only three basic types of fractures that have been observed in metals:

1. Intercrystalline fracture (along the grain boundaries)
2. Transcrystalline fracture through the grains due to cleavage
3. Transcrystalline fracture through the grains due to shear.

At ordinary temperatures just as at low temperatures, the fracture path is normally through the grains rather than around them, i.e. shear or cleavage in type. At the higher temperatures, the reverse is true with fracture occuring along grain boundaries. Fracture by shear is "slip," as described in Chapter 5, which is much like the sliding of a deck of cards, one over the other. Cleavage may be thought of as the splitting into sheets of mica or similar material. Each of the three types of fracture can be revealed and identified by either macroscopic or metallograhic examination in the laboratory.

Fractures due to shear are usually fairly dull and appear as gray silky surfaces, while cleavage fractures, on the other hand, appear as a bright, granular structure after fracture. The cleavage fracture, also termed brittle fracture, usually shows a minimum of plastic flow before separation, while the shear (or ductile) fracture surface shows some evidence of some plastic flow before separation takes place.

Fig. 14-11. *Another pressure vessel made of H11 sheet steel, heat treated to yield strength of 200,000 psi showing brittle failure as revealed by the fracture surface. (Courtesy of* Metals Progress, *American Society for Metals.)*

Fig. 14-12. *By the absence or suppression of the shear lip, the origin of the fracture is clearly indicated. Both the chevron markings and radial lines point to the point of fracture origin. (Courtesy of* Metals Progress, *American Society for Metals.)*

Fig. 14-13. *A driveshaft that failed in a ductile manner when overloaded, fibrous markings such as result with slow crack growth being evident on the surface of the fracture.* (*Courtesy of* Metals Progress, *American Society for Metals.*)

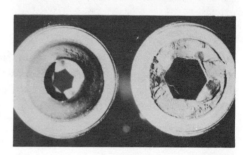

Fig. 14-14. *A case of hydrogen embrittlement because of too heavy cadmium plating. The bolt at right is the one that fractured 6 weeks after tightening, the extra heavy cadmium permitting too much hydrogen to enter the bolts. (At left is a ductile failure for the purpose of comparison.)* (*Courtesy of* Metals Progress, *American Society for Metals.*)

Fig. 14-15. *How corrosion pits may also serve to reveal the origin of cracks. In this H11 part which was heat treated to 200,000 to 220,000 psi, the brittle failure began at a corrosion pit. The radial lines point to the origin.* (*Courtesy of* Metals Progress, *American Society for Metals.*)

Fig. 14-16. *A crack that originated in this titanium part because of an electric pencil marking thereby resulting in a localized melting situation. When the material that was heated up to melting temperature solidified, a brittle structure was formed at which the crack originated as shown, when the first load cycle was introduced. This was a most unusual situation brought about by a manufacturer who, knowing that steel stamped marks are stress raisers, used the electric pencil for marking with these results.* (*Courtesy of* Metals Progress, *American Society for Metals.*)

Fig. 14-17. *Illustration showing how some fractures have more than one origin. Here is seen such a condition where the fracture shown has two points of origin as noted by the arrows. This fractured part shows the conventional markings and suppression of the shear lip.* (*Courtesy of* Metals Progress, *American Society for Metals.*)

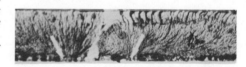

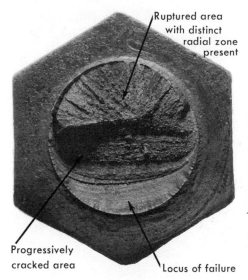

Ruptured area
with distinct
radial zone
present

Progressively
cracked area

Locus of failure

Fig. 14-18. *A fatigue failure in a steel bolt showing clearly that the locus of failure is at the origin of the oyster-shell markings. The progressively cracked area is shown at the bottom of the photo, and the ruptured area at the top was formed by sudden fracture of sound metal when the cross-sectional area was not sufficient to carry the load. The beginning of failure (fatigue) is usually at the outer surfaces of the part in question with ultimate fatigue failure occurring because of localized hardening and embrittlement of the piece resulting from repeated plastic deformation caused by the applied load. A small crack grows larger with repeated loading until finally sudden fracture takes place in the part. (Courtesy of* Metals Progress, *American Society for Metals.)*

14-4 How Fractures Occur in Metals and Alloys

Even though many fracture characteristics are qualitatively understood, fracture theory has not yet reached the point where any of the existing theories can give a full explanation of all the results obtained experimentally. This is due primarily to the fact that fracture is a far more complex phenomenon than any existing theories postulate, so that the laws have not yet been entirely formulated that will permit exact calculation of exacting fracture conditions.

Actual metals are not as strong as theory predicts; tests with metals reveal that maximum theoretical strength invariably exceeds the actual test values by a factor ranging from 100 to 1000 depending, of course, on the test involved. It is this lack of agreement between theory and experimentation that has led to the conclusion that real crystals in metals are not perfect. On the basis of experimentation with glass fibers, some scientists have concluded that microcracks are the cause of the low values of fracture strength, their findings indicating that microcracks are present in real materials and will grow, or propagate, only when such growth would reduce the free energy of the system.

A review of a few recent concepts as to how cracks in metals form include the following all of which have some merit:

1. The theory advanced by Zener says that as an array of dislocations moves along a slip band and meets an obstacle, such as a grain boundary or a hard particle of matter, the dislocations begin to accumulate and pile up at the obstacle. Then the shear stress relaxes in the slip band behind the piled-up dislocations, and the stress concentration increases ahead of the piled-up array. As a result of this increase in stress concentration, several possibilities present themselves. If the dislocations pile up at a grain boundary, the stress may merely initiate a new slip band in the next grain. However, whether the dislocations pile up at a grain boundary or at a hard particle of nonmetallic inclusion, the stress concentration may actually initiate a crack. Unless the

crack has such a high stress concentration that it becomes self-propagating, however, complete relaxation of shear stress in the slip band will result in the termination of the microcrack.

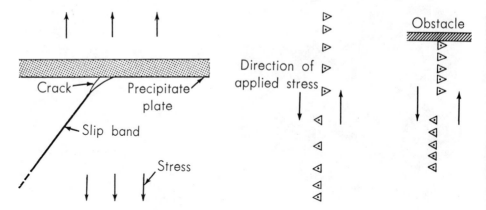

Fig. 14-19. *Slip band may initiate a crack upon striking a precipitate plate (Zener). (Courtesy of Materials in Design Engineering, Reinhold Publishing Company, New York.)*

Fig. 14-20. *Dislocation representation of a slip band. Left—normal condition: note higher density of dislocations at ends of bands. Right—dislocation density increases when slip band strikes an obstacle, such as a grain boundary. As dislocation density increases, stress at head of slip band also increases. (Zener). (Courtesy of Materials in Design Engineering, Reinhold Publishing Company, New York.)*

2. The formation of crack nuclei, based on the dislocation possibility, was also suggested by Zener. The introduction of edge dislocations into the lattice causes many small crack nuclei to form as shown in Fig. 14–21. With the stressing of the lattice, these nuclei may coalesce into larger nuclei whose volumes substantially exceed those of the original ones.

3. Another experimenter has shown that if a bar of metal is twisted in torsion until brittle, further pulling of the bar in tension will produce a helical fracture surface. Then, if the twisted bar is untwisted before being tensile tested, the bar will evidence a normal cup-and-cone, or ductile fracture as might be expected. Behavior such as this is consistent with the assumption that microcracks existed prior to the testing of the bar. In case microcracks were already present in the bar twisted in torsion, they would become oriented as in a helix, and any subsequent untwisting, or straightening, would realign the cracks into their original orientations. Fig. 14–21 shows how a possible fracture nucleus is formed by dislocations, the circles representing the positions of the atoms (Zener).

Fractures in components that fail when they are overstressed are brittle, ductile, or combinations of both, depending on the characteristics of the component and the types of stresses acting upon it. A close examination and analysis of fractures help in the correction and elimination of failures in the future. A careful and correct analysis of a fracture will often give a great deal of information about the contributing factors and assist in eliminating the causes for future failure of a similar nature. All too often, the needed information is not obtained because of a lack of technical background by the analyst or accidental destruction of valuable but unrecognized

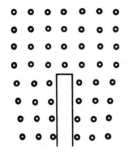 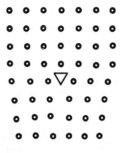 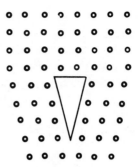

a. Edge dislocation is formed by inserting extra half plane of atoms.

b. Free energy of system is lowered when major portion of crack closes leaving nucleus for potential fracture.

c. When two dislocations coalesce, the resulting crack nuclei are more than double the original size.

Fig. 14-21. *How a possible fracture nucleus is formed by dislocations. Circles represent atom positions (Zener). (Courtesy of* Materials in Design Engineering, *Reinhold Publishing Company, New York.)*

evidence. It is imperative wherever possible to preserve for investigation both parts of the fractured part, and, if possible, the investigator should have access to the entire machine such as an automobile, truck, aircraft, etc., prior to the removal of the parts that were actually fractured; in many cases, other portions of the assembly may well lead to the cause or causes of the failure of a specific part.

As previously stated, metal parts fracture because of shear forces producing slip movement along certain crystallographic planes, or tensile forces that cause cleavage or splitting. Both of these modes of fracture are present in varying degrees in most fractures.

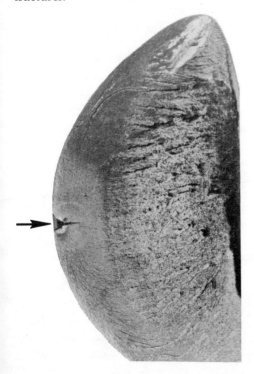

Fig. 14-22. *Steel shaft that failed as a result of torsion fatigue, showing the origin of the shear, marked by arrow. (Courtesy of D. J. Wulpi, Research Engineer, International Harvester Co., Hinsdale, Illinois.)*

Shown in Fig. 14–24 are two steel bolts deliberately pulled to fracture in a tensile machine to illustrate both ductile and brittle behavior. As indicated below the illustrations, the bolt on the left was brittle and had a hardnessof Rockwell C57; the bolt on the right was ductile with Rockwell of C15. It is clear that the softer, more ductile bolt failed in the typical ductile manner by shear, resulting in extensive deformation. The brittle bolt on the left failed in a brittle fashion and with no apparent plastic flow.

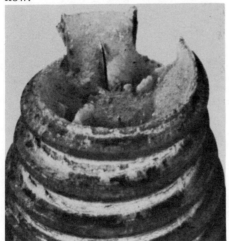  

Fig. 14-23. *Ductile fractures are dull gray and fibrous with much deformation, as shown in this close-up of the fracture surface of the bolt on the right in Fig. 14-24. (Courtesy D. J. Wulpi, Research engineer, International Harvester Co.)*

Fig. 14-24. *These two steel bolts, intentionally pulled to failure in tension, demonstrate brittle and ductile behavior. The brittle, left, was hard (Rockwell C57); the ductile bolt was soft (Rockwell C15). (Courtesy of D. J. Wulpi, Research Engineer, International Harvester Co.)*

14-5   Shear Fractures

Shear fractures that are caused by a single load are usually dull gray and fibrous with edges which are deformed plastically. Fig. 14–23 is a close-up of the ductile fractured bolt in Fig. 14–24 showing that there is a considerable amount of deformation present. This type of fracture (shear) occurs on slip or shear planes such as the diagonal plane across the unit cell of a body-centered cubic crystal of iron, while fracture by cleavage is shown at the right side of Fig. 14–25; these planes lie across the faces of the cubic crystal as shown. Inasmuch as a metal crystal is made up of millions of such units, all oriented in the same direction, an atom is located at each corner of the cube and at the center. Slip or plastic flow occurs by the shearing of certain crystallograhic planes over one another. The iron lattice shown has three slip planes, all of them having common slip directions—the diagonals of the cube.

14-6   Fractures by Cleavage

Cleavage or brittle fractures generally have a bright and crystalline appearance. Each crystal tends to fracture on a single plane, and this plane varies only slightly from one crystal to the next in the aggregate. For this reason it follows that a cleavage fracture in a polycrystalline specimen will generally sparkle in the light when rotated in the hand. Many times the surfaces of cleavage (brittle) fractures have distinctive appearances, as previously pointed out, with the characteristic "chevron" or "herring-bone" pattern emanating from and pointing toward the origin of the fracture. Such markings are readily discernible when illuminated by a grazing light at an angle. Since different crystallographic planes are involved in the two mechanisms of fracture by shear and cleavage, the nature of individual fractures can often be determined by metallographic examination in the laboratory. It is seldom that a fracture is either shear or cleavage, for the variable stress state that usually exists in a struc-ture, the changing of stress patterns during the progress of fracture, and also the microscopic differences in orientation of crystal units generally produce fractures made up of both shear and cleavage.

In most cases, all load carrying members in a structure provide resistance to the load imposed on it. As they do so, an internal stress condition is created in the member. This condition may vary from the simple uniaxial stresses to the more complex system multiaxial stresses, depending on the type of load and the configuration and geometry of the part involved. The way in which the load is applied may vary from a single-load application to a series of fluctuating loads which may alternate over wide magnitude and frequency ranges. In order for the part to perform satisfactorily and retain its original functional shape and resist fracture, the stresses developed within the member must be properly balanced by the strength characteristics of the material in question.

14-7   States of Stress and Strain

The term *stress* is used to denote the intensity of the force reactions which are set up within a body by the application of external loads or retained in a body after some procedures of fabrication. These retained stresses are referred to as "residual stresses." The changes in dimension that accompany the development of stresses are known as *strains* and they may be either elastic, which disappear upon the dissipation of the stress, or plastic, which remain in the specimen or part after the stress has been relieved. Stresses and strains are divided into two groups for convenience: normal and shear, depending on whether they tend to produce separation or translation respectively. Normal strains lie in the direction of normal stresses, while shear strains are measured as the displacement of one plane relative to another plane that is parallel to it and separated from the first by a unit distance.

It is customary to use Greek letters to represent stresses, the letter sigma (σ) indicating normal stress and the letter tau (τ) referring to a shear stress. In a body there are an infinite number of planes about which a stress system may be described; however, regardless of the complexity of stresses that are present, the stress con-dition at one point in the body can always be described by a set of three mutually perpendicular vectors, these representing the *maximum normal stresses*. They are re-ferred to as *principal stresses* and are indicated by the designations, σ_1, σ_2, and σ_3. Depending on whether they are tensile or compressive, they are indicated as being positive or negative as shown in Fig. 14–26. It is customary to designate the largest stress as σ_1 and the smallest as σ_3. No shear stresses exist in the three mutually per-pendicular planes normal to these vectors; therefore, the stress system is completely identified.

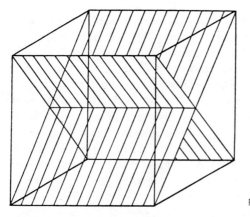

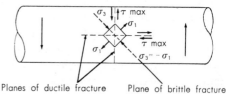

Planes of ductile fracture   Plane of brittle fracture

Fig. 14-25. *Here the planes of maximum shear stress are shown as they lie in the lattice of a body-centered cubic crystal. (Courtesy American Society for Metals.)*

Fig. 14-26. *A bar has been twisted indicating that torsional forces are developed within it. Maximum stresses act along the planes as indicated. (Courtesy American Society for Metals.)*

The principal stresses are always accompanied by shear stresses, except where there is total triaxiality where $\sigma_1 = \sigma_2 = \sigma_3$. As shown in Fig. 14–26, the maximum shear stress occurs at a 45° angle to the initiating principal stresses and has a value of half the difference between the greatest and the least principal stresses which may be represented by the following:

$$\left(\tau_{max} = \frac{\sigma_1 - \sigma_3}{2} \right)$$

In the case of a uniaxial tensile test, there are an infinite number of planes for which the shear stress is maximum, all of them making an angle of 45° with the axis of tension of the specimen. Inasmuch as materials have tensile (cohesive) strengths and shear strengths, their behavior is governed to a large extent by the relationship between the corresponding stresses. In bending or tension, the relationship between σ and τ is: $\tau_{max} = \frac{1}{2}\sigma_{max}$ and for torsion it is, $\tau_{max} = \sigma_{max}$. This means that for a given value of σ max, τ max will be twice as great in torsion as in tension. It follows that since the shear strength of ductile materials is less than the cohesive strength, the shear stress will exceed the shear strength of a material in a smooth test bar loaded to failure in torsion. Shown in Fig. 14–26 is the state of stress for a bar in torsion and the planes on which the maximum stresses act.

14-8   Strength of Material

When a bar of steel is subjected to a load, there is an elastic reaction proportional to the load regardless of how large the load might be. Furthermore, if a large enough load is applied to a ductile material, flow by crystallographic slip takes place, and the metal may finally fracture either by shear or cleavage. In really brittle materials, crystallographic slip or flow does not develop and fracture by cleavage is always present. Although the relationship between flow strength and stresses causing flow is quite well understood, fracture is much more complex even though the laws governing fracture are fully understood in a qualitative way. In brief, yielding occurs when the shear stress becomes greater than the shear yield strength; ductile or shear fractures develop when the shear strength is overcome by the shear stress; and brittle fractures occur when the cohesive strength is overcome by the principal or tensile stresses.

In Fig. 14–26 this principle is shown graphically; two materials are considered and their shear strengths and cohesive strengths are represented by the horizontal and vertical lines respectively. The behavior of these materials when a load is applied depends on the stress system or ratio of the normal stress to shear stress. The diagonals in the graph indicate the three stress ratios.

The foregoing discussion has been based on the maximum shear theory which states that fracture will take place when the maximum shear stress is the same as that present in bending or tension that would bring about the same fracture. It may be understood that this has been an oversimplication of the maximum shear theory, and that in actual tests the stress-strength relationships that cause fracture may vary somewhat with these conclusions referred to in this discussion.

14-9 Fatigue Failure—Analysis and Prevention

In trying to answer why fatigue failures occur, there are many channels of explanation that might be pursued. For example, the engineer would more than likely attribute the origin of fatigue failure to a stress raiser in a part. The metallurgist, on the other hand, along with the solid-state physicist, would likely look at the cause or causes in the light of stresses, strains, slip, and with a submicroscopic scale of analysis of from 1 to 10^3Å units. It is well to define a fatigue failure (fracture) as a fracture that has been associated with stresses whose magnitudes vary with time.

The old adage that "a chain is no stronger than its weakest link" may aptly be applied to fatigue failure in two significant ways:

1. The fatigue strength or fatigue life of a machine or structure depends on the weakest link of the design, manufacture, service, and material of the part. For example, a machine element may have been designed, manufactured, and serviced properly; however, the user of the machine may have subjected it to an environment for which it was not designed or intended.
2. More specifically, a fatigue fracture depends on the weakest link in the chain of material strength, for a fatigue fracture will invariably start at some point or points of weakness in the machine component, in those areas that are subjected to the highest stresses which are generally of a localized character.

Although, as was stated previously, the origin or origins of a fatigue fracture in a component are often readily recognizable by visual inspection of the fractured surface or by microscopic inspection at low-powered magnification, one exception to this general rule is the identification of fatigue origins in rolling-element bearings and the origins in the spalling of gear teeth. In these cases, the progressive failures obliterate the origins.

Strictly from the point of view of strength, the most serious degradations of the fatigue strength of a part are caused by:

1. Notches or similar discontinuities that serve as stress raisers
2. Corrosion or other chemical attack of surfaces
3. Fretting and fret-corrosion
4. High residual tensile stresses introduced in manufacture or thermal treatment
5. Imperfections in the material itself.

A few conditions causing reduction in fatigue strength are as follows:

Condition	*Result*
Stress concentrations due to improper design (small fillet radii in shafts or changes in sections)	The reduction in fatigue strength depends on the geometric factor and the sensitivity of the material to notches. Can be as high as 4 to 1.
Stress concentrations due to improper manufacture (file marks, roughly machined surfaces)	More difficult to evaluate since geometry of the notch is usually of a nonstandard form.
Residual tensile surface stresses caused by grinding	Poor and improper grinding can introduce high tensile stresses causing a decided loss of fatigue strength.
Residual tensile stresses due to cold forming of metals	Although beneficial compressive stresses can be introduced by cold forming, in some cases tensile stresses are introduced causing a loss of fatigue strength.
Fretting or galling of surfaces that are simultaneously subjected to fatigue stresses	Fretting or galling can cause a severe loss of fatigue strength. All clamped or riveted joints are subjected to this condition.
Corrosion	Corrosion from moisture or liquids in general causes a substantial loss of fatigue strength. Most metals require an adequate surface protection.
Plating of metal surfaces	Plating usually reduces the fatigue strength of the part, the amount depending on the type of plating, the thickness, and the method of plating.
Surface conditions introduced by heat treatment (oxide penetration, decarburization, etc.)	Only by the most careful control can the surface be protected during the process of heat treating.
Size effect	Most of the published fatigue data on materials are based on small laboratory specimens which do not adequately represent the fatigue strength of the larger parts.
Effect of speed	Although speed has only a minor effect over a large range of speed or stressing, very high or very low speeds will *usually* cause lower strengths.
Effect of shape	It has been found that shape has some influence on fatigue strength.
Assembly stresses	Tensile stresses induced by assembly have an adverse effect on fatigue strength.

Fracture vs crack S-N curves	Laboratory S-N data are usually obtained on the basis of complete fracture of the specimens.
Material variability	Fatigue properties of a material depend on many details associated with the making (melting) and processing (casting, forging, rolling, etc.) of the material. Essentially, the fatigue strength of a material depends on its chemistry, its purity, the homogeneity of its elemental particles, and the microstress distribution between these microscopic or submicroscopic particles, in addition to the tensile strength of the material.

14-10   Fractography Using the Electron Microscope

Fractures, particularly those associated with service failures, have been examined routinely for some years with the unaided eye and with optical microscopy. Electron microscopy, however, affords some distinct advantages, although it has been used extensively only within recent years. The examinations of fractures with the unaided eye are limited to the recognition and classification of fractures into broad categories as cystalline, fibrous, or fatigue. Optical microscopic studies permit the analyst to distinguish such things as intergranular fracture surfaces, cleavage facets, and fatigue striations; however, the optical microscope has severe limitations for studies of this type, including the limited depth of focus, which makes examinations of rough surfaces, such as fractures which contain hills and valleys, most difficult. Also, the limited resolution of optical microscopy makes recognition of features, such as fine precipitates or inclusions commonly present on fracture surfaces impossible.

Many of the limitations of the other means of fracture analysis have been largely overcome by the application of the electron microscope; however, this is not meant to imply that electron fractography (study of fractures by means of the electron microscope) has eliminated the need for the more conventional types of analyses. On the contrary, the information obtained by all of the various techniques must be used to complement one another. The scale revealed by the unaided eye and the optical microscope are still important ones and cannot be ignored any more than can features seen on any other scale that might be used. In fact, the interpretation in electron fractography would be very difficult without complete lower magnification studies.

Since most electron microscopes are of the transmission type, fractures cannot be examined directly but only indirectly by using the replica techniques. This replica to be studied must be an exact duplicate of the original as-fractured surface which will be visible at the magnifications used. Furthermore, the replica must be structureless and free from artifacts and, of course, must be transparent to the electron beam. In order to obtain such a replica, it is imperative to exercise extreme care and employ certain techniques at all stages of handling from the time the fracture is produced until the replica is placed in the electron microscope for study.

W. R. Warke and James L. McCall, metallurgists with the Battelle Memorial Institute, presented a paper at the Western Metal Congress in Los Angeles, California in 1965, in which they brought out the usefulness of fractography with a special emphasis on the application of the electron microscope. This is covered in full in the American Society for Metals Technical Report No. W 3–3–65, and the reader is referred to it for a discussion of both the standard and special techniques for the examination of fracture surfaces in the electron microscope. Also shown in the report are examples of the use of fractography in basic and applied research programs as well as in service failure analyses.

14-11   Preparing the Replica for Study (Replication)

The three techniques of replication which are more commonly used for fractographic studies are as follows:

1. Plastic-carbon technique
2. Direct carbon technique
3. Oxide replica technique.

Each of these replication techniques has its limitations and its areas of maximum applicability. For example, the plastic-carbon technique is quite rapid and non-destructive, the fracture surface being preserved for further study if desired. However, plastic-carbon replicas are more susceptible to artifacts (imperfections made by the analysis) than are the direct carbon replicas. The direct carbon and the oxide methods give the maximum obtainable fidelity of reproduction of the surface, but do require etching of the surface to free the replica. (A complete description of all three of these replication methods is given in the report by Warke and McCall, and the student is referred to the report for further study.) Magnifications of 1500X to 6000X are normally used in fractographic work although the maximum useable magnification for plastic-carbon replicas is about 12,000X and about 40,000X for direct carbon replicas. The resolutions of the replica limit studies at higher magnifications. Several electron fractographs of various materials and at indicated magnifications are shown on the following pages.

The *plastic-carbon replication* technique consists of the preparation of a plastic primary replica from which a final secondary carbon replica is made. The most common plastic employed for fractography is *cellulose acetate* sheet from 0.003 to 0.025-in. thick. One surface of a sheet of cellulose acetate is softened by dropping acetone on to it. When it is soft, the plastic is placed over the desired area, and pressure is applied with the thumb or medium soft eraser. The pressure is maintained for about a minute and the replica is allowed to dry in place for about 10 to 15 minutes. Then the replica is stripped from the specimen and if sufficiently dry and if the fracture face does not contain many large re-entrant angles or cracks, the replica may be removed easily by a slight lifting of one edge.

The next step is the production of what is known as "shadowing" which is the deposition of a heavy metal at an angle, usually at about 45°, to the surface of the replica; however, lower angles are used for very flat fractures. The metal, such as chromium, platinum-carbon, or uranium, is deposited by evaporation from an incandescent wire or an arc used to deposit a structureless base which will be inert in the electron beam. The shadowing phase of the replica method has three purposes:

1. Increases contrast by depositing at varying thicknesses on facets at varying orientations.
2. Assists in interpretation of depressions and protrusions on the fracture through a study of the shadow they cast.
3. Maintains orientation of the replica. The shadowing is usually done in a direction related to the macroscopic propagation direction (very often parallel).

After the shadowing procedure, carbon, the material which makes up the bulk of the final replica, is deposited by evaporation from an arc in a vacuum chamber. This is followed by the most critical step in the replication, i.e., the freeing of the carbon film from the plastic sheet, which is best accomplished by immersing the composite in acetone which dissolves the plastic and leaves the shadowed carbon replica to be picked up on a specimen grid of from 100 to 200 mesh and stored in a clean, dry place until ready for the examination in the electron microscope.

(a) 3000X

(b) 3000X

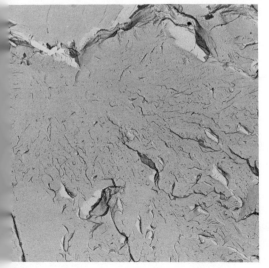

Fig. 14-27. *Electron fractographs of low carbon gray iron: (a) pearlite inter-colony fracture and (b) cleavage fracture initiating at a graphite flake.*

Electron microscopic fractography is an extremely useful tool for the metallurgist for studying fractures; however, being a rather new technique, the total usefulness is not known, and the important information that it can provide is just beginning to be appreciated. One of the most important areas for future reseach and study is that of the initiation of various types of fractures by locating and examining their origin areas—something that previously has been unobtainable.

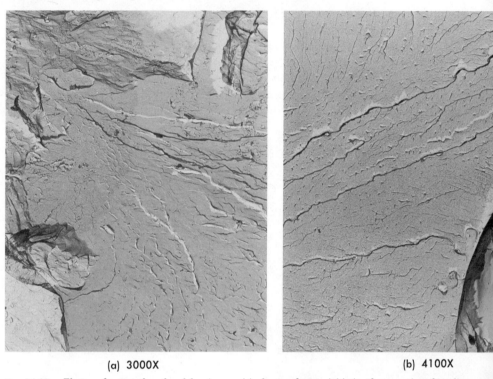

(a) 3000X   (b) 4100X

Fig. 14-28. *Electron fractographs of nodular iron:* (a) *cleavage fracture initiating from a region of pearlite intercolony fracture and* (b) *cleavage fracture propogating toward a graphite nodule.*

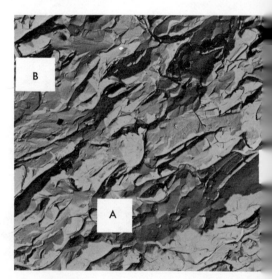

Fig. 14-29. *Electron fractograph of the W-5Re-2.2ThO$_2$ specimen with three visible fracture areas:*

   A — Grain boundary fracture
   B — Cleavage fracture
   C — Platelets on featureless facets

This fractograph was made of a Thoriated Tungsten-Rhenium Alloy to reveal the effect of structure on fracture. The fractograph was taken at 3000X.

Fig. 14-30.   *Photomicrograph of the W-$5Re$-$2.2ThO_2$ specimen showing a nonpropagating surface crack. Magnification was 5000X.*

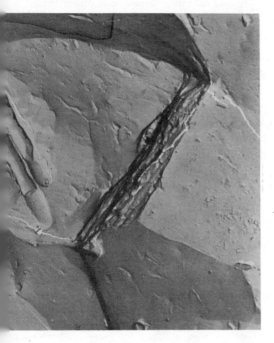

Fig. 14-31.   *Electron fractograph of a steel aircraft part which failed intergranularly because of hydrogen-stress cracking. Magnification 5660X. The material, AISI 4140 steel, heat treated to Rockwell "C" 50, was found to have cracked within 24 hours after installation. The parts were cadmium plated, and it was found that they were under a high sustained load after installation. The fracture surface was found to be completely intergranular. Steps were taken to reduce sustained loads and the processing of the parts was changed to minimize the likelihood of a recurrence of the problem. Electron fractography played an important part in determining the cause and nature of cracking in this critical aircraft part. (Fractographs shown in Figures 14–27, 14–28, 14–29, 14–30 and 14–31 through courtesy of American Society for Metals, Metals Park, Ohio.)*

14-12   Fractures at Elevated Temperatures

About fifty years ago Zay Jeffries demonstrated that the fracture characteristics of metals at elevated temperatures varied as the time required for fracture varied. He used an ordinary tensile testing machine as described in Chapter 12, except that a furnace was placed around the specimen for heating to the desired temperature during the test. In this manner, he obtained variations in the fracture time by running the machine at different strain (elongation) rates; the slower the rate, the longer the time required for the specimen to break, and the lower the fracture stress. Jeffries found that for the shorter fracture times at elevated temperatures the path of fracture, when examined under the microscope, travelled across the grains *transgranularly* or, as it is sometimes referred to, *intragranularly*, but that for the longer fracture periods, the path of fracture travelled around the grains *intergranularly*. He corroborated with his experiments what had been known for many years, i.e., that when specimens were broken at room temperature, the path of fracture was across the grains, while specimens fractured at high temperature broke with a fracture path that travelled around the grains. Jeffries thereby proved that it was the time element in the high temperature testing that caused a difference in the path of fracture at the same temperature.

Fractures that occur transgranularly, i.e., through the grains as at room temperature and for the short fracture times at elevated temperatures, indicate that the grains themselves are weaker than the grain boundaries. Similarly, when the path of fracture is intergranular, i.e., around the grains, such as for medium or long periods of time at elevated temperatures, it indicates that the grains are stronger than the grain boundaries at the higher temperatures.

14-13   Relationship Between Equicohesive Temperature and Nature of Fractures

Inasmuch as there is a change in relative strength of the grains and grain boundaries with elevated temperature, it follows that there must be some temperature at which the strength of the two would be approximately equal in value. This is shown schematically in Fig. 14–32, in which strength is plotted against temperature. As indicated, the line representing the strength of the grains is below the line representing grain boundary strength at lower temperatures, and their relative positions are reversed at the elevated temperatures. The point at which these two lines intersect has been termed the *equicohesive temperature*, "equi" meaning equal and "cohesive" meaning strength.

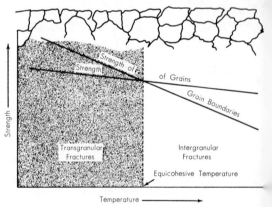

Fig. 14-32. *The relationship between equicohesive temperature and the nature of fractures. The strength of the grains and grain boundaries decrease with increasing temperature at different rates and intersect at a point referred to as the equicohesive temperature. At higher temperatures the grains are found to be stronger, and failures occur in the weaker grain boundary zones (intergranularly) while at low temperatures, the grain boundaries are stronger and failures take place across the grains with transgranular types of fractures.*

The equicohesive temperature therefore is the one at which the grains and grain boundaries have equal strength, and fractures there would be transgranular or intergranular depending on other variables such as strain rate, the time of the test, the alloy composition, and perhaps others. It also follows from this diagram in Fig. 14–32 that the path of fracture would be expected to be intragranular at low temperatures and granular at temperatures above the equicohesive temperature.

The equicohesive temperature is influenced by the fracture time and composition of the material; the longer the fracture time used, or experienced, the lower will be the equicohesive temperature up to a certain minimum value. In the case of carbon steels, for example, regardless of the fracture time employed, the position of this point of intersection would never reach room temperature. Furthermore, the effect of composition of the steel or alloy on the equicohesive temperature is extremely important for both carbon and alloy steels. A study of microstructures of a series of carbon steel specimens broken at 1000 F over time periods ranging from a few minutes, as in the short time tensile test, up to nearly 14,000 hours reveals that in the short time tensile test specimen and in the specimen that required 6.4 hours before fracture occurred, the fracture was found to be transgranular, thereby indicating that for these fracture time periods, 1000 F is below the equicohesive temperature. But for this same SAE 1020 carbon steel fractured at the same temperature in longer time periods of from 1,556 and 13,960 hours, the path of fracture was intergranular. These studies and tests showed that for fracture times above 1,500 hours, 1000 F is above the equicohesive temperature for low carbon steels. Further studies of microstructures of steels that are quite similar to the SAE 1020 grade but with additions of 1.25 per cent chromium, 0.75 per cent silicon, and 0.50 per cent molybdenum reveal that these moderate additions of alloying elements cause the equicohesive temperature to be in excess of 1000 F, as revealed by the fact that all such specimens broke with a transgranular fracture at 1000 F and up to 6,151 hours.

QUESTIONS

1. What are the questions that must be reviewed and answered in the investigation of every failure of metals?

2. Name all of the areas in which metals must be 100 per cent reliable.

3. Of all of the thirty or more types of corrosion, which one is more common and in what kinds of environment can it occur?

4. What should be done immediately after a metal failure has been reported to the metallurgist who is going to investigate the cause or causes of the failure?

5. Define just what is meant by the term "fatigue" in metals.

6. Name some of the several methods of analyzing fractures when they occur.

7. Why is it essential to examine first the fractured surfaces prior to examining polished, mounted, and etched specimens under the microscope? Must both parts of the fractured piece be studied? If so, why?

8. Discuss the differences between transcrystalline and intercrystalline fractures in metals.

9. Name and describe the several "zones" of fractured surfaces.

10. Will these "zones" be the same under varying temperatures of testing? If not, how will they differ?

11. Explain the significance of herringbone or chevron marks in the fractured surface. What is meant by the "shear lip" zone?

12. Do both flat and round specimens have the several significant zones in fractured metal parts? What is the difference in them, if any?

13. Referring to Fig. 14–5 of the AISI 4340 steel test bars, how does the lineal zone size change with increased stresses? What effect, if any, does hydrogen embrittlement have on the fibrous area and radial zone?

14. In Fig. 14–7 how is the degree of fibrosity in fractured surfaces of impact specimens related to the impact strength of the metal?

15. In what ways does the information relating various features of fractured surfaces and the markings on the same assist us in our investigation of the causes of failure?

16. Before beginning examinations of fractured surfaces what important precautions should be observed for best results?

17. How do the general appearances of markings of ductile and brittle failures differ, if at all?

18. In what ways does a fracture caused by excessive hydrogen resulting from too heavy an electroplated coating identify itself?

19. Is it possible to reveal the origin of the cracks by studying a fractured surface that has been in a structural part that was subjected to pit corrosion? Explain.

20. It is recognized that the use of steel stamped marks on castings or forgings often results in stress raisers that may well be the cause of ultimate cracking and failure. In the case of certain nonferrous parts would it be best to use an electric pencil for making such identifying markings? Explain.

21. Is it ever possible that some fractures have more than one point of origin?

22. Basically, there are three types of fractures that have been observed in metals. Name and define them.

23. What is another name for cleavage fractures? How do they differ from other types of fractures?

24. Discuss a few of the recent concepts as to how cracks in metals originate and illustrate with sketches in each case.

25. How may we determine whether a metal rod or bar which has been stressed in tension was brittle or ductile in nature?

26. Do shear fractures resulting from a single load differ in appearance from fractures caused by cyclical, repetitive loading? Explain.

27. What is meant by the term "residual stresses."

28. Into what two groups may stresses and strains be divided? Define each.

29. Is the shear strength of ductile materials greater or less than the cohesive strength of the materials?

30. What is meant by the term "maximum shear theory"?

31. In making an investigation of the cause of fatigue failure of metal parts, how would the approach of the engineer differ from that of the metallurgist and solid-state physicist?

32. It was said many years ago that "a chain is no stronger than its weakest link." Does this have any significance now in the analysis of fatigue failures that occur? If so, in what ways?

33. Looking at the strength of the material, what are the causes of the most serious degradations of fatigue strength of metals?

34. Name several conditions that cause a reduction in fatigue strength of metals. Explain also the results of these conditions.

35. What added advantage is gained by the use of the electron microscope in the study of fractures? Does this new tool eliminate the need for studies by means of the unaided eye and the microscope in the metallurgy laboratory? Explain the reason for your answer.

36. Describe the techniques of replication used today in the studies of fractures in metals by means of the electron microscope.

37. Define "equicohesive temperature" and show the relationship between it and the nature of fractures.

38. At elevated temperatures are the grains of steel stronger than the grain boundaries? How do fractures occur in steels at room temperature? Explain the reasons for your answers in each case.

References

Cazaud, Roger, *Fatigue of Metals* (translated by A. J. Fenner). New York: Philosophical Library, 1953.

Clark, Charles L., *Characteristic Behavior of Metals at High Temperatures*, Metals Engineering Institute, Metals Park, Ohio: American Society for Metals, 1956.

Forrest, Peter R., *Fatigue of Metals*. Reading, Massachusetts: Addison-Wesley Publishing Co., 1962.

Freudenthal, Alfred M., *Fatigue of Aircraft Structures*. New York: Academic Press, 1956.

Gray, Allen C., (ed), *What You Can Do About Metal Fatigue*. Metals Park, Ohio: American Society for Metals, *Metals Progress*, 1956.

Grover, Harry J., S. A. Gordon, and L. R. Jackson, *Fatigue of Metals and Structures*, NAVAER 00–25–534, Washington, D. C.: Government Printing Office, 1954.

Harris, William J., *Metallic Fatigue*. New York: Pergamon Press, 1961.

Heywood, Roland B., *Designing Against Fatigue of Metals*. New York: Reinhold Publishing Co., 1962.

LaBelle, Jack E., *Practical Aspects of Fatigue*. Metals Park, Ohio: *Metal Progress*, American Society for Metals, May, 1959.

Larson, Frank R., and Frank L. Carr, *How Failures Occur*. Metals Park, Ohio: *Metals Progress*, March 1964, American Society for Metals.

Moore, Herbert F., and J. B. Kommers, *The Fatigue of Metals*. New York: McGraw-Hill Book Company, 1937.

Murray, William M., *Fatigue and Fracture of Metals*. New York: John Wiley & Sons, Inc., 1952.

Ogden, Paul, *Case Histories of Materials Failure*. Metals Park, Ohio: *Metal Progress*, July 1963, American Society for Metals.

Peckner, Donald, *Why Metals Break and What to Do About It*. Associate Editor, *Materials in Design Engineering*, New York: Reinhold Publishing Company, April 1960.

Pelloux, Regis M. N. , *The Analysis of Fracture Surfaces by Electron Microscopy*. Metals Park, Ohio: Technical Report No. 19–3–64, American Society for Metals.

Plantema, Frederik J., and J. Schijve, *Full-Scale Fatigue Testing of Aircraft Structures*. New York: Pergamon Press, 1961.

Pope, Joseph A., *Metal Fatigue*. London: Chapman and Hall, 1959.

Rassweiler, Gerald M., and William L. Grube, *Internal Stresses and Fatigue in Metals*. Amsterdam and New York: Elsevier, 1959.

Sines, George, and J. L. Waisman, *Metal Fatigue*. New York: McGraw-Hill Book Company, 1959.

Stulen, Frank B., and W. C. Schulte, *Fatigue Failure Analysis and Prevention*. Metals Park, Ohio: *Metals Engineering Quarterly*, American Society for Metals, August 1965.

Weibull, Waloddi, *Fatigue Testing and Analysis of Results*. New York: Pergamon Press, 1961.

Powder Metallurgy

15-1 Methods of Processing Powder Metal Parts

Until 1945 to 1950 parts produced by powder were made in a rather simple manner —compact or press the powders in question, then sinter as required. Today, however, there are at least fifteen production routes that can be adopted to produce a part by the powder metallurgy method, each one being tailored to exact requirements. Fig. 15–1 is a chart illustrating the wide latitude that is available to production engineers and designers at one of the most modern facilities in this country.*

There are, as shown in the chart, seven major processing routes which can be modified in many different ways to alter the characteristics of the product; four of these are:

1. Press-sinter (for parts with low density)
2. Press-sinter-coin
3. Press-sinter-infiltrate
4. Press-sinter-coin-resinter-heat-treatment (for parts of high density).

As stated, Process 1 usually produces low density structural parts, mainly ferrous materials, where moderate mechanical properties and maximum cost savings are desired. High density parts, usually of iron or steel components, are produced by means of Process 4 where the parts are to have greater strength, ductility, impact resistance, and wear characteristics. Then by selection of the powders and pressing and sintering techniques, variations in mechanical properties are obtained.

---

* Mallory Metallurgical Division of P. R. Mallory & Co., Inc., Indianapolis, Indiana.

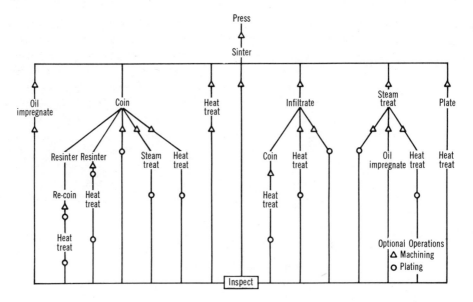

Fig. 15-1. *Diagram of operations at Mallory Metallurgical Co. illustrates the wide variety of production routes by which powder metal parts are made. Each sequence imparts a special combination of properties and characteristics. Sintering and infiltration can be, and often are, combined.*

For nonferrous production and for higher density iron parts where good strength and close dimensional tolerances are required, Process 2 would be best adapted as it includes the extra step of coining. This, obviously, adds to the total cost of production over the Process 1 method; however, parts produced by this technique have closer tolerances, smoother surfaces, much better mechanical properties, and excellent uniformity from one part to the next. For example, a dimensional tolerance of ± 0.001 in. can be held for inside diameters that do not exceed 0.50 in.

Powder metallurgy provides the engineer and designer a means of obtaining a wide range of characteristics in a variety of metallic compositions and at reasonable costs. By this method it is possible to create parts of two or more elements, capitalizing on the special properties of each in a powder metal compact, where such elements otherwise could not be fabricated into an alloy since they perhaps may be partially or completely immiscible in the molten and/or solid state. In order to use the process of powder metallurgy effectively and efficiently, it is important to know the advantages and disadvantages of the technique. A few of the advantages of producing parts by the powder metallurgy method are as follows:

1. Control over the properties of the parts involved is possible. For example, sintered iron powder yields parts having tensile strengths in the order of 30,000 psi compared with 50,000 to 80,000 psi for the parts made of cold rolled steel. However, by certain procedures, higher strength iron powder parts can be obtained by increasing the density in one of four ways: using pressure of a higher order in briquetting; using powders with greater compressibility; coining after sintering; or infiltrating the part with a lower melting point metal such as copper. By following treatments of these natures tensile strengths of 50,000 to 100,000 psi can be obtained without too much difficulty.

2. Porosity, of course, is the reciprocal of density, and this characteristic may be either useful or detrimental if not properly controlled. It may be useful

when the voids are filled with liquids such as oil for purposes of lubrication or to prevent corrosion of the parts. It is detrimental in the case of other structural parts since the properties of elongation and hardness are seriously reduced. Because voids or pores are usually interconnected in parts with low density, porosity may well result in internal corrosion and shorter service life for the parts, and in some cases it results in a destruction of the finishes that may have been applied to the surface. Porosity also prevents the use of some powder metals parts in pressure systems inasmuch as liquids and gases can leak through the voids. Increasing the pressure of the compact up to a point will decrease the porosity in the sintered part; however, excessive pressures can also produce excessive porosity. A high degree of control is required. The sintering temperature also affects the porosity of the finished part.

3. Another advantage of making certain parts by the powder metallurgy method is where they cannot be made by any other technique or process on an economical basis. For example, a giant computer uses hundreds of thousands, and in some cases as many as two and a half million, tiny memory cores made of ferrites (magnetic compounds of iron oxide) by the powder metallurgy method. Ferrites are the basis of an industry that grossed less than $1 million in 1949, $15 million in 1958, and over $100 million in 1964. TV cores are the biggest single item of ferrite production, memory cores for computers is second, and antenna materials is third. Number four on the list is the item of barium ferrites, used as permanent magnets. Until fairly recently most permanent magnets were made of Alnico, an aluminum, nickel, and cobalt alloy; however, nickel and cobalt must be imported and are therefore on the critical list of strategic materials. Furthermore, cobalt has a high affinity for radioactivity, whereas barium ferrite does not have this hazardous property. Furthermore, there is ample supply of it in this country.

A few of the disadvantages or limitations of powder metal products are as follows:

1. Inasmuch as dry powders do not transmit pressure uniformly in all directions, undercut sections and very high compacts cannot be pressed satisfactorily.

2. Although higher sintering temperatures result in greater density of the powder metal part, it is also true that in certain cases it is not uncommon for expansion of trapped gases in the compact to cause a decrease in density at certain temperatures of sintering.

3. Because of the high cost of dies and tooling, the powder metals method is not inexpensive and will only pay off when there is a large volume of parts involved or where the parts simply cannot be made by any other technique.

4. The corrosion-resistance of powder metal parts is usually poor because of the large area of exposed pores. As stated before, this can be overcome or at least minimized by impregnation with low melting point metals such as copper, or alloys, or in some cases with nonmetallics.

In order to take advantage of powder metallurgy to the fullest extent, the engineer and designer should determine the strength, ductility, and hardness required, all of which are related to the density required. Heat treatment will be found to be necessary in certain cases, but in other cases powder metal parts can be used without subsequent heat treatment. By determining the properties that are required, the engineer can avoid paying a higher price than necessary to produce a part that will function just as well.

15-2   Four Groups of Metal Powder Products

Metal powder parts can be divided into four general categories:

1. Parts having densities of the order of 50 per cent. Such parts are used as filters and for similar applications.
2. Those parts having densities in the order of 75 per cent such as the well-known and broadly used self-lubricating bearings.
3. Parts having densities ranging from about 80 per cent to 95 per cent such as those used in structural applications.
4. Infiltrated parts having practically 100 per cent density when finished; such parts are also used largely in structural applications.

Parts made from ferrous powders are iron, copper-infiltrated iron, steel, and stainless steel compositions. Many of these materials are covered by ASTM specifications as shown in Table 15–1 which lists typical compositions and physical properties.

Shown in Table 15–1 are the properties of some ferrous metal powder parts in the various categories based on densities. These values were collected from many sources throughout the country, so that they may not be strictly comparable since in some cases neither the heat treatment or the fabricating conditions were furnished by the source. These values, however, do indicate the effects of density on mechanical properties and also the range of properties obtainable by pressing and sintering.

Fig. 15-2. *This atmosphere furnace at Mallory Metallurgical Co., Angola, Indiana, heat treats powder metallurgy parts for added strength and wear resistance. (Courtesy of P. R. Mallory & Co., Inc., Indianapolis, Indiana.)*

TABLE 15-1. ASTM Requirements and Typical Properties*

Material	Specified Density, gm/cu cm	ASTM Number	ASTM Class	Composition, % [a] Fe	Cu	C	Other	Density, gm/cu cm	Typical Properties [e] Ten Str, 1000 psi	Elong (in 1 in.), %	Compr Yld Str (0.1% offset), 1000 psi
Low Density Iron	5.7–6.1	B310-58T, Type 1	A....	96.25[b]	—	0.25[c]	3.0[d]	5.7	14	1.5	10
			B....	95.9[b]	—	0.25–0.60	3.0[d]	5.7	17	1.0	15
			C....	95.5[b]	—	0.60–1.0	3.0[d]	5.7	22	0.5	20
Medium Density Iron	6.1–6.5	B310-58T, Type II	A....	96.25[b]	—	0.25[c]	3.0[d]	6.5	24	4.0	18
			B....	95.9[b]	—	0.25–0.60	3.0[d]	6.5	27	2.0	23
			C....	95.5[b]	—	0.60–1.0	3.0[d]	6.5	35	0.5	27
High Density Iron	6.90–7.29, 7.30[b]	B309-58T, B309-58T	A.... B....	97.9[b] 97.9[b]	— —	0.15[c] 0.15[c]	1.5[d] 1.5[d]	6.9 7.3	30 37	7.0 11.0	25 30
Copper Infiltrated Iron	7.1–7.6	B303-58T	A....	71.25–85.00	15–25	0.25[c]	3.0[d]	7.35	65	1.0	70
			B....	70.90–84.75	15–25	0.25–0.60	3.0[d]	7.35	75	1.0	90
			C....	70.50–84.40	15–25	0.60–1.0	3.0[d]	7.35	100	0.5	120
Iron-Copper	5.8–6.2	B222-58	......	86.5[b]	7.0–11.0	0.3[c]	2.5[d]	5.8 6.2	29 34	0.5 1.0	28.5 30
Bronze	6.4–6.8, 6.8–7.2	B255-58T, B255-58T	A.... B....	1.0[c] 1.0[c]	87.5–90.5 87.5–90.5	1.75[c] 1.75[c]	Sn 9.5–10.5 Sn 9.5–10.5	6.4 7.2	13.5 20	1.0 3.0	11 20
Brass	7.2–7.7, 7.7[b]	B282-58T, B282-58T	A.... B....	0.25[c] 0.25[c]	77.0–80.0 77.0–80.0	— —	Pb 1.0–2.0, Zn Bal; Pb 1.0–2.0, Zn Bal	7.2 8.0	20 27	9.0 13.0	10 14

[a] For minor constituents see specification. [b] Minimum. [c] Maximum. [d] Unspecified elements determined by differences, maximum.
[e] Not specification values.

* Courtesy of *Materials in Design Engineering* published by Reinhold Publishing Company, New York, New York.

TABLE 15–2.   Properties of Some Ferrous Metal Powder Parts

Nominal Composition, %	Density, gm/cu cm	Ten Str, 1000 psi	Elong (in 1 in.), %	Compr Yld Str (0.1% offset), 1000 psi	Rockwell Hardness
LOW DENSITY IRON (5.7–6.1 gm/cu cm)					
Fe 100	6.0	18	3.0	—	F65
Fe 99.5, C 0.5	5.7–6.1	25	1.5	20	B20
Fe 99, C 1.0	5.7–6.1	15–35	0.1–1.0	13–35	B30–40
Fe 99, Cu 1.0	6.0	16	1.0	22[a]	H60
Fe 96.5, Cu 3, C 0.5	6.0	32	0.1	—	B30
Fe 94.5, Cu 5, C 0.5	6.0	32	1.5	—	B30
Fe 95, Cu 4, C 1.0	5.8–6.1	25	0.5	20	B25–45
Fe 94, Cu 5, C 1.0	6.0	37	1.0	—	B50
Fe 90, Cu 10	5.8–6.2	30–40	0.5	32–45[b]	H94–B35
MEDIUM DENSITY IRON (6.1–6.5 gm/cu cm)					
Fe 100	6.5	22–26	2–5	18–21	F20–30
Fe 99.4, C 0.6	6.5	35	0.5	27	B35–45
Fe 99, C 1.0	6.2–6.5	25–42	0.5–1.0	23–40	B40–50
Fe 97, Cu 2, C 1.0	6.5	60	1.5	—	B60
Fe 95, Cu 5, C 1.0	6.5	42	0.5	—	B50
Fe 94.5, Cu 5, C 0.5	6.2–6.5	64	0.2	60	B90
Fe 93, Cu 7	6.2–6.5	45	1.0	40	B48
Fe 60, Cu 40	6.3	15	6.5	18[b]	H65
HIGH DENSITY IRON (6.8 gm/cu cm min)					
Fe 100	6.9–7.6	30–45	7–18	20–25[b]	B42
Fe 99.5, C 0.5 (heat treated)	7.0	120	1.0	150	—
Fe 99, C 1.0	6.8–7.6	45–75	1.0	40–90	B50–85
Fe 97, Cu 2, C 1.0	7.0	100	2.5	—	B75
Fe 94, Cu 5, C 0.7	6.8	80	1.0	—	B82
Fe 93, Cu 7	6.9	52	2.5	—	B56
Fe 92, Cu 7, C 1.0	6.8	104	1.0	—	B89
COPPER-INFILTRATED IRON					
Fe, C 1.0, Cu[c]					
Infiltrated	7.1–7.6	75	1.0	90	B85
Heat Treated	7.1–7.6	120	0.4	100	C40
Fe 85, Cu 15					
Infiltrated	7.9	60–75	16	—	—
Heat Treated	7.9	60–125	14	—	—
Fe 84, Cu 15, C 1.0					
Infiltrated	7.9	80–110	6	—	—
Heat Treated	7.9	85–185	11	—	—
Fe 75, Cu 25					
Infiltrated	8.0	50–65	13	—	—
Heat Treated	8.0	50–100	18	—	—
Fe 74, Cu 25, C 1.0					
Infiltrated	8.0	70–90	7	—	—
Heat Treated	8.0	80–160	10	—	—

TABLE 15–2. *

LOW ALLOY STEELS

C 0.30, Mn 0.50, Si 0.25, Ni 1.7, Mo 0.25	6.9	60	0.5	60[b]	C25
C 0.30, Mn 0.50, Si 0.25, Ni 1.85, Mo 0.25	7.5	115	1.5	80[b]	C30
C 0.75, Ni 3.5					
Sintered	6.6–7.2....	50–68	2.5–5	—	B66–B71
Heat Treated	6.6–7.2....	100–148	1–2.5	—	C22–C50
C 0.75, Ni 7.0					
Sintered	7.23	93	4	—	B90
Heat Treated	7.26	138	2.5	—	C52

STAINLESS STEELS

Cr 14.5	6.7	45	20	—	—
Cr 18, Ni 8	6.4	40	7	45	—
Cr 17, Ni 11, Mo 2.5	6.7	50	7	35[b]	B55

[a] These data are not strictly comparable since they were obtained from many different sources which gave little information on fabricating conditions.
[b] 0.2 offset.
[c] Composition not specified.

* Courtesy *Materials in Design Engineering* published by Reinhold Publishing Company, New York, New York.

TABLE 15–3. Comparison of Heat Treated Iron Powder Parts and Parts Made of Wrought Carbon Steels*

Material	Heat Treatment	Ten Str, 1000 psi	Yld Str, 1000 psi	Elong, %	Rockwell Hardness
Iron Powder[b] (0.95% C)	O.Q., Temp 600 F	170	160	1	C48
AISI C1095	Same	182	119	10	C42
Iron Powder[b] (0.95% C)	O.Q., Temp 800 F	138	120	2	C36
AISI C1095	Same	175	112	12	C36
Iron Powder[b] (0.95% C)	O.Q., Temp 1000 F	100	86	4	C25
AISI C1095	Same	158	98	15	C31
Iron Powder[b] (0.80% C)	O.Q., Temp 600 F	160	155	4	C46
AISI C1080	Same	189	143	11	C39
Iron Powder[b] (0.40% C)	O.Q., Temp 400 F	125	104	3	C50
AISI C1040	W.Q., Temp 400 F	130	97	16	C51

[a] Data determined on parts of different cross section. Therefore they indicate only relative properties of materials.
[b] Iron powder parts pressed to density of 7.5 gm/cu cm, through-carburized to carbon content indicated.
Source: *Doelker.*

* Courtesy of *Materials in Design Engineering* published by Reinhold Publishing Company, New York, New York.

TABLE 15–4. Properties of Some Nonferrous Metal Powder Parts*

Nominal Composition, %	Density, gm/cu cm	Ten Str, 1000 psi	Elong (in 1 in.), %	Compr Yld Str (0.1% offset), 1000 psi	Rockwell Hardness
COPPER					
Cu 100	8.0	20	8	15	—
	8.3	26–27	15–19	14–18	H70–75
BRONZE					
Cu 95, Sn 5	7.6–8.0....	22	5	20	H47
Cu 90, Sn 10	6.6–7.2....	15–20	2–3	13–20	H35–65
Cu 89.5, Sn 9.5, C 1.0	6.4–6.8....	15	1.5	13	H24
Cu 88, Sn 10, Pb 2	6.8–7.2....	19–26	10–13	—	H55–65
Cu 86, Sn 10, Pb 4[a]	6.6–6.8....	12–14	3–4	—	H32–44
Cu 77, Sn 8, Pb 15[a]	5.8–6.2....	4–6	3–4	—	—
Cu 68, Sn 10, Pb 22[a]	6.7–7	10–12	5	—	H19
BRASS					
Cu 90, Zn 10	7.6–7.9....	22	10	—	H65
Cu 88.5, Zn 10, Pb 1.5	7.6–7.9....	20	12	—	H50
Cu 85, Zn 15	7.6–7.9....	27	12	—	H74
Cu 80, Zn 20	7.7	33	20	—	—
Cu 78.5, Zn 20, Pb 1.5	7.5	21	15	12[b]	H70
Cu 70, Zn 30	7.3–7.6....	27	8	—	H80
NICKEL SILVER					
Cu 70, Zn 20, Ni 10	7.5–7.8....	29	10	—	H78
Cu 64, Zn 18, Ni 18	7.3–7.8....	20–32	2–10	18	H75–92
Cu 64, Zn 16.5, Ni 18, Pb 1.5	7.5–7.8....	23	15	—	H80
NICKEL					
Ni 100	6.7–7.7....	18–27	7–9	—	—
	7.4–8.1....	30–37	7–10	—	—
TITANIUM					
Ti 100	4.1	74–77	6	—	B50
Ti 100 (hot pressed)	....	58	35[c]	—	A48
TUNGSTEN					
W 90, Ni 6, Cu 4	16.9	85–120	2–10[c]	—	C10–40
W 90, Cu+Ni 9, Other[d]	16.7–17.1..	120	6[e]	—	C20–30

[b] Plus graphite.　　[b] 0.2% offset.　　[c] In 2 in.　　[d] Unspecified.　　[e] In 4D.

* Courtesy of *Materials in Design Engineering* published by Reinhold Publishing Company, New York, New York.

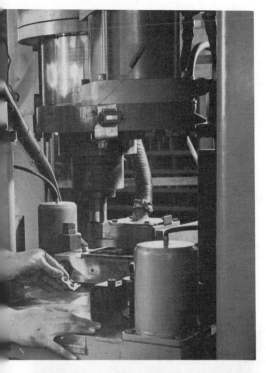

Fig. 15-3. *A 200 ton press can turn out powder metallurgy parts at the rate of 10,000 per 8 hour day at the new powder metallurgy plant of Mallory Metallurgical Co., Angola, Indiana. (Courtesy of P. R. Mallory & Co., Inc. Indianapolis, Indiana.)*

Fig. 15-4. *This 2 in. diameter ratchet is a component of a photo-copying machine with 92 teeth around the perimeter. The main reason for making it by powder metallurgy is the accurate reproducibility and close tolerances that can be attained (0.001 in. inside diameter). (Courtesy of P. R. Mallory & Co., Inc., Indianapolis, Indiana.)*

Fig. 15-5. *Critical dimensions on cam made of iron powder for an electric typewriter must be held to 0.001 in. (Courtesy of P. R. Mallory & Co., Inc., Indianapolis, Indiana.)*

Fig. 15-6.   *Timer gears and pawls made of sintered iron powder with small additions of carbon are produced to tight tolerances and high hardness by sintering and heat treating. (Courtesy of P. R. Mallory & Co., Inc., Indianapolis, Indiana.)*

Fig. 15-7.   *These detent cams for television tuners are made by powder metallurgy to give superior resistance to wear. (The cost is lower than if made of heat treated wrought steel as it can be made all in one piece without any machining required.) (Courtesy of P. R. Mallory & Co., Inc., Indianapolis, Indiana.)*

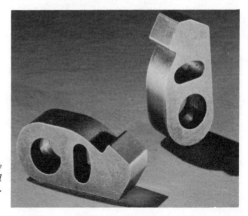

Fig. 15-8.   *Seat belt latch made by powder metallurgy process is stronger than the mating lock plates of hardened steel. (Courtesy of P. R. Mallory & Co., Inc., Indianapolis, Indiana.)*

Although not at all a disadvantage of using powder metal parts, there are some limitations that must be recognized. For example, there are certain configurations and shapes that must be given secondary machining or processing in order to be used for the purpose intended. Three typical configurations of this kind are shown in Figures 15–9, 15–10, and 15–11.

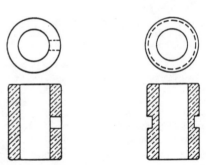

Fig. 15-9.   *Holes at right angles and external grooves cannot be molded. They must be machined afterward.*

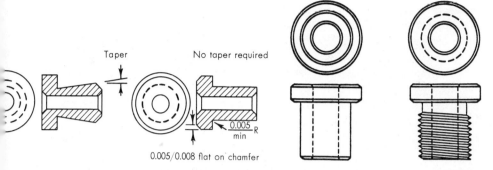

Fig. 15-10. *Reverse tapers cannot be molded. They must be formed as shown at the right and then machined.*

Fig. 15-11. *Threads cannot be molded. Both external and internal threads must be machined after sintering.*

The technique of making metallic products from metal powders is applied to three different areas of application, depending on certain factors, as follows:

1. As a method of manufacturing machine parts or structural parts that can also be made by the conventional methods of casting, forging, cutting from metals etc. but for which the powder metallurgy technique is used because of its minimum loss of materials and, in some cases, its lower cost of production.
2. For the manufacture of special materials with unusual properties that cannot be achieved by any other metallurgical method, often because the component metals are immiscible and therefore cannot be alloyed in the molten state.
3. As a research tool for investigating solid state reactions and phenomena.

The second category is perhaps the most important for consideration since it deals with some special materials (combinations of metals and nonmetals) which cannot be fabricated by any other method than by powder metallurgy techniques.

15-3 Methods of Producing Metal Powders

Metallic powders are produced by a number of different methods, and the resulting shape and size of powder particles vary from one method to the other. Therefore, the properties also vary to an appreciable extent. The more common methods of producing metal powders are the following:

1. *Reduction of compounds.* When a compound of a metal (usually an oxide) is reduced in the solid state by the use of a reducing gas, the size of the particles and size distribution depend largely on the original size of the compound. The shape of the oxide, for example, is generally jagged and irregular, and the particles are quite porous. Metal powders commonly produced by this method are iron, molybdenum, nickel, cobalt and copper.
2. *Atomization.* This process uses a swift moving stream of air, steam, gas, or water and impinges it onto a stream of the molten metal involved. The metal is scattered immediately and solidified in the form of droplets. The size of the particles is relatively coarse and depends a great deal upon the speed and type of the atomizing medium. The shape is irregular, ranging from spherical to elongated droplets. Atomizing is used to make powders of iron, lead, copper, aluminum, silver, cadmium, zinc, tin, brasses, bronzes, and complex alloys of the aforementioned.

3. *Condensation from gases.* The metal to be powdered is vaporized and then made to condense in the form of droplets. The shape of the condensed particles is more or less spherical. This technique is largely used for the low boiling point metals such as zinc, lead, cadmium, etc. Some of the high boiling point metals for compounds which can be easily decomposed form volatile compounds and therefore are most useful in the production of metallic powders. A typical example of this is nickel whose carbonyl $Ni(CO)_4$ boils at 110F and decomposes on further heating thereby yielding nickel powder.

4. *Electrodeposition.* When electrodepositing metals from solutions, conditions can be so adjusted that a brittle, spongey, or a loosely adherent deposit can be obtained. The production of deposits by this method that will be suitable for powder metallurgy requires:

(a) A high cathode current density
(b) Either a very high or very low acidity of solution
(c) A low amount of agitation of solution
(d) Low metal concentration.

The conditions just enumerated are most favorable for powders of the best quality. In some cases, the metallic deposit is already in powder form so that only washing, drying and screening are needed prior to using it. Other metals, on the other hand, form continuous deposits that are brittle and can be pulverized only by a grinding operation. Powders produced by this method are dendritic and have a large surface compared to their mass. Some of these are soft and spongey, while others are hard and require annealing treatments to improve their compressing properties. Metals commonly produced by this method include iron, copper, nickel, cadmium, tin, zinc, silver, antimony, and lead. Highly reactive metals can be electrodeposited from molten salt solutions. Such metals as vanadium, niobium, tantalum, zirconium, titanium and thorium can be produced in powder form by this method.

5. *Mechanical.* There are several methods for powdering metals mechanically; however, crushing and grinding in impact or ball mills are the ones most used. Brittle metals, such as bismuth, antimony, chromium, silicon, cobalt, and brittle alloys do not need any pretreatment prior to grinding. Ductile metals, however, require an embrittling heat treatment before grinding in which case hammer mills are employed for this type of conversion of the ductile metals to powders. In general, the powders produced by this method are in flake form and usually are not suitable for powder metallurgy. These ductile metals include zinc, lead, and cadmium.

Another method of converting metals to powder mechanically is that of grinding by attrition, i.e., wearing down simply by a grinding process, which utilizes the abrasive effect of the particles working on themselves. These particles suspended in a stream of air or inert gas are made to collide with one another at high velocity. The principal advantage of this method is that wear on the mill, and therefore the contamination of the powder, is negligible. Particles produced by the attrition method are rounded or saucer-shaped, and the size and size-distribution are much the same as those of the other grinding methods.

Two other methods of producing metal powders should be mentioned although they are not in the same realm of importance as the ones aforementioned:

6. *Decomposition of alloys.* Certain alloys with a two-phase structure consisting of primary crystals surrounded by a eutectic at the grain boundaries can be powdered

effectively by dissolving the matrix phase in the eutectic. In addition, alloys in which one of the components can be volatilized readily can be powdered by distilling off the volatile metal. Iron and nickel powders are made by the decomposition of iron carbonyl or nickel carbonyl. The metallic carbonyls which are gaseous at the operating temperature of the process are readily decomposed to iron or nickel resulting in very pure powders; this is because the formation and subsequent decomposition of the carbonyls are actually refining measures, eliminating substantially any foreign atoms from the system. Carbonyl nickel and iron powders are usually spherical in shape.

7. *Intergranular corrosion.* As was discussed in paragraph 13-41 intergranular corrosion is usually avoided in metals; however, where it is done intentionally and completely, it is an effective method of producing metal powders. Those materials which are susceptible to intergranular corrosion can be powdered by corroding away the grain boundaries. Obviously, the resulting powder is then composed of the individual crystals of the alloy with the size and shape of the crystals being dependent on the original grain size of the alloy in question. This method, in general, wastes a substantial amount of the metal but may be used for making stainless steel powders.

15-4   A New Stainless Steel from Powder

In their search for a high strength, high temperature alloy with good corrosion and oxidation resistance for bearing and other frictional parts that operate dry at elevated temperatures, aerospace engineers recently developed a stainless steel from powder that is dense and compares favorably with wrought material in strength and ductility.* Furthermore this alloy, termed NM-100 and containing 17.5 Cr, 10.5 W, 9.5 Co, 1.25 C, and 0.75 V, is forgeable, machinable, hardenable by heat treatment, and also resistant to wear and galling. The mechanical properties of NM-100 are as follows:

Temperature	Yield Strength	Tensile Strength	Compressive Strength	Elongation
70 F	246,000 psi	277,000 psi	275,500 psi	1.5%
600 F	220,000 psi	268,500 psi	234,000 psi	2.0
1000 F	182,000 psi	242,000 psi	174,500 psi	3.7
1200 F	79,500 psi	111,000 psi	70,500 psi	11.2

In the manufacture of this material a pre-alloyed powder of high quality made by the commercial atomization process was used. The two problems that presented themselves in the development of NM-100, namely the nonmetallic inclusions as contaminants and also the contaminations from foreign powders, were overcome after considerable experimentation. The problem of the nonmetallic inclusions was solved by using high temperature nozzles of alumina and controlling the

* From article, "A new Stainless Steel from Powder," by Elihu Bradley and Robert Sprague with Pratt & Whitney Co. and Wilson Tuffin with Nuclear Metals Division of Textron, Inc. by courtesy of *Metals Progress* of September 1965, published by American Society for Metals, Metals Park, Ohio.

pouring temperatures more closely. The second problem of the foreign powder particles was resolved by using a separate set of screens, filters, ducts, and gaskets that were used only for the NM-100 powder and also by carefully cleaning the collection chamber and all other permanent equipment which the powder contacted during the process.

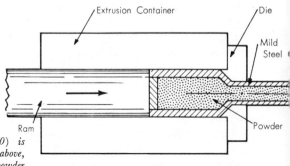

Fig. 15-12. *Stainless steel powder (NM-100) is densified by canning in a steel container as shown above, which is then sealed and extruded. The resulting powder metal is equivalent to wrought material.*

Fig. 15-13. *Compared to conventionally processed type 440C stainless shown on the left above, the NM-100 has a much finer structure and much smaller carbides. (Courtesy Metals Progress, American Society for Metals, Metals Park, Ohio.)*

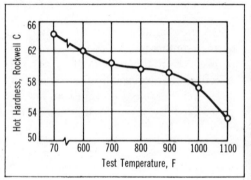

Fig. 15-14. *This graph of the hot hardness tests of NM-100 shows that the densified powder retains usable hardness up to high temperatures, a characteristic that is badly needed in certain critical applications such as in bearings.*

15-5   Important Products Made by Powder Metallurgy Techniques

Powder metallurgy plays an important role in the manufacture of electrical contacts simply because there is no other way by which the needed and desired properties—electrical conductivity and resistance to heat—can be incorporated in one piece. Electrical contacts have three main tasks to perform—make a circuit, break a circuit and carry a current. A typical application is that of a circuit breaker. Since success or failure of the contact is dependent on the mechanical properties of the particular contact device and on the electrical characteristics of the contact materials, it is significant that powder metallurgy was found to produce the superior material for these electrical contacts. These are usually composed of tungsten or molybdenum plus copper or silver, the refractory metal providing the hardness and wear-resistance, and the copper or silver giving the electrical conductivity required. The composite contacts obtained by the powder metallurgy techniques are made either by mixing the constituent powders, pressing, and sintering in the usual way, or by infiltrating a refractory sintered "skeleton" with a high conductivity, lower melting point metal.

A satisfactory refractory and conductive metal combination cannot be made by melting and casting because the metals are not mutually soluble, and furthermore, the melting points of tungsten and molybdenum are very high. In developing techniques for producing duplex materials, it has been found that if the proportion of refractory material exceeds 60 per cent, machining and cold working become difficult; even when materials contain less than 60 per cent refractory content, forging, machining and grinding are difficult and increase the cost. However composites of virtually any refractory content can be made from metal powders as shown in Fig. 15–15.*

It is of interest and importance that the first product to be made by the powder metallurgical method was *tungsten* and, furthermore, that it is still made by this

Fig. 15-15.   *Microstructure of composite made of silver and tungsten shows virtually unlimited alloy capability of powder technique. Left, 85W–15Ag; right, 20W–80Ag. Uniform, homogeneous microstructures are seen in both cases. Etchant used was equal parts of 10 per cent NH_4OH, 30 per cent H_2O_2 and water. 125X.*

---

* George A. Meyer, Product Development Engineer with Stackpole Carbon Co., St. Marys, Pennsylvania, has done a great deal of research in this area.

method. In fact, this is the only way in which tungsten can be produced. Tungsten is produced from its oxide by reaction with hydrogen at temperatures (1500 to 2000 F) well below its melting point (6100 F). The oxygen in the oxide of tungsten is removed as water vapor, and tungsten in the form of a fine powder is collected and subsequently pressed and sintered to a solid bar. Inasmuch as no melting takes place, all the impurities present in the oxide remain in the metal. For this reason it is imperative that only purified oxides be used in the production of tungsten powder.

The principal use of tungsten is for the manufacture of high speed tool steel, in which tungsten may range from 2 per cent to about 22 per cent. In addition, it is used in the production of steels for hot working dies for certain high temperature alloys and is also used to a limited extent in permanent magnet steels. Another important use of tungsten is in the filaments in tungsten light bulbs which have replaced the old carbon filaments that were short-lived and of poor lighting quality.

The alloy commonly used for adding tungsten to steel is ferrotungsten, although tungsten metal powder is also used as well as some tungsten compounds such as calcium tungstate. Tungsten metal powder, like ferrotungsten, is available in a number of grades suitable for the production of tungsten steels, as well as in grades of very high purity with closely controlled, extremely fine particle sizes suitable for the production of tungsten carbide tools and similar applications.

Another product of increasing importance made by powder metallurgy is tiny memory cores, about the size of the head of a pin, thousands of which are used in every electronic computer today. These are made from powdered ferrites, molded, compacted, and sintered on a high production basis. In fact, if it were not for powder metallurgical techniques and capabilities, the production of these tiny memory cores would be slow and the costs extremely high if made by any other method.

Commercial *cemented carbides*, another product made by the powder metallurgy techniques, are very finely divided carbide particles of the refractory metals, cemented together by a metal or alloy of the iron group to form a body of great hardness and high compressive strength. Cemented carbides were first used for wire-drawing dies, from which the application expanded to include all types of drawing dies for round and irregular shapes as well as cutting tools for machining all kinds of materials. They have also been used for machine and instrument parts and for a wide variety of products where high rigidity and resistance to wear are of utmost importance.

Cemented carbides may be classified into two general categories, depending on their uses:

1. The straight tungsten carbide with cobalt binder is used in tools for cutting cast iron, nonferrous metals and nonmetallic materials; in addition, in dies for drawing wire, bar, tube and sheet metal, and for blanking; also for machine parts where wear-resistance is important.

2. The steel-cutting grades of cemented carbides consist largely of tungsten carbide with additions of titanium carbide, tantalum carbide, or both, or of columbium carbide. These added constituents produce a material that resists cratering much better than the straight tungsten carbide grades. ("Cratering" caused by the hot steel chip is the formation of a cavity in the top surface of the carbide blank, slightly behind the cutting edge.)

The process of making cemented carbides consists, basically, of preparing the powder carbides of tungsten, titanium, or tantalum; mixing one or more of these carbides with a binder, such as cobalt powder; and subsequently sintering molded shapes to achieve consolidation. Two tungsten carbides, WC and W_2C, are used in the manufacture of cemented carbides, both of which have a very high hardness value in excess of 9 (based on Mohs' Scale of Hardness), next to the diamond which has a hardness of 10. Both WC and W_2C are used by one of the large manufacturers

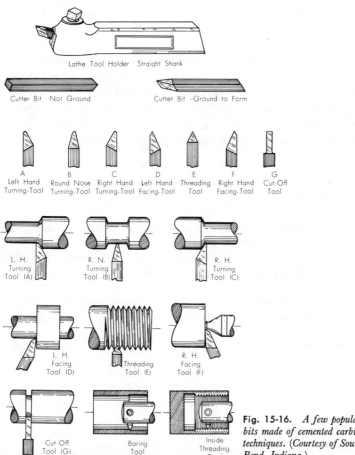

Fig. 15-16. *A few popular shapes of lathe tool cutter bits made of cemented carbides by powder metallurgical techniques.* (*Courtesy of South Bend Lathe Works, South Bend, Indiana.*)

of drilling tools in Houston, Texas, who, in fact, is reported to be the largest single user of tungsten in this country. Tungsten monocarbide can be prepared by any one of three methods:

1. By heating a mixture of tungsten powder or tungsten oxide with a measured amount of carbon powder in a hydrogen atmosphere containing carbon. The carbon powder may be lampblack or sugar carbon, either one giving good results if properly processed.
2. By heating tungsten powder or tungsten oxide in a carburizing atmosphere.
3. By forming tungsten carbide by reaction of the constituents in a molten metal that does not form a stable carbide.

Tantalum and titanium carbides may also be produced by any of the three methods used to produce tungsten monocarbide and may also be prepared in either an inert atmosphere or in a vacuum. Cobalt powder is obtained by reduction of either the oxide or the oxalate in a hydrogen atmosphere at a temperature not high enough to cause an appreciable coarsening of the particles through sintering. Where desirable, mechanical means may be used to reduce further the particle size. Denver Research Institute (DRI, division of Denver University) has been doing some significant work in the development of new cemented carbides on an Air Force Contract using 15 per cent Ni, 85 per cent Cb, and also 15 per cent Co and 85 per cent Mo as binders in conjunction with WC-TiC solid solution carbides plus TaC monocarbide.

Powder metallurgy enhances the ability to produce cemented carbide tool bits of high hardness and wear resistance. Many shapes and sizes of lathe tool cutter bits can be manufactured and used in conjunction with the lathe tool holder, which is usually made of a forging of sufficient alloy content to give it strength, toughness, and shock-resistance for long service. See Fig. 15–16 for a few of the popular shapes of lathe tool cutter bits, all of which are made of cemented carbides, and their applications.

QUESTIONS

1. Name some of the changes in the methods of producing parts from powders (metal) that have occurred during the past ten or fifteen years.
2. Although there are seven major processing routes shown in Fig. 15–1, some of these may be altered and modified depending on the endproduct desired. What are some of these alterations?
3. What method or process would be used to produce low density structural parts of ferrous materials where it is essential to obtain moderate mechanical properties and low cost production?
4. Which process would be best for producing metal parts of iron or steel powders where high density properties are desired?
5. Close dimensional tolerances may be best obtained by what means?
6. Name several of the advantages of producing parts from metal powders.
7. State the disadvantages that accrue in producing metal parts from the powders, including some of the limitations of this method.
8. Before considering the use of parts made from metal powders, what must the engineer and designer determine to take the utmost advantage of this process?
9. Is it usually necessary to heat treat metal compacts after they come from the molds? What are the determining factors in this respect?
10. By studying Table 15–2 showing the properties of some ferrous metal powder parts in several categories, what do you conclude about the effect of density on the mechanical properties?
11. From observing Table 15–2, what do you find concerning the range of properties obtainable by pressing and sintering?
12. After studying Table 15–3 what are your conclusions about to the comparison of iron powder parts that have been heat treated with those made of wrought carbon steel?
13. The technique of making metallic parts from metal powders is applied to what three different areas of application depending on certain factors?
14. Name the more common methods of producing metal powders and describe each of them.

15. In the production of metal powders by the electrodeposition method what criteria are essential? Is this method one that produces only one type of deposit?

16. Is it possible to produce a high strength, high temperature alloy with good corrosion and oxidation resistance by means of metal powders? Explain.

17. Why is it that the powder metals process plays an important role in the manufacture of electrical contacts?

18. Describe the production of the new NM–100 stainless steel powder illustrating by means of sketches.

19. How has powder metallurgy solved the problem of producing a satisfactory refractory and conductive metal combination?

20. What success has been achieved in producing metal powder parts of metals with high and low melting points such as tungsten and silver?

21. Describe the production of cemented carbides and tell why they are important to industry.

22. Into what two general categories may cemented carbides be classified? Describe each category.

References

Clark, Frances H., *Advanced Techniques in Powder Metallurgy*. New York: Rowman and Littlefield, 1963.

DeGroat, George H., *Tooling for Metal Powder Parts*. New York: McGraw-Hill Book Company, 1958.

Goetzel, Charles G., *Treatise on Powder Metallurgy*, vols. 1,2, and 3. New York: Interscience Publishers, Inc., 1949–1952.

Hoyt, Samuel, L., *Hard Metal Carbides and Cemented Tungsten Carbide*. New York: Reinhold Publishing Co., 1952.

Kingston, Walter E., *Symposium on Physics of Powder Metallurgy*. New York: McGraw-Hill Book Company, 1951.

Mallory, P. R. & Company, Indianapolis, Indiana, *Powder Metallurgy in Production Applications*. New York: Reinhold Publishing Company, 1965. (*Materials in Design Engineering*.)

Samans, Carl H., *Powder Metallurgy*. Metals Park, Ohio: *Metals Handbook*, American Society for Metals.

Toeplitz, William R., *Tolerances of Finished Metal Powder Parts*. New York: Metal Powder Industries Federation, 1962.

Modern Methods
of Metal Forming,
Shaping
and Machining

16-1 Metal Forming

Once metals have been cast into ingots, billets or slabs they may either be used in these forms or converted to other more usable forms such as angles, channels, bars, rods, etc. as required. Along with the more conventional methods of forming are those of casting by the many processes discussed in previous chapters.

The types of metal forming to be discussed in this chapter are the more unconventional methods including electrical-discharge machining, explosive forming (high-energy metalworking), automatic machining, electronic machining, electroforming (production of articles by electrodeposition), and machining with numerical-controlled machines. In recent years, a variety of novel and effective processes for forming and removing materials have been used as alternatives to the conventional methods. Although some of these techniques find their widest use and application in the processing of such materials as carbides or ceramics and high-strength and temperature resistant alloys that are difficult to form and/or cut, they also have important applications in the processing of fragile or flimsy workpieces since most of these unconventional machining processes develop comparatively low mechanical forces. These alternative techniques are expanding in their use because they can economically perform jobs which are difficult or impossible by the conventional methods.

16-2   Electrical-Discharge Machining

Although the erosion of metals by spark discharges was observed by Priestly in 1762 and was used by Svedberg in 1906 for disintegrating metals, the bulk of research on spark-discharge processes has been accomplished in the past ten years. In contrast to the electric arc, which is a stable thermionic phenomenon, the spark is a transient electric discharge through the space between the two charged electrodes. The discharge takes place when the potential difference between the two electrodes is large enough to cause a breakdown in the medium between the electrodes and to produce an electrically conductive bridge or spark channel. When the electrodes are separated by a distance of approximately 0.001 in. and the gap is filled with a dielectric hydrocarbon oil, a spark will occur at a potential of 25 to 100 v. The breakdown voltage is lower for narrower gaps. The breakdown potential can be obtained by connecting the two electrodes to the terminals of a condenser charged from a packaged power source. Other types of power supply may also be used to produce the spark.

This procedure is used for metal cutting since each discharge removes a minute amount of material from the electrodes, and furthermore, the discharges can be repeated rapidly. Electrodes of the desired shape are used as tools to control the shape of the work. These tools may be made from copper, aluminum, iron, titanium, brass, and alloys of tungsten-silver, as well as of copper-carbon. Depending on the material being cut, these tools may be made by many different methods including casting, extruding, machining, powder-metallurgy processes, and other techniques. Electrical-discharge machining processes are applicable to all materials which are sufficiently good conductors of electricity. In commercial machines the output voltage ranges up to 400v. The spacing between the tool and workpiece electrodes is critical and is usually adjusted along with the feed by means of servomechanisms. The voltage across the gap normally is used to control the servomechanism, which in turn advances or retracts the tool electrode in its attempt to maintain constant operating voltage.

The dielectric bath in which the workpiece is submerged must provide an efficient cooling medium and also carry away particles produced by the electrical discharge. In addition, the fluid must remain nonconductive until the proper breakdown voltage is reached and then deionize the spark gap rapidly to permit rapid rates of repetitive discharges. Sparking is usually forced to occur at a rate between 20,000 and 300,000 electrical discharges per second.

Fig. 16–1 shows the electrical circuit for electrical discharge machining. Fig. 16–2 illustrates a heavy-duty design of an electrical discharge machine as manufactured by one maker, this one having a servo-controlled, high-pressure hydraulic cylinder that delivers extremely fine sensitivity and response.

The energy in each spark discharge depends on the following relationship:

$$E = \frac{CV^2}{2}$$

where E equals the energy of the discharge in microjoules, C equals capacitance in microfarads, and V equals voltage in volts. The spark discharge causes the positive electrode to erode faster than the negative electrode, and the workpiece is positive in all spark-erosion processes. Since the spark has a small cross-section, the current

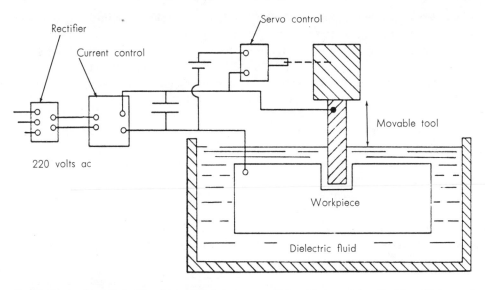

Fig. 16-1. *An electrical-circuit used for electrical discharge machining. (Courtesy of Battelle Memorial Institute.)*

Fig. 16-2. *Current Model HRP-103 electrical discharge machine with a 40 amp power supply, manufactured by ELOX Corporation of Michigan, and used in small and large industries around the world.*

density is high, in the order of 10^6 amp per sq in. Temperatures in the spark have been estimated to exceed 10,000 F. As the spark discharge proceeds, the spark channel increases in the arc; after a few microseconds, the discharge tends to develop an arc-like character. Obviously, arcing is undesirable because it causes melting on the surface of the workpiece and structural damage in subsurface layers.

Rates of metal removal by spark-discharge machining processes depend on the electrical parameters, shape, composition, and physical properties of the electrodes, as well as the nature of the dielectric fluid. The rates of metal removal by this process usually do not exceed 0.06 cu in. per min. As a rule, faster rates of metal removal produce rougher surfaces, as shown in Table 16–1. As machining current is increased for a particular discharge frequency, metal removal increases. For example, when the current is doubled, the energy in the spark is doubled, and twice the volume of workpiece material is removed.

TABLE 16–1. Performance Data for Spark-discharge Machining of Heat Treated Steel Workpieces.

CONDITIONS	Cutting Rate Cu in./minute	Surface Finish Microinch	Dimensional Tolerance in Inches
Roughing	0.06	50	0.004
Semi-finishing	0.008	18	0.003
Finishing	0.0005	5	0.001
Super-finishing	0.0001	2	0.0005

Data are for cutting operations with a 2.758 in. diameter copper electrode cutting to a depth of 0.473 in. (Sundstrand Corporation.)

To control dimensions and minimize tool costs, the ratio of material removed from the tool to the volume removed from the workpiece should be low. This ratio will vary with the different combinations of tool and work electrodes and with operating conditions involved. Table 16–2 contains data furnished by The Cincinnati Milling Machine Company showing that tools significantly better than brass are known for some applications and also that a particular tool material may not prove to be best for all workpieces. Table 16–2 also shows that the tool-workpiece combination affects the stability of the cutting operation and of the servo-system. The advantages of electrical discharge machining are manifold, a few of which are the following:

1. Ability to machine quickly and accurately materials otherwise difficult, if not impossible.
2. Close tolerances may be held with this process; in fact, tolerances as low as 0.0005 in. can be held with slow rates of metal removal.
3. Hundreds of man-hours can be saved over the conventional machinng techniques.
4. Electrical discharge machining is basically a toolmaking process. Over 85 per cent of the EDM machine tools used in industry today produce tooling of all sorts including stamping dies, forging dies, extrusion dies, and molds of various metals.
5. Holes of almost any shape and size can be produced by this method because tool rotation is not essential.

Originally used in industry merely as a "tap-remover" from dies in which taps became broken, this process has come into its own as a production tool in industries around the world—effecting substantial savings in costs as well as producing a superior finished product.

TABLE 16-2. Electrical-discharge Machining Characteristics of Various Electrode-Material Combinations.

Electrode Combination		Current amperes	Removal Rate 0.001 cu in./min	Wear Ratio*	Machine Stability
Tool	Workpiece				
Copper	Copper	8	0.39	0.30	Poor
Copper	Iron	12	0.95	0.50	Fair
Copper	Titanium	10	2.80	0.10	Poor
Aluminum	Copper	12	0.88	1.60	Good
Aluminum	Iron	8	0.53	1.70	Fair
Aluminum	Titanium	10	0.16	8.00	Fair
Iron	Copper	12	2.00	1.30	Good
Iron	Iron	8	0.20	2.50	Poor
Titanium	Iron	10	0.30	2.00	Poor
Titanium	Titanium	22	0.03	2.00	Poor
Brass	Steel	(15)	2.90	1.00	—
Brass	Cemented Carbide	(15)	2.00	3.00	—
90 W-10 Ag	Steel	(15)	2.80	0.05	—
90 W-10 Ag	Cemented Carbide	(15)	3.40	0.14	—
65 WC-10 Ag	Steel	(15)	2.20	0.08	—
50 Cu-50 C	Cemented Carbide	(15)	—	—	—
50 Cu-50 C	Steel	(15)	10.00	0.34	—

* The wear ratio is the ratio of volume of metal removed from the tool to the volume of metal removed from the workpiece. Lower wear ratios are preferable.

16-3   Electroforming

Another method of manufacturing a product is *electroforming* which involves the electrodepositing of metal on a mandrel or master form of a predetermined size, shape, accuracy, and finish. The metal being electrodeposited builds up to the required thickness after which the mandrel is removed, thus leaving the desired product, often without the necessity of further finishing of any kind. Given the correct electrolytic bath, mandrel material and operating conditions, the metallurgical properties of an electrodeposited metal can be controlled and selected over a considerable range.

Parts of intricate design with accurate dimensions and smooth surface finishes up to 1 to 2 microinches can be produced by the electroforming method. Complex parts are much less expensive when produced by the electroforming method than by other methods of manufacture, and, furthermore, these parts can often be produced in a single piece and without the necessity of welding or brazing.

Tolerances as close as 0.001 in. can be held in electroforming through long production runs and may be held even closer by using accurately machined mandrels made of Invar or Kovar. There is almost no limit to the shapes that may be made by electroforming, and internal stresses in such articles are often lower than those found in cast, forged, spun, or injection molded parts. Many metals, including nickel, copper, silver, iron, gold, rhodium and chromium, may be selected to conform with a variety of specific engineering requirements such as electrical or thermal conductivity, optical reflectivity, strength, corrosion, or wear-resistance.

So far as the electrolytic baths used are concerned, various types that have been developed for heavy nickel plating are used in the electroforming of nickel, including the Watts and fluoborate baths as well as the newer nickel sulfamate solutions, which produce a lower-stressed deposit.

A wide range of products are being formed by the electroforming method, and still others will be so formed in the future. For example, current production parts range from giant missile bulkheads to small portable appliances and builder's hardware. Considerable savings may be effected by electroforming methods over other manufacturing techniques in the mass production of automotive trim, provided the product is designed with electroforming in mind. Nickel electroforms have corrosion resistance superior to that of many other materials used for trim or functional components, and at the same time gives the designer greater flexibility in design. Automotive companies are starting to use tools and dies made of nickel electroforms, and recently electroformed nickel (and copper) molds have been used to produce vinyl plastisol skins for arm rests, sun visors, and crash pads as well as rubber weather strips and floor mats.

Fig 16–3 shows a typical electroplating process which produces or reproduces an article by electrodeposition of metal on a *cathode* called the mandrel or mold to result in the electroforming process (in this case with nickel). As indicated, the anode is connected to the positive pole, the mandrel to the negative pole of a DC source. Flow of electricity or electrons results in the oxidation of the nickel to nickel ions at the anode and reduction of nickel ions to nickel metal at the cathode.

Fig. 16–4 shows a typical electroplating (electroforming) tank which should be equipped with an automatic device to control solution level and temperature, as well as an electrolyte purification compartment. It is well to apply a nickel coating to copper bus bars in order to minimize contamination of the electrolyte with copper. Illustrated in Figures 16–5, 16–6, 16–7, and 16–8 are typical parts that are being made by the electroforming process showing the wide ranges of size and tolerances as well as surface finishes resulting.

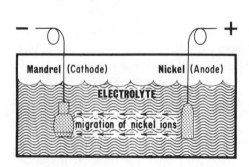

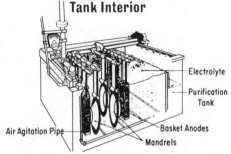

Fig. 16-3. *Typical nickel electroforming tank. (Courtesy of International Nickel Co.)*

Fig. 16-4. *Cut-away view of an electroforming tank showing components. (Courtesy of International Nickel Co.)*

Fig. 16-5. *Mirror-like finishes may be produced by the electroforming method as shown in this photo. (Courtesy of International Nickel Co.)*

Fig. 16-6. *Large radar wave guides such as shown here are made by this electroforming method. (Courtesy of International Nickel Co.)*

Fig. 16-7. *Intricate screens and grids as shown here are made by this electroforming process. (Courtesy of International Nickel Co.)*

Fig. 16–9 shows the mandrel and electroform upon completion. As nickel atoms deposit on the mandrel, the thickness of the deposit increases, and when the deposit reaches the required thickness, the mandrel-deposit combination is removed from the electrolyte. The built-up material, called the *electroform*, is then removed from the mandrel. The surface of the electroform off the mandrel is an exact reproduction in reverse of the mandrel surface. The basic equipment used in electroforming—tanks, filters, pumps and sources and control of Direct Current—are the same as used in electroplating.

Mandrels are classified generally as either *permanent* or *expendable*. The permanent mandrel is reusable after separation from the electroform; the expendable mandrel is destroyed during separation. The type of mandrel (permanent or expendable) and its material of construction are important factors in the cost of the electroformed product. By far the most widely used mandrels are metallic, especially for high production runs. Low melting-point materials, alloys, and nonmetallics, as well as metals such as aluminum which can be chemically dissolved, are used as

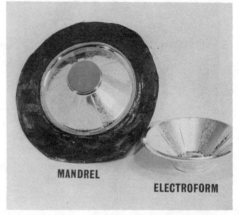

MANDREL

ELECTROFORM

Fig. 16-8. *Highly polished utensils are made by the electroforming process in mass production. (Courtesy of International Nickel Co.)*

Fig. 16-9. *View of the mandrel with the electroformed product still encased in it and also the finished product after removal from mandrel. (Courtesy of International Nickel Co.)*

expendable mandrels. Nonmetallic materials are used for both permanent and expendable mandrels, but they must be metallized to provide an electrical-conducting surface. Stainless steels are commonly used for mandrels which are to be withdrawn from the electroform and used repeatedly; such types as 316, 416 and 17–4PH are the best so far as corrosion-resistance is concerned. Machinability and low coefficient of thermal expansion compared with copper indicate 17–4 PH to be best suited for permanent mandrels, especially when used in the acid-sulfate electrolyte bath. Permanent mandrels made of stainless steels offer a high scratch-resistance and do not require a conductive coating; however, their use is limited to electroforms allowing their complete removal as integral mandrels or mandrel components.

Expendable mandrels in use today include polystyrene and methyl methacrylate, or plexiglas materials. Such plastics are easily molded and readily dissolved, thereby permitting intricate electroforms; however, they are readily scratched, must be made electrically conductive, and may warp with a change of temperature (i.e. in an evaporative coating process). In order to render these plastics conductive, they are subjected to evaporation of approximately 1000 Å (approximately $4 \cdot 10^{-6}$ in.) of gold. Gold is chosen, as a rule, because of its better conductivity, tarnish-resistance, and ease of vacuum deposition; however, other metals may also be used.

Just as in the case of other types of metal forming, electroforming claims several advantages over other processes, including:

1. Production of intricate shapes
2. Reproduction with great fidelity
3. Achievement of detail in intricate designs
4. Mirror-like surfaces
5. Adaptability to large-scale production.

16-4   Electrolytic Machining (ECM)

Electrolytic machining or grinding, electrochemical machining or grinding, and anodic machining or grinding are all names for the same phenomenon—removal of metal by electric current flow. They should not be confused with electrodischarge or spark-arc machining methods, previously discussed in this chapter.

The principle of metal removal which underlies electrolytic machining is governed by laws of physics that are well understood. It has been known since the work of Michael Faraday (1791–1867) that if two metal poles are placed in a conductive electrolyte bath and energized by a direct current, metal can be plated onto the negative pole (the cathode) and deplated from the positive pole (the anode). The cathodic side of the process is extensively used, of course, in electroplating. The anodic side of the process, where metal is removed instead of being added, was not used at all for industrial metalworking until the advent of the electrolytic machining process. It is, however, a potent force for metal removal and in time may become as useful as the plating of cathodic side of the Faraday cell.

Faraday established not only the basic idea of electrolysis, but also the rule that the amount of metal deposited on the cathode or deplated from the anode is directly proportional to the current used in electrolytic action on the metals. In fact, so basic is this idea that the ampere is defined by reference to it; "An ampere is that amount of current which when flowing for one second will deposit (or deplate) 0.001118 grams of silver." This number is called the electrochemical equivalent of silver. Every other metal has its own electrochemical equivalent, that is, for a given current a fixed quantity of metal will be removed. Since current is the only factor in Faraday's law, it is not difficult to estimate the current or amperage required for a given rate of metal removal.

Ordinarily, the electrochemical equivalents are expressed in grams per ampere; however, since these values are not too handy for the engineer in industrial metalworking, the values shown in Table 16–3 have been prepared to show the theoretical maximum removal rates expressed in cubic inches per 1000 amperes, for a number of the more common industrial metals.

TABLE 16–3.   Electrochemical Equivalents of Industrial Metals

Work Material	Removal Rate*
Aluminum	0.128
Beryllium	0.094
Chromium	0.137
Cobalt	0.125
Columbium	0.205
Copper	0.134
Iron	0.134
Molybdenum	0.119
Nickel	0.125
Tantalum	0.103
Titanium	0.133
Tungsten	0.121
Zirconium	0.133

* Cu in. of metal removed per 1000 amp minimum.

As shown in Table 16-3 the electrochemical removal rates of many common alloying metals—chromium, cobalt, iron, molybdenum, nickel, tungsten—are closely bracketed. In practice the variations among the different alloys can be neglected in computing electrolytic removal rates, despite the fact that the mechanical properties of the alloys may be different when various kinds and amounts of the alloying materials are used.

In electrolytic machining the current efficiency is remarkably high, ranging from about 75 per cent to over 90 per cent, depending on the material, the electrolyte, and the work configuration. These values are computed after measuring and making allowance for the relatively small amount of material removed by abrasion. These high values are surprising because many electrolytic plating baths necessarily operate at much lower current efficiencies. As a practical matter, it is usually safe to assume a removal rate of 0.100 cu in. per min for each 1000 amp of current. This value is applicable to most steel materials and to most of the so-called "superalloys" of the high temperature type. For tungsten carbide the values range from 0.100 cu in. per min for some of the newer steel-cutting grades to values as low as 0.061 cu in. per min for each 1000 amp for some of the "straight" carbides with low cobalt content.

Fig. 16–10 shows one of the medium sized models of ANOCUT Engineering Co. electrolytic machining units, and Fig. 16–11 shows a larger capacity unit. The ANOCUT Company manufactures a full line of standard and special purpose tools capable of accomplishing many cutting jobs with speed and accuracy on metals such as tungsten carbide and others. In fact, this company when asked to assist in computing the requirements for machining a steel wing spar some 60 ft long to an

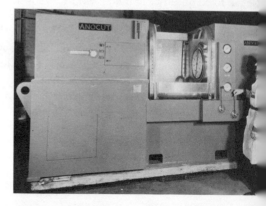

Fig. 16-10. *This is a 10,000 ampere lathe. The workpiece is mounted on the spindle (to the right) and rotated while being machined. (Courtesy of ANOCUT Engineering Co.)*

average depth of 0.150 in. was told that the job was to be done "as fast as possible." They computed that the job could be completed with one of their tools in about 90 sec—with 720,000 amp of current! A full year's production could be accomplished in one working day; however, the equipment would stand idle most of the time, incurring substantial depreciation charges and doing no work. The speed of electrolytic machining must always be balanced with other machining facilities and with production requirements. Only two or three years old, this process has been doing difficult jobs of shaped electrode drilling and cavity sinking in mass production and is more recently being used for another difficult job—that of making "anode cuts" on concentric shapes on rotating work up to 19 1/2 in. OD from any electrically conductive metal and at rates up to 0.30 cu in. per min with ANOCUT's 3000 amp electrolytic lathe. Figures 16–12, 16–13, and 16–14 show some of the typical work being done by this process for many industries today.

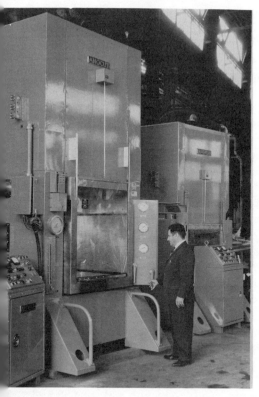

Fig. 16-11. *A 30,000 amp machine capable of handling large workpieces in this vertical unit. (ANOCUT Engineering Co. Chicago, Ill.)*

Fig. 16-12. *Integrally-bladed turbine wheels made of titanium alloy or of waspaloy. One blade is machined in two wheels simultaneously, at a feed rate of approximately 1/4 in. per min. (Courtesy of ANOCUT Engineering Co.)*

Fig. 16-13. *Airfoil forms such as those shown are easily machined with a single axis plunge of a shaped electrode tool. The tool does not wear. All of the convex surfaces of these high temperature alloy blades were machined within an envelope tolerance of 0.002 in. with the same electrode. (Courtesy of ANOCUT Engineering Co. Chicago, Illinois.)*

Fig. 16-14. *This pipe elbow forging die was machined into hardened die steel in 20 minutes to the shape and finish shown. (Conventional machining and polishing would require several hours to produce the same form.) (Courtesy of ANOCUT Engineering Co.)*

16-5   Chemical Milling

The process of *chemical milling* permits the removal of large amounts of metal by etching selected areas of somewhat complex parts. Developed in the aircraft industry as a means of fabricating lightweight parts of large areas and thin sections, it has become a practical method of milling in many other industries, including automotive, transistor, and others. Chemical milling involves four steps: cleaning the parts to be milled, masking out those parts not to be etched, the etching process, and, finally, the demasking. Neoprene rubber or vinyl plastic is used effectively as a maskant and is sprayed over all surfaces and subsequently baked. The maskant is then cut in accordance with a templet and stripped off the areas to be etched. By removing parts of the maskant at different times during the etching process, different surfaces can be milled to various depths as required.

The etching tank into which the material is dipped is the only limiting factor that controls the size of parts that can be processed by chemical milling technique. In milling aluminum by this method, caustic soda is the usual etchant; the etchant for steel, magnesium, and titanium is one of the more active acids such as sulfuric acid (25 $\pm$5 per cent H_2SO_4 by weight), with the etching solution operating at room temperature as a rule. In some plants where large castings or forgings are processed, the etching solution is heated to accelerate the operation.

The rate of etching is about 0.001 in. per min in the solution, providing it is held at proper concentration throughout the process. By means of deoxidizing and rinsing, the black smut that forms on the surface of the work may be readily removed. In some of the aircraft industries, tolerance of $\pm$0.001 in. are being held, although it is more practical to hold to $\pm$0.060 in. on the length and width and +0.005 and −0.000 in. on the depth and thickness of the work. Surface finish ranges from 28 to 126 microinches; the deeper the cut, the rougher the finish produced, although the finer-grain material etches more smoothly in most instances.

Chemical milling is being done on all types of parts including rolled sections, castings, forgings, and preformed pieces. There are no limitations as to shape, direction of cut, or cutter, and various sizes and shapes of cuts can be produced at one time. Where indicated by the nature and end product, the work can be etched on both sides at the same time to reduce danger of warpage. Since work that has been chemically milled does not have any of the scratches on the surfaces that conventionally milled parts have, it appears to possess higher fatigue strength after chemical milling. It is also most advantageous for complex cuts and parts having very large areas to be milled very readily. Necessary tanks are now available for parts up to 12 $\times$ 50 ft thus opening the door to the design engineer for such applications. For simple, straightforward milling, however, the conventional method can usually be accomplished more economically using standard machine tools.

Chemical milling, being very simple, can be accurately controlled by automatic operations. Costs of equipment, preparation time, and actual operations are quite low; in fact, chemical milling has reduced these factors of production rates by over 60 per cent in many plants. An aircraft manufacturer states that costs of milling by the conventional method using standard machine tools have been cut from $32.32 per piece to $10.64 using the chemical milling process where the parts are being run in lots of from 75 to 200 pieces. Just as in most of the other modern machining and fabricating processes today, there are some parts which are best produced by one method rather than another. Each process has its advantages and disadvantages but there is a place for each of the many processes, and the advantages of one outweighs the disadvantages for certain types of work.

In this chapter the author has endeavored to describe the newer and most modern methods of metal forming, shaping, and machining and has not included any of the more conventional processes of these operations. There are many good references for the student on the orthodox methods of machining, etc., including those listed at the end of this chapter as well as the following:

Engineering Materials and Processes, by Donald S. Clark, International Textbook Company, Scranton, Pennsylvania, 1958.
Metal Processing by O. W. Boston, John Wiley & Sons, Inc, New York, New York, move in 1951.
Metal Machining by L. E. Doyle, Prentice-Hall, Inc. Englewood Cliffs, New Jersey, 1953.

16-6 Explosive Forming of Metals

Explosive-metalworking operations can generally be classified as either *confined* or *unconfined* systems. The confined system has distinct advantages for the forming of thin materials to close tolerances; however, the nature of the operation imposes a size limitation. Unconfined systems are less efficient because only a small portion of the total energy from the explosive is utilized in the forming operation. This method is particularly attractive, especially for very large pieces, since tooling requirements are greatly simplified. A wide variety of explosives and detonators are employed in explosive-forming operations; however, the secondary high explosives are of considerable importance.

Explosive forming is a process in which metal parts are formed by the high pressures resulting from the detonation of chemical explosives. In the course of development of new forming methods, a number of high-energy-rate techniques have been categorized as explosive forming. Such methods have included the use of chemical high and low explosives, pneumatic systems, electrical discharge systems, and magnetic devices. There are many types of explosives available and used for explosive-forming operations; however, in selecting explosives it is imperative to consider handling and storage characteristics, sensitivity to shock and heat, tendency to be hydroscopic, and the effect of storage time and conditions on homogeneity, as well as the more obvious characteristics of behavior upon detonation and suitability of physical form. Although consideration of cost of explosives can be important under some circumstances, in most instances the explosive cost is only a small fraction of the total expense of the operation.

Fig. 16–15 is a graphic illustration of the confined or closed system, consisting of a die completely enclosing the energy source. This system has been used with propellant charges and for some small-diameter tube forming and piercing operations with high explosives. The closed system has distinct advantages for the forming of thin materials to close tolerances, as stated previously, because the sustained pressure tends to set the material to the die. The confined system has been used with explosive charges for some close-tolerance sizing operations on thin-wall tubing. However, limits on part size maximum which can be produced, die erosion, and possible

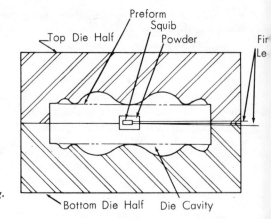

Fig. 16-15. *Confined system of explosive forming. (Courtesy of Olin Mathieson Chemical Corporation.)*

hazards of operation have been prime factors limiting its use. As the part size is increased with the closed-die system, the thickness of the die-wall must be increased proportionately, and a point of uneconomical die construction is reached quickly, usually at around 2 in. for a tubular section. When forming a part with a shape other than tubular, the critical size will be reached at an even smaller size. Deterioration of the die cavity is common with the closed-die systems as a result of continued gas erosion. Furthermore, die failure in a closed-die system is much more likely to result in a shrapnel hazard from the fragmented die than in an unconfined system. For these reasons the confined system has had limited use up to now, and the unconfined systems are more widely used today.

Fig. 16–16 shows the unconfined system which consists of a single female die with a blank held over it and an explosive charge suspended at a predetermined position over the blank of metal to be formed. The complete assembly may be immersed in a water tank, or a plastic bag filled with water may be placed over the blank.

The unconfined system is inherently inefficient because only a small portion of the total energy released from the explosive is used in the forming operation. With explosive forming the explosive force acts equally in all directions, sending out shock waves radially from the charge. Although the unconfined system may be inefficient in the utilization of energy, it has other advantages which make it economically attractive. For example, tooling for explosive forming can be made simple, with

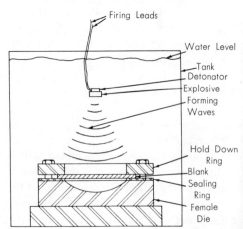

Fig. 16-16. *Unconfined system of explosive forming. (Courtesy of Olin Mathieson Chemical Corporation.)*

a reduction in cost of up to 80 per cent over that for tooling required to perform the same operation by conventional methods. The tooling is simplified since only the female member of a die set is required, with the explosive shock waves acting as a punch. The tooling is loaded in compression to a greater extent than in tension. Inasmuch as most die materials can be loaded much greater in compression than in tension, lighter dies can be used.

Table 16–4 gives the characteristics of a number of explosives used in explosive forming of metals, all of which must be studied and considered prior to proceeding with an actual operation. Explosives have an initiation sensitivity which requires not only that a sufficient force be applied but that the application be sufficiently

TABLE 16–4. Characteristics of High and Low Explosives

Property	High Explosives	Low Explosives
Method of initiation	Primary high explosives—ignition, spark, flame, or impact. Secondary high explosives— detonator, or detonator and booster combination.	Ignition
Conversion time	Microseconds	Milliseconds
Conversion rate	6,000 to 28,000 ft per sec.	A few inches to a few feet per second.
Pressures	Up to about 4,000,000 psi.	Up to about 40,000 psi.

Properties of High Explosives (After Ref. 2 and 3)

Explosive	Detonation Temp (°C)	Detonation Velocity (ft/sec)	Detonation Pressure (psi)
RDX	5450	27,400	3,750,000
PETN	5400	27,200	3,300,000
TETRYL	4400	25,700	2,900,000
PICRIC ACID	3900	24,100	2,650,000
TNT	3900	22,600	2,250,000

Velocities of Elastic Waves in Materials

Material	C_L (ft/sec)	C_P (ft/sec)	C_R (ft/sec)	C_T (ft/sec)
Aluminum	20,900	17,800	16,800	10,200
Beryllium	42,300	42,200	42,200	29,100
Brass	14,100	12,500	11,500	6,700
Copper	14,900	12,800	11,700	7,400
Lead	7,100	4,300	4,000	2,300
Magnesium	21,100	17,800	15,700	10,100
Molybdenum	20,900	19,850	18,000	11,200
Nickel	18,800	16,800	16,300	9,800
Steel	19,500	17,800	16,400	10,500
Tin	9,500	8,300	8,200	4,800
Titanium	19,700	16,900	15,900	9,700
Zinc	12,300	11,900	11,600	7,500

(Reprinted from *Journal of Metals*, September 1960, by permission.)

brisant (shattering effect) in character to assure detonation of the explosive. It is possible to use less powerful caps on the less sensitive explosives if an intermediate booster is used between the cap and the explosive. The use of a booster, however, is normally undesirable since it complicates the explosive setup. The best approach is to select a cap which has sufficient power for the direct initiation of the explosive.

Fig. 16–17 shows an explosive-forming facility consisting of one concrete tank 12 ft in diameter by 10 ft deep with 1-ft thick walls. The tank is equipped with a bubble curtain, and 1-lb charges have been fired in it without damage to the tank.

Fig. 16-17. *Production facility for explosive forming. (Courtesy of Astronautics Division of General Dynamics Corporation.)*

Fig. 16–18 illustrates a slightly different type facility where the water tank is completely above the ground, and an air curtain is used to reduce stresses in the steel tank wall. The water tank is 13 ft in diameter and 13 ft deep. The most desirable type of facility will depend on the local conditions and needs estimated for present and future production requirements. Most of the facilities for explosive forming are located in the western part of the country, where outside operations are possible.

Fig. 16-18. *Elevated water tank for explosive forming on a production basis. (Courtesy of Lockheed Aircraft Corporation.)*

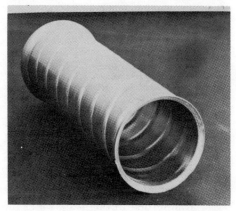

Fig. 16-19. *A large Kirksite die for forming antenna reflectors in the plant of a large aircraft company. (Courtesy of North American Rockwell Corporation.)*

Fig. 16-20. *Explosive-formed hexagonal tube before and after trimming. Formed from a 5-in. diameter Type 321 stainless steel tube measuring 38 in. long with a 0.020 in. wall, fabricated in a single operation using 6 oz of Primacord in a water medium and an AISI 4340 steel die. The final configuration represented a stretch of approximately 20 per cent with finished tolerances of +0.000 and −0.010 in. (Courtesy of General Dynamics, Fort Worth, Texas.)*

Fig. 16-21. *End view of outer thrust chamber shell. Formed in a single operation with 150 grains of PETN Primacord and a Solar tool-steel die in a water medium. The initial 4-in. diameter Type 321 stainless steel tube with a 0.063 in. wall yielded approximately a 7 per cent stretch with a finish tolerance of ±0.0005 in. on the inside diameter. (Courtesy of Rocketdyne, a Division of North American Rockwell Corporation)*

Fig. 16–22 shows a large completed pylon made by explosive forming at the Rocketdyne plant of North American Rockwell Corporation. Shown in Figure 16–20 is an explosively-formed hexagonal tube before and after trimming, and Figure 16-21 shows the end view of an outer thrust chamber shell, which was formed in a single operation with 150 grains of PETN Primacord and a Solar tool-steel die in a water medium. The shell was made of 4–in, diameter Type 321 stainless steel tube with a 0.063-in. wall. It yielded an approximate 7 per cent stretch with finish tolerances of ±0.0005 in. on the inside diameter.

High-energy-rate forming (explosive forming) has at least four advantages over ordinary forming methods:

1. Parts and materials that are difficult to form at low energy rates are readily formed at high energy rates.

Fig. 16-22. *A completed pylon for a large missile system. Made of 6061 aluminum alloy, the final part which measured 48 in. in length by 18 in. diameter at the base had a 0.063 in. wall with a final tolerance of ±0.010 in. with a maximum of 20 per cent stretch. Over 100 of these parts were made in this manner with the same die setup. (Courtesy of Rocketdyne, a Division of North American Rockwell Corporation)*

2. High-energy-rate forming requires only simple tooling. In explosive and electrohydraulic forming, only a female die is required—the explosive energy, transmitted through the water medium, acts as the punch. Electromagnetic forming of tubes is done without tooling. Although punches and dies are used for pneumatic-mechanical forming, they are much lighter than the tools used for conventional forming.

3. Equipment and floor space requirements are at a minimum.

4. No machines or presses are needed. Even for pneumatic-mechanical forming, the machines are compact and relatively low in cost, considering their capabilities.

High-energy-rate metalworking techniques are not limited to forming operations. Explosive engraving, welding, powder compaction, hardening, and cutting are also possible. These are contact operations which take advantage of the fact that materials exhibit many unusual properties in their behavior patterns when worked under very high pressures.

16-7   N/C (Numerically Controlled) Machining

Any consideration of the forming of metals must include N/C Numerically Controlled Machining which effects not only substantial cost savings in production but minutely exact duplication of parts in very large quantities. Introduced to the market only ten years ago, the continuing revolution that is numerical control must be described as the most significant manufacturing development of the century.

Several manufacturers of numerically controlled equipment now furnish machines that perform milling, drilling, reaming, tapping, and boring in a single setup, the setup and cycle time being accurately controlled by the use of multi-channel punched tape which provides the memory for the system, never making a mistake, never misinterpreting the instructions. The following functions are performed automatically by numerical control:

1. Starting and stopping the machine cycle
2. Starting and stopping coolant (flood or mist as required)
3. Sequence and changing of tools
4. Position index table
5. Stopping or starting the spindle at programmed speed and direction of rotation
6. Positioning any axis at any feed rate—1 through 79 in. per min, or rapid transverse rate—200 ipm.
7. Feeding in any axis at programmed feed rate
8. Two-axis contouring (optional)

With this system it is possible to perform all operations required to finish a part completely, ready for assembly, and it can be repeated over and over with accuracy. The tape controls all the operations automatically.

Most machines in the higher precision class today possess not only a tape mode panel which includes function indicators, sequence number display, and feed rate override, but also a manual mode panel which provides the operator with full manual control of all functions with the same accuracy as tape control. All data contained on tape can be duplicated or changed manually, including speeds and feeds. Furthermore, manual jogging, from zero to 100 per cent of programmed feed rate, can be performed. Tape readers are also a part of some of the machines; this is a photoelectric compact reel-type unit capable of reading 300 or more characters per second.

By way of comparing costs of producing two typical parts on the MILWAUKEE-MATIC Series E_b and on conventional machines, both parts being machined complete including contouring, the following data are of interest:

JOB #1   Material—aluminum   Lot Size—30
Six sides of part worked on in two setups

	Conventional	*MILWAUKEE-MATIC*
Setup	8.6 hours	0.50 hours
Cycle	5.8 hours	1.10 hours
Tooling	$9,600.00	$1,700.00

JOB #2   Material—magnesium   Lot Size—20
Seven sides worked on in two setups

	Conventional	*MILWAUKEE-MATIC*
Setup	17.8 hours	0.50 hours
Cycle	6.5 hours	1.70 hours
Tooling	$9,500.00	$1,450.00

Photographs of the MILWAUKEE-MATIC and those of other makers are shown on following pages.

Fig. 16-23. *Kearney & Trecker MILWAUKEE-MATIC 3-axis Model II with solid state numerical control. (Courtesy of Kearney & Trecker Corporation.)*

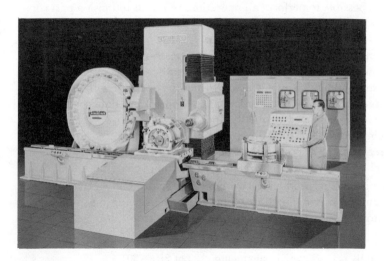

Fig. 16-24. *Kearney & Trecker MILWAUKEE-MATIC 5 axis Model III with automatic tool changer that provides fast, error-free random selection of tools from the rotary tool storage magazine as shown.*

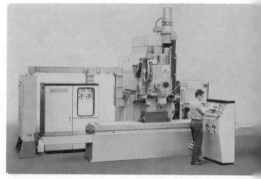

Fig. 16-25. *Numerically controlled 30 in. HYDRO-TEL Milling Machine with three axis contouring operations for conventional vertical milling or the duplication of dies for aerospace, die-sinking, automotive industries, or job shops. (Courtesy of Cincinnati Milling Machine Co.)*

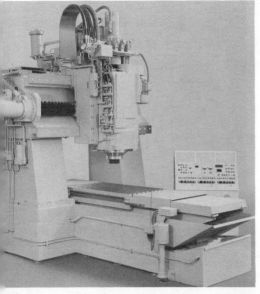

Fig. 16-26. *Numerically controlled Bridge-Type Profile Milling Machine. (Courtesy of Cincinnati Milling Machine Co.)*

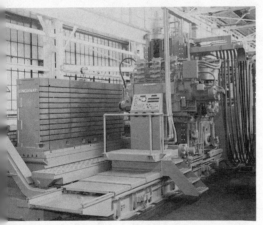

Fig. 16-27. *Cincinnati Travelling Column Milling and Profiling Machine N/C and Tracer controlled for manufacturing mirror image steel die blocks, air frame parts, automotive components, etc. (Courtesy of the Cincinnati Milling Machine Co.)*

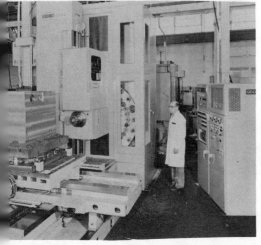

Fig. 16-28. *NUMERICENTER-H N/C Machining Center with automatic tool changer and Numeripoint Control. (Courtesy of Giddings & Lewis Machine Tool Company.)*

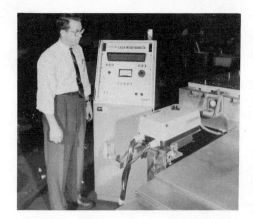

Fig. 16-29. *Laser Interferometer shown here to check Numeri Mill N/C Contour milling machine illustrated at the right. This atomic-age instrument utilizes light waves for millionth-of-an-inch measurement of machine tool movements and numerically controlled positioning. A high degree of quality control is assured with this system. (Courtesy of Giddings & Lewis Machine Tool Company.)*

Fig. 16-30. *SC-25 SERVOFEED 4-Axis Turret Lathe with G. E. Mark Century Numerical Control. (Courtesy of Warner & Swasey Company.)*

Fig. 16-31. *Closeup of the SC-25 movable control console showing complete hand controls which can be positioned anywhere along the front rail permitting the operator to observe clearly both the workpiece and cutters as he maneuvers the slides. (Courtesy of Warner & Swasey Company.)*

QUESTIONS

1. Describe the method and function of metal forming by the electrical-discharge process.

2. Upon what factors do the rates of metal removal by spark-discharge machining processes depend?

3. In order to minimize tool costs and to control dimensions, what must be observed so far as the ratio of the material removed from the tool used for cutting to the volume of metal removed from the work-piece is concerned?

4. State some of the advantages of the electrical discharge method of metal forming.

5. Give the essentials of the electroforming process of metal forming including the wide range of products being formed by this method.

6. In the electroforming process the mandrels or master forms may be either permanent or expendable. Explain the difference in construction and properties of each type.

7. Name some of the advantages of the electroforming process.

8. Describe the electrolytic machining (ECM) method of metal forming giving the basic principle on which it was founded.

9. As a rule, the electrochemical equivalents of metals are expressed in grams per ampere. On what basis are the electrochemical equivalents of industrial metals given for the ease and convenience of engineers in the metalworking field?

10. Upon what does the current efficiency depend in the process of electrolytic machining? Is it usually high or low?

11. As a rule of thumb, what is the safest assumption regarding the removal rate of metal with the electrolytic machining process? Is this applicable for all grades of steel?

12. Into what categories may explosive-metalworking operations be classified? Is there any advantage of one method over the other?

13. Define explosive forming of metals and state the various types that are categorized under this heading.

14. What factors must be considered when choosing an explosive for a particular application?

15. In explosive forming does the explosive force act only in the downward direction?

16. What are the advantages of the unconfined system of explosive forming?

17. Where is the greatest savings effected in the explosive forming of metals?

18. What are the basic requirements of the explosives that are used in explosive forming metal parts?

19. What media can be used in the explosive forming process? Which one is more commonly used? Why?

20. Can the explosive forming process be used for production as well as for prototype parts for models?

21. Name some of the advantages of explosive forming of metals over conventional forming methods.

22. Is the high-energy-rate metalworking process limited to forming operations? If not, what other operations are being done by means of explosives? On what factors are these other techniques based?

23. Why has the N/C numerically controlled machining process been acclaimed as the most significant manufacturing development of the century?

24. Name some of the operations that are being performed by the numerical control of machines in industry. What are the unique differences between these techniques and conventional methods?

25. In addition to the types of machining called for in the preceding question, name some of the functions that are being accomplished automatically by means of numerically controlling the machines.

26. Describe the numerical control of machines in the higher precision class in regard to the method of their operation from start to finish.

27. Name some of the substantial advantages of numerical controlled machines as compared with conventional methods in doing the same jobs.

28. Define "chemical milling" and describe the process.

29. State the advantages and disadvantages of chemical milling.

References

American Society for Testing Materials, *Standards of Mechanical and Chemical Milling*, Philadelphia, Pennsylvania, 1964.

Battelle Memorial Institute, Columbus, Ohio: DMIC Report 213 Defense Metals Information Center, *Metal Removal*, 1965.

Cina, Bernard, "The Effect of Surface Finish on Fatigue," *Metallurgia*, 55 (327), 11–19, January 1957.

Doyle, Lawrence E., J. L. Morris, J. L. Leach, and G. F. Schrader, *Manufacturing Processes and Materials for Engineers*. Englewood Cliffs, New Jersey: Prentice-Hall, Inc., 1964.

Lockheed Aircraft Company, Technical Division, Marietta, Ohio: *Chemical and Electrochemical Milling of Aircraft Parts*, 1965.

Oeldoetz, Paul A., and G. A. Clark, *Chemical Milling*. Los Angeles: Society of Aerospace Material and Process Engineers, 1962.

Taylor, Lyman, (ed), *Metals Handbook*, Metals Park, Ohio: American Society for Metals, 1948 and 1961 editions.

The Joining of Metals

17-1 Metallurgy of Joining Metals

Many articles that are too large or too costly to be made in one piece are best made by bonding (joining) several individually made parts. Such parts may be made by casting or metalworking or may be cut from sheet or plate material. This bonding may be accomplished by riveting, bolting, welding, soldering, and brazing. In addition to these methods of joining either similar or dissimilar metals there are several newer techniques that are now being developed and, in some cases, used, including welding by means of the electron beam, the laser beam, ultrasonic methods, and capacitor-discharge welding. These latter methods are particularly useful in the joining of dissimilar metals. There is also welding by means of the plasma arc and explosion welding; both have applications all of which will be described briefly in this chapter.

In the previous discussion of metallic binding it was stated that metals are held together by the electrostatic attraction or bond between negatively charged free electrons and the positively charged ions and that the atoms are held apart from each other by an electrical repulsion between neighboring ions. It was also stated that these electrical forces are balanced in such a way that the atoms are strongly bonded together and that plastic deformation of metals is possible because of this unique type of bonding. Upon these metallurgical bonding mechanisms depend the entire field of joining separate metallic components successfully by sintering, in the case of powder metallurgy techniques, and by the various types of welding, including arc, gas, electrical resistance, etc. The basic mechanism of metallurgical bonding of metals makes it imperative that the metals to be joined comply with the following characteristics as much as possible:

1. That they be placed in intimate contact with each other.
2. That they be so close that the atoms of one piece will be separated from the atoms of the other piece by approximately the same interatomic spacing that is found normally in the component metal parts involved.
3. That the surfaces to be joined are well cleaned.

Under these conditions, the interatomic forces will cause immediate bonding from one surface to the other and will permit the joining of any metal to another metal, the strength of the joint being proportional to the surface areas to be joined and to the intimacy of contact with each other.

Metals may be bonded together by processes in which only the joining medium is melted in which case the strength of the joint depends upon adhesion or some small degree of alloying by diffusion. Soldering, which will be discussed in detail in this chapter, is an example of such adhesion. In brazing, some of the filler metal atoms diffuse into the solid base metal being joined.

In the case of arc welding both the filler metal and the parent metal are melted so that after solidification the joint resembles the crystal structure of a casting. Resistance welding uses pressure and only sufficient heat to cause the joining and bonding of the mating parts, without the fusion of either the filler metal or the parts. Powder metallurgy combines both mechanical working and joining by compacting and sintering in metal dies as was discussed in Chapter 15.

After parts are produced by any of these methods of bonding, they are often heat treated and finished to give them the mechanical properties desired as well as the attractive finish sometimes required for better sales appeal, such as electroplating, hot dipping, spraying of one metal on another, or coating with nonmetals such as lacquers, paints, etc.

In order to obtain surfaces as clean as possible prior to joining, it is essential that every effort is made to remove any oxides and adsorbed gases from the surfaces of each part to be joined. It is well to heat the parts sufficiently to get rid of the adsorbed gases, and either gaseous or liquid fluxes are used to remove the oxide film. In extreme cases it is necessary to resort to considerable pressure, and, at times, grinding or polishing are necessary to eliminate the oxides.

Joining metals together with good firm joints is possible both for similar as well as dissimilar metals under the following conditions:

1. While both parts being joined are in the liquid state such as is the case in fusion welding
2. While one metal is liquid and the other is in the solid state, such as in the case of sintering operations
3. While both are solid—also by sintering as well as by pressure weld bonding at either room temperature or higher temperatures.

Most metals and alloys, with only few exceptions, can be joined to similar metals by fusion, in which case the liquid metal from one part flows into the liquid metal of the other part resulting, upon solidification, in a welded joint. Here, in fusion, the atoms of the fused metals join the crystal structure of the parent metals resulting in the inception and growth of dendrites, growing from the interface of the liquid and solid metal to the center of the joint. Such dendritic crystal growth continues toward the center until all the liquid metal is used up and the result is a strong, bonded weld.

The fusion method results in a sound metallic weld with a strong bond between adjacent atoms within the molten metal when solidified and in the parent metal throughout; the only question in the bonded strength occurs at the primary interface of the first layer of the atoms in the molten metal, after solidification, and the parent metal. This critical area can be rendered more perfect if every caution is taken to insure cleanliness and proper preparation of the joints to be bonded together.

Most metals form oxides upon heating where any oxygen is present as it is in air, and it is understood, furthermore, that these oxides usually have higher melting points than the original parent metal; for this reason these oxides must be removed by fluxing, grinding, polishing, etc. In those cases where the oxides have lower melting points than the parent metal, they will usually be displaced by the added filler metal and will therefore not be too troublesome, since in such cases no flux is necessary.

The bonding of solid to solid is very common, as was stated in a previous chapter, where any two-phase alloy has the type of bond and can come together by the formation of a coherent, homogeneous structure at the interface. Incomplete coherence, however, is often caused by brittle, intermetallic compounds that result in a reduction in the ductility of the joint.

In pressure welding the cleaned surfaces of the two metals to be joined are brought closely together, and by applied pressure the two pieces are welded together. Inasmuch as it is next to impossible to get an interfacial junction between two metals to be joined so that they are separated from one another by just an amount of the normal interatomic spacing, we apply heat to our pressure joints and thereby break down the unsmooth surfaces and bring them into more intimate contact. The use of heat and pressure results in favorable weld conditions. When the temperature is raised high enough, recrystallization takes place, and joining similar metals results in welds in which there are an entirely new set of crystals that form across the interface of the joint so that there is very little left to show any indication of the junction between the two pieces. No appreciable fusion takes place in pressure welding, alloying taking place when the applied pressure brings the two pieces to be joined at a temperature above the recrystallization temperature of the metal.

17-2 Three Important Zones in Welds

In welds there are three important zones as follows:

1. The weld itself, right at the point of fusion.
2. The heat-affected zone—that area directly adjoining the weld zone.
3. The non-affected zone which is remote from the heat of the weld.

The weld zone in either fusion or pressure welding shows a coarse structure which is usually columnar in character. Because a structure very similar to the "as-cast" condition is obtained, the weld zone is less ductile and somewhat harder and stronger than was the original material.

The heat-affected zone varies depending on the composition of the material involved as follows:

(a) In pure metals and solid-solution alloys without allotropic transformation, the heat-affected zone usually shows grain growth because of the high temperature to which it has been subjected. In this heat-affected zone, the mechanical properties are lowest, and failures occur when the weldment is subjected to stresses, provided, of course, that no defects are present in the weld itself.

(b) Castings generally are not susceptible to grain growth, so little or no coarsening of the grain is present in welding.

(c) In those metals in which allotropic transformation takes place, like iron and steel (BCC, FCC, and HCP), three different structures are found in the heat-affected zone:

   1. The part heated well above the critical range shows a coarse grain such as is found in the weld zone itself.
   2. That part heated just above the critical range is very fine-grained.
   3. The part heated below the critical range is the softest, and, therefore, failures are found in this area when under stress.

(d) In those alloys containing eutectics, the heat-affected zone shows a gradually changing structure if the welding is accomplished after heat treatment.

(e) When cold-worked materials are welded, recrystallization and grain growth take place in the heat-affected zone. The material in this zone has properties that are unlike the cold-worked material. In fact, the properties are more like those of the annealed condition.

In fusion welding, which is essentially a casting process in which the metal is melted, the parent metal is often embrittled by welding, or a high degree of shrinkage may occur because of the use of an incorrect type of welding rod in the process. For these reasons it is of utmost importance that a welding rod suitable to the material being welded be selected. For example:

(a) In welding cast iron and malleable iron, a rod with high content of nickel is used.

(b) For the welding of high carbon steels, a rod with stainless steel content is best.

(c) To weld aluminum, a rod with aluminum-silicon alloy content performs better than others.

In some cases no filler rod is used, such as in the welding of thin sheets of metal in which part of the sheet is melted in fusion to furnish its own filler metal.

17-3 Arc Welding Processes

The transformation of electrical energy into heat in the form of an electric arc and the application of this liberated heat to fuse metals to be joined is comparatively new. In 1881 De Meritens first used arc welding for joining metals in the form of storage battery plates. The workpiece which was lead was connected to the positive source of current, and a carbon rod was connected to the negative pole to complete the circuit. Some modifications of this followed with the work of Bernardos, Olszewski, and others, but several years later (1887) Bernardos received a patent on the carbon-electrode process of arc welding. Two years later (1889) a man named Coffin received the important Coffin patents for his metallic-electrode process of arc welding. During the past twenty-five years there have been many important improvements in both equipment used and electrodes and techniques that have brought arc welding to a position of high importance in industry, especially during the war years when ships, tanks, weapons, ponton-bridges, etc. had to be constructed on a large scale with highest reliability.

A basis for the arc welding process is that every current of electricity generates heat—however small. The relation between electrical energy and heat may be stated simply as:

$$1 \text{ kwhr} = 3413 \text{ BTU}$$

One BTU equals 1/180 part of the heat required to raise the temperature of 1 lb of water from 32 to 212F. This is substantially equal to the heat required to raise one lb of water from 63 to 64F.

An arc drawn between a metal plate and a carbon electrode will operate at a potential of approximately 35 to 50 v, and an arc drawn between a metal plate and a metallic electrode will operate at approximately 15 to 45 v. Inasmuch as most commercial electric circuits operate at a higher potential, a transformer must be used to step down the voltage. For example, 30 v·250 amp·2 hr (the time used) equals 15,000 whr or 15 kwhrs; 15 kwhrs·3413 BTU equals 51,195 BTU which is the heat developed in this situation. In arc welding there must be a continuous supply of electrical current, i.e., sufficient and of the proper voltage to maintain the arc. The voltage across the arc, in general, will range from 17 v minimum to 45 v, maximum. The current will range from 10 amp to as high as 1200 amp in case of automatic operations.

Either AC or DC can be used; however, DC is, of course, more common today, and the most common source of DC current is the motor generator set of the variable

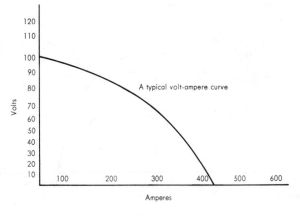

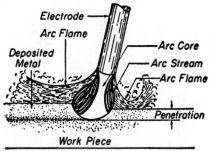

Fig. 17-2. *Arc welding with bare electrode. (Courtesy of American Society for Metals.)*

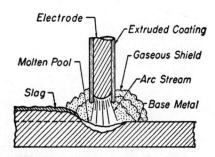

Fig. 17-1. *A typical volt-ampere curve.*

Fig. 17-3. *Arc welding with shielded or coated electrode. (Courtesy of American Society for Metals.)*

voltage type. The more common source for AC is the voltage transformer type welder with separate reactance since it is small, compact, and highly efficient.

An actual curve taken on a standard arc welding generator would look like that shown in Fig. 17–1.

In the modern generator with proper controls, literally hundreds and thousands of curves can be plotted. For example, if the voltage control has 30 voltage steps to it and if the current control has 100 steps, we could plot $30 \cdot 100$ or 3,000 v-amp curves.

The welding process, which is the ability of the arc to weld a good joint economically, depends on the *arc Watts*, i.e. the arc-length or voltage, and the arc current. If the arc voltage, that is, the closed circuit voltage, is held constant and the arc current is varied, the arc Watts will increase directly with the arc current because the arc Watts equals the arc amperes times the arc volts. This relationship may be expressed by the welding performance curve shown in Fig. 17–4.

In this welding performance curve, when the arc current is low the welding performance is also low because there is not enough current to melt the electrode and the edges of the joint to be united quickly enough. As the arc current increases, the electrode melts more readily, and the joint is melted deeper, giving a better penetration and fusion. The welding current increases with the arc current until the point P is reached which is the maximum welding performance. If the arc current is increased still further, the electrode melts faster than it can be deposited, resulting in an excess puddle of molten metal and the burning of the metal. If the arc

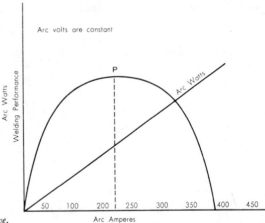

Fig. 17-4. *Welding performance curve.*

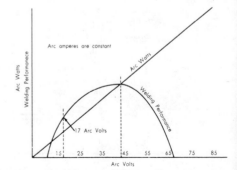

Fig. 17-5. *Welding performance curve.*

current is held constant at its best value P and the arc voltage is varied, a curve such as shown in Fig. 17–5 results.

In this curve in Fig. 17–5 the arc Watts will vary directly with the arc voltage or arc length and develop a straight line as shown. The arc Watts curve does not start at 0 voltage as an arc cannot be maintained unless the arc voltage is approximately 17 v as indicated.

17-4 Advantages of Arc Welding Over Gas Welding

Although, as will be shown later, gas welding has numerous advantages over electric arc welding, the latter has certain advantages over gas welding including the following:

1. The heat is more intense and concentrated thereby permitting a faster rate of welding and less distortion.
2. The important heat-affected-zone is much smaller than in gas welding.
3. Electric arc welding is better suited to continuous and automatic operations in which the bare rod is fed from a coil through a bath of the special flux required.
4. The procedures of arc welding produce much cleaner welds, especially with the use of gas shields.
5. It is much less costly than gas in continuous operations after the initial costs of equipments are amortized.

One consideration regarding safety in arc welding is that there must be proper shielding provided for the operators, since large amounts of radiation are produced.

17-5 Gas Welding

In gas or flame welding processes, the heat is supplied by combustion of a suitable fuel-gas with air or pure oxygen. These gases are mixed in a welding torch and regulated to produce an impinging flame with the necessary characteristics. The gases most used for this type of welding are acetylene and oxygen; however, hydrogen and other combustible gases are also used in some applications. The use of the welding torch is not a new development, for a crude form of blow-pipe was used as a torch by the early Greeks, Romans and Egyptians, to work the precious metals as well as those metals with low melting points such as lead, zinc, etc. The flame was derived from alcohol and similar fluids; however, the later discovery of gases giving the higher temperatures (up to 5,000 to 6,000F) really brought about the present development of the welding torch as it is known today.

Although acetylene was discovered as early as 1836, it was not widely used, except in laboratories, until 1892 when the method of producing calcium carbide (CaC_2) in large quantities was discovered. Acetylene itself is produced from calcium carbide (CaC_2) in the following manner:

$$CaC_2 + 2H_2O \longrightarrow C_2H_2 + Ca(OH)_2$$

calcium carbide   water   acetylene   hydrated lime

Actually the year 1903 marks the beginning of the oxyacetylene process for general use in welding and cutting of steel. The properties of the constituent gases and the methods of producing them are basically as follows.

Oxygen is a colorless, odorless, tasteless gas that supports and intensifies combustion. It is very active at ordinary pressures and even more so at higher temperatures and pressures. It combines violently with oil or grease even at ordinary temperatures. Oxygen is produced mainly from liquid air. Since air is approximately one-fifth oxygen, it can be liquified, then separated into oxygen and nitrogen, argon, helium, and its other components by a process of rectification. From the separation plant oxygen goes into storage holders and then into cylinders where it is compressed as a gas and made ready for the ultimate consumer. The distribution of liquid oxygen is becoming increasingly popular, and by this method it is then vaporized at the place of use.

Acetylene is also a colorless gas, but it is combustible as well and has a characteristic odor. It is a compound of carbon and hydrogen (C_2H_2). It forms highly explosive mixtures with air and oxygen so that the laws and regulations forbid the generation or use of acetylene fuel at pressures above 15 psi because any higher pressures may cause explosions under certain conditions. As was previously stated, acetylene is produced by the chemical reaction between water and calcium carbide. When a piece of calcium carbide is dropped into water, bubbles of acetylene gas will rise to the surface.

With commerically pure oxygen and acetylene the hottest known flame from gases can be produced, its estimated temperature being in the neighborhood of 6200F. The chemical reaction for complete combustion of oxygen and acetylene is as follows:

$$2C_2H_2 + 5O_2 \longrightarrow 4CO_2 + 2H_2O \text{ (water vapor)}$$

This means that two volumes of acetylene together with five volumes of oxygen combine and react to produce four volumes of carbon dioxide and two volumes of water vapor. Therefore, for *complete combustion* of acetylene and oxygen the ratio of oxygen to acetylene is 2–1/2 to 1.

For oxyacetylene welding and heating, however, the most suitable mixture is generally obtained by using a 50–50 mixture of equal proportions of oxygen and acetylene through the torch. Such a mixture when burned at the tip of a properly designed torch produces what is known as a *neutral flame*, because its action is neutral in effect, being neither oxidizing nor carburizing in nature. In the combustion of this 50–50 mixture of gases there is a double chemical reaction as follows:

(1) $\quad C_2H_2 + O_2 \longrightarrow 2CO + H_2 + 193{,}000$ BTU of heat which is approximately one-third of the heat available.

(2) $\qquad\qquad\qquad 2CO + O_2 \longrightarrow 2CO_2$

(3) $\qquad\qquad 2H_2 + O_2 \longrightarrow 2H_2O$ (water vapor)

The reaction represented by equation (1) takes place at the inner cone of the flame where the highest temperature is developed.

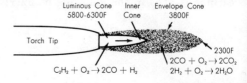

Fig. 17-6. *A typical oxyacetylene torch, showing flames and temperatures produced.*

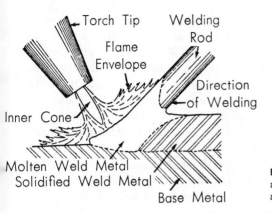

Fig. 17-7. *The addition of filler metal in form of welding rod, also various components of oxyacetylene welding. (Courtesy of American Society for Metals.)*

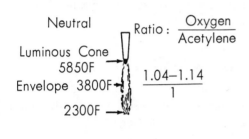

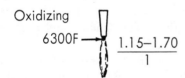

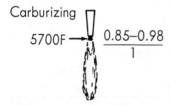

Fig. 17-8. *Characteristics of oxyacetylene welding flame. For complete combustion of acetylene, 1 molecular volume (380 cu ft at 60F) of acetylene, plus 2-1/2 molecular volumes of oxygen burns to form 2 molecular volumes of carbon dioxide plus 1 molecular volume of water vapor, liberating 542,700 BTU of heat. (Courtesy of American Society for Metals.)*

Then, as shown in equation (2) the carbon monoxide is burned to CO_2, and in equation (3) the hydrogen is burned to water vapor. The net result is a neutral flame as desired for welding and heating. The neutral flame is generally used for all heating and welding operations; however, there are uses for both the carburizing and oxidizing flames. With the carburizing or excess acetylene flame, free carbon is deposited in a very fine form and this free carbon has been utilized in the welding of steel. In such cases, a thin layer of highly carburizing iron is formed which will melt at a lower temperature than the steel itself so that the presence of this mixture is conducive to fusion and shortens the period of heating; therefore, rate of welding is faster than with the neutral flame. As the carburizing effect of the flame increases, however, the flame temperature drops and the amount of carbon deposited increases. Therefore, only small amounts of excess acetylene are used in welding operations.

The oxidizing flame with excess oxygen is used where the maximum flame temperature is desired and where the oxidizing effect is not detrimental, but in fact may be beneficial. Therefore, this oxidizing flame is used for preheating in the process of cutting operations with the oxyacetylene torch. It is also desirable in the welding of nonferrous metals, particularly brasses and bronzes, as it forms a tough oxide film over the molten metal to prevent any vaporization of the zinc and to curtail turbulence. This results in less oxidation of the molten metal once the oxide film is formed. The oxidizing flame is therefore generally used for this purpose.

Welding by means of the oxyacetylene flame is a form of fusion welding in which the heat required is furnished by oxyacetylene gas flame. At times in fusion welding, in fact, as a rule, a filler metal is added in the form of a welding rod to form the welded joint, although joints in some instances are formed in oxyacetylene welding merely by fusing the parts to be welded together without the addition of any welding rod or filler metal. In the welding of some metals a flux is used as a means of floating out the impurities and as an aid in securing a better bond.

17-6   Advantages of Gas Welding

Because of its flexibility, the oxyacetylene process has several distinct advantages over other processes of fusion welding, including the following:

1. Because the source of heat and the metal to be added (welding rod) are separate, this technique of welding may be used for it distributes the heat and rod in the best possible manner for controlling the molten puddle and preparing the parts to be joined in fusion.
2. The pressure of the flame helps a great deal in the control of the molten puddle of metal. This flexibility is particularly useful in position welding, such as in overhead welding, where the molten metal must be prevented from falling away from the point of fusion.
3. The molten metal is protected from atmospheric attack by the outer envelope of the flame. As previously stated, the surrounding oxygen at this point is consumed in the final combustion stage of the flame.
4. The advantage accrued by reason of its intense heat, of being able to cut through steel even as thick as 30 in. thick easily, is important to those firms in structural steel fabrication. For cutting with the oxyacetylene flame a special tip is used with several small holes placed around the end and a large hole located at the center. A large stream of oxygen is sent through the center hole while the combustible mixture of $C_2H_2 + O_2$ passes through the smaller outside holes. Burning of oxyacetylene gas mixture preheats the metal to over 1600F at which temperature the iron and other oxidizable elements are kindled to their ignition point and burned by the oxygen stream. The resulting combination of the force of the oxygen stream and the quick oxidation caused by the oxyacetylene flame cuts a path through the iron or steel. The equation for such burning is as follows:

$$3Fe + O_2 \longrightarrow Fe_3O_4 + 480,000 \text{ BTU/lb/molecule of } Fe_3O_4$$

It requires 4–1/2 cu ft of O_2 to burn 1 lb of Fe to Fe_3O_4.

17-7   Thermit Welding

Thermit welding is another important method of joining metals. The process grew out of a discovery by Vautin in 1894 that by mixing finely powdered aluminum with metallic oxides, sulfides, and chlorides and then igniting the mixture, he could get temperatures of 5000F and even higher. He also found that at the same time the metal was readily reduced and remained at a high degree of purity. The equation for this reaction is as follows:

$$8Al + 3Fe_3O_4 \longrightarrow 9Fe + 4Al_2O_3 + 179,000 \text{ BTU per lb mol of Al}$$

Thermit welding is principally used for welding heavy sections of iron and steel as well as cast iron. In fact, they may be actually joined together by this method. The process is low in cost and only a short interval of time is needed. Furthermore there is no need for stress relieving, as stresses are relieved by the thermit welding process itself. Thermit welding can produce tensile strengths of from 70,000 to 75,000 psi in the weld if the proper technique and care are used in the process.

17-8   Metallizing

Metallizing is the spraying of metals in the molten state onto metals that have first been roughed up by sandblasting, machining, or grinding. It is used extensively for building up worn shafts, thus effecting a substantial savings in not having to purchase new shafts. All metals, except magnesium, titanium, and tungsten, can be sprayed by blowing fine drops of molten metal through the nozzle of a spray-gun. Either wire or powder can be used as the source of metal being sprayed. An intense gas flame is used to melt the metal just before it is blown out of the end of the nozzle. At times the metallized parts require a heat treatment subsequent to the metallizing in order to make a denser deposit and a tighter bond.

The equipment required for metallizing include:

1. Equipment to prepare the surface such as sandblast, shot blast, grinding machines, etc.
2. Spraying equipment
3. Gas and oxygen equipment
4. Source of air
5. A means or equipment for exhaust
6. A lathe, in the case of metallizing a round shaft

Actually, in the metallizing process, the bonding between the sprayed metal and the base metal is purely mechanical, since the sprayed metal does not, as a rule, fuse with the base metal. Each tiny particle of molten metal while in transit from the spray-gun to the work is spherical in shape but flattens out and solidifies when it reaches the work of base metal.

There are several advantages of metallizing:

1. A faster rate of forming coatings as compared with electro-plating
2. Portable equipment so that it is possible to coat with metals those structures that are too large to treat by any other means except painting. Tank cars, storage tanks, turbines, dock-gates, etc. may be metallized without difficulty because of the portability of the equipment.

3. The ability to hard-surface shafts and other bearing surfaces that become worn down. Certain alloys, such as the nickel-base alloys containing boron and chromium may be sprayed onto the surface of such shafts for which a hard surface is desired, and then they may be melted and actually alloyed with the base metal by means of a torch, a furnace treatment, or by induction heating. Hard-surfaced shafts can be made to wear for years by such methods.

Although it is true that metallic coatings applied by means of a spray-gun are somewhat porous, in most cases this is not so much a detriment as an advantage; this porosity permits the retention of a suitable lubricant to a better advantage. In certain applications, the pores must be filled by subsequent heat treatment or by mechanical working.

17-9   Submerged-Arc Welding

This is a method whereby the electrode is shielded by means of a fluxing material applied to the electrode as a coating not only for the purpose of providing a flux but also for rendering it fusible at a lower rate than the rod itself, thereby excluding the atmosphere in the vicinity of the arc. Welds made by this process are freer from blowholes and are more dense and ductile.

In the submerged-arc welding process, a bare metal electrode is used, and an arc is formed between the electrode and the workpiece just as in normal arc welding. In this latter process, however, the area around the arc is entirely submerged in a finely crushed mineral that serves as the flux, and the entire process takes place submerged within this fluxing material. Since this crushed mineral-medium is a highly resistant conductive material when hot, a great deal of heat is generated by the resistance of conduction of this medium. Those instances requiring continuous and automatic operation are particularly suited to this submerged-melt process. Because of the problems of handling the powdered mineral-flux, the process is limited to horizontal welds; however; it is the means of cutting costs in such instances and results in high-quality welds.

17-10   Arc Welding with Inert Gas Shielding

There are two more important methods of arc welding where an atmosphere is provided to protect and shield the material being welded. These are the helium-shielded arc process and the atomic-hydrogen arc process. The arc in the atomic-hydrogen arc welding process is formed between two tungsten electrodes, and then molecular hydrogen is admitted to the arc through the electrode holder. Atomic hydrogen is formed by the dissociation of the molecular hydrogen in the arc; then molecular hydrogen is again formed by the recombining of the atomic hydrogen. A separate rod supplies the filler metal in those cases where required; however, atomic-hydrogen welding gives an oxide-free weld with excellent homogeneity. This process is used frequently in hard facing with tungsten carbide in lump form to assure a highly reducing atmosphere to prevent the formation of oxides of tungsten carbides. In fact, atomic-hydrogen welding is used for welding all materials which oxidize easily, although it is also used for other types of hard-surfacing as well. Since hydrogen itself is a reducer, it is not necessary to use a flux in atomic-hydrogen ard welding processes.

At times referred to as the "Heliarc" process, the helium-shielded process of welding consists of arc welding in an atmosphere of helium which is introduced into the arc through the electrode holder. Argon, another of the inert gases, is also used as a shielding gas. Such methods have been used satisfactorily in the welding of magnesium and other nonferrous alloys.

Gas Tungsten-Arc Welding

Gas-shielded arc welding using a tungsten (nonconsumable) electrode is referred to as "TIG" welding, indicating "tungsten inert gas" welding. Because of the increasing use of gases other than helium or argon in the shielding mixture, this term "TIG" is somewhat inaccurate. This method is used especially for joining relatively thin sections of strip, sheet, or light-wall tubing. The tungsten-arc electrode holder shown in Fig. 17–8a is often used for fusing the abutting edges of a square-groove weld to form a weld without the necessity of adding filler metal. The tungsten-arc holder can also be used effectively to fuse a joint in a heavier section and melt wire introduced to provide filler metal into the groove. The molten metal can be controlled to leave a solid weld joint that requires very little subsequent finishing.

The liberation of heat from the tungsten-arc operating in a protective gas shield is especially intense near the poles where steep voltage drops are present. When operated with direct current on straight polarity, approximately two-thirds of the heat is liberated at the base metal which is the anode. The decidedly lower heat liberation at the cathode is due to the fact that tungsten is a thermionic metal and a good electron emitter when at elevated temperatures and therefore minimizes the voltage drop at the cathode pole.

The three kinds of tungsten electrodes available for use in nonconsumable electrode welding are (1) pure tungsten, (2) thoriated tungsten, and (3) zirconiated tungsten. Since tungsten melts at approximately 6200F, the extreme tip of a pure tungsten electrode will melt superficially and form a molten ball that clings to the end with only little loss of tungsten because of its high boiling point (10,700F), unless the molten droplet becomes dislodged. Although the formation of the molten ball changes the shape of the tip of the electrode, causing the cathode spot to shift its location from time to time, this change in area of electron emission results in small, but significant, fluctuations in the temperature of the arc. To insure an electrode that will maintain a fixed shape at the tip and, therefore, a steady cathode spot, small additions of certain oxides such as thorium and zirconium are used to improve greatly the ease of electron transmission by reducing the thermionic work function. This is the amount of added energy required by an electron to permit it to escape from the surface. Electrons are provided more profusely to the welding arc, by the addition of a very small amount, as little as 1 or 2 per cent, of thoria or zirconia to the tungsten.

Weld metal formed by the gas tungsten-arc process can be remarkably clean and sound if the base metal and any added filler metal are killed steels. The welding conditions not only prevent any significant oxidation or nitrogen pickup, but also insure the elimination of many of the nonmetallic inclusions (dirt) in the base and filler metals.

Gas Metal-Arc Welding

This process is commonly referred to as "MIG" welding since it originated as a "metal inert gas" arc-welding operation; however, the users of the process also turned to gases other than inert argon or helium, and therefore, the term "gas metal-arc," as eventually adopted by the American Welding Society, is more nearly correct according to present-day practice. Shortly after the gas tungsten-arc process (nonconsumable electrode) proved so successful, attention was given to the development of a modification of the process that would provide filler metal for more efficient filling of a groove or joint. One of the early changes was simply to replace the tungsten electrode with a consumable metal wire to serve the dual role of the electrode and also the filler metal. This was not immediately successful, however, because the electrode wire melted off in large globules producing considerable spatter and an uneven weld bead. This was later found to be due to the welding current which in early experimentation was the same as used for normal arc welding with a given size of electrode wire. Later on, welding engineers discovered that if a much higher welding current was used, the electrode wire melted off as a steady spray or stream of tiny droplets of metal and formed a satisfactory weld deposit. Accordingly, a current-density transition point was determined for the various sizes and kinds of welding wire, and a commercially useful process was the result, still using the inert gas for shielding as before.

Gas metal-arc welding process ("MIG") using the metal, consumable electrode under the inert gas shield is shown graphically in Fig. 17–8b. In addition to changes in the nature of gases used for shielding, an important development in the technique of metal transfer has occurred. In addition to the "spray-type" arc which was in use for about ten years, it was found that the gas metal-arc process could be operated with a substantially different "shorting" or "droplet" type of metal transfer. This mechanism of transfer extends the range of usefulness of the process to much lighter thicknesses of base metal making it necessary to identify two distinctly different kinds of gas metal-arc welding. These are (1) spray-arc metal transfer, and (2) shorting-arc metal transfer. The first of these is based on the fact that for each combination of shielding gas and metal electrode a welding current density can be found above which a stiff, stable, relatively spatter-free arc will operate. The second method is the newer form of gas metal-arc welding, and it has been found particularly useful for welding thin base metal because a markedly lower heat input is generated during the deposition of weld metal. This is the fundamental change which results in the following operating advantages:

1. The penetration into the joint can be controlled to avoid excessive melt-through, even in light gages of sheet metal.
2. Deposits of weld metal can be made to bridge sizable gaps caused by poor fit-up of joints.
3. Welding is performed in all positions with equal ease.
4. Important changes in microstructures and properties in the heat-affected zone are held to a minimum.

For further information on TIG and MIG welding the student is referred to *Welding Handbook*, 5th edition, published by the American Welding Society, 1965, *Inert-gas Shielded Arc Welding of Ferrous Metals* by Gilbert R. Rothschild and Alexander Lesnewich; and also *Welding Metallurgy*, by George E. Linnert, 1965.

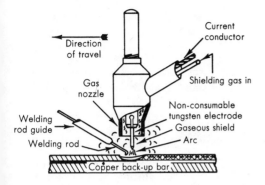

Fig. 17-8a.   *Diagrammatic sketch of gas tungsten-arc welding, "TIG," using a non-consumable electrode of tungsten with inert gas shielding.*

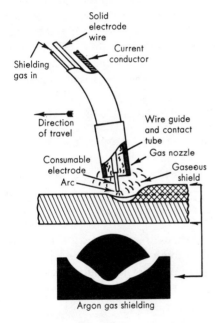

Fig. 17-8b.   *Gas metal-arc welding process, "MIG," using a consumable metal electrode under inert gas shield.*

17-11   Brazing and Soldering

Brazing and soldering are both fusion joining processes, and both are methods of uniting metals by means of a different metal. The joints in each case are made without pressure being applied, the joining metal being merely introduced into the joint in the liquid state and allowed to solidify. Both brazing and soldering are good for joining small assemblies, electrical parts, etc.

The brazing alloys are mainly the high-zinc brasses (Tobin Bronze) and also the nickel-zinc-copper alloys. In this process a nonferrous alloy in the liquid state is introduced between two pieces of metal to be joined and allowed to solidify. The filler metal has a temperature of over 800F melting point, but one that is lower than the melting point of the parent metal. The filler metal is distributed between the surfaces by capillary action. *Braze welding* is similar to conventional brazing, except that the filler metal is not distributed by capillary action. In both instances, special fluxes are required to give the filler metal the fluidity necessary to wet the joint between the surfaces completely. The brazing metals and alloys more commonly used are as follows:

1. Copper—melting point of 1982F
2. Copper alloys such as the brasses and bronzes with melting points of from 1600 to 2250F. Also the low-fusing bronze such as nickel-zinc-copper alloy and the high-zinc brass referred to as Tobin Bronze.
3. Silver alloys with melting points of from 1165 to 1550F
4. Aluminum alloys with melting points from 1025 to 1785F.

The procedure for brazing consists of first cleaning the joint of oil, dirt, and oxides and then fitting the pieces together with just the correct amount of clearance for the filler metal to enter. Chemical or mechanical cleaning may be necessary in addition to the flux used during the process (such as borax either used alone or with other salts). The strength of the brazing joint depends on the design of the joint and the brazing alloy selected for that design. The strongest joint results from a definite clearance between the parts being joined of about 0.0015 in. The strength obtained is more than double the strength of the brazing alloy being used. It is important to see that the gap is completely filled by the liquid brazing alloy. It is not essential or necessary to hold the temperature after the joint has been made.

There are three types of joints that are made:

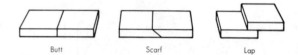

Fig. 17-9.   Butt   Scarf   Lap

The lap joint is used more than the others because it gives joints of high strength and good quality as to pressure-tightness. The more the area of the lap the greater the strength of the brazed joint. The shear-strength of lap joints is calculated by the equation:

$$T = LS$$

where T equals tensile strength of the weakest member, L equals length of the lap, and S equals shear strength of the brazing alloy. The amount of lap required can be calculated by the equation

$$L = \frac{FTW}{S}$$

where W equals thickness of weakest member and F equals the factor of safety incorporated.

Soldering differs from brazing in that lower temperatures of the filler metals are used (those with melting points below 800F) in the joints. Lead and tin alloys with melting points of from 300 to 700F are most commonly used as filler metal. The strength of the joint in soldering is determined by the adhesive qualities and strength of these alloys. Although any heating method that is used in brazing can be employed in soldering, much of the soldering is done with the common soldering iron especially on small parts and light gage metals. Heat is supplied by the iron, and solder is fed into the joint in the form of a stick or wire. Again, it is of utmost importance to have a good, clean joint surface, and a flux is also used. In soldering there is very little alloying by solid-state diffusion such as in brazing, so the strength depends mainly on the forces of adhesion between the two metals being joined and the filler material used.

Since soft-soldering is not as strong as brazing or welding alloys, it follows that joints do not have high mechanical strength. The most important use of soldering is the production of leakproof joints and joining metal parts where high electrical conductivity is essential. The lead-tin-base alloys are known as the "soft-solders." Those alloys with 50 per cent lead and 50 per cent tin are the most common. The alloys with appreciable amounts of silver are known as silver solders or "hard solders." However, the term "solders" is usually restricted to the soft solder with melting points under 850F.

17-12   Electron Beam Welding

The electron beam welding process is a fusion welding process in that the mechanism of welding is to join two or more pieces of metal by local melting, which results in coalescence. Filler metal and base metal, or base metal only, may be melted together to produce a joint.

The heat required for welding is produced by the bombardment of the work by a dense beam of high velocity electrons. That is, the electron beam is directed upon the area to be fused, and the electrons upon striking the surface of the metal give up their kinetic energy almost completely in the form of heat energy.

Since a vacuum in the order of $1 \cdot 10^{-4}$ mm Hg is needed to produce a stable electron beam, the welded joints are extremely pure and singularly free from absorbed gases. As a result, electron beam welding is uniquely suited for welding the refractory metals (tungsten, molybdenum, columbium, tantalum, etc.), the highly oxidizable metals (titanium, beryllium, zirconium, uranium, etc.), and also the vacuum melted alloys (M–252, Rene 41, Udimet 500, hastelloys, etc.) Any weldable metal or alloy, and possibly some ceramics, can be fused by means of the electron beam process.

In addition to welding by fusion, the process and equipment can also be used for melting, grain refining, stress-relieving, out-gassing, cutting, overlaying, metallizing, crystal-growing, vacuum brazing, etc. Containers enclosed by electron beam welding retain an internal vacuum when removed from the welding chamber.

Electron beam welding has many advantages over the older arts of joining metals including the following:

1. It is possible to weld otherwise almost impossible metals, both similar and dissimilar, such as those mentioned above. In addition the precious metals such as gold, silver, platinum, etc., and of course the stainless steels and refractory metals.

2. The welding is accomplished in a vacuum so that many of the metals that are highly reactive to oxidation can be joined and with satisfactory, strong welds.

3. Narrow and deep welds can be easily produced with the proper equipment with the desired high power density at electron voltages below 30 kv and without the inherent danger from radiation resulting from very high voltage systems.

Fig. 17–10 shows a typical electron beam gun column with the various components marked for identification. Fig. 17–11 shows the newest type electron gun developed by one large manufacturer of this equipment. The typical Sciaky electron beam welding system includes:

1. A vacuum chamber
2. A vacuum pumping system
3. An advanced design of electron gun
4. A special mechanism for remotely manipulating the electron gun without breaking the vacuum
5. A work table providing power translation motion
6. A work holding chuck providing powered rotational motion
7. A high voltage power supply
8. An electrical control system and panel.

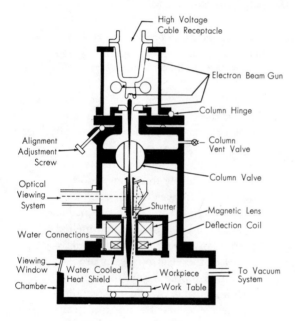

Fig. 17-10. *A Hamilton Standard Electron Gun Column showing the various components parts. (Courtesy Hamilton Standard Division of United Aircraft Corporation, Windsor Locks, Connecticut.)*

Fig. 17-11. *Electron Gun that achieves a desired high powered density at electron voltages below 30 kv without the inherent danger from radiation resulting from very high voltage systems. (Courtesy of Sciaky Bros., Inc., Chicago, Illinois.)*

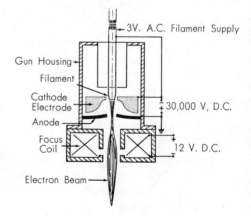

Fig. 17-12. *Electron Beam Welder with vacuum work chamber 52 in. by 36 in. by 36 in. in size with complete mechanical and electrical systems operated by one man as shown. (Courtesy of Hamilton Standard Division of United Aircraft Corporation.)*

Fig. 17-13. *Electron Beam Welder in service in the plant of a large manufacturer with vacuum work chamber and 6 kw electron gun. (Courtesy of Hamilton Standard Division of United Aircraft Corp.)*

17-13   Advantages of Electron Beam Welding

The added advantage of electron beam welding over the conventional types of welding is that the weld is accomplished so rapidly and in the vacuum; thus the heat generated in the conversion of kinetic energy into thermal energy takes place so quickly that there is little or no heat-affected zone, such as gives trouble with most other welding processes. This means much stronger welds and life-long reliability since the welds are free from oxidation and excessive heating.

Until recently electron beam welding has had one major drawback in that the welding had to be accomplished inside a vacuum chamber. This meant that the workpieces had to be small enough to fit inside the chamber. If the electron beam could be brought into the atmosphere, these restrictions could be removed. For several years, research engineers have been working to find some way to take the electron beam out of the vacuum chamber and operate it in a normal atmospheric environment. One large manufacturer has just built equipment which will weld 0.60 in. thick austenitic stainless steel on a continuous basis, and the welds are very similar to those made in a vacuum chamber. This would be a major achievement and will undoubtedly come soon as the engineers predict that they will be building a 25 kw unit capable of welding 3/4 in. wall steel pipe in a single pass at the rate of 100 in. per minute.

The electron beam welding units are not inexpensive; however, where a superior weld of metals and alloys that cannot be joined in any other way is required for any application, this process is without a peer. So important are the electron beam welding systems to the space program that the National Aeronautics and Space Administration has recently awarded a contract of considerable size to Hamilton Standard to design and build a hand-held electron beam welder that works in the vacuum conditions of space. The welder will join metals by firing a highly concentrated beam of electrons traveling 50,000 miles per second. Astronauts one day could conceivably use such a tool to repair and assemble spacecraft during prolonged flights.

Cylindrically-shaped, the portable part of the welder housing the electron gun, its electro-magnetic focusing lens, and a transparent shield through which the welding can be observed, will be 5 in. in diameter, 10 in. in length and will weigh 10 lb. A cable will connect it to a separate power supply designed to function in the earth's atmosphere or on board a spacecraft. The electron beam process promises to be very adaptable for space use because it normally works in a vacuum and is extremely fast so that very little heat goes into the welded metal. The hand-held welder will have a trigger to turn the electron gun's 1.5 kw beam power on and off. Weld tests are to be made on stainless steel, aluminum, and titanium alloys in thicknesses of less than 0.10 in. as the majority of the metals from which our spacecraft are made fall into this thickness range. The task in the development of such a small unit is that of miniaturization—the reduction of the size and weight of the essential components in order to be adaptable for spacecraft usage.

Recently, some very large structures have been electron beam welded successfully, and a development program by the engineers at the Space Flight Center, National Aeronautics and Space Administration, Huntsville, Alabama, indicates that the process will assume a primary role in the near future. Aluminum rings 23 ft in diameter are being welded in a split vacuum chamber which clamps around the joint and allows the work to protrude through rubber seals. These rings are 23 in. high, have a 4–1/2 in. maximum profile width, and are made of 2219 aluminum with the following analysis:

> Copper . . . . .6.50 per cent
> Manganese. 0.32
> Titanium 0.07
> Vanadium 0.12
> Zirconium 0.16

These large rings join cylindrical sections to end domes and skirts of fuel and oxidizer tanks for the S-1C stage of the Saturn V booster.

The electron beam system used in this application is rated at 30 kw and employs 1000 ma and 500 ma guns, each of them capable of traversing 32 in., for the making of butt welds. The interest in electron beam welding at the George C. Marshall Space Flight Center began while the Saturn vehicle was being designed, for it became apparent that there were only a few shops in the United States capable of machining some of the large shapes that would be necessary for the huge rocket. To adapt electron beam welding to the fabrication of the Y ring, however, a clamp-on vacuum chamber and a method for sealing around a complex configuration to maintain the vacuum had to be devised, along with a mobile electron gun and machining practice to obtain a good joint fit-up.

In the early tests, electron beam welding proved capable of producing a square butt joint in 2 in. thick aluminum with only one pass from one side. The resulting weld was only about 1/16 in. wide, yet it penetrated the full thickness of the 2 in. plate. One of the great advantages of the electron beam method is that it develops a very narrow heat affected zone and minimized shrinkage and distortion. Table 17–1 compares the electron beam welding technique with the inert gas metal arc process.

TABLE 17–1. Comparison of Welding Processes for Saturn S-IC Y Rings

Operations	Electron Beam	Inert Gas Metal Arc
Passes	2	100
Setup and welding time	8 hr.	80 hr
Filler material used	None	300 cu in.
Weld quality	Potentially high	Moderate
Depth-to-width ratio	19 to 1	1 to 5
Joint efficiency	75%	50%
X rays per joint	2	20
Welding speed	40 in. per min	4 in. per min

Welding parameters were studied and established with the knowledge that power is directly proportional to thickness of material being welded and on the basis that 2.4 in. thick 2219 aluminum requires 30 kw of power. As the weld was made, the variables were controlled by electronic circuitry. Machine settings depended on the change in the profile as the gun traversed the shape and on the variation in thickness. (Each of the four Y rings on the vehicle has a different thickness.)

As may be concluded from the above brief description of the welding of large structures by means of electron beam techniques, this method has a tremendous potential for many applications where high quality joints with a minimum heat affected zone are required.

17-14 Safety in Use of Electron Beam Equipment

Any time a moving electron is stopped, X radiation is generated. The penetrating power of the X ray generated is a function of the kilovoltage between the anode and cathode. Radiation standards require: "The shielding integrity of the machine shall not exceed 2 mrem per hour at any surface of the machine when it is operating at its maximum kilovoltage." Every precaution must be taken to shield the operator of the electron beam welding machine, including the selection of the material used for the vacuum chamber, the thickness of the same, and the sealing of every port and opening by means of "O" rings, tongue and groove joints, etc.

17-15   Non-Vacuum Electron Beam Welding

The necessity of having a vacuum chamber in which to do the electron beam welding has presented limitations on the application of this outstanding method of joining metals, as the size of the chamber is the limiting factor for this technique. Research is being carried on at this time, and prototype equipment is available for electron beam welding at atmospheric pressure which passes the beam from a thermionic electron source gun through a differentially pumped labyrinth. The beam then passes through a thin inert gas shield and into the weld area. Successful welds have been produced by at least two independent groups by this method. Equipment of this type is designed to operate at more than 100 kv. The main problem is projecting the electron beam through the inert gas and into the metal with minimal scattering produced by electron collisions with gas atoms which results in a reduction of power density and the power entering the weld.

The versatility of an electron gun that does not have to be operated in a large vacuum chamber and that will produce welds at atmospheric pressure is the incentive for continuing research in which some engineering students using this textbook may well participate and perhaps help to solve the problems involved. The ultimate in electron gun development is a portable gun for use in space, where the vacuum is much higher than that used in a chamber, for the assembly and repair of space vehicles. Extensive research is also being done in this area on a gun and power supply to provide components of light-weight and reduced size to permit easy maneuverability. This, too, is a challenging field in which young engineers of today will play an important part.

17-16   Filler Metals in Electron Beam Welding

Unlike the more conventional fusion welding processes, electron beam welding does not require the addition of filler metal in the weld seam. There are exceptions to this statement, particularly when dissimilar metals are joined together. In such cases, the filler metal shim strip can be preplaced between the abutting surfaces, or a filler wire feed system can also be used to supply metal to the joint. Filler wire feeders, such as those used for automatic TIG welding systems, are entirely satisfactory and require only minor installation innovations to permit their use.

When there is incomplete filling of the joint without filler wire, then its addition is necessary. Also, when it is necessary to add oxidizers, scavengers, or absorbants to prevent the formation of brittle intermetallics in the welding of dissimilar metals, it is imperative that filler wire additions be used.

17-17   Electron Beam Welding Cycle

A typical electron beam welding cycle would consist of loading a configuration to be welded in an appropriate welding fixture in the vacuum chamber. Assuming that all welding parameters have been established, the next step would consist of roughly aligning the weld seam beneath the electron gun. In cases where a movable gun system is employed, the gun carriage device is electromechanically "jogged" to move the gun into correct position. Where a fixed gun system is used, the weldment is electromechanically "jogged" transversely and or longitudinally into position beneath the fixed gun by moving the base carriage on which the welding fixture is resting or bolted. After the weld joint has been approximately aligned beneath the electron gun, the vacuum chamber door is closed and the chamber evacuated. As initial evacuation starts, a heavy white "cloud" forms inside the chamber but soon disperses. The visible "cloud" is caused by condensation of water-vapor within the chamber as the pressure drops. The automatic cycling of the roughing, diffusion, and holding pumps generally requires approximately 10 minutes, to attain a a vacuum within the chamber of $1 \cdot 10^{-4}$ mm of Hg. At this point, the electron beam may be started with no danger of filament contamination or high voltage flashover.

In those machines where no optical system is available, the electron beam energy is gradually increased in intensity until a definite small spot appears on the part to be welded. At that time, the gun or the part is then positioned over the center of the joint. If an optical system is used, the weld joint can be located with respect to a reference on a reticle in the eyepiece of the optics. This assures very accurate joint alignment with respect to the beam. One system permits continuous viewing of the weld through the optical telescope while another has a shutter that blocks the mirror while welding is progressing.

The welding cycle would then be continued by increasing the beam energy at the weld seam until a molten spot begins to appear, at which time the part or the gun is caused to traverse the entire length or circumference of the seam to be welded. In some instances, particularly on circumferential configurations, the part to be welded is in motion prior to increasing beam energy to obtain the best molten weld puddle. After the seam has been completely welded, most systems incorporate a current decay or beam energy down-slope cycle which is automatically initiated by the technician by pressing the appropriate button on the operator control panel. For longitudinal or other discontinuous welds, runoff tabs should be used to prevent "wash-out" on the ends of the weld.

After a required cooling down period (some metals and alloys have a very high oxidation rate if exposed to the atmosphere while at elevated temperature and must therefore remain under vacuum in the chamber for a predetermined period of time), air is admitted into the chamber to bring it up to atmospheric pressure and the workpiece and welding fixture are removed from the chamber. This completes the welding cycle.

17-18 Laser Welding

Laser welding is one of the most exotic of the new space-age processes. It is somewhat like welding with a white-hot needle in that it uses a carefully focused beam of light which concentrates tremendous amounts of energy on a small spot to produce fusion. The process is similar in many respects to electron beam welding, but has unique features that permit the welding of designs difficult to produce by any other process including the electron beam.

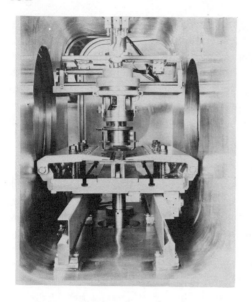

Fig. 17-14. *An electron beam welder with a view through the chamber showing the traverse carriage and electron beam gun. (Courtesy of AiResearch Manufacturing Div., The Garrett Corporation, Los Angeles.)*

Fig. 17-15. *Electron beam welding fixture for aid turbine wheel shaft assembly. (Courtesy of AiResearch Div., The Garrett Corporation, Los Angeles.)*

Fig. 17-16. *Piston assembly in a multiple fixture mounted within the chamber of electron beam welding machine as viewed through the port-hole just prior to welding. (Courtesy of AiResearch Div., The Garrett Corporation, Los Angeles.)*

Fig. 17-17. *Here is shown an idea of the versatility and range of the electron beam welder with the largest and smallest turbine assemblies being electron beam welded at AiResearch Div. They are approximately 16 and 3 in. in diameter respectively and are made of high nickel alloy for the wheels and steel for the shafts. (Courtesy of AiResearch Div., The Garrett Corporation, Los Angeles.)*

Fig. 17-18. *The electron beam welding of a heat exchanger with a full penetration type weld in AISI 347 stainless steel. (Courtesy of AiResearch Div., The Garrett Corporation, Los Angeles.)*

Fig. 17-19. *An enlarged view of the heat exchanger shown in Fig. 17–18 after it has been electron beam welded. This is the end cap unit and shows how small the weld is compared with what it would be if welded by some of the more conventional methods. (Courtesy of AiResearch Div., The Garrett Corporation, Los Angeles.)*

Fig. 17-20. *Test plates 9/16 in. thick made of 18 per cent nickel maraging steel that have been electron beam welded. Notice the very thin weld zone and negligible heat affected zone next to it. Diffusion is evident in the photo insuring a strong joint. 5.2X orig. mag. and 2X enlargement. (Courtesy of Sciaky Bros., Chicago, Illinois, builders of electron beam welding equipment.)*

This new technology is the result of the mastery of the light beam, and the word *laser* means "Light Amplification by Stimulated Emission of Radiation." In the field of metallurgy, it is already an accomplished fact that laser beams have been used for some time to cut and weld metal with a precision previously unattainable. In fact, lasers have made it possible to drill holes into steel with a diameter of only one micron.

The laser allows excellent control of heat input, and this accounts for most of the present applications—largely in aerospace and electronic industries. For example, it fuses metal adjacent to a delicate glass or ceramic seal without damaging the seal as shown in some of the photos that follow. It also welds close to varnish-coated wires without impairing the insulating characteristics of the varnish. It produces welds in heat-treated alloys without affecting the heat-treated condition any further than 0.010 in. from the weld. All this is done without chilling devices of any sort.

A major limitation of laser welding is the shallow penetration of the laser beam into metals. It will not weld materials thicker than 0.020 in. with typical present-day equipment; however, with certain joint designs and with improved laser equipment, this limitation will undoubtedly be overcome. At present almost every new application requires a new development program, and yet the process has proved that it provides reliable welds on a repetitive basis even on difficult-to-weld configurations. It has been accepted as a production tool for electronic packaging and soon will be a common method for joining major structural components of aerospace hardware.

17-19 Laser Welding Processes

This process focuses monochromatic light consisting entirely of a pure color into extremely concentrated beams. The heart of laser welding hardware is a high-purity rod, usually a ruby (trivalent chromium in aluminum oxide) which has seemed to be most promising. Fig. 17–21 is a laser welding unit with the various component parts identified. Fig. 17–22 is a diagrammatic sketch of the basic laser

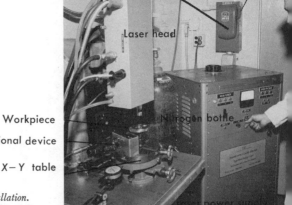

Fig. 17-21. *A conventional laser welding installation. The manipulator allows longitudinal and circumferential welds. (Courtesy of AiResearch Div., The Garrett Corporation, Los Angeles.)*

head system which is somewhat self-explanatory. The average duration of a laser weld beam is 0.002 sec. Because of the short duration, two basic welding methods are used. In one method, the workpiece is rotated or moved fast enough so that the entire joint is welded with a single burst of light. The other method uses many pulses of the laser to cover the joint. With the pulse technique, the weld is comprised of round, solidified puddles, each overlapping the previous one by about half a puddle diameter. The pulse method is the one most commonly used.

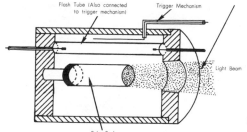

Fig. 17-22. *A simplified schematic of a ruby-rod type laser welding head.*

Most laser systems pulse an average of 10 times per sec, so that each point on the weld line melts and solidifies in microseconds. As a result, total energy input is small, and the workpiece does not get hot which means that there is little or no heat-affected zone such as experienced in all other processes with the exception of electron beam welding. Weldments can be held in the bare hand after laser welding. Just as with other fusion-welding processes, the workpiece can be moved beneath the energy source or the energy source can be made to move across or around the workpiece. Holding the laser head stationary is usually most economical. The laser beam is focused to a spot less than $100\,\mu$ in diameter, so the welding fixtures must track within this accuracy. However, when the parts to be welded are more than 0.010 in. thick, the tracking precision can be somewhat relaxed simply by changing the focus to produce a larger spot. A larger spot has less ability to penetrate.

Joint preparation requirements for laser welding are more stringent than for most other fusion-welding processes. The process is extremely intolerant of any oxides or foreign inclusions such as dirt, oil, greases, and even fingerprints. The reason is simple metallurgy as the weld puddle is at liquidus temperature for only about 0.001 sec. which is not enough time to vaporize and boil off impurities as other processes do.

17-20   Joint Design

In general, any joint can be laser welded if it can be fusion welded by any other process—except for the limitation on material thickness. The process is suitable for straight-line welds and for circumferential welds on cylinders. The drawings shown in Fig. 17–23 show typical joint designs used with laser welding. The flange joint is especially suited to laser welding and is particularly useful for closure welds where header materials include ceramic or glass feed-through seals and where header materials are thick. To join thick materials, a lip must be machined into the flange because the laser cannot penetrate deeply into the metal. An important advantage

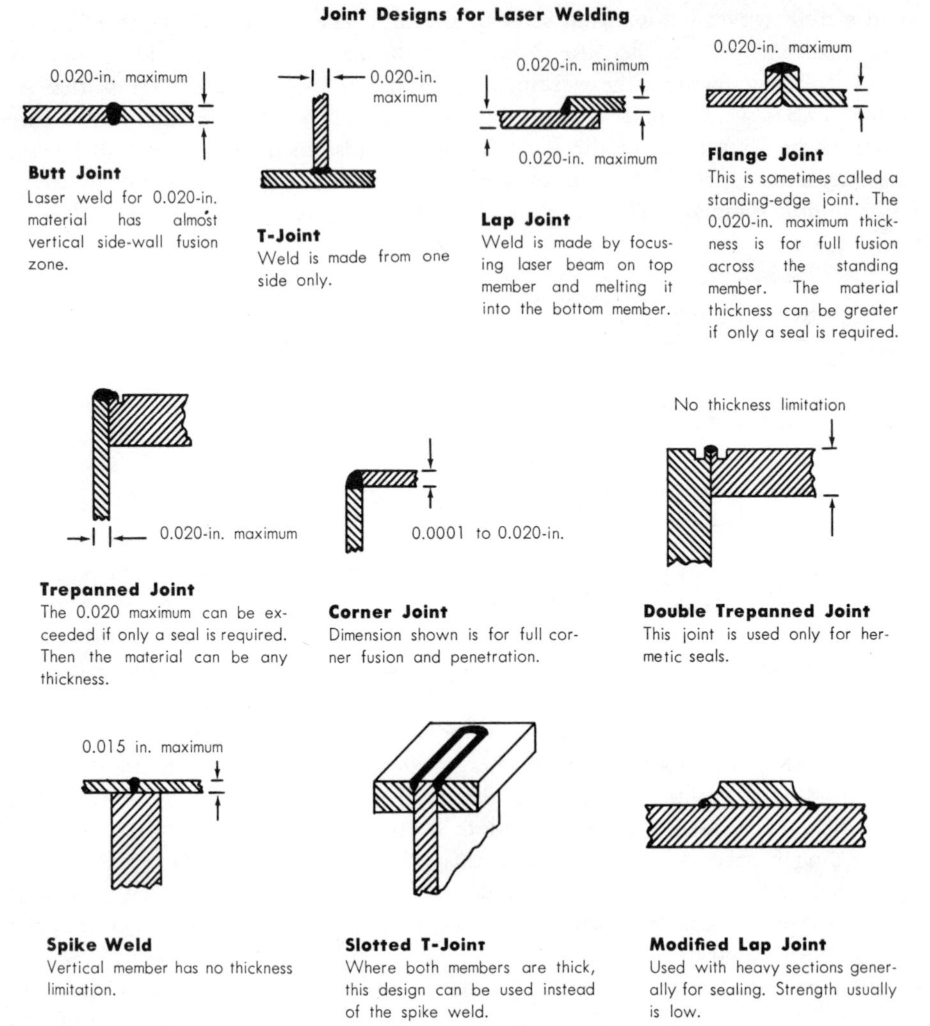
Joint Designs for Laser Welding
0.020-in. maximum
Butt Joint
Laser weld for 0.020-in. material has almost vertical side-wall fusion zone.
0.020-in. maximum
T-Joint
Weld is made from one side only.
0.020-in. minimum
0.020-in. maximum
Lap Joint
Weld is made by focusing laser beam on top member and melting it into the bottom member.
0.020-in. maximum
Flange Joint
This is sometimes called a standing-edge joint. The 0.020-in. maximum thickness is for full fusion across the standing member. The material thickness can be greater if only a seal is required.
0.020-in. maximum
Trepanned Joint
The 0.020 maximum can be exceeded if only a seal is required. Then the material can be any thickness.
0.0001 to 0.020-in.
Corner Joint
Dimension shown is for full corner fusion and penetration.
No thickness limitation
Double Trepanned Joint
This joint is used only for hermetic seals.
0.015 in. maximum
Spike Weld
Vertical member has no thickness limitation.
Slotted T-Joint
Where both members are thick, this design can be used instead of the spike weld.
Modified Lap Joint
Used with heavy sections generally for sealing. Strength usually is low.

Fig. 17-23. *Typical joint designs used in laser welding.* (*Courtesy of AiResearch Div., The Garrett Corporation, Los Angeles.*)

offered by the laser welding process is its ability to "reach" into recesses to make welds at the bottom of deep cavities, which is difficult or impossible with all other welding methods except the electron beam process.

17-21 Materials Joined by Laser Welding

The materials which can be joined by laser welding are about the same as those joined by electron beam processes, the only difference being in the joining of dissimilar metals. Here, the electron beam is excellent, but the laser is even better. Also, an added advantage is the fact that the laser does not need the protection against atmospheric contamination that is required by electron beam processes. Aluminum and aluminum alloys are weldable by the laser process, including alloys 7075 and 2024, which are not considered easily weldable even by the tungsten inert-arc welding process. Other nonferrous alloys such as copper, Monel, brass, and bronze are also easily welded by the laser.

All 300 series stainless steels are weldable—even alloys with high sulfur content such as 303. Although sulfur-stringers develop in welds in the high-sulfur alloys, the stringers do not cause cracks as they do with the electron beam and other fusion welding processes. The conventional 400-series stainless steels such as AISI 410, for example, offer no problems for laser welding, and alloys steels such as AISI 4130 and 4340 also are readily weldable. Both the laser and electron beam processes are ideal for the precipitation-hardening stainless steels such as 17–7 PH, 17–4 PH, and 15–7 Mo because both processes produce minimum heat-affected zones that are troublesome in welds made by most of the other fusion welding processes. The reactive and refractory alloys such as titanium, zirconium, molybdenum, tungsten, and columbium are weldable by laser beam. Furthermore, with laser welding, these alloys do not require special protection against atmospheric contamination.

17-22 Costs of Laser Welding

Equipment costs for laser welding are considerably less than those for an electron beam facility. The principal saving results from the fact that the laser process requires no vacuum chamber and pumping equipment. The accessory items cost about the same for both systems. A typical electron beam gun costs about the same as a typical laser head, but welding operators must be careful not to damage the ruby rod in the laser system. It costs about $1000 to replace. Fixture costs are slightly higher for electron beam welding because the larger heat input tends to distort the workpiece being welded. Distortion must be minimized to maintain precision tracking under the welding head. In fact, the low heat imput with laser welding allows tools to be made of wood and other nonmetallics. The typical power source for laser welding is a conventional capacitor-discharge, stored-energy system which is much less costly than the high-voltage power sources typically used with the electron-beam process. There are many jobs a laser does well, and making welds is one of them. Like all processes, it excels in some jobs but cannot handle others.

(The author is indebted to Kenneth J. Miller, President of Metals Joining Corporation, Redondo Beach, California, and to Joseph D. Nunnikhoven, Senior Welding Engineer, AiResearch Mfg. Div., Garrett Corporation, Los Angeles, California, for photos and resource material furnished for this section of Chapter 17.)

17-23 Ultrasonic Welding

In the *ultrasonic welding* process, the welder converts electrical energy to high-frequency mechanical vibrations. These vibrations are delivered to the parts being welded in such a way that dynamic stresses are induced in a limited area near the interface between the workpieces. When these dynamic stresses reach sufficient intensity, they cause local plastic deformation of the interface material in such a way that adhered moisture, organic, and oxide films are broken up and dispersed. The irregularities of the original interface material surfaces are also eliminated in order to create an area of intimate nascent metal contact. This results in a true metallurgical bond, formed in the solid state, with no melting of the materials being joined.

Because ultrasonic welding is a solid state process, it has many advantages including the following:

1. Thermal degradation of the materials being joined is practically eliminated.
2. Close dimensional tolerances in assembly can be obtained because thermal distortion does not occur.
3. Brittle, high-resistance intermetallic compounds are not formed during welding as often occurs with other welding processes.
4. A wide variety of dissimilar material combinations can be joined.
5. Very small parts and wires can be welded to each other and to very large component parts with ease.
6. No filler metal or fluxes are required.
7. Costly precleaning, postcleaning, or other treatments are not required as a rule.
8. There is no arcing, outgassing, or other contaminations of the workpieces.
9. No closed circuit through the weldment is required, since no electric current passes through the joint.
10. High yields can be obtained in complex electronic assembly operations.

Shown in Fig. 17–26 is a ring-spot ultrasonic welding equipment for metal container packaging and for structural joint applications. It is particularly suitable for encapsulating materials where true hermetic sealing is required, especially where the temperature rise associated with fusion welding is intolerable. The equipment may be controlled manually, or automatically sequenced as desired.

Fig. 17-24. *A dramatic photo of a high energy density laser pulse (0.002 sec) impinging on a 7075 aluminum alloy. (Courtesy of AiResearch Mfg. Div., Garrett Corporation, Los Angeles.)*

Fig. 17-25. *A few typical welds made by the laser beam including t-joint, circumferential, glass seal-weld, and power transistor. (Courtesy of Metals Joining Corp., Redondo Beach, California.)*

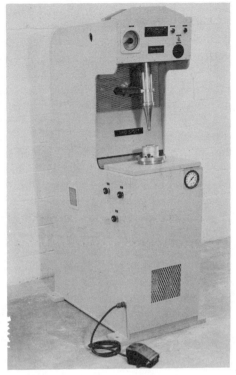

Fig. 17-26. *Ring-spot ultrasonic welder. (Courtesy of Sonobond Corp. a subsidiary of Aeroprojects, Inc.)*

Fig. 17-27. *A closeup of the ultrasonic ring-spot welder. (Courtesy of Sonobond Corp., a subsidiary of Aeroprojects, Inc.)*

17-24   Explosive Welding

The fastest growing application of chemical explosives as a fabrication energy source is for explosive welding. In this process, a chemical high explosive charge is used to impinge the mating surfaces together at very high velocities and under extremely high pressures. Once the dynamic parameters of the collision have the proper relationship, the surface films and perhaps a small amount of the substrate are, for a very short period of time, subjected to a very high energy density pulse which compresses these layers under essentially adiabatic conditions. From the laws of physics it is known that the effective temperature of these layers will reach a very high level permitting them to become mobile. Where the collision has been made to occur so that an angle is created between the impinging surfaces which preceeds along the interface, the mobile surface films are extruded into the area ahead of the closure angle and ultimately are ejected from the interface leaving behind film-free surfaces in intimate contact. This procedure is essentially, for all practical purposes, a highly efficient cold welding technique, and as such, it is essentially independent of the usual welding or bonding requirements of fusion or diffusion across the interface.

As was stated in a previous chapter, it has long been generally agreed that where two metal surfaces, completely free of surface films, are brought into sufficiently intimate contact, a metallurgical bond or weld will take place. The nature of the interatomic or intermolecular attractions across the interface are essentially the same as those in the component materials being joined.

A large number of alloy combinations have been explosively welded successfully including the following:

> 4330 steel to Ta-10 per cent W alloy
> Zircaloy to Inconel
> Be-Cu to Be-Cu
> Aluminum to aluminum
> Titanium to Inconel X
> Steel to steel
> Copper to steel and stainless steel
> Magnesium to magnesium
> Stainless steel to stainless steel.

From present indications it is apparent that most metallic systems can be metallurgically welded using explosive techniques so long as they possess sufficient ductility to withstand the explosive shock.

17-25   Characteristics of Explosive Welding Affecting Applications

1. Welds can be produced between incompatible materials which have properties equal to the weaker of the base materials.
2. Properly produced explosive welds do not have heat affected zones or cast metal structures.
3. Welds can be produced between highly cold-worked materials without affecting their mechanical properties.

4. Large surfaces, such as those between concentric tubes, can be metallurgically bonded.
5. In many instances, the explosives themselves are the only equipment, tooling, and energy source required making explosive welding systems compact, lightweight, and independent of supporting services.
6. Elaborate surface preparation of the components is not generally required.

It will be observed from the above list that there are at least three application criteria which would recommend consideration of explosive welding techniques. The first of these is where metallurgically incompatible alloys must be joined. In this situation there are often few or no alternatives that will satisfy the service requirements of the weldment. A second circumstance would be where the properties of the components to be joined are, in part, the result of cold-work or heat treatment, and it is inconvenient or impossible to treat the components after joining so that again there may be few or no other alternatives. The third situation is where remote fabrication might be required, i.e. where the weld is inaccessible or a logistic problem exists. An example of the latter case would be an inaccessible joint in a complex plumbing assembly of a rocket engine so that welding in outer space might represent a situation presenting a logistic problem. Although there is still a great deal of reseach and development ahead, it is a certainty that explosive welding will eventually develop into an increasingly valuable tool in the joining of materials in the years ahead.

17-26 Adhesive-bonding of Materials **

Adhesive-bonding is a rather new technique and development of an old art that was used by aircraft manufactures in the days of early plywood planes. The use of structural adhesives for joining metallic airframes and members began with the development of better and more satisfactory thermosetting resin and rubber adhesive combinations in the early 1950's. This combination of resin and rubber resulted in an adhesive after curing with the high strength of the thermosetting resin and the resilience and vibration resistance of the rubber. By this means the joining of metal-to-metal bonded components of aluminum, titanium, and magnesium is possible. Convair's B58 is an outstanding example of structural adhesive bonding as it has adhesive-bonded structures on 95 per cent of its surface area. Furthermore, the B58 is one of the first manned aircraft to use adhesives in its primary structures.

There are many reasons for the increasing interest and use of structural adhesives; they produce continuous bonds which distribute stress loads evenly over the entire joined area, local stress concentrations are eliminated, and joints of greater strength and rigidity are produced. This permits the use of thinner materials. Adhesives are flexible and this, along with uniform distribution of stresses, improves resistance to vibrational fatigue and permits the transfer, distribution, and absorption of these stresses. Dissimilar metals can be joined with adhesives. Acting as a continuous insulating barrier between the two metals, the adhesive minimizes galvanic corrosion and corrosion from moisture trapped between surfaces.

** For more information on Adhesives, see Chapter 19.

17-27   Selecting the Adhesive

The type of bonding material to be used is governed by the function of the completed structure. Factors to consider include bond strength (shear, tensile, cleavage, peel), aging characteristics (service life), fabrication techniques, application procedures, equipment for fabrication, and cost. The ability of the adhesive to resist oxidation and to retain greater strength than the stresses produced by flexural or compressive loading are also very important in many instances.

There is no all-purpose bonding agent (adhesive) for every design and service requirement. Structural adhesives are formulated to produce a balance of properties with emphasis on certain features. Four basic factors should be considered when selecting a suitable adhesive:

1. *The materials being joined.* The adhesive must be one which will wet the surface and have the required adhesion to the surfaces being bonded.
2. *The requirements of the job.* The initial shear, tensile, cleavage, and peel strength requirements are important. Also, the ability of the adhesive to withstand weathering, moisture, chemicals, temperature differences, and fatigue should be considered. Adhesives should not be expected to do what the structure cannot do; the one chosen must provide a bond with adequate strength to permit the structure to perform the functions for which it is designed.
3. *The design of the joint.* The joint should be designed to take full advantage of the properties of the adhesive. Adhesives seldom display their best properties when substituted directly for other fasteners.
4. *The cost of the adhesive.* This involves preparation for use in the bonding operation, waste, personnel needed for inspection and production, and also the adaptability of present bonding equipment. The equipment and means available to produce bonds of the desired performance levels are important selection factors. For economical production, the method of application, time and temperature involved, and speed of curing must be well chosen.

17-28   Types of Structural Adhesives

Thermosetting structural adhesives are made in the form of solvent solutions and of dry films having controlled thickness and width. The films (elastomer resins) are placed on a nonadhering liner and stored in rolls. When properly stored, these films remain stable and usable for long periods.

Film adhesives offer many design and cost-saving advantages, such as uniform thickness throughout the joint, confinement of cement to the immediate bonding area, and a clean and simple operation. This material does not contain a solvent—which eliminates fume disposal and drying problems. Film adhesives are available in varying thicknesses and widths and can be die-cut into complicated shapes. They give the best compromise of shear strength, peel strength, shock and fatigue resistance. Film adhesives adhere well to metals and plastics and offer good flexibility, impact strength, vibration absorption, and other properties as listed in Table 17–2. Many of them have excellent resistance to fuels, lubricants, humidity, and salt spray. Depending on the application and formula, certain of these films can be used for high strength bonding applications at temperatures as low as −80F.

In some instances, shear strengths of 7200 psi have been achieved at −67F. Generally, these materials can be used in continuous service up to 250 to 300F. Some films (especially modified elastomeric phenolics) withstand moderate stresses at temperatures as high as 500F for short periods.

TABLE 17–2. Properties of Typical Structural Adhesives * **

Type of Adhesive	Overlap Shear Strength, Psi†					Peel Strength at 75 F (Lb/in. Width)	Optimum Cure		
	−67 F	75 F	180 F	300 F	400 F		Time, Min	Temperature, F	Pressure, Psi
Thermosetting Films‡									
A	3700	3000	1700	700	50	50 to 70	60	350	150
B	2800	3800	2800	2100	1050	20 to 50	60	350	150
C	7300	6000	3600	500	200	80 to 110	60	350	25
Liquid Adhesives—One-Part, Heat Curing									
D	3000	5500	4600	700	200	8 to 10	30	350	Contact
E	2600	2600	3800	2500	300	3 to 5	60	350	Contact
F	3500	5500	5300	800	475	8 to 10	60	350	Contact
Liquid Adhesives—Two-Part, Room Temperature Curing							Days		
G	1500	2800	700	—	—	3 to 5	7	75	Contact
H	1400	2300	800	150	—	4 to 5	7	75	Contact
I	1600	2700	600	410	—	4 to 5	7	75	Contact

* Courtesy of *Materials in Design Engineering*, published by Reinhold Publishing Co., New York.
† Tested per MIL-A-5090D.
‡ 10 mils thick before being cured.
** For more information on Adhesives, see Chapter 19.

Thermosetting film adhesives require heat and pressure to accomplish the bond. Pressure brings the metal parts into contact and helps contain the volatile by-products of the curing reaction. If pressure is not maintained, this vapor will cause a porous bond. When cured under pressure, film adhesives soften to a semifluid state and wet the surfaces they contact. Pressure applied uniformly to the part as the bond line heats to 180F forces the adhesive (in its thermoplastic state) to flow wet and fill small mismatched areas. Depending on the rate of heat input to the bond line and the composition of the adhesive, pressures of 25 to 150 psi are required.

High strength adhesives are being used in many ways in structural applications to improve product performance and reduce costs. The aircraft industry is probably the largest single customer—thermosetting adhesive films bond leading and trailing edges of wings, helicopter rotor blades, and primary and secondary structural components such as bulkheads, floors, rudder and aileron members. High strength structural adhesives play a vital role in sandwich construction both in the assembly of core materials, such as aluminum honeycomb, and in the attachment of metal skins to the cores. Wings, speed capsules and honeycomb control surfaces of the Convair 990 jetliner are assembled and sealed with high strength film adhesives.

QUESTIONS

1. Why has so much importance been placed on the joining of metals?

2. Upon what metallurgical bonding mechanisms does the entire field of joining separete metallic components depend?

3. The basic mechanism of metallurgical bonding of metals makes it mandatory that the metals to be joined comply with what specific characteristics?

4. Under these specific conditions referred to in the previous question, upon what factors does the strength of the joint depend?

5. At times, as required, what is done to the parts that have been joined by one of the several processes enumerated? Why?

6. Under what conditions is it possible to join metals with good firm joints? Is this true for dissimilar as well as similar metals?

7. What are the three important zones in welds? Why are they important? Which zone is the most important? Why is this true?

8. Discuss the heat-affected zone as related to the composition of the materials being joined.

9. Discuss the importance of the selection of the correct welding rod to be used in fusion welding.

10. Give a description of the arc-welding process including the real basis for this type of joining metals.

11. Draw a curve such as might be taken from a standard arc welding generator so far as the voltages and amperages are concerned.

12. Upon what factors does the success of making a sound joint with the arc welding depend, keeping costs in mind?

13. What are some of the advantages of arc welding over gas welding?

14. In arc welding what safety precaution must be taken? Why?

15. By means of charts and equations, describe and discuss the gas welding process in general, using oxygen and acetylene as the gases.

16. Although acetylene was discovered in 1836, why was it that it was not widely used until 1892?

17. Describe the two important gases, oxygen and acetylene, as to their source, properties, characteristics, etc.

18. State the chemical reaction for the complete combustion of oxygen and acetylene. Why is this not the one that is used in oxyacetylene welding since it has the hottest known flame from gases of 6,200°F?

19. What is the most suitable mixture of oxygen and acetylene for oxyacetylene welding and heating? Why is this true?

20. State the advantages of the oxyacetylene process for heating and welding over other fusion welding processes.

21. Define and describe thermit welding and state when it is used to best advantage.

22. Discuss *metallizing* including the equipment required, advantages, and limitations.

23. What is the submerged-arc process of welding? What distinct advantage does it have over some of the other processes of welding?

24. Describe the atomic-hydrogen process of welding and state when it is particularly suitable. What flux is best to use in this process?

25. What is the principal difference between brazing and soldering?

26. Name some of the more commonly used brazing metals and alloys and tell for what purposes they are particularly suited.

27. Discuss the three types of joints that are made in brazing using sketches of each as well as the method of calculating the shear-strength of the lap type joints.

28. In the soldering of joints, upon what factors does the strength of the joint depend?

29. What is the most important use of soldering in industry? What are the solders termed "soft-solders" and "hard-solders"?

30. Draw a sketch of the electron beam welding gun and discuss the process.

31. Name some of the many advantages of electron beam welding over other conventional fusion welding processes. What are some of the limitations of electron beam welding?

32. What do the letters L A S E R stand for? Briefly describe the laser beam welding process giving its advantages and limitations.

33. Because of the short duration of the laser weld beam, two basic methods of welding with lasers are used. What are they?

34. Are there any limitations as to the joint design in laser welding? If so, explain.

35. How do costs of equipment and production compare between the electron beam and laser welding?

36. What is the basis of ultrasonic welding? In what fields does it find its most useful applications at present?

37. What are a few of the advantages of ultrasonic welding over some of the conventional methods? Basically, why are these advantages possible?

38. Describe the explosive welding process and state the characteristics of the process that affect its applications.

39. Why are adhesives important in metal joining?

40. What four basic factors must be considered when selecting suitable adhesives for structural applications?

41. Discuss the types and properties of structural adhesives.

References

Anderson, J. E., *Laser Welding*. Detroit, Michigan: University Research Conference, May 6, 1964.

Crane, T. H., *A Commercial Electron Beam Welder*. New York: American Welding Society, 1959.

Dobratz, B. E., R. S. Congleton, and W. R. Sooy, *Dynamic Limitations on the Attainable Inversion in Ruby Lasers*. New York: Columbia University Press, Proceedings of the Third International Congress on Quantum Electronics, 1964.

Harper, M. E. and E. G. Nunn, "Electron Beam Welding," *The Welding Journal*. New York: American Welding Society, 1963.

Hess, E. F., "Adhesives for Fabricating High Strength Structures," *Metal Progress*. Metals Park, Ohio: American Society for Metals, June 1963.

Lander, H. J., and W. T. Hess, *Electron Beam Welding of Rocket Cases*, Alloyd General Corporation, Medford, Mass. 1961.

Lincoln Electric Company, Gorham Woods (ed), *Procedure Handbook of Arc Welding Design and Practice*. Cleveland, Ohio: 1961.

Miller, Kenneth J. and J. D. Nunnikhoven, *Laser Welding*. AiResearch Manufacturing Division of The Garrett Corporation, Los Angeles, 1964.

Miller, Kenneth J. and T. Takenaka, "Electron Beam Welding," New York: *Bulletin for Welding Research Council No. 100*, October 1964.

Morris, Joe L., *Welding Principles for Engineers*. Englewood Cliffs, New Jersey: Prentice Hall, Inc., 1951.

Platte, W. N., and J. F. Smith, *Laser Techniques for Metals Joining*. New York: Supplement to the *Welding Journal*, Nov. 1963.

Reich, Sherman, *Laser (Optical Maser) Beam Fusion Welding*. Interim Engineering Progress Report No. IR-7-985 (VII), ASD Project No. 7–985, U.S.A.F., May 1964.

Rossi, Boniface E., *Welding Engineering*. New York: McGraw-Hill Book Company, 1954.

Schawlow, A. L., "Infrared and Optical Masers," New York: *The Solid State Journal*, June 1961.

Shell Chemical Company, "Epoxy Tape Adhesives Provide High Strength with Low Heat Cure," Adhesives Division, Pittsburg, California from *Materials in Design Engineering*, February 1966.

Schwinghamer, Robert J., *Laser Welding*, Huntsville, Alabama, NASA George C. Marshall Space Flight Center, 1965.

Snitzer, Edward E., *Neodymium Glass Laser*. Southbridge, Massachusetts: American Optical Co., U. S. Army Research Office. 1964.

Udin, Harry, E. R. Funk, and John Wulff, *Welding for Engineers*. New York: John Wiley & Sons, Inc., 1954.

Welding Handbook, New York: American Welding Society, 1950.

Use of Computers
in Metallurgy

18-1 Applications of Computers
to Metallurgical Problems

The first industrial revolution was a consequence of the great extension of man's capabilities through his discovery of methods for converting the chemical energy stored in fossil fuels to mechanical and electrical energy. We are now entering a second industrial revolution, with the appearance of the stored-program electronic digital computer.

The computer provides a powerful tool in the programming and solving of complex abstractions, constituting an invaluable aid in the area of logical problem solving. However, the role of the computer is not confined to providing support in solving mathematical and nonmathematical problems. Coupled with other machines and processes, computers become flexible and comprehensive task performers with a scope vastly exceeding machines and processes. The word *cybernetics* is used to describe the emerging technology born of this marriage of the machine, processes, and the computer.

The use of computers by the metallurgical engineer is a reality of today, not a dream of tomorrow. Several metallurgical applications of computers will be discussed in this chapter. Engineering students in our colleges and universities are increasingly required to take courses in computer uses and applications. It has been said that within five years computer courses will be required for graduation from every engineering school in the country. The practicing engineer of today would be wise to take advantage of the courses offered by universities on the capabilities, potential usefulness, and actual practical uses of the computer. In Chapter 16 was outlined the uses of the computer in numerically controlling industrial machines by programming and putting on tape all of the machining information required for particular applications. There are many scientific and research applications in which the computer saves many man-hours and turns out high-quality products answers, including countless applications in the metallurgical field.

18-2 Studies of Solidification Patterns in Steel Castings Using the Computer

Design engineers in foundries are faced with the difficult problem of designing castings that are shrinkage-free on the first run. At the present time many high-quality steel castings are evaluated, as to design, by destructive or nondestructive inspection techniques, i.e., X ray, ultrasonic tests, magnetic particle inspection, sectioning, etc., as discussed in Chapter 12. Most of these inspection tests, however, are after the fact, for if the casting fails these tests, it must be redesigned and reproduced until the required acceptance standards are met. Although this trial and error method can sometimes be justified in the production of small castings, this technique involves considerable expense for the manufacturer of large, high-quality castings. For this reason, methods of predicting casting soundness in advance by means of the computer are desirable, if not imperative.

The solidification of steel castings is affected by a number of variables, including section size, shape, alloy composition, pouring temperature, chill distribution, sand conductivity, density, specific heat, the heat of fusion, etc. For several years the foundry department of General Electric Company has been developing a computer method by means of which all of these pertinent variables are used to predict solidification patterns during the freezing of a casting. The ability of the computer, analog or digital, to predict casting soundness by analysis of solidification patterns depends to a large extent upon the thermal properties of the metal and mold materials used as input data. The solving of such problems has been approached by both analytical and approximation methods, and there has been a great deal published about these in studying the solidification of castings. The analytical methods attempt to study the process of solidification through analysis of exact heat-transfer equations. These equations, however, in their most general form, are almost impossible to solve, and simplifying assumptions, such as one-dimentional solidification, constant interface temperature, semi-infinite mold wall thickness, and thermal properties which do not vary with temperature, must be made. The result is that their application, while valuable, is limited, and the answers are subject to errors introduced by the several assumptions required.

Graphic and numerical approximation, on the other hand, has received wider usage in recent years because these techniques can provide solutions to many problems unsolvable by analytical methods. Basically, the geometry of the problem is divided into nodes and equations describing the flow of heat from one node to the next, written and solved for small increments of time by means of known thermal properties, node size, and boundary conditions. This method can handle problems in two-dimensional heat flow and those where heat of fusion is involved. Even some variation of material properties concerned with temperature, can be taken in account, but the corrections required are complicated, and, indeed, a considerable amount of labor is needed.

By combining the principles of numerical approximation with the ability of the digital computer to rapidly solve many equations simultaneously, J. G. Henzel, Jr., and J. Keverian, both affiliated with the Applied Research and Development

Laboratory of the General Electric Foundry in 1964, wrote a paper stating that their company had designed a general transient heat transfer program of even greater versatility, speed, and accuracy than was previously possible. Their method of formulating the necessary network for the finite difference equations was to divide manually the geometry of the problem into nodes, and to supply the dimensions of each node to the computer. By way of example, in their studies of the heat flow in a long insulated rod of square cross-section, they first divided it into cubicle nodes similar to the method described by G. M. Dusinberre in his paper on the "Numerical Analysis of Heat Flow," 1949 (McGraw-Hill).

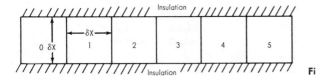

Fig. 18-1.

A heat balance may be expressed about node 2:

$$\text{rate heat accumulated in node 2} = \begin{pmatrix}\text{rate heat conducted}\\ \text{into node 2}\end{pmatrix} - \begin{pmatrix}\text{rate heat conducted}\\ \text{away from node 2}\end{pmatrix}$$

The corresponding basic equation describing this flow of heat is the Fourier equation. For one-dimensional heat flow this equation is as shown below:

$$(1) \quad \frac{\partial T}{\partial \tau} = \alpha \frac{\partial^2 T}{\partial x^2}$$

where

T = temperature

τ = time

α = thermal diffusivity = $\dfrac{K}{\rho C}$

K = thermal conductivity

ρ = density

C = specific heat

Computer analysis is typified by the finite difference technique. As a result Equation (1) must be rewritten in finite difference form:

$$\frac{\partial T}{\partial \tau} = \frac{T_2' - T_2}{\Delta \tau},\text{ where the prime indicates the unknown temperature after the time}$$

increment $\Delta \tau$ is finished.

and

$$\frac{\partial^2 T}{\partial X^2} = \frac{T_1' - 2T_2' + T_3'}{\Delta X^2},$$

The Fourier equation in finite difference form becomes:

$$(2) \quad \frac{T_2' - T_2}{\Delta \tau} = \alpha \frac{(T_1' - 2T_2' + T_3')}{\Delta X^2}$$

or when rearranged,

$$(3) \quad T_2' - T_2 = \frac{K}{\rho C}\frac{\Delta \tau}{\Delta X^2}(T_1' - 2T_2' + T_3').$$

This is one equation in 3 unknowns, which is of the form used in relaxation methods. Similar equations may be written about each node of the problem. The temperature T_2' is the unknown central node temperature which is used to replace T_2 after time increment $\Delta \tau$ is finished. Thus at the beginning of the transient, T_2 is known from the initial temperature distribution and T_2' is calculated from the system of simultaneous equations that are set up. At the end of the first time increment $\Delta\tau$, temperature T_2' just found will be substituted for T_2 as the known temperature for the second time step and is repeated until the temperatures at the node centers have been calculated for all desired times. Two programs are now available for solving solidification heat transfer problems. One program has a capability for solving 200 equations simultaneously with 30 time steps in less than 11 minutes. A second program can solve up to 1,000 equations in about 50 minutes.

For problems involving freezing, the above basic Fourier equation is modified to include the release of heat of fusion. The method of solution, however, remains the same.

To use these programs, the authors:

(1) Divide the geometry of the problem into a number of nodes.
(2) Specify the co-ordinate dimensions of each node on the computer input sheets.
(3) List the thermal conductivity, and specific heat of the node materials (sand, steel, etc.) as functions of temperature and
(4) State the boundary conditions as a function of time or temperature (i.e., shop wall temperature, flask surface heat transfer coefficient, etc.)

This information is then transferred from the sheets to key punch cards and used as input to the computer. The computer is programmed to calculate automatically the surface areas and volumes of the nodes, interpolate for the thermal properties listed, assemble a heat balance for each node, and apply an accelerated iteration technique to solve simultaneously a system of n equations in n unknowns. The output is printed out and lists the temperature at the center of each node for each time specified. By this method data are provided similar to that recorded by a thermocouple placed at the center of each node, allowing a path of the liquidus and solidus isotherms to be easily traced.

In order to obtain "effective" heat transfer properties of the steel and sand in question, basic thermal measurements are made in the laboratory, and cooling curves obtained throughout the steel; heating curves are also obtained for the sand surrounding the cylinder castings being studied. The THT (transient heat transfer) program is then used actually to calculate equivalent thermal curves, using thermal property data originally obtained from a study of the literature on the subject. In the analysis of the valve casting here in question, the closest agreement between calculated and measured data is found after some modification of the thermal properties of the sand in order to include the effects of moisture and air gap.

The chemical composition of this Cr-Mo-V Steel was:

Carbon	0.18 per cent
Manganese	0.60
Phosphorous	0.025 max.
Sulfur	0.015 max.
Silicon	0.40
Chromium	1.25
Molybdenum	1.00
Vanadium	0.22

(The analysis shown above is an average for several castings involved.)

The theory of a transient heat transfer (THT) digital computer program has been very briefly described above. Using this program the solidification pattern of a production steel valve casting was calculated and compared to measured data:

1. It has been shown that this program is capable of calculating solidification patterns in a production steel valve casting with reasonably accurate results, providing that the appropriate thermal properties are used.

2. It has also been shown that there is excellent agreement between calculated and measured cooling curves, during and after solidification.

3. The thermal arrest at 200F that occurs in dry-sand molds and cores because of residual moisture driven off by the casting heat wave, can be accurately simulated in a digital computer. Therefore, heating curves, even in partially moist dry-sand mold and cores, can be calculated with reasonable accuracy.

4. Air gap formation, occurring between the cast steel and a chill placed in the mold sand, can also be accurately simulated in a digital computer. Additional information, however, is needed in this area in order to correlate chill size and design, with corresponding air gap width.

5. It may also be said, in conclusion, that although still in its infancy, the digital computer is a powerful tool for analyzing and predicting solidification phenomena in steel castings. It should prove equally helpful in solving such problems in malleable iron, gray-iron, and nonferrous foundry operations.

18-3 Computing Charges for Electric Furnaces with the Computer

The necessity for knowing the most economical usage of material in producing alloy steel in electric furnaces led to the investigation of current practices using computers. The furnaces considered in this study are charged with cold materials, more than 90 per cent of it steel scrap, coming either from the companies' rolling mills or purchased from outside sources. Mill scrap (tops and bottoms of billets) is segregated according to alloy content. Grades containing chromium, molybdenum, and nickel (singly or in combination) are stored separately at the electric furnace shop, according to alloy content, when not needed currently. Chemical specifications for the steel to be produced dictate the amount of the various types of scrap to be charged, the melter adding cold pig iron to assure a satisfactory carbon content for proper working of the heat. He also makes up the balance of the metallic charge with scrap of carbon steel.

After the charge melts down, oxygen is blown into the bath to reduce the carbon to the desired level. Unfortunately, as the carbon content drops, desirable elements, such as manganese and chromium, oxidize and enter the slag. In order to investigate these losses, it was decided to study the conditions occurring during the oxygen blow, and special tests were made at the beginning, during, and at the end of several blows, the results analyzed to determine the losses incurred in carbon, manganese, and chromium. As shown in Fig. 18–1, the loss rate was different for each element. Inasmuch as alloy losses varied with the carbon level of the steel, it was necessary to separate the steel grades into low, medium, and high carbon in order to make proper mathematical analyses of each.

After the oxygen blow, a manganese reboil is used on most grades of alloy steel, to stabilize the bath before removal of the first slag. (Manganese deoxidizes the bath and helps lower the sulfur content.) If the specification permits, a predetermined amount (0.20 per cent) of manganese is added. The efficiency of this addition is about 60 per cent; therefore, it warrants separate consideration. After the reboil, the bath is slagged off. The oxidizing slag which results from the oxygen blow is removed from the furnace, and with it (in the form of oxides) the alloys are lost. The metal is then refined under a reducing slag. As a consequence, the efficiency of materials used to adjust alloy contents is high and consistent—95 per cent or more in the case of some materials. For this purpose standard ferroalloys and virgin metals (nickel and molybdenum) are used. The basic steps in the process briefly stated above are then expressed in basic linear program.

By means of linear programming, a mathematical technique, the levels of variables which optimize a given objective are determined. Optimizing equations include any necessary restrictions, and these are termed linear restrictions, or inequalities. Variables in the electric furnace process are the charge and additional materials used in making up an alloy heat. Restrictions and limiting conditions are chemical specifications, operating and metallurgical process requirements, and the available supply of materials. The objective is to determine the best combination of materials to make up a heat at a minimum of cost.

A model was set up and seven of the 26 equations in the model included inequalities which concerned scrap availability; each equation involved a different scrap. Two other material equations referred to the amount of pig iron and calcium silicon used. Various operating parameters, such as the chemical requirements of the specifications, chemical relationships among the elements, and other metallurgical restrictions, were included in 17 equations. In the first two, phosphorus and sulfur contents were limited by inequalities so that inferior scrap would be culled out at the start. Amounts of chromium, nickel and molybdenum in the charge were restricted to assure that melts which were out of specification would not be made because of scrap contamination. Restrictions on metallurgical practice were also incorporated, one equation fixing the carbon in the process so that the carbon from the charge materials would be high enough to meet that required in the melt. Carbon remaining after the oxygen blow was regulated (in another equation) to meet the specified objective. The rest of the equations were concerned with alloy contents and requirements.

Models for low and high carbon alloy grades are similar to the model for medium carbon grades described above. Equations are formulated to make more scrap types available to the low carbon grades, and less to the high carbon grades. Regardless of the extent of scrap availability, material selection is made on a basis of cost; therefore, cost equations are included in the models.

The computerized programs mentioned above have resulted in many improvements in electric furnace operation and practice. It is now possible to determine

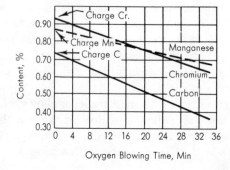

Fig. 18-2. *During oxygen blows, baths of molten steel lose carbon, chromium and manganese at different rates. The above chart depicts loss of elements as computed for melting AISI 4340 steel. (Courtesy of Materials in Design Engineering, August, 1965, published by Reinhold Publishing Company, New York.)*

Table 18-1. Material Usage Combinations, AISI 4340 Heat of Steel

Run	1	2	3	4	5	6	7	8	9	10	11	12	13
Charge, Lb													
043 Scrap	155,191	100,000	60,000	40,000	20,000								
086 Scrap		69,000	119,000	139,671	159,099	178,528	120,000	80,000	40,000	20,000			
041 Scrap							56,213	97,661	137,309	157,133	176,956		
051 Scrap	27,700	12,359	1,240									178,178	
001 Scrap													174,128
Pig iron	10,000	10,000	10,000	10,000	10,000	10,000	10,000	10,000	10,000	10,000	10,000	10,000	10,000
Coke	92	168	222	245	267	288	290	291	292	293	293	111	476
Nickel		1,255	2,164	2,660	3,167	3,674	4,226	4,604	4,981	5,170	5,358	5,358	5,358
Molybdenum				14	33	52	53	54	56	56	57	647	647
Additions, Lb													
Coke	15	5										16	
FeMn*	320	310	302	298	294	291	445	550	656	708	761	293	615
FeCr*	830	1,045	1,165	1,170	1,174	1,179	967	823	678	606	513	867	720
FeCr†			34	93	147	202	129	79	30				1,497
FeMo	154	154	154	154	154	154	154	154	154	154	154	154	154
Nickel	710	710	710	710	710	710	710	710	710	710	710	710	710
FeSi	1,010	1,003	999	998	997	996	1,002	1,006	1,010	1,012	1,014	1,009	986
CaSi	123	123	123	123	123	123	123	123	123	123	123	123	123
% of Optimum Material Cost	100	103	105	107	109	111	114	116	118	118	119	128	133

Reboil: 504 lb high carbon FeMn in all heats.

* High carbon.

† Low carbon.

(Courtesy of *Materials in Design Engineering*, August 1965, published by Reinhold Publishing Company, New York.)

the best possible combination of charge materials in order to assure lowest cost, and this has been the prime object. Also, the optimum combination of a limited supply of charge materials can be determined as the best practical solution at a given time. Usage for a day's production may be established in advance by use of the scrap allocation model. Because a minimum of expensive raw materials is required for adjustment purposes, material and production costs are low. By means of this mathematical, computerized approach to steel production in the electric furnace, many advantages have accrued. The system is both practical and efficient and should be considered by steel producers engaged in a highly competitive race.*

Fig. 18-3. *View of Control Data Corporation equipment at Great Lakes Steel where computer control of equipment and processes is used extensively. (Courtesy of Control Data Corporation, Minneapolis, Minnesota.)*

Fig. 18-4. *Mill operator at the controls of Computer Control Station at Great Lakes Steel. (Courtesy of Control Data Corporation, Minneapolis, Minnesota.)*

---

* Much of the above material is incorporated in an article by Ben T. Bernacchi and Edward F. Dudley, Jr. with United States Steel Corporation. The article appeared in the June 1965 issue of *Metal Progress* (American Society for Metals) by the special permission of Mr. Bernachi, Mr. Dudley, and the A.S.M.

Fig. 18-5. *View of a large rolling mill at Great Lakes Steel, completely controlled by Control Data Corporation monitoring systems. More consistent operation, using, computer control, guarantees a uniform product and overall quality. (Courtesy of Control Data Corporation, Minneapolis, Minnesota.)*

Fig. 18-6. *A GE/PAC 4060 process computer manufactured by General Electric Company, such as might be used in solving the type of metallurgical problems discussed in this chapter. (Courtesy of General Electric Company, Process Computer Section, Phoenix, Arizona.)*

Fig. 18-7. *The IBM 1130 computing system, capable of performing 120,000 additions a second, with great internal computing power, to assist engineers and metallurgists in the solving of many types of problems. (Courtesy of International Business Machines Corporation, Data Processing Division, White Plains, New York.)*

18-4   Computer Control for the Blast Furance

In France, IRSID (l'Institute de Recherches de la Siderurgie) has endeavored during the past few years to obtain a full understanding of elementary blast furnace phenomena by means of theoretical studies and operational results. This has led to the development of a functional model of the blast furnace in static and dynamic states, and finally to a continuous operational control method, utilizing the computer.

The research has been based largely on a program of experimental work, employing a series of test programs undertaken by the French steel industry. Methods have been perfected for direct investigation of furnace operations by means of shaft probings. It has been possible to transmute the results of this work in the laboratory, for the study of elementary processes. The results have provided sufficient data to project a general model for heat and oxygen exchanges in the blast furnace. A study of transitional phenomena was then undertaken, consequent to operational disturbance, which led to the definition of a relatively simple method ensuring uninterrupted control of the operation.

A simple, functional outline of an ideal blast furnace would be (1) a furnace charged with a highly reducible, 100 per-cent self-flexing burden and (2) a furnace characterized by a uniform distribution of gas in the shaft. Given such a furnace, it is possible to define three distinct heat-exchange zones and three oxygen-exchange zones. Fig. 18–8 is a schematic of such a blast furnace in two zones. Fig. 18–10 is a schematic of a blast furnace processing zone.

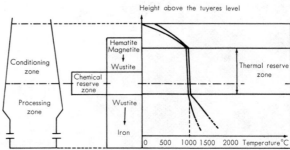

Fig. 18-8. *Schematic of an ideal blast furnace in two zones. (Courtesy of United States Steel Corporation.)*

1   Temperature of solids
2   Temperature of gas

Heat-Exchange Zones:

In terms of heat exchange, the three zones are as follows:

1. Upper zone: Solids charged at the top of the furnace are rapidly heated to about 1000C; the temperature differential between the gas and solids decreases progressively, attaining a value close to zero.

2. Intermediate zone: Heat exchange becomes almost insignificant as both burden and gas remain at about 1000C for an appreciable furnace height. This isothermal column is referred to as either the intermediate or the thermal-reserve zone.

3. Lower zone: Heat exchange becomes intense once more; the temperature difference between gas and solids increases, down to the level of the tuyers. This zone is characterized by the thermal capacity of solids greater than that of the gas.

SOLIDS OR LIQUIDS	Ideal	Non Ideal
	G A S	
CONDITIONING ZONE		
Initial state	Final state	Final state
Coke and oxidized burden	Top gas	Top gas
	↑	↑
Final state ↓	Initial state	Initial state
Burden preheated to θ_c and prereduced to wustite	θ_c and $CO_2/CO + CO_2 = \lambda^*$	$\theta_c + \epsilon$ and $\dfrac{CO_2}{CO + CO_2} = \lambda$
PROCESSING ZONE		
Initial state	Final state	Final state
Burden preheated to θ_c and prereduced to wustite	θ_c and $CO_2/CO + CO_2 = \lambda^*$	$\theta_c + \epsilon$ and $\dfrac{CO_2}{CO + CO_2} = \lambda$
	↑	↑
Final state ↓	Initial state	Initial state
Pig iron and slag	Hot blast	Hot blast

θ_C = critical temperature

ϵ = temperature difference between gas and solids (for θ_c)

λ^* = equilibrium constant wustite-Fe at θ_c °C

λ = effective gas composition when solids are assumed to have the degree of oxidization of wustite.

Fig. 18-9. *Basic reactions of the mathematical model. (Courtesy of United States Steel Corporation.)*

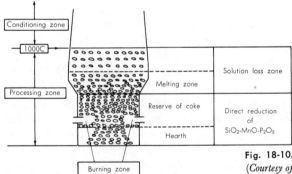

Fig. 18-10. *Schematic of blast furnace processing zone. (Courtesy of United States Steel Corporation.)*

The thermal profile indicates that at the beginning of the lower zone the heat requirements of the burden, which is still in a solid state, increase significantly. This increase is due to the highly endothermic solution-loss reaction:

$$C(coke) + CO \leftrightharpoons 2CO$$

Temperature plays an important part in this reaction, because of its high activation energy. And the 1000C temperature of the thermal reserve zone is assumed to be the temperature below which the solution-loss reaction proceeds at an imperceptible rate.

Oxygen-Exchange Zones:

Under the ideal conditions considered, the three oxygen-exchange zones are as follows:

1. Upper zone: The oxides, hematite and magnetite, are reduced by CO to wüsitte ($FeO_{1.05}$); thus, the only chemical reactions taking place are those of

indirect reduction. Practically no heat exchange is required and this zone is in the isothermal column (1000C).

2. Intermediate zone: Iron exists entirely in the form of wüstite in this zone. The gas phase is such that the ratio of per cent CO_2 to per cent CO, plus CO_2, is 0.238—a value set by the equilibrium: iron—wüstite—gas. This chemically inert zone is known as the chemical-reserve zone; it lies in the lower part of the heat-reserve zone.

3. Lower zone: This oxygen-exchange zone occupies part of the lower heat exchange zone. In it wüstite is reduced to iron, a reaction that entails a partial solution loss. From the above analysis it appears that the solution-loss reaction plays a decisive role in the blast furnace. In the first place, this reaction causes a downward extension of a mean-temperature zone that is favorable to reduction. Moreover, the solution-loss reaction regenerates the reducing potential of the furnace gas sufficiently for the charge, still in a solid state, to be reduced at temperatures above 1000C.

Using the above information and data, with the added data on the organization of heat and oxygen exchange into the concept of a two-cycle functional scheme for the blast furnace, a mathematical model is designed to test certain operating techniques and to judge the performance of the furnace.

PROVISIONAL MATHEMATICAL MODEL

The mathematical model is designed to test certain operating techniques and to judge the performance of the blast furnace. Furthermore, it constitutes the basis of thermal control in the operation. Theoretical calculations leading to the mathematical model are noteworthy but there is not room for a discussion here. They are available in an article by J. Michard: "Etude théorique de l'injection de fuel à témperature de vent constant," *Journées Internationales de Sidérurgie*, Luxembourg, October 1962.

Fig. 18–9, showing the basic reactions for the mathematical model, is the basis for these calculations; it gives a simple representation of the role of the two functional zones under both ideal and non-ideal conditions. The conditioning zone has a mere recovery function—its only requirement is a sufficient sensible heat input supplied by highly reducing gas. The processing zone, on the contrary, has severe requirements, specified by two equations, one based on the over-all heat balance of the processing zone, and the other based on the oxygen balance of the same zone.

The following assumptions are made for the functional outline of the processing zone as shown in Fig. 18–10:

1. The reduction of iron oxides is achieved prior to melting the sinter, using an indirect process, followed by the *solution-loss reaction*. The *solution-loss zone* is the upper part of the processing zone in which the solid-state reduction takes place.

2. Nonferrous oxides are reduced after slag melting, while in contact with coke fragments.

3. Melting of slag and metal is simultaneous, i.e., there is only one melting zone in the furace.

A mathematical model of the blast furnace like this one makes possible a qualitative and quantitative description of transitional states connected with operational disturbances, and permits us to program all of the data and to provide a continuous control of the thermal aspects of the furnace, as well as the blast input and molten output. When the blast input is not constant, operation control is more difficult; the top gases and their analyses are then the only characteristics by which a diagnosis may be established with any degree of reliability. Again, the electronic computer permits blast furnace operators to approach the concept of the ideal furnace by means of accurate controls that are impossible by any other means.

18-5 Use of Computers in Metalworking Operations

In Chapter 16 this use of computers was introduced in the consideration of numerically controlled machines and processes, wherein the entire program was taped and operated all the equipment with precision and speed unheard of prior to the advent of the computer. In fact, the metalworking world is in the midst of a computer revolution, and as more is learned about computers and what they can do, even more use will be made of them.

When large amounts of data must be handled (in multiple correlation problems, for example), or if the mathematical procedures must be repeated over and over (most industrial processes fall into this category), computers are invaluable. Control of machining operations is accomplished, with the computer converting the holes in punched tape to machine movements. In fact, the tape itself is often produced by computer methods.

General Electric Company has devised GE-ADAPT, a machine language program designed for their medium range computers, the GE 215, 225, and 235. This program permits tapes that otherwise might take two to three days to prepare by manual methods, to be completely punched in about ten minutes. The program comprises two sections: one translates the required machine tool operations into computer language, and the other converts this second language into perforated tapes for operating specific tools. As stated in Chapter 16, examples of numerically controlled machine tools include drills, borers, punches, horizontal boring mills, lathes, dye mills, and profilers. Over 3000 numerically controlled machine tools are in use today and the number is increasing.

In a large foundry operation, the Symington Division of Symington Wayne Corporation, in Depew, New York, an IBM 1401 computer is making significant savings by controlling data on each heat produced, direct and indirect labor hours, shop costs, manufacturing schedules, sand characteriscs, heat treating temperatures and times, job classifications, machine usage and breakdown, maintainance costs, overhead, and countless other items.

Complex computers now supervise rolling mills, calculate charges for basic oxygen converters, and perform numerous complex integrations and differentiations. Today, almost all installations for making basic oxygen steel utilize computer facilities to aid in calculating the effects of the many production variables. The IBM 1620 unit at McLouth Steel Corporation, for instance, receives manually entered data on such variables as hot metal charges, temperatures, and the like, along with the required steel composition, and employs it to inform the melter of the correct amount of oxygen needed to produce the desired end point. The computer can handle, in seconds, as many as 20 process variables for each heat poured.

Sharon Steel Corporation, the American pioneer in the use of the Stora-Kaldo technique for oxygen steel making, was also first to apply computer methods to monitor the melting process from charge to tap.

Elaborate analog-digital computers are also employed on research problems. With these, programmers use equations to set up mathematical models of the process in question—blast furnace, open-hearth or basic oxygen—so that they can determine the theoretical effects of the many variables. Digital computers now supervise production and output of the mills of Bethelehem Steel Co., Colorado Fuel and Iron Corporatian, and Great Lakes Steel Corporation's new hot strip mill near Detroit. In fact in the last named installation, by means of Daystrom Systems Division's most complex computer control system, the computer does the controlling directly instead of by means of punch cards. Daystrom's computer runs the roughing mill stands through a Westinghouse PRODAC digital control system, and the seven-stand finishing mill using General Electric controls. This is said to be one of the most significant computer systems in the metals industry and worth watching.

Many other computer controls are already in use in other metallurgical systems, including the following:

1. Quantitative metallography for polyhedral-shaped particles.
2. Computer programs for the analysis of positions and profiles of X-ray powder patterns
3. Calculation of the cohesive energy of solids, using computers
4. Unidirectional analysis of heat transfer during continuous casting
5. Simulation of a basic oxygen furnace.

These and others applications are discussed in detail in *Computer Applications in Metallurgical Engineering* published by American Society for Metals, in 1964, edited by Dr. Robert D. Pehlke and Dr. Maurice J. Sinnott—a book highly recommended to the student of metallurgy for further reading about the new world of computer controls used in the metals fields, a world that is becoming greater and more complex with each passing day.

18-6   Computer-Controlled Hot Strip Steel Mill

The steel industry is almost made to order for computer supervision. In the broadest sense, making iron and steel is a process, and processes are well adapted to computer control, while mechanically complex jobs, such as assembling a product, are not. At the same time, the steel industry's products are batches of separate items, in such a variety of composition and shapes, that computers are needed just to keep track of them all.

At first computers were used in steel mills in much the same way as in dozens of other industries, for accounting, inventory control, production scheduling, and research. About 10 years ago computers began to move in the direction of production operations; the first production job involving digital equipment, but not computers, was simple routine. Sets of punch cards were made that, through reading devices, automatically adjusted the rolling mill for each pass as a metal piece was run back and forth through the several passes necessary to convert it into sheet or plate. The first step in the steel mills' use of computers was to use an on-line computer to recalculate the number of passes and the roll pressures, according to changes in temperature that occurred in the process. Several rolling mills are now almost completely controlled by computers. When an ingot reaches the roughing mill from the holding furnace, its temperature, weight, and measurements are taken automatically and fed to the computer. In a split second the computer calculates the roll settings and the number of passes through the rolls that will be required. All the computer needs to know in advance is the composition of the alloys and the size and gauge of the coil or sheet to be produced. Then, as the metal passes through the rolls, its temperature is recorded continuously, and so is the rolling pressure. In cases where this information does not conform to the prearranged program, the computer automatically recalculates the entire program and requests corrects from the control center, all automatically. At the completion of a run, the computer prints a ticket identifying the coil of steel—its dimensions, weight, and metallurgical analysis, along with other characteristics. It also provides accounting, payroll, and inventory data.

Fig. 18–3 shows a view of the Control Data Corporation equipment now in service at Great Lakes Steel Corporation's new hot strip mill near Detroit. Fig. 18–4 shows the mill operator at the controls of the system and Fig. 18–5 shows a view of the rolling mill, completely controlled by the Control Data Corporation monitoring and controls systems, assuring the mill a uniform product and over-all quality.

18-7 Functional Features of Monitoring and Control System

The following a few of the functional features of the information supplied, automatically and almost instantaneously, at Great Lakes and other steel mills today:

Slab Tracking and Cobble Detection	Temperature Control
Mill Control	Inventory Control
Furnace Control	Production Control
Mill Safety	Payroll Information

The prerequisite for rolling mill control is a description of the process in mathematical terms, giving the controlled variables as a function of the input variables. By using known theoretical relationships between variables, and refining these relationships, the necessary information is developed, gathering and reducing plant data through regression analysis. This procedure is known as setting up the mathematical model, a term is familiar to all engineers who work with computers, both on and off of the campus. Fortunately, more and more engineering students are learning the functions and operations of the computer through actually solving problems with them. In 1964, 76 per cent of all engineering students attended schools that required a computer training course in at least one department; 22 per cent were at schools that were "considering" such a course; and 2 per cent of the students attended schools that were not considering computer training. Undoubtedly these figures have changed during the past two or three years as industries today demand that the engineering students they hire know something about computers and are able to use them effectively. It is a matter of self-defense today for engineers to know how to use these machines effectively.

Two typical problems exist at this point, relating to the type of metallurgical problems the young engineer of today might be called upon to solve or to assist in their solution.

18-8   Problem-Solving Capabilities
of Digital Computers

In addition to the problem-solving capabilities of the digital computer, there are other important applications not strictly analytical in nature. Two such applications are critical path programming and process control. Others include literature surveillance, information retrieval, data logging, and various schemes for compiling data and display, all of which relieve the engineer of time-consuming repetitive tasks and reduce substantially the time necessary for drawing conclusions and making decisions.

An examination of the steps normally taken throughout the course of an investigation suggests several areas for computer application. Preliminary steps include a review and analysis of the literature and the design of the experiment. Raw data are collected during the investigation and converted to parameters of interest, tested for bias and significance, applied to existing theory, or reduced to new fundamental relationships. Finally, the data are displayed in tabulated form and pertinent information is assembled in a report.

The larger and more involved the investigation, the greater is the justification for combining one or more of the above data processing steps into a multipurpose computer program. In the field of metallurgical engineering, and specifically in the development of alloys used for specific purposes, long-term surveillance tests of component materials and process development are extensive enough to benefit from use of the comprehensive computer program. In many cases, the programming effort consists of merely providing transfer paths and a common data reference among existing computer routines.

18-9   Problem Based on the Unidirectional Analysis
of Heat Transfer During Continuous
Steel Casting

The continuous casting of metals was discussed in Chapter 8 (8.16), and a generalized sketch of the process was shown in Fig. 8–17, showing how liquid metal persists in the center of a continuous casting for a considerable distance after the casting (slab) leaves the water-cooled mold. A more detailed sketch of the process is shown in Fig. 18–11, consisting of two distinct heat transfer stages:

1. A water-cooled copper mold that oscillates to maintain its separation from the continuously downward-moving slab of steel.
2. A high-velocity water spray located immediately below the mold, to promote rapid heat transfer from the surface of the hot slab.

Two critical aspects of the process are related to these heat transfer units. The first is the extent of solidification; that is, the thickness of the frozen skin; this is important because, as the slab emerges from the water-cooled copper mold, the skin must be thick enough to support the head of liquid metal extending from the bottom of the mold up to the surface of the liquid. Secondly, the thickness of the solidified layer of metal leaving the water-spray zone should be such that the solidification process is nearly complete. The liquid metal well (crater) through the center of the slab should not extend far below the water spray; the slab is completely solidified when it reaches the cutoff or bending station of the casting strand.

Heat Transfer Analysis

Copper Mold

Heat transfer in the copper mold can be analyzed on the basis of assumed heat transfer coefficients at each of the physical interfaces, and on thermal conduction both through the slab as its solidified thickness builds up, and through the wall of the copper mold. This path for heat transfer has been chosen, disregarding any heat transfer between liquid and solid steel within the slab. The rate of energy transfer from the liquid-solid interface to the water stream at any point along the mold, assuming steady-state conditions, may be stated by equation 18–1, as follows.

$$q = \frac{[(KS/X) * (TF - TW)]}{[1 + (KS/X * (1/HMS + XM/KM + 1/HWM)]} \tag{18-1}$$

where q equals the rate of heat transfer in BTU/hr, KS equals thermal conductivity of solid steel in BTU/ft-hr °F, X equals thickness of the frozen layer in ft, TF equals liquidus temperature of the steel in °F, TW equals average temperature of the water flowing in the mold, HMS equals heat transfer coefficient between mold and slab in BTU/hr °F, XM equals mold thickness in ft, KM equals thermal conductivity of the mold material, and HWM equals heat transfer coefficient: cooling water—mold, BTU/hr °F.

Assuming steady-state heat transfer, the temperatures at each interface can be computed from thermal resistances, and are given by:

$$TWM = q/HWM + TW \tag{18-2}$$
$$TMS = q * (XM/KM) + TWM \tag{18-3}$$
$$TSM = q/HMS + TMS \tag{18-4}$$

where TWM equals temperature of the mold on the water side in °F, TMS equals temperature of the mold on the slab side in °F, and TSM equals temperature of the slab on the mold side in °F.

The slab moves downward through the mold. By consideration of each discrete point along the vertical dimension of the mold as a point where unidirectional steady-state heat transfer takes place, the heat extracted can be equated to the solidification of a given amount of steel. As solidification progresses, the heat extracted is equal to that sufficient to

1. Remove the liquid superheat; that is, to cool the steel from the pouring temperature to the liquidus temperature
2. Remove the heat of fusion, assuming that this heat is extracted at a specific temperature
3. Remove the heat from the already frozen steel in order to provide a linear temperature gradient throughout the slab.

In the present analysis, a specific thickness of metal is chosen to be frozen per iteration, and the heat that must be removed is

$$\begin{aligned} QREQD = {} & (TS - TF) * (CPL) * (DX) * (RHO) + (HF) * (DX) * \\ & (RHO) + (TF + TSM/2) * (X) * (CPS) * (RHO) + \\ & (TF) * (DX) * (CPS) * (RHO) - (TF + TSM/2) * \\ & (X + DX) * (RHO) \end{aligned}$$

where QREQD equals heat in BTU required to freeze a steel increment of DX thickness in ft, CPS equals specific heat of the solid steel in BTU/lb/°F, RHO equals density of solid steel in lb/ft³, TS equals temperature of the liquid steel in the well in °F, and HF equals heat of fusion of the steel in BTU/lb.

The time required to remove the quantity of heat computed in equation 18–5 is determined by the rate of heat transfer q under the physical conditions assumed to exist at any point along the vertical of heat, thus,

$$t = \text{QREQD}/q \tag{18–6}$$

where t equals the time in hours to freeze an increment of thickness DX. The vertical movement of the slab can then be computed from the expression

$$\text{DIST} = (t) * (\text{VEL})/(60) \tag{18–7}$$

where DIST is the vertical distance in feet that the slab moves downward during the freezing of the layer of thickness DX, and VEL is the average downward velocity of the slab in ft per min.

In actual operating practice, the mold is usually given a vertical oscillating movement in order to prevent sticking of the slab to its walls. This movement has been ignored in this problem analysis, as we will assume that its effect is of secondary importance. Also, an average heat transfer coefficient between mold and slab has been assumed.

Water Spray

Heat transfer in the spray section of the strand can be computed in a manner parallel to that employed for calculating heat transfer in the copper mold. A heat transfer coefficient between the water spray and the slab is assumed. This surface resistance to heat transfer is added to that related to thermal conductivity in the solid portion of the slab, permitting a calculation of the rate of heat transfer q by the relationship

$$q = \frac{(\text{KS}/\text{X}) * (\text{TF} - \text{TW})}{1 + (\text{KS}/\text{X}) * (1/\text{HSPS})} \tag{18–8}$$

where HSPS is the heat transfer coefficient between the water spray and the slab surface in BTU/hr-°F. In a manner parallel to equations 18–2, 18–3, and 18–4, the surface temperature of the slab can be estimated as

$$\text{TSSP} = (q/\text{HSPS}) + \text{TW} \tag{18–9}$$

The heat that must be removed in order to effect the freezing of a layer of thickness (DX) during passage through the water spray, can be calculated by considering the same heat terms as in the case of the copper mold. The heat that must be removed by the spray is

$$\begin{aligned}
\text{QREQD} = &(\text{TS} - \text{TF}) * (\text{CPL}) * (\text{DX}) * (\text{RHO}) + (\text{HF}) * (\text{DX}) * \\
&(\text{RHO}) + ((\text{TF} + \text{TSSP})/2) * (\text{X}) * (\text{CPS}) * (\text{RHO}) \\
&+ (\text{TF}) * (\text{DX}) * (\text{CPS}) * (\text{RHO}) + ((\text{TF} + \text{TSSP})/2) * \\
&(\text{X} + \text{DX}) * (\text{CPS}) * (\text{RHO})
\end{aligned} \tag{18–10}$$

Equations 18–6 and 18–7 can then be employed to compute the vertical movement of the slab during the time period required to freeze an increment of thickness DX.

Computer Program

Employing an iterative procedure in which the transfer at each successive point along the mold surface is computed, based on the heat flow at the previously computed point, the thickness of the shell as a function of position in the mold and spray system is to be estimated. The flow diagram for this iterative procedure is shown in Fig. 18–12, and a summary of the input data used in the calculation is presented in Table 18–2. The computer output data is to be calculated by the student. The results of the computer calculation, employing the data given in Table 18–2, are shown in Fig.

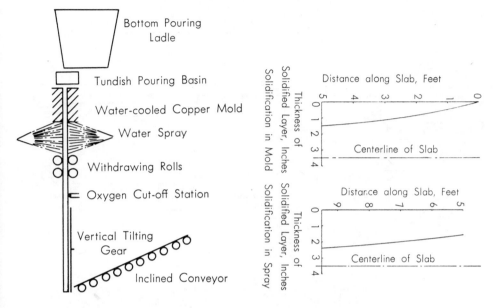

Fig 18-11. *Schematic diagram of continuous casting process, (Courtesy of Dr. Robert D. Pehlke, University of Michigan, and American Society for Metals.)*

Fig. 18-12. *Predicted profile of solidification front in mold and spray sections of a continuous casting strand, given in problem. (Courtesy of Dr. Robert. D. Pehlke, University of Michigan, and American Society for metals.)*

Table 18–2. Input data for computer calculation.*

Water-mold heat transfer coefficient, BTU/hr-sq ft-°F = 3000
Thermal conductivity of mold, BTU/hr-ft-°F = 200
Mold-slab heat transfer coefficient, BTU/hr-sq ft-°F = 300
Spray-slab heat transfer coefficient, BTU/hr-sq ft-°F = 1500
Thermal conductivity of steel, BTU/hr-ft-°F = 25
Mold length, ft = 5.00
Mold thickness, in. = 0.50
Slab thickness, in. = 7.00
Spray length, ft = 4.50
Slab velocity, ft/min = 2.50
Density of steel, lb/cu ft = 490
Water temperature, °F = 100
Liquidus temperature of steel, °F = 2760
Tapping temperature of steel, °F = 2840
Heat of fusion of steel, BTU/lb = 118
Specific heat of liquid steel, BTU/lb-°F = 0.1840
Specific heat of solid steel, BTU/lb-°F = 0.1550
Increment of freezing thickness, in. = 0.0100
Iterations for printout = 5

* Courtesy of Dr. Robert D. Pehlke, University of Michigan, and American Society for Metals.

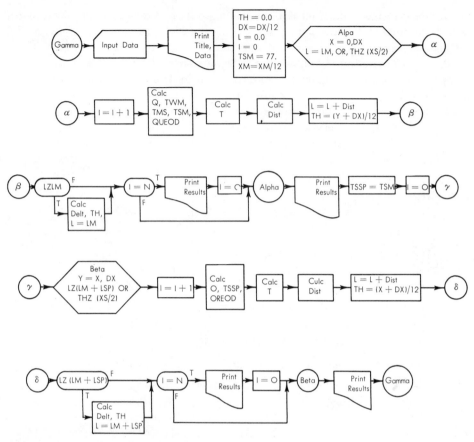

Fig. 18-13. *Flow diagram for computer program given in problem. (Courtesy of Dr. Robert D. Pehlke, University of Michigan and American Society for Metals.)*

18–13. The estimated thickness at the exit of the copper mold is approximately 1.55 in., and the thickness at the bottom of the water spray is approximately 2.40 in.

Several assumptions must be made in deriving this unidirectional pseudo-steady-state heat transfer simulation. One particular aspect that should be considered is the heat transfer between the liquid metal contained in the well and the solidifying shell. This heat transfer may be neglected in the student's calculation, and the temperature in the metal liquid may be assumed to remain constant. This is, of course, not the case in practice; furthermore, there is some liquid circulation in the well promoting heat transfer and delaying the initial buildup of the shell, at the expense of a decreasing temperature in the metal well. It may not be possible in this problem to estimate the influence of this error.

Another rough assumption that may be made is that the temperature gradient through the solidified layer of the slab is linear. Although this assumption is known to be in error, the first order correction—correcting the heat removal term for the energy removed from the solidified layer as it becomes thicker and the temperature gradient is found to level out—is sufficient to give the liquid-solid surface a nearly parabolic shape in the mold and spray heat transfer zones. A parabolic interface is predicted theoretically if no superheat is present in the liquid, by the relationship

$$X = k(at)^{1/2} \qquad (18\text{--}11)$$

where k is a constant and a is thermal diffusivity, $KS/((RHO) * (CPS))$.

This agreement between the assumed simulation and conditions amenable to theoretical analysis is a good indication that the error did not have a marked influence on the results found for the continuous casting simulation.

Using all of the aforementioned facts and figures, the student is to proceed with the solution of this interesting and practical problem.*

QUESTIONS

1. What was the nature of the great impact made by the first industrial revolution?

2. Explain the significance of the second Industrial Revolution and what it involves.

3. Define the term *cybernetics* and state its significance to our age.

4. Why is it essential that engineering students should study the theory and applications of computers?

5. Explain briefly the application of computers as a means of studying solidification patterns in steel castings.

6. Define and explain the term THT (transient heat transfer).

7. Discuss the use of computers in the calculation of charges for electric furnaces.

8. In the application of computers in calculating electric furnace charges, why is it essential to separate the steel grades of the materials going into the furnace into low, medium and high carbon?

9. What are some of the restrictions on metallurgical practice in the electric furnace operation that must be resolved into equations before going into the models?

10. In setting up the outline of an ideal blast furnace in preparation for computerizing its control and operation, what would be its simple, functional outline?

11. Name and explain the three distinct heat-exchange zones and the three oxygen-exchange zones in an ideal blast furnace.

12. What are some other areas where the computer saves many man-hours in operations in and control of metallurgical processes?

13. Referring to the book entitled *Computer Applications in Metallurgical Engineering*, by Robert D. Pehlke and Maurice J. Sinnott, write a paper on one of the many applications given in which the computer serves a real function in industry and research.

14. Discuss the importance and operation of the automatic information retrieval in *Metallurgy and Related Subjects*, as provided by American Society for Metals, Metals Park, Ohio.

---

* This problem made available through the courtesy of Dr. Robert D. Pehlke, Professor of Engineering, Department of Chemical and Metallurgical Engineering, University of Michigan, Ann Arbor, Michigan, and the American Society for Metals, Metals Park, Ohio.

References

Bement, Albert L., and J. E. Irwin, *Automatic Processing of Mechanical Properties Data*. Richland, Washington: Hanford Atomic Laboratories, General Electric Company.

Darken, L. S., *Kinetics of Metallurgical Reactions with Particular Reference to the Open Hearth*, Technology Press, 1958.

Dusinberre, G. M., *Numerical Analysis of Heat Flow*. New York: McGraw Hill Book Company, 1949.

Fischer, G. A., *Solidification and Soundness Prediction for Large Steel Ingots*, Proceedings of the American Society for Testing and Materials, Vol. 62, 1962, pp. 1137–1155.

Foreman, James H., *Mathematical Model for Copper Converter Control*, Golden, Colorado: Colorado School of Mines, Quarterly, 1965.

Henzel, J. G., Jr., and J. Keverian, "The Use of a Digital Computer in Calculating Solidification Patterns within a Sand Cast Steel Cylinder," Cleveland, Ohio: *Steel Foundry Facts*, Steel Founders Society, Feb. 1964, No. 243.

Calculating Solidification Patterns within Sand Cast 8 and 12 inch Diameter Steel Cylinders by Means of a Digital Computer, Cleveland, Ohio: Transactions of American Foundrymens Society, 1965.

Hubbard, John W., *Computer Availability for the Metallurgical*. New York: Computing Sciences Division, The Service Bureau Corporation, 1965.

Korotkov, K. P., H. P. Mayorov, A. A. Skvortsov, and A. D. Akimenko, *The Continuous Casting of Steel in Commercial Use*. London: Pergamon Press, 1960.

Lippitt, D. L., *Simulation of a Basic Oxygen Furnace*. Metals Park, Ohio: American Society for Metals, 1964.

Maatsch, J., E. Plockenger, and M. Wahlster, *Materials Balance and Heat Balance in the LD Basic Oxygen Top-Blowing Process*, Tech Mitt Krupp, 17, No. 6 (1959), Brutcher Translation 4808, 1959.

McBride, D. L. and T. E. Dancy, *Continuous Casting*. New York: American Institute of Mining, Metallurgical and Petroleum Engineers, 1962.

Pehlke, Robert D., *Unidirectional Analysis of Heat Transfer During Continuous Casting*. Metals Park, Ohio: American Society for Metals, 1964.

Plastics,
Adhesives,
Elastomers (Rubbers)

19-1 Plastics, Adhesives, Elastomers (Rubbers)

Simply stated, *plastics* is the name given to a family of *synthetic* materials which have large molecules made up of chains of atoms. Although they are soft and moldable during manufacture, they solidify in time. Plastics come in many different forms, being found as sheeting, film, fibers and filaments, liquids and adhesives and also as molding pellets and powders.

According to the official definition accepted by the Society of Plastics Engineers (SPE) and the Society of the Plastics Industry (SPI), the term plastics applies to "a large and varied group of materials which consist of or contain as an essential ingredient, a substance of high molecular weight which, while solid in the finished state, at some stage of its manufacture is soft enough to be formed into various shapes—most usually through the application (either singly or together), of heat and pressure."

Thermoplastic and Thermosetting Plastics. The thermoplastic plastics become soft when they are exposed to heat and harden when cooled regardless how often the process is repeated. By alternating heating and cooling they can be reshaped many times. In this respect, they may be compared to wax. When heated they are moldable; when cooled they are hard and rigid, but upon reheating they once again become soft and pliable. A few important members of this family group are acrylics, cellulosics, Nylon, polystyrene, polyethylene, fluorocarbons and vinyls.

The *thermosetting* plastics, (thermosets) are set or cured into a permanent shape by heat and once they have set, they cannot be remelted and returned to their original state. However, they do not retain their hardness at extreme heats, most of this group softening somewhat at temperatures above 305° F, but they will not return to their original flow condition. Prominent members of this group of plastics are phenolics, aminos, polyesters, epoxies, and alkyds.

19-2   Structure of Plastics

To understand the reaction of plastics to heat, it is essential that we understand something of their molecular structure. In the formation of plastics many atoms are combined to form molecules, each atom being connected to the next atom by connecting links called *valence bonds.* Their chemical structure is *chain-like.*

In *thermoplastics,* the atoms and molecules are joined, end-to-end into a series of long chains, each chain being independent of the others. When subjected to heat, the individual chains slip, causing *plastic flow.* Upon cooling, the plastic chains of atoms and molecules are once again held firmly, but with subsequent heating, we find that slippage once again takes place. There are practical limitations to the number of heating-cooling cycles to which thermoplastics can be subjected, an excessive number of such cycles many times resulting in a loss of color or plasticizer thereby affecting the appearance and the properties.

The structure of *thermosetting plastics* is also chain-like and prior to molding, very similar to thermoplastics. The curing or hardening, occurring, as a rule during molding, consists of the formation of *cross-links* between adjacent molecules resulting in a complex, interconnected network. These cross-bonds prevent the slippage of individual chains, thus preventing plastic flow with the addition of heat. Fig. 19.1 shows the structure of *thermoplastics* and *thermosetting* plastics.

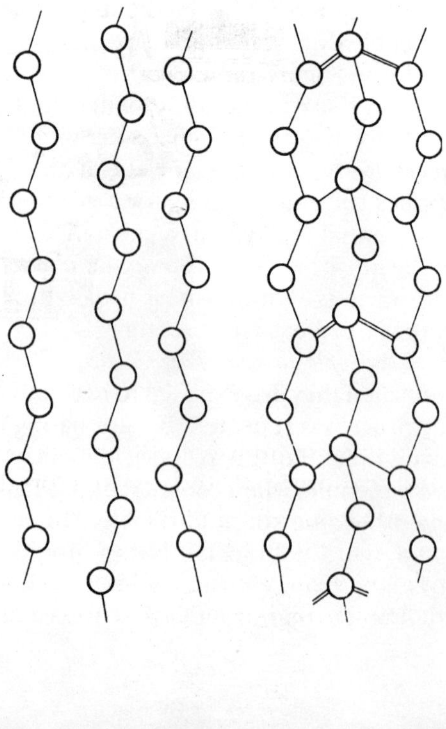

Fig. 19.1.   *Structure of thermoplastics* (left) *thermosetting plastics.* (right)

19-3   Manufacture of Plastics

Although plastics are synthetics, they are made from many common natural materials such as wood, air, water, petroleum, natural gas and salt. Complex chemical reactions are necessary to produce a great number of plastics by slightly altering the processes and ingredients. Actually, the chemist literally takes the natural materials apart by separating their basic molecules and atoms, then subsequently recombining in different ways with the aid of heat, pressure and chemical action. A graphic description of the manufacture of polystyrene is shown in Fig. 19.2. The raw materials used are coal and petroleum or natural gas. Benzene is extracted from the coal and then are linked to form ethyl benzene. In the last stage of the process, the ethyl benzene is subjected to heat and pressure followed by milling and grinding to form the finished product, polystyrene. If ethylene gas is combined with chlorine, obtained from common salt, the result is one of the common vinyl resins, vinyl chloride as shown graphically in Fig. 19.3.

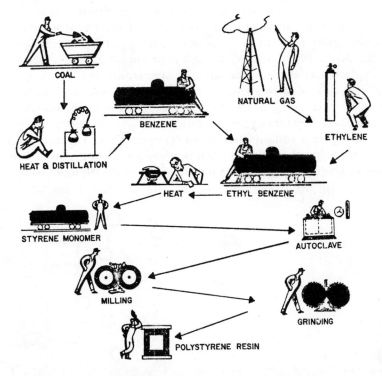

Fig. 19.2.   *Manufacture of polystyrene. (Courtesy Union Carbide Corp.)*

As shown above, if ethylene gas, obtained from natural gas, is subjected to heat and pressure, the resulting product is polyethylene, which is the base for many of our thermoplastics. The very common use of the *squeeze bottle* as a container for all types of fluids has led to the development of an important piece of equipment, i.e. the *blow-molding machine* for the actual forming process. Blow molding is one of the few processes by which a hollow, one-piece article can be

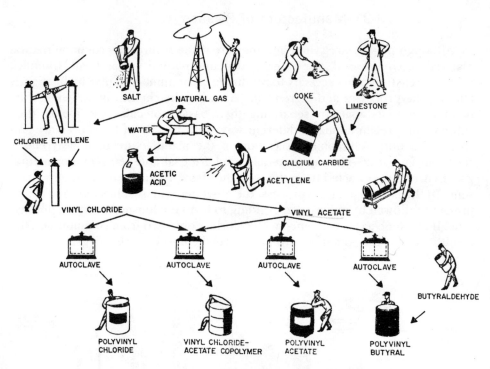

Fig. 19.3. *Manufacture of vinyls. (Courtesy Union Carbide Corp.)*

made. This is a very high-speed process and consists of machines, as a rule, with several mold stations so that as one article is cooling, others are in various stages of manufacture, the extruder portion of the process, running continuously. More will be given on this important blow-molding process on subsequent pages.

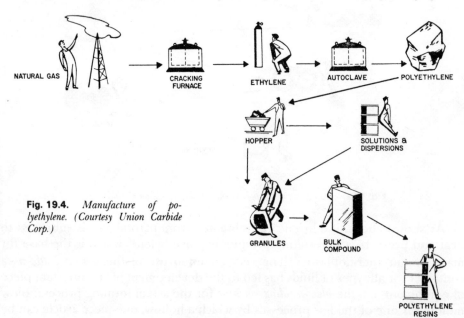

Fig. 19.4. *Manufacture of polyethylene. (Courtesy Union Carbide Corp.)*

19-4   Constituents in Plastics

Resin is usually the principal constituent of most plastics, however other materials are also present such as *fillers, solvents, plasticizers* and *colorants.* The resin or binder serves to bind the plastic together and impart some of the significant characteristics to the finished product. A plastic is usually named by the resin involved in its manufacture, the resin determining whether a plastic is thermoplastic or thermosetting.

Before being processed into finished products, most plastics make use of a *filler,* such as wood flour which gives very good surface appearance and excellent electrical properties. Asbestos provides resistance to fire and acid. In their natural state, many resins are hard and brittle, however, others are soft and rather tacky. All of the resins must first be made fluid and their component particles must weld together. For this purpose, a *solvent* is used. There are over 300 solvents that are employed for various types of plastics.

Many plastic resins possess high viscosity and are rather stiff in final form. For this reason, *plasticizers* are used to lower viscosity at high processing temperatures and to give the final product, the necessary plasticity.

Due to the fact that plastics are subjected to heat and light during their manufacture and when in service, *stabilizers* are often added to prevent degradation by heat, light and aging. Since most plastics are not left in their natural color, over 800 *colorants* are on the market today that are most effective.

Undboutedly, the greatest single advantage of plastics is that they can be molded into finished products at a relatively low cost compared to the machining and fabricating necessary with metals and wood. Although plastic materials are more costly then some metals, this higher cost is many times offset by the low cost of plastic molding, extruding, rolling, blowing etc.

Other advantages of plastics are inherent in their properties. In general, they resist chemicals well and are nonconductors of electricity. Furthermore, they have a relatively high strength to weight ratio as a rule and do not corrode like ferrous metals. They also have some disadvantages that msut be considered.

Plastics materials include a wide range of products with different properties and costs—being highly competitive between themselves as well as with some of the previously used materials. There is an ever increasing demand for plastics and we find them in general use, today, replacing parts that were formerly made of other materials.

19-5   High Polymers—Polymerization

In general, the chemical reactions by which *high polymers,* the essential part of all plastics, are formed are referred to as *polymerization.* Polymers are large molecules and are sometimes referred to as macromolecules. The polymers embrace substances commonly known as plastics, the latter being those materials which are plastic or continuously deformable at some point in their manufacture. Those polymers that are capable of being subjected to large elastic strains are termed, *elastomers.* Natural and synthetic rubbers described on later pages, are elastomers.

There are two general types of chemical reactions involving high polymers:

addition polymerization and *condensation polymerization*. A combination of these two reactions is also possible, resulting in a single polymer. *Addition* polymerization is the reaction which results in the bonding of two or more molecules without the elimination of any by-product molecules. There are two general types of such reactions that are recognized, (1) those involving a single molecular species and (2) those involving more than one molecular species.

19-6 Types of Molecular Structures

The long, linear straight chains of molecules, formed by addition polymerization may be bundled together in random manner like straws in a stack. However, the atoms in the chain are held strongly together by primary valences. The bonds between chains are secondary bonds or van der Waals' forces resulting from the state of unbalance or unsaturation at the surface. These van der Waal bonds, varying considerably in strength, are normally much weaker than most primary bonds. They are effective only where the surfaces of adjacent chains of molecules are in contact, one with another. In a purely mechanical manner, the interlacing of the chains may add some strength to the mass involved.

This haphazard, unoriented structure produces an amorphous material. Amorphous solids in general, do not have definite melting points, and when solid, breaking with a conchoidal fracture, and tending to flow under stress. Furthermore, the magnitudes of the physical properties are not dependent upon direction. When the chains are parallel, the polymer tends to be crystalline. The symmetry of the chains also affects the crystallinity. On the other hand, if the chains are perfectly uniform, they lie close together, thereby producing a stronger attraction and greater crystallinity than if they were irregular.

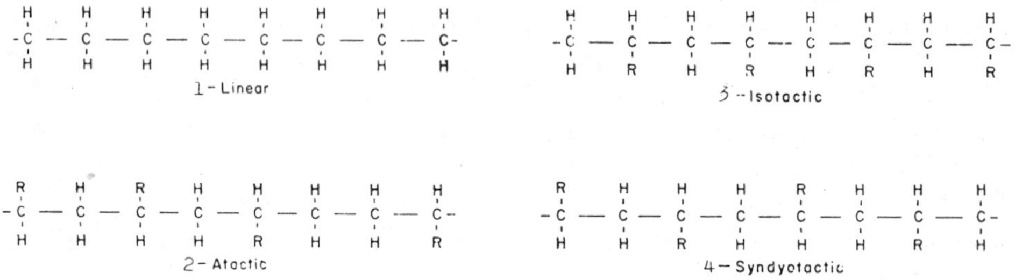

Fig. 19.5. *Types of chain structure.*

Reprinted by permission from 'Introduction to Plastics' by Lionel K. Arnold,
© 1968, Iowa State University Press, Ames

In Fig. 19.5-1 we see "linear" polyethylene chain which is this type of polymer. If part of the hydrogen atoms are replaced by radicals and the radicals so substituted are large, they may hold the chains apart somewhat, reducing the crystallinity. We see this latter type arrangement of the radical R, on the chain at random in Fig. 19.5-2, this type being referred to by the brilliant research chemist, G. Natta, as "atactic", which has a low degree of crystallinity. "Atactic" polypropylene, for example, has a random distribution of side chains, which leads to poor molecular symmetry, thereby reducing or eliminating entirely its crystallinity. A regular arrangement of the atoms and radicals in the chain such as in Fig. 19.5-3, or its inverted form called "isotactic," is crystalline. Such polymer, with a dilotometric melting point of about 175°C (347°F) in the case of solid, crystalline polypropylene, has all side-chain methyl groups appearing on alternate carbons of the polymer chain but located on the same side of the backbone of the chain as shown. Such arrangement of the polymer chain produces a highly crystalline product. Another arrangement in a chain structure is designated as "syndyotactic," as shown in Fig. 19.5-4. At times the polymer is made up of both crystalline and amorphous areas, with the crystallinity varying with conditions under which solidification takes place.

Table 19.1

PROPERTIES OF THERMOPLASTICS

	ACETALS	ACRYLICS	CELLU-LOSICS	FLUORO-CARBONS	POLY-AMIDES	POLY-OLEFINS	STYRENES	VINYLS
Specific Gravity	1.4	1.17–1.20	1.15–1.40	2.1–2.2	1.09–1.14	.91–.97	.98–1.1	1.2–1.55
Tensile Strength (1000's psi)	10	7–14.5	1.9–8.5	6.5–9.9	7.0–11.0	1.5–5.5	3.5–12.0	1.5–9.0
Compressive Strength (1000's psi)	18	12–18	13–36	1.7–80.0	7.2–13.0	2.5–10.0	4.8–16.0	1.0–13.0
Impact Strength	Excellent	Excellent	Good	Excellent	Excellent	Excellent	Good	Good
Clarity[1]	Trl–O	T–O	T–O	Trl–O	Trl–O	Trl–O	T–O	T–O
Electrical Resistance	Excellent	Good	Good	Excellent	Excellent	Excellent	Good	Good
Heat Distortion Point (Degrees F.)	338	150–210	115–250	250	300–360	105–230	165–225	100–165
Maximum Service Temp. (Degrees F.)	185–250	140–200	115–200	390–550	175–400	212–320	140–250	115–200
Low Temperature Properties	Good	Good	Good	Excellent	Good	Good	Excellent	Good
Burning;Rate[2]	S	S	S to SE	None	S to SE	S	S	S to SE
Water Absorption Rate	Low	Low	High for plastic	None	None	Low	None	Low
Effect of:								
Weak Acids	Attacked by some	Little	Little	None	Little	Little	None	Little
Strong Acids	Attacked	Attacked by some	Decompose	None	Attacked	Slowly attacked	Attacked by some	Attacked by some
Weak Alkalies	Attacked by some	Little	Little	None	None	Little	None	Little
Strong Alkalies	Attacked	Attacked by some	Decompose	None	None	Little	None	Little
Solvents	None	Soluble in some	Soluble in many	None	Little	Soluble in some	Soluble in some	Little
Outdoor Conditions (Sunlight)	Little, "chalks"	None	Little	None	Slight discolor	Crazes discolor	Discolor	Little

[1]T — transparent, Trl — translucent, O — Opaque   [2]S — slow, SE — self-extinguishing

(Courtesy, Robert S. Swanson, PhD; copyright McKnight Publishing Co.)

ABS Acrylonitrile-Butadiene-Styrene Plastics

The major classes of thermoplastic materials are given in Table 19.3 and include their typical properties, applications and important characteristics. Although all twelve of the plastics listed have an important place to take in industry, perhaps none is more important for its particular applications than the one designated as ABS, so named because the plastics in this classification are copolymers of Acrylonitrile-Butadiene and Styrene resins. As noted in the Table, these are employed in the manufacture of cams, knobs, push-buttons, instrument cluster housings, radio grills, battery caps and many other items including automobile dashboards, refrigerator door liners etc. wherever good strength, toughness and weather resistance are required.

Table 19.2

PROPERTIES OF THERMOSETS

	AMINOS	CASEIN	EPOXIES	PHENOLICS	POLYESTERS	SILICONES	URETHANES
Specific Gravity	1.47–1.55	1.35	1.11–1.8	1.25–1.55	1.3	1.6–2.0	1.15–1.20
Tensile Strength (1000's psi)	5.0–13.0	10.0	4.0–13.0	4.0–9.0	4.5–25.0	4.0–35.0	Varies with rigid and flexible
Compressive Strength (1000's psi)	25–45	27–53	13–28	15–50	12–34	9–15	
Impact Strength	Good	Fair	Excellent if reinforced	Good	Excellent if reinforced	Good	
Clarity[1]	Trl–O	T–O	T–O	Trl–O	T–O	O	O
Electrical Resistance	Good (low freq.)	Fair	Excellent	Good	Good (low freq.)	Excellent	Good
Heat Distortion Point (Degrees F.)	266–400	300	250–290	150–260	140–425	500–900	does not apply
Maximum Service Temp. (Degrees F.)	210–400	275	200–300	160–300	250–350	450	400
Burning Rate[2]	None SE	S	S to SE	S to none	S to SE	S to none	S to SE
Water Absorption Rate	Low	High for plastic	Very low	Low	Low	Very low	Very low
Effect of:							
Weak Acids	Little	Little	None	Little	Little	Little	Little
Strong Acids	Decompose	Decompose	Attacked by a few	Attacked	Attacked	Little	Little
Weak Alkalies	Little	Decompose	None	None	Attacked by some	Little	Little
Strong Alkalies	Attacked by some	Decompose	Little	Decompose	Attacked	Little	Little
Solvents	None	Little	Little	Little	Attacked by some	Attacked by some	Little
Outdoor Conditions (Sunlight)	Discolor	Discolor	None	Discolor	Discolor	Little	Discolor on some

[1]T — transparent, Trl — Translucent, O — Opaque   [2]S — slow, SE — self-extinguishing

(Courtesy, Robert S. Swanson, PhD; copyright McKnight Publishing Co.)

The ABS resins were originally blends of 60 percent or more of styrene-acrylonitrile copolymer with butadiene-acrylonitrile rubber. Now they are commonly copolymer of the three monomers. The properties of the ABS products can be altered considerably by changing both the relative amounts of the monomers and the way in which the monomers are attached to each other in the polymer structure. Collectively, they are characterized by improved shock resistance and improved elongation, with good electrical and mechanical properties.

The ABS polymers are processed by injection molding, extrusion, blow-molding, and calendering, making them ideal for such items as fan blades, heads of golf clubs, battery cases, bobbins, wheels and pipe of certain sizes. They are marketed under the trademark names of Cyolac, Cycolon, Kralastic, Lustran and others.

It is anticipated the market segments of ABS that will show the greatest growth are DWV (drain-waste-vent) pipe, appliance and transportation applications. Although its use in DWV pipe is tied to construction, even if there is a reduction in construction, this is expected to be offset by an increasing number of remodeling projects. The outlook for increased uses of ABS plastics is bright in the days ahead.

19-7   Physical Properties

Weight: Most plastics are somewhat light in weight, in fact, polyethylene and a few others, will float on water. The fluorcarbons are the heaviest and have specific gravities of about 2.3 or a little more than twice as heavy as water. This compares with 7.7 specific gravity for iron and 2.67 for aluminum and as a result, there are many applications that make use of this very advantageous property of plastics.

Hardness: Plastics are not very hard, the hardness types comparing with brass and aluminum. As a rule, thermosetting plastics are harder than the thermoplastics. The temperature of the material substantially affects this property: elevated temperatures soften most plastics considerably—even thermosetting plastics are softened considerably. The engineering tests to determine and report hardness fall into two categories: (1) *fracture hardness,* which is the resistance of the material to the penetration of the test indentor on its surface, and (2) *deformation hardness,* which is a measure of the amount of deformation the surface of the material sustains when a weight of a certain amount is concentrated on a specified area by dropping the weight from a given height. Usually, this property is reported in terms of a number on one of the several hardness scales such as Brinell or Rockwell. Most plastics will fall in the range of from 5 to 50 on the Brinell scale (15 to 105 Rockwell on the M scale.)

Tensile Strength   As stated on page 306, the tensile strength is the ability of a material to resist a pulling force. Compared with metals, the tensile and compressive strengths of plastics fall below the values for magnesium. Ductile plastics are, in some respects, similar to metallic materials in their response to loading conditions, in that higher rates of tensile loading raises the elastic limit. Fatigue loading causes failure of plastics at lower loads than short-time static loading. By way of comparison: tensile strengths:

Vinyl Chloride - 1000 to 9000 psi tensile strength
Polyamides (Nylon) - 9,000 to 10,500 psi
Cellulose acetate (Cellophane) - 1500 to 2500 psi
Phenol-formaldehyde (Bakelite) - 7,000 to 10,000 psi

Compressive Strength: This is the ability of a material to resist crushing when a squeezing force is applied to it. We find a wide range of compressive strengths among the plastics, polyesters, reinforced with glass rovings, being able to resist forces of 70,000 psi as compared to aluminum which has a value of 12,000 psi and steel of 50,000 psi.

Impact Strength: As noted on previous pages, this is the ability of a material to resist sharp blows or sudden shocks, as found in the laboratory by means of the Izod and Charpy tests.

Electrical Properties: Dielectric strength represents the electricalinsulating value of a plastic. It specifies the maximum voltage necessary to cause a current to flow through a given thickness (usually .001"). Plastics with high dielectric strengths are recognized as being good electrical insulators. Practically all plas-

Table 19.3 — Typical Properties and Applications for Plastics

Source: Ralph P. Schmuckal, Ford Motor Co.

Type of Plastic	Tensile Strength, psi	Tensile Modulus, 10⁵ psi	Rockwell Hardness, R	Elongation, %	Impact at RT, Izod-Notched, ft-lb	Impact at -40 F, Izod-Notched, ft-lb	Heat Distortion Temp. at 264 psi, °F	Coefficient of Thermal Expansion, 10⁻⁵ in./in./°F	Important Characteristics	Applications
Nylon	11,700	3.9	117	60	1.1	0.4	150	5.0	Strong and rigid; resistant to oils, fuels and abrasion; good electrical properties	Bushings, cams, small gears, fuse holders, lamp bases
Acetal	10,000	4.1	120	40	1.5	1.2	212	4.2	Strong, hard and rigid; low creep under load; resistant to oils, fuels, and abrasion; moisture resistant; dimensionally stable	Interior door handles and window regulators, windshield washer pump housing, instrument cluster housings, small gears, "greaseless" bearings
Polycarbonate	9,700	3.2	118	80	14.0	2.2	275	3.9	Exceptionally tough; maintains high load-carrying ability at high temperatures; good electrical properties, transparent in some types	Transparent housings, covers and dials; impact-resistant gears, propellers and impellers, wheels
Methacrylate	10,400	4.5	127	5	0.4	0.4	160	3.0	Weather resistant; lustrous appearance; exceptional optical properties, colorable	Light lenses, instrument lenses, instrument cluster dials, horn button medallions, decorative items
Polyethylene (high density)	4,000	1.1	45	30	2.0	0.8	115	6.5	Very low friction; resistant to oils and fuels; colorable; good gloss; easily fabricated; low cost	Seat side shields, window washer reservoirs, cowl kick panels, heater and cold air ducts, lightly loaded bushings, decorative items
ABS	8,700	4.4	116	20	1.5	0.4	200	3.2	Strong, hard and rigid; creep resistant; relatively insensitive to moisture; resists alcohols and oils (not resistant to aromatic hydrocarbons); can be integrally colored, metalized or painted	Cams, knobs, push buttons, instrument cluster housings, dome light bezels, radio grilles, electrical condenser housings, battery caps
Polypropylene	5,000	1.6	95	350	1.1	0.1	140	4.7	Heat resistant at low stress levels, resists stress cracking. "stretchable", good flex life, less tendency to warp than polyethylene, low cost	Dome light lenses, cable connectors, seat side shields, kick panels, upholstery, tubing, radio grilles, integrally hinged accelerator pedals, air ducts, clips
Polyethylene (low density)	1,700	0.25	11	570	16	0.4	—	9.5	Good flex life; better transparency and resistance to stress cracking than other polyethylenes; colorable; low cost	Limited auto usage. Temporary seat covers and moisture barriers in car doors
Cellulose acetate	4,500	2.0	100	45	2.5	0.4	130	7.0	Tough, high resistance to impact; produces lustrous translucents, transparents and opaques; self-extinguishing	Electrical parts and housings, knobs, handles
Butyrate (cellulose acetate)	4,500	1.5	100	70	3.6	1.2	130	8.0	Tough, highly resistant to impact, resilient, high surface luster, crystal-clear; easily colored; weather resistant; dimensionally stable	Steering wheels, interior knobs, taillight lenses, arm rests
Polytetrafluoroethylene (TFE)	4,500	0.6	20	300	4.0	2.5	130	5.5	Chemically inert; heat resistant; low friction	Power steering piston rings, carburetor bearings, low-friction coatings and seals
Vinyl (rigid PVC)	7,000	3.6	120	60	0.8	0.5	165	3.0	Chemically inert, abrasion and impact resistant, color stable, flame resistant, good dielectric properties	Window frames and sash, moldings

Typical Properties

Table 19.4

Comparison of Properties of Plastics

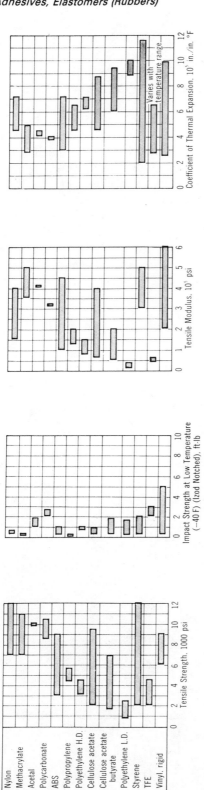

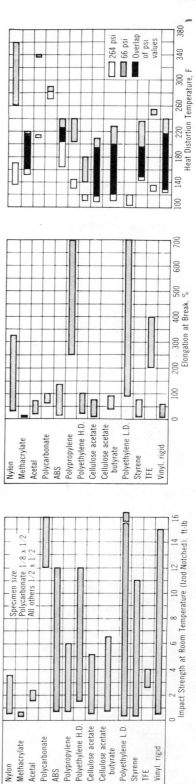

tics, when dry, are excellent insulators. Some have been developed which retain their insulating values even after long immersion in water. In fact, some have been developed that actually conduct a current, i.e., they are conductors of electricity. With an increase in temperature the dielectric strength is generally lowered. The same thing is true when a load is placed on the plastic.

Thermal properties: Plastics are found to fall in the group of heat insulators, that is, they have very low thermal conductivities. Copper transmits over 2000 times as much heat as most plastics; cast iron 250 times as much; asbestos four times as much, and wood about twice as much. Because of this property, plastics, in general are pleasant to touch. For example, a plastic handle on a hot pan transmits relatively little heat from the hot pan to the hand. A plastic refrigerator tray transmits little heat from the hand to the ice cubes in the tray.

Chemical properties: The "resistance ratings" to various chemicals are important to the considerations of chemical properties of plastics. Many plastics have been developed that are acid-resistant and can endure chemicals for long periods of time. This is done without corrosion problems such as we get in metals and alloys.

19-8   Methods of Producing Plastic Parts

Plastics are processed to form various parts by several methods:

1. Compression molding
2. Injection molding
3. Transfer molding
4. Cold molding
5. Extrusion
6. Laminating
7. Casting

The method selected depends upon the shape and size of the part to be formed,

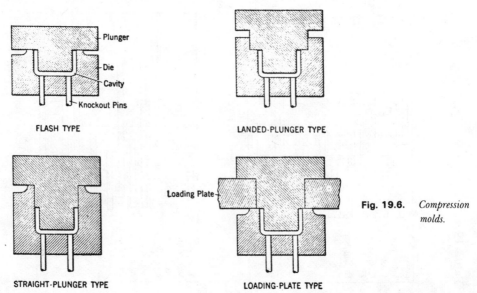

FLASH TYPE

LANDED-PLUNGER TYPE

STRAIGHT-PLUNGER TYPE

LOADING-PLATE TYPE

Fig. 19.6.   *Compression molds.*

the number of pieces to be made, and the type of material to be molded. In the case of the molding processes, a die and a means of applying adequate pressure and heat are necessary. The dies are usually made of steel, either the case-carburizing types of steel, SAE 1020, 3110, 3115, and 3312, or else an oil-hardening nondeforming tool steel. The dies or molds, as they may be called, are prepared either by machining with milling machines or special die-sinking machines, or by a hobbing operation. The latter *hobbing* method of producing dies for molding plastics, involves forcing a hardened punch of the desired shape, into the surface of a low carbon steel die block. Subsequent to minor finishing operations, the die is carburized and then heat treated.

Compression molding is most commonly used in the forming of parts to be made from thermosetting plastics. The plastic, in the form of a powder, granules, or a precompressed pill, is placed in the heated mold cavity. The mold closes, thus applying pressure to the plastic, causing it to flow and to fill the cavity completely. After the plastic remains in the heated mold for the correct length of time to permit curing or *polymerization,* the mold is opened and the part ejected. The pressure and temperature employed depend on the shape, size and complexity of the part and on the characteristics of the plastic being molded. Thermoplastic materials can be and usually are molded by compression, but when this is done, the mold must be cooled after the pressure is applied, such that the part will maintain the shape imparted by the die.

The molds used for forming plastics by compression are generally of four types: (1) flash types, (2) straight-plunger type, (3) landed-plunger type, and (4) loading-plate type. These four types of molds are shown in Fig. 19.6. In the case of the flash mold, an excess amount of charge is squeezed out, and after the hot piece has been ejected by the knockout pins, the die is cleaned of flash debris by compressed air, making it then ready for the next charge. Parts made by the straight-plunger type mold are usually those requiring exact size and here, the

Fig. 19.7. *Plastic injection molding machine 400–IB. (Courtesy of Reed-Prentice, Div. of Package Machinery Co.)*

charge takes the full force of the ram, thereby sacrificing, to some extent, uniform density of the finished product. The landed-plunger type mold is used where the charge is just sufficient to fill the mold, and therefore the finished part is quite exact as to dimensions. The full force of the ram is not carried by the charge, and only a small amount of flash is squeezed out of the land. In the case of the loading-plate type mold, this is used when the part being molded requires that a large space is provided for the charge used, thereby eliminating the necessity of machining a large space in the die itself. In all of these four types of compression molds, a rather complex assembly of parts is necessary on the press for quantity production of plastic parts.

Injection molding is very adaptable to thermoplastics, this process being very similar to die casting of metals, as shown in Fig. 19.6, the plastic, in granular or powder form, being forced into a heating chamber, a charge at a time, in precise measured amounts. With each plunger injection, the previously heated charge is forced into the mold. The process is fully automatic, the dies are water-cooled, and the production rates are kept as high as possible. Heating is carefully controlled, with the temperature of the charge held as low as possible to avoid burning the plastic. Injection pressures, even higher than in die-casting, up to 20,000 psi or more, are not uncommon. For this reason, the machines must be very rugged (Fig. 19.10) as even a small casting may require a clamping force of a million pounds or more to hold the mold halves in position. Pressure and

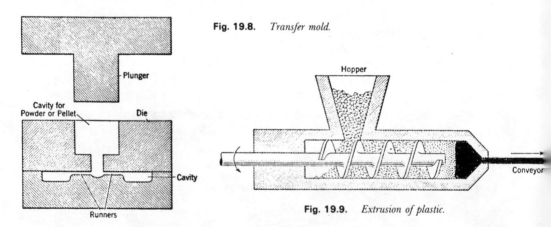

Fig. **19.8.**   *Transfer mold.*

Fig. **19.9.**   *Extrusion of plastic.*

temperature control are independent, since viscosity varies with the temperature. Production rates will vary from 100 to 850 parts per hour for each mold cavity. Small parts are often injected in multiple cavity molds with from 2 to 8 cavities in a mold.

Transfer molding is usually used for thermosetting plastics and it is very similar to the injection molding of thermoplastics, except that a heated mold is used to receive an injected charge of a moderately heated material. This method has been developed as a result of better control over the thermosetting reaction. Shown in Fig. 19.9 diagrammatically is indicated how the heat-softened material is injected into the heated mold and held there under high pressure until the setting reaction takes place and is completed. This equipment is more expensive but the finished parts are cleaner and have a better surface, and with faster

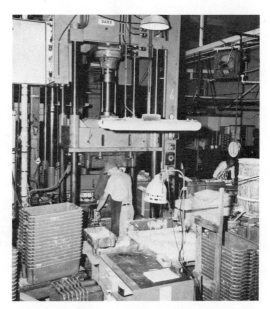

Fig. 19.10. *25-ton automatic molding press, air-operated. Molds thermosets such as phenolic, ures, bakelite, etc. (Courtesy of Dake Corp., Grand Haven, Mich.)*

Fig. 19.11. *100-ton fiberglass molding press making tote boxes. (Courtesy, Dake Corp.)*

production cycle. This process has one particular advantage over compression molding of the thermosetting plastics, i.e. there are no fins or flashes resulting.

Cold Moulding consists of the formation of plastic parts by the compression of the material in a cold die of the straight plunger-type. Upon the removal of the compressed plastic from the die it is baked in an oven at the correct temperature for from 1 to 4 days. This method is restricted to the thermosetting plastics and is effective for parts requiring heat resistance and strength at elevated temperatures, where a higher asbestos content is employed. Many small but important parts are made by this process, including switch bases, rheostats, handles for cooking utensils, connector plugs for flat-irons, etc.

Casting of plastic materials is the method generally used where there are a relatively few parts to be made as it makes the unit cost of the pieces much lower than if one of the more expensive methods previously described, were used. The technique is very similar to sand casting of metals, except that a steel arbor or mandrel is machined to the desired shape and the arbor is dipped in molten lead, the lead so solidifying around the arbor and cools when removed from the bath. The lead is then stripped off from the arbor forming the mold. In the case of phenol formaldehyde resin, the resin is then placed into the mold and cured for 2 to 6 days at a temperature of 160 to 200 F. Parts made in this manner are restricted in shape to simple forms with no undercut surfaces. Articles made by the casting process include novelty items, decorative pieces, jewelry, lighting fixtures etc.

Extrusion of plastic rods, tubes, angles and narrow sheets is accomplished in an extrusion machine shown schematically in Fig. 19.9 and supplied to the market in lengths as required. The heated plastic, in pellet form or as a powder,

Fig. 19.12. *Thermoformer—rugged four-post press designed for continuous high speed operation. 100 psi forming pressures. (Courtesy of Plastic Machinery, Div. NRM Corp.)*

is forced through the die opening at a continuous rate and is cooled by means of an air blast as it comes out of the die. This process is best adapted to the thermoplastic materials as thermosetting extrusions are more difficult to make, since the chemically intermediate plastic must be set by additional heating upon leaving the die. Small cross sections have been made from phenol formaldehyde and with the latest development of improved controls even larger shapes are being made quite satisfactorily, by the extrusion method.

Lamination of Plastics is a favorable method of processing casein, most of the aldehydes, and some of the other resins by dissolving them in organic solvents and subsequently using them as varnish for coatings and for impregnating sheets of paper, cloth or other fabrics. Layers of these sheets may then be cemented into a unit mass by pressing. Flat laminates can be produced very rapidly and inexpensively. The casein solution may be applied at room temperature by dipping, spraying or brushing and then the pressure applied either hot or cold. Although casein laminates are strongly bonded, they have a very poor resistance to moisture. The aldehyde laminates, while overcoming this disadvantage, require heat and close temperature control. The flat laminates may be sawed or cut to shape to produce such items as cams and gear blanks. Resin-bonded laminated shapes are largely used for such items as terminal boards, acid-resistant tubing, bearings, silent gears, bearings, radio and television parts, etc.

19-9   Foamed Plastics

These important products may be either thermosetting or thermoplastic and are made by expanding the plastic to a spongelike structure during processing. This is accomplished by incorporating chemicals which decompose with the liberation of gas at a critical point in the fabrication. This expansion may also be accomplished by dissolving a gas in the plastic under conditions that will allow the gas to come out of solution later with the formation of bubbles. Plastisols and plastigels are also used for producing foams by the above techniques. The work of German scientist, Wurtz back in 1848 was the forerunner of the foam plastics although his knowledge and experiments were not fully appreciated until just

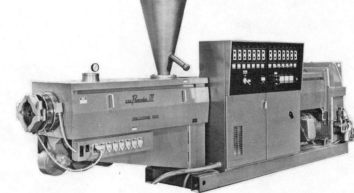

Fig. 19.13. *Air-cooled Pacemaker III Twin Screw Extruder.*

(Courtesy of Plastic Machinery, Div. NRM Corp.)

Fig. 19.14. *Dake 300-ton structural foam molding machine with 100% solid state controls.*

prior to World War II by the plastics industry.

Urethane plastics are produced as hard resins, solid elastomers, and adhesives, however, their primary use to date has been in the form of flexible or rigid foams. *Urethane foam* is the term adopted by The Society of the Plastics Industry, for materials that were previously called isocyanate, polyurethane or polyester foam. The foams are very useful for cushioning, packaging and thermal insulation, being found today in foam mattresses, liners for crash helmets, in randomes of aircraft and guided missiles, due to their near-perfect radar transmission properties. Their heat insulating properties as well as their tear-resistance qualities make the urethane plastics invaluable as lining materials for winter clothing. Foam liners only one-sixteenth inch thick provide excellent warmth for even arctic temperatures, being useful over a temperature range of from –50° to 250° F. Most of the foams are self-extinguishing and are not ignited by a glowing cigarette. They have good chemical resistance as well and are unaffected by most acids and alkalies.

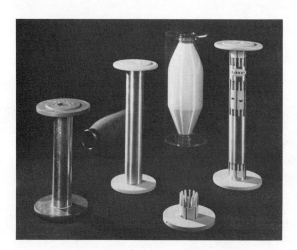

Fig. 19.15. *Textile bobbins produced by LHP Corp. are molded from Monsanto Vydyne R–240 mineral reinforced nylon resin. (Courtesy Monsanto Co.)*

Fig. 19.16. *Comfortable and contoured plastic handles on the Contura-Lite series of sheers from J. Wiss & Sons Co. are molded from Monsanto's Lustran ABS–240 plastic. (Courtesy Monsanto Co.)*

19-10   Plastic-Bonded Plywood

This is an important industry in this country developed substantially by the fact that the aldehyde resins are so superior to all other adhesives yet found for this purpose. Layers of plywood, bonded with casein and animal glues have been on the market for numbers of years and have been found to give good service and at the same time, to be comparatively low in cost. Resin-bonded plywoods are not only low in cost but they are also stronger and have moisture-resistance besides. They are also resistant to fungus and bacterial attacks and do not, of themselves, support combustion.

Bonded plywood is used extensively in some aircraft due to the fact it has a low specific gravity, being about half that of aluminum, so we find it used in wings, ailerons, struts, fins, ribs, rudders, bomb doors, floors and propellers where there is often a decided strength or stiffness advantage for a given weight. Bonded plywood sheets may be curved and still made to stand up and retain their forms even under extreme stress conditions in storms and at varying extremes of stratosphere to elevated humid air conditions such as in the tropics.

19-11   Aerospace Adhesive Bonded Systems

These have come a long way due to the in depth research on the part of such scientists as Raymond B. Krieger, Jr., Richard J. Dauksys, Michael J. Bodnar and others within the past few years. Their uses and importance are increasing at a

Code	Area	Material
	A	Aluminum Skin, Fiber-Glass Core
	B	Aluminum Skin, Aluminum Core
	C	Aluminum Skin, Aluminum Core
	D	Aluminum Skin, Full Depth Core*
	E	Aluminum Skin, Aluminum Core
	F	Aluminum Skin, Aluminum Core
	G	Aluminum Skin, Fiber-Glass Core
	H	Aluminum Skin, Fiber-Glass Core

*Wing Tips and Rudder Contain Aluminum Core, Resolution Surfaces and Fin Tip Contain Fiber-Glass Core

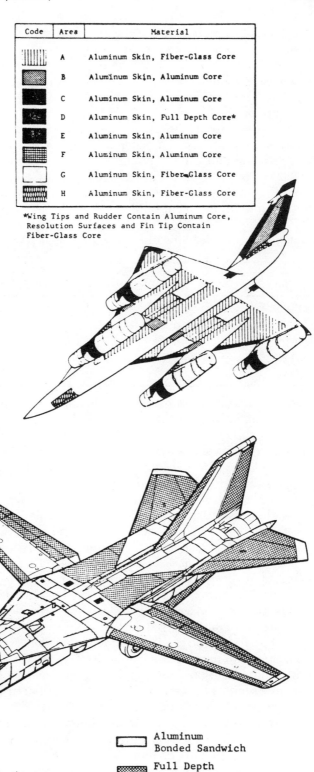

Fig. 19.17. *B–58 bonded structure areas.*

Fig. 19.18. *F–111 bonded construction.*

	Aluminum Bonded Sandwich
	Full Depth Honeycomb Core

rapid rate. The B-58 is cited as the first military aircraft to use extensive adhesive bonding, as shown in Fig. 19.17. Approximately 80% of the F-111 is adhesive-bonded sandwich structure shown in Fig. 19.18 and the C-5 contains over 1 acre of adhesive bonded assemblies. The F-15 contains a structural adhesive empennage. (tail section of aircraft) Table 19.5 shows the extent of usage of adhesive structure on the Boeing 700 Series aircraft. Adhesives, because they lend themselves to design and fabrication of minimum weight constructions and joining of a wide variety of dissimilar materials, are used extensively in aerospace systems. It is estimated for every 1 pound saved in fabrication of hardware, $10,000 to $20,000 would be saved in launching the system. (Much of this section on Aerospace Adhesive Bonded Systems is by courtesy of Dr. R. J. Dauksys and the Society for Advancement of Material and Process Engineering (SAMPE).

Table 19.5   Bonded Structure Utilization Boeing Aircraft

Airplane	Area Bonded Structure (Ft.^{2})			Hightime Airplane (hours)
	Honeycomb	Metal to metal	Fiberglass	
707	250	1,000	250	49,100
727	1,500	3,500	700	28,400
737	1,000	3,000	2,000	14,000
747	3,600	9,960	12,000	11,000

The main reason for moving into adhesive bonded systems in aircraft is due to the substantial cost savings by virtue of elimination of holes and mechanical fasteners, such as bolts, rivets etc., which typically accounts for 30% to more than 70% of total manufacturing costs. Other advantages of adhesive bonding are associated with lower weight, and depending on desired performance and design, resulting greater payload and/or maneuverability and/or flight times. Furthermore, aerodynamically smooth parts are possible by the joining of structures with adhesives. Adhesive bonding permits facile joining of thin and contoured sheets, minimizes stress concentrations, and reduces galvanic corrosion effects when joining dissimilar metals, the adhesive, no doubt, acting as a sealant as well.

   Methods of testing Bonded Adhesive Joints is of major importance and new advances have been made to determine the stress field of various design and compositions. For example, the Air Force Flight Dynamics Laboratory (AFFDL) has developed a linear closed form finite element analysis and accompanying computer program referred to as BONJO which will provide distribution of normal and shear stresses in bonded composite lap joints. A major problem associated with implementing adhesive laminated structures (Fig. 19.19, 19.20, 19.21) for primary structural applications is that adequate fracture mechanics or fracture criteria and associated with NDT (non-destructive testing) are just now becoming available to assess flaws such as voids, edge cracks, and debond areas. However, it is a fact that this type of bonded structure, should it develop gross defects, offers formidable problems of repair, as aircraft builders are reluctant to scrap 1000 pounds or more of machined and formed adhesive laminated titanium sheet and therefore determine the most economical method of salvaging the assembly.

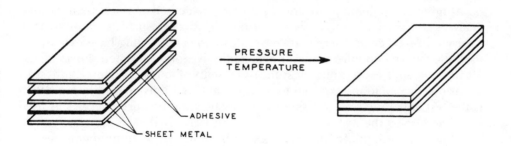

ADVANTAGES

EXCELLENT FRACTURE TOUGHNESS QUALITIES

EXCELLENT FORMING QUALITIES

EXCELLENT DAMAGE TOLERANCE CHARACTERISTICS

Fig. 19.19. *Adhesive laminated sheet structures.*

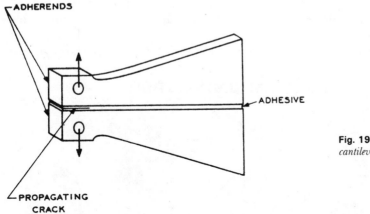

Fig. 19.20. *Tapered double cantilever beam specimen.*

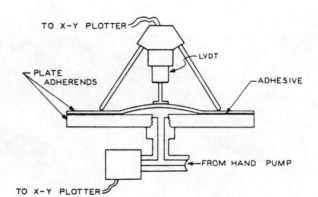

Fig. 19.21. *Blister adhesive joint fracture energy test.*

Although slow coming, advances are being made in flaw assessment. Several analyses are available for flaws of various geometries such as penny-shaped internal defects, edge cracks and voids. Mostovoy and Ripling have extensively used the tapered double cantilever beam adhesive joint specimen shown in Fig. 19.18 to obtain fracture toughness measurements of joints containing adhesives of various formulations exposed to a variety of conditions. Shown in Fig. 19.19 is the test apparatus and test specimen for obtaining fracture energies as used by a scientist by the name of W. Jones which were used very effectively.

It must be recognized that basic research studies are a continuing necessity, and that although they are usually longer term insofar as payoff is concerned, must be continued in the months and years ahead. The problems associated with advancing adhesive bonding to its fullest extent and potential are complex but not insurmountable. Progress made to date in research and exploratory development of adhesives and adhesive bonding promise high payoffs in advanced design/manufacturing programs which will ultimately result in economical and reliable aerospace systems of unparalleled performance.

High Temperature Resistant Adhesives up above 400°F. are a necessity which means that the chemist is faced with designing polymers for use as adhesives that are tough, do not produce volatiles and that cure at modest temperatures, at the same time displaying high temperature properties.

Three adhesives which have received the greatest attention to date, for applications that require greater than 500° F service temperature are polyimide (PI), polyimidazoquinazoline (PIQ). Further research and development are of paramount importance.

FUNDAMENTALS OF ADHESIVE TECHNOLOGY. From shoes to space

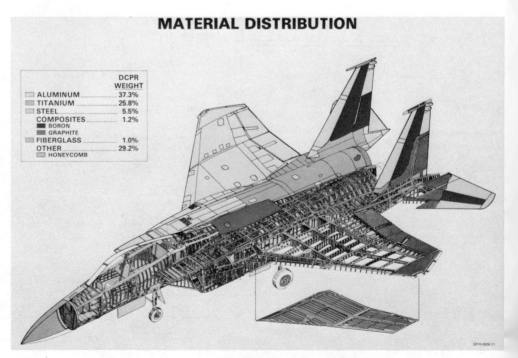

MATERIAL DISTRIBUTION

	DCPR WEIGHT
ALUMINUM	37.3%
TITANIUM	25.8%
STEEL	5.5%
COMPOSITES	1.2%
BORON	
GRAPHITE	
FIBERGLASS	1.0%
OTHER	29.2%
HONEYCOMB	

Fig. 19.22.   *F-15 EAGLE*

Fig. 19.23. *Adhesive bonded structure is utilized extensively on the F–15 aircraft. (Courtesy of McDonnell-Douglas Corp., St. Louis, Mo.)*

Fig. 19.24. *There are three areas on the F–15 where high strength and stiffness of boron/epoxy composites are applied to good structural advantages: Vertical fin torque box skins; horizontal stabilator torque box skins; rudder skins. (Courtesy of McDonnell-Douglas Corp., St. Louis, Mo.)*

ships, as shown on the preceding pages—adhesives perform the fundamental function of holding things together. But that is not as simple as it sounds. For a workable understanding of adhesion, and its benefits and limitations, knowledge of the fundamentals is essential. One of the common laboratory tests to measure adhesive performance is to "pull at" or stress the bond, the purpose being to see at what point, stress overcomes adhesion and the bond breaks. With some adhesives the materials stretch or break before the adhesive bond.

ADHESION vs STRESS - that's what a great deal of adhesive technology is all about. Adhesion is the force that holds materials together. There are three basic types:

1) *SPECIFIC ADHESION* - is the molecular attraction between contacting surfaces.
2) *MECHANICAL ADHESION* - occurs when an adhesive is applied to rough or porous surfaces.
3) *EFFECTIVE ADHESION* - combines specific and mechanical adhesion for optimum strength.

Stress, on the other hand, is the force pulling materials apart. The basic types of stress in adhesive technology are:

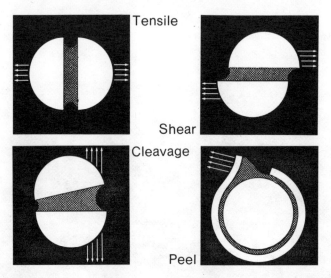

1) *TENSILE* "Pull" is exerted equally over the entire joint. "Pull direction" is straight and away from the adhesive bond. All adhesive contributes to bond strength.
2) *SHEAR.* "Pull direction" is across the adhesive bond. The bonded materials are being forced to slide over each other.
3) *CLEAVAGE* "Pull" is concentrated at one edge of the joint and exerts a prying force on the bond. The other edge of the joint is theoretically under zero stress.
4) *PEEL.* One surface must be flexible. Stress is concentrated along a thin line at the edge of the bond. This line is the exact point where an adhesive would separate if the flexible surface were peeled away from its mating

surface. Once peeling has begun, the "stress line" would stay out in front of the advancing bond separation.

Most adhesives perform better when the primary stress is tensile or shear. However, in most industrial applications, a combination of stresses are involved. For best performance, the entire bond area should carry the bulk of the stress. Resistance to stress is one general reason for the rapid increase in the use of adhesives for product assembly.

19-12 *Elastomers, or rubbers*

Elastomers, like the plastics, are made into organic polymers, however, they differ from the plastics in that they have a colloidal rather than a crystalline

Adhesives, Coatings and Sealers Division 3M COMPANY PRINTED IN U.S.A. — 3M CENTER, ST. PAUL, MINN. 55101 — **ADHESIVE SELECTION CHART**

FOR BONDING:

ABS	ACETAL	ACRYLIC	CELLULOSE ACETATE	EPOXY	NYLON	PHENOLIC	POLYCARBONATE	POLYESTER (GLASS REINFORCED)	POLYESTER FILM	UNTREATED POLYETHYLENE (LINEAR)	UNTREATED POLYPROPYLENE	STYRENE	STYRENE (HI-IMPACT)	VINYL (RIGID)	*VINYL (FLEXIBLE, UNSUPPORTED)	*VINYL (SUPPORTED)	3M SUGGESTS:
•				•	•	•		•							•	•	PLASTIC ADHESIVE 1099
•				•	•	•		•							•	•	PLASTIC ADHESIVE 1359
		•													•	•	PLASTIC ADHESIVE 2262
																•	PLASTIC ADHESIVE 4213
	•	•		•		•	•	•					•	•	•		PLASTIC ADHESIVE 4475
•	•	•	•	•	•	•	•	•	•	•	•	•	•	•	•		PLASTIC ADHESIVE 4693

structure. They can be molded into forms which tend to hold their shape, like the plastics, however in the case of the elastomer forms, they can undergo great elastic distortion without plastic yielding. Table 19.6 shows the comparative properties of rubbers and indicates that there is not a sharp line between them and other plastics.

The essential elastomers may be considered as being polymers or copolymers of 1,3 butadiene ($CH_2 = CH - CH = CH_2$) or one of its derivatives. The natural rubber, isoprene ($CH_2 = C - CH - CH_3 = CH_2$). As indicated, this natural rubber monomer is the 2-methyl derivative.

Another group of elastomers is composed of ethylene derivatives, or copolymers, and yet others are polyurethanes, polysulfides, and polyacrylates.

Up until World War II, natural rubber was the only elastomer used in appreciable amounts in the United States, with the exception of a relatively small amount of neoprene used in special applications. When our supply of natural rubber from Asia was cut off during the war, the manufacture of styrene-butadiene copolymer rubber was developed in government plants in this country as an emergency measure. Since the war, the production of this and other types of rubber has increased rapidly. Now, only about 20 percent of the rubber consumed in the United States and about 40 percent consumed in the word, is natural rubber. About 75 percent of synthetic rubber used in this country is the styrene-butadiene copolymer made largely by the emulsion polymerization process, although the use of the new stereospecific catalysts in solution polymerization have produced better control of the rubber structure along with the use of new raw materials. At this time, it appears to show a trend away from the styrene-butadiene product to some of the newer methods and products.

Natural rubber is a vegetable product which may be obtained from a variety of plants, its chief source being a tropical tree, *Hevea brasiliensis,* a native of the Upper Amazon River Valley. A substantial amount of the natural rubber today comes from the cultivated Hevea rubber trees in Southeastern Asia, with lesser amounts coming from Africa and South America. A shrub, guayule, which grows on dry land in southwestern United States and in Mexico shows some possibility as a rubber source, however it has not been commercialized to date.

Natural rubber from the Hevea tree comes as an emulsion or disperson, known as *latex,* the rubber constituting about 35 percent of the latex obtained. Most of the latex is treated with acetic or formic acid to precipitate the rubber. Formerly, the separated rubber was formed into sheets and dried by hot air or smoke, however the more modern method employs the use of extruders to squeeze out the water, then passing the coagulated rubber through three or four pairs of creping rolls which cut it into granule form, these granules being subsequently baled for shipment to the market.

The raw rubber is processed either by milling between heavy rolls or by employing a Banbury mixer (Fig. 19.25) to obtain a uniform product and yet soften it such that it can be mixed with additives then processed in operations such as calendering and extruding. Specific plasticizers, both chemical and mechanical in their operation are added to assist in the softening, the former including certain petroleum sulfonates, aromatic mercaptans, and pentachlorothiophenol, along with vulcanization accelerators which may also act as plasticizers.

Natural soft rubber is used in applications where both its mechanical properties, such as flexibility and extensibility, and its resistance to chemicals and toxic conditions, makes it especially desirable. Included in such applications for natural soft rubber are, automobile tires and tubes; air hose for water, steam and air; "rubbers" and overshoes; raincoats; floor tile and mats; tubing; protective

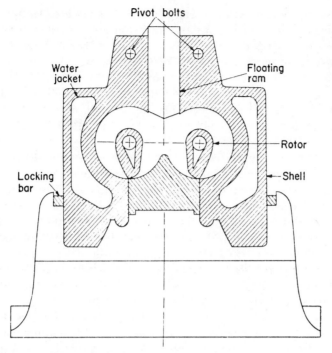

Fig. 19.25. *Banbury Mixer*

Table 19.6   Comparative Properties of Rubbers

Property	Natural	SBR	Butyl	Polysulfide*	Nitrile	Neoprene	Chlorosulfonated polyethylene†	Fluorocarbon‡	Urethane§	Ethylene-propylene‖	Silicone
							Types of Rubbers				
Tensile Strength (1000 psi)	3.0	2.0	2.0	...	2.0	3.0	3.0	2.0	4.0	3.0	1.5
Specific Gravity	0.9	0.9	0.9	1.3	1.0	1.2	1.2	1.9	1.1	0.9	...
Vulcanizing Properties	E	E	G	F	E	E	E	G	E	E	...
Adhesion (to metals & fabrics)	E	G–E	G	F–P	E	E	G–E	G–E	E	G	...
Tear Resistance	G	F	G	P	F	G	F	F	E	G	P
Abrasion Resistance	E	G–E	G	P	G	E	E	G	E+	E	P
Gas Permeability	F	F	VL	L	F	L	L–	VL	F	F	F
Dielectric Strength	E	E	E	F	P	G	E	G	E	E	G
Chemical Resistance:											
Acids	F–G	F–G	E	F	G	G–E	G–E	E	P	E	F–E
Petroleum products	P	P	P	E	E	G	G	E	E	P	F
Fat and oil solvents	P–G	P–G	E	E	E	G	G	E	E	G	F
Aliphatic	P	P	P	E	E	G	G	E	E	P	P
Aromatic	P	P	P	G	G	F	F	E	F–G*	P	P
Oxygenated	G	G	G	G	P	P	P	P	P	G	F
Lacquer	P	P	P	G	F	P	P	P	P	P	P
Resistance to:											
Oxidation	G	G	E	G	G	E	E	E+	E	E	E
Sunlight	P	P	VG	G	P	VG	E+	VG	G	E+	E
Heat	G	E	E	P	E	E	E	E	G	E	E
Cold	E	E	G	F	G	G	G	G	E	E	E

P=poor; F=fair; G=good; E=excellent; L=low; V=very.
* Thiokol
† Hypalon
‡ Viton
§ Adiprene
‖ Nordel

gloves; hot water bottles; erasers, etc. It also has many uses, industrially including protective linings in tanks, pumps, and other equipment; rubber belting and various types of seals and closures. In the case of hard rubber, this is used in electrical insulating parts, chemically resistant pipes and equipment as well as combs and similar products.

Foam rubber is made by incorporating gas into latex and then vulcanized. Many products are made from this material including, toys, pillows, furniture cushion, mattresses, automotive pads and gaskets. (see Fig. **19.14** for DAKE 300 Ton Structural Foam Molding Machine)

Sponge rubber is produced from dry natural or synthetic rubber, into which a blowing agent such as sodium bicarbonate and fatty acid are injected. Where an *open-cell* structure is desired, the compounding and curing are regulated to produce gas before vulcanizing, thereby rupturing the cell walls and producing an interconnecting structure. In the case of a *closed-cell* structure, the rubber is partially cured prior to expansion of the gas. *Open-cell* types of sponge rubber are used in sealing, heat insulating, cushioning and shock absorption. The *closed-cell* types of sponge rubber have similar uses as aforementioned and also find uses where buoyancy in water are required.

Rubber is reclaimed from old tires and tubes by treating in a satisfactory manner, to recover *reclaimed rubber* for subsequent use. The usual method of processing discarded tires and tubes is grind the rubber items between corrugated rolls revolving at unequal speeds. The ground rubber material is digested 5 to 24 hours in an aqueous solution of sodium hydroxide at from 370° to 405° F, thereby hydrolyzing the fiber and softening the rubber. This material is then washed and dried followed by a milling and blending operation with plasticizer, clay, and carbon black. After additional milling and straining to remove foreign matter, the rubber is formed into thin sheets which are wound into rolls. Reclaimed rubber is blended with new rubber to form many new products, and has numbers of advantages including low cost, short mixing time, low power consumption, low heat generated in processing, high rate of cure and good aging.

Neoprene is an elastomer that is produced from acetylene gas and hydrogen chloride, forming a monomer called *chloroprene* which can be polymerized to a form that possesses rubber-like properties. Its mechanical properties are quite similar to rubber, whether in the pure gum or the vulcanized state. It can be compounded with carbon black to make very durable tire treads. It is far superior to rubber in its resistance to deterioration in the presence of oils and other organic solvents or when exposed to air and sunlight. Neoprene also has better heat resistance than rubber and the chlorine atom in its molecule makes it relatively nonflammable. Although the materials from which neoprene are made are comparatively costly and the chemical process somewhat complex, nevertheless it has found a ready market for such products as diaphragms, gaskets, valve seats, grommets and oil seals due to its excellent properties.

Neoprene latices are used in production of gloves, balloons, industrial parts, foam items and in adhesives.

Vulcanization of rubber was first discovered by Charles Goodyear in 1839 when he found through experimentation, that when sulfur and rubber are mixed and heated, the properties of the rubber underwent a remarkable change. This process of heating the compound rubber to bring about the desired properties is called *vulcanizing.* At first, some 20 to 40 percent of sulfur was required, and a heating period of many hours, however, it was later discovered that the amount of sulfur could be materially reduced and the heating period shortened, by additions of zinc oxide or magnesium oxide. Then in 1906 it was learned that 1 percent of analine oil, added to the sulfur-zinc oxide mixture again reduced the amount of sulfur needed and resulted in a more uniform product. In most cases, a mixture of 3 percent or less of sulfur is now required and the vulcanizing temperature ranges from 200 F to 320 F. Furthermore, the vulcanizing time has been found to be best, from just a few minutes to several hours, depending upon the hardness desired and on the thickness of the part. The additives of zinc oxide, magnesium oxide and analine oil are known as *accelerators* and their action is a chemical one. Together with the sulfur, the process results in a complex cross-polimerization of the rubber.

19-13   Search for Improved Tires Underway

An important news item in January 1976 out of Dayton, Ohio states in part as follows: "Growing use of carbon brakes in aircraft is raising the temperatures that tires are experiencing, especially in the bead area, thus pushing the search for higher thermal resistance of parts of the tire that are subject to relatively little wear. At the same time, the nearly universal employment of grooving to prevent hydroplaning on wet runways is increasing the cut, wear and abrasion experienced by tire treads and requiring new materials to counteract this."

To counteract the high temperature environment of sidewalls, DuPont *Kevlar* has been used as a reinforcement and two types of rubber: *styrene-butadiene* (SBR) and *carbonitrile* (CBR) are employed. In addition, heavy metallic heat-sinks on the aircraft wheels are being provided to soak up the heat generated by the carbon brakes. For the most part, however, the temperature resistance is being built into the tire-wheel interface. A mixture of natural rubber and SBR with a curing system seems to give the best high temperature performance. The properties of the two materials complement each other nicely—at high temperatures, the SBR hardens while the natural rubber softens, thereby maintaining the strength of the tire. Chopped *Kevlar* is used as a reinforcement, mixed with the rubbers, whereas DuPont Nylon 66 is used on the cords.

In order to reduce cut, wear and abrasion on tires, Alfin-SBR appears to be promising in blends with natural rubber. *Alfin* is a catalyst that gives a high molecular weight rubber that is tougher than ordinary rubber.

Tire testing has improved also with a facility in Texas for testing the durability of tires on a 2-mile long track of granite chips. There is also important testing at Langley Airforce Base on wet-runways that is proving important to the development of better tires.

QUESTIONS

1. What is the "official" definition of plastics? (State in your own words.)
2. What are the two classifications of plastics in terms of the way heat affects them? Name a plastic from each group.

3. What are the ingredients of most plastics? What is the function of each ingredient?
4. List the forms in which plastics can be found. Give an example of where each could be found.
5. State the four general groups of properties that should be considered when studying a plastic.
6. Are plastics usually hard or soft as compared to most metals?
7. How does the weight of plastics compare with that of metal? of wood?
8. Name a plastic that is very clear.
9. What is likely to cause a plastic to warp?
10. Are plastics usually good or poor insulators? Why is this?
11. How do plastics compare with metals in general so far as conduction of heat is concerned? What term is used to indicate the heat insulating value of a plastic?
12. How do most plastics react to freezing temperatures?
13. What effect does heat have on the size of a plastic article?
14. How do plastics generally react to acids? to alkalies?
15. Give an example of a product where its physical properties would be of great importance. Its electrical properties. Its thermal properties. Its chemical properties. Give examples of each.
16. Name a material that is not a plastic but acts like a thermosetting plastic when subject to heat or cold.
17. What combination of properties makes plastics ideal for refrigerator tray?
18. Make a list of plastics belonging to the family of thermplastics. After each plastic list two or three of its outstanding properties.
19. Make a list of thermoset plastics and list a few properties of each.
20. What fundamental difference is there betwen plastics and elastomers (rubbers)?
21. Considering the comparative properties of rubbers, where is the line of difference between them?
22. Which one of the various elastomers was used in appreciable amounts prior to World War II?
23. During World War II, what was it that brought about the development and manufacture of styrene-butadiene?
24. After World War II did the use of natural rubber return to what it was prior to the war? Why was this?
25. What is the major source of natural rubber in this country?
26. Give some of the important uses of natural rubber and give the reasons why this is true in each case.
27. Explain the process of making sponge rubber and state how many types there are of such sponge rubbers.
28. Is it profitable to reclaim old tires? If not why not? If it is, how is this accomplished?
29. What is neoprene and how is it produced?
30. What was it that led to the vulcanization of rubber? How is this done now? How was it accomplished prior to 1906?
31. Describe in detail the importance of plastic-bonded plywood in domestic and aircraft production.

32. How far has the use of adhesive-bonded systems in aerospace come during the past few years? Give details.

33. Are adhesive-bonded systems considered satisfactory for use in military aircraft? Give specific examples.

References

Arnold, L. K. *Introduction to Plastics.* Ames, Iowa. The Iowa State University Press, 1968

Allcott, John V. *Plastics Today.* Oxford University Press. New York

Bick, Alexander., *Plastics: Projects and Procedures with Polyesters.* The Bruce Publishing Co. Milwaukee 1962

Brenner, Walter, et al. *High Temperature Plastics* Reinhold Publishing Co. New York 1962

Buyer's Guide to Plastics Materials and Machinery and Equipment for the Plastics Industry London. British Plastics Federation.

Cherry, Raymond, *General Plastics* Bloomington, Ill. McKnight & McKnight Publishing Co. 1967

Edwards, Lauton. *Industrial Arts Plastics,* Peoria, Ill. Charles A. Bennett Co., Inc. 1964

Facts and Figures of the Plastics Industry, the Society of the Plastics Industry, Inc. New York N.Y. 1975

Cellular Plastics in Transportation Technomic Publishing Co. Inc. Westport, Connecticut. 1975

Structural Plastic Foams. Chemical Business Development Co. Montclair, N.J. 1975

Plastics Engineering; Society of Plastics Engineers. Dec. 1975

Modern Plastics Encyclopedia Vol. 51 No. 10A 1974–75 McGraw-Hill, Inc.

Lawrence, J. R. *Polyester Resins* Reinhold Publishing Corp. New York

Plastics, (Reference Issue of Machine Design,) 1964–65

Skeist, Irving, editor *Handbook of Adhesives,* Reinhold Publishing Corp. 1962

SAMPE QUARTERLY, The Society for the Advancement of Materials and Process Engineering Special Issue October 1973 on Adhesives Technology William G. Long, Editor. Lynchburg, Va.

Dauksys, Richard J. *Research and Development of Aerospace Adhesive Bonded Systems and Concepts.* 1973

Beemer, Roger D. *Introduction to Weld Bonding,* S A M P E 1973

Ziska, James L. and Robert S. Thomas, *A B S Plastic,* Modern Plastics Encyclopedia 1974–75

Swanson, Robert S. *Plastics Technology,* McKnight Publishing Co. Bloomington, Ill. 1965.

Smith, W. Mayo *Manufacture of Plastics* Vol. 1 Research Center, Escambia Chemical Corp. Wilton, Conn. Reinhold Publishing Corporation, New York 1964

Klein, Imrich and Donald I. Marshall, *Computer Programs for Plastics* Engineers, Reinhold Book Corp. 1968

Kaye, S. Leon *The Production and Properties of Plastics* International Textbook Company 1947

Clark, Donald S. *Engineering Materials and Processes,* International Textbook Company 3rd edition 1966

Keyser, Carl A. *Materials Science in Engineering,* Charles E. Merrill Publishing Co. 1968

Bateman, Leslie, *Chemistry and Physics of Rubberlike Substances* New York, Interscience Publishers, John Wiley & Sons, Inc.

Morton, Maurice, *Introduction to Rubber Technology,* Reinhold Book Division, New York

PERIODICALS

Modern Plastics, McGraw-Hill Publishing Company 770 Lexington Ave. New York, N.Y. 10021

Plastics World, Cahners Publishing Co. 221 Columbus Ave., Boston, Massachusetts, 12116

Rubber Age, Palmerton Publishing Company 101 West 31st Street, New York, N.Y. 10001

Rubber World, Bill Brothers Publishing Company 630 Third Avenue, New York, N.Y. 10017

SPE JOURNAL, Society of Plastics Engineers, 65 Prospect Street, Stamford, Connecticut 06902

APPENDICES

APPENDIX A

TEMPERATURE-CONVERSION TABLE

°C	°F	°C	°F	°C	°F	°C	°F	°C	°F
−273	−459	400	752	1000	1832	1600	2912	−268	−450
−250	−418	410	770	1010	1850	1610	2930	−240	−400
−200	−328	420	788	1020	1868	1620	2948	−212	−350
−150	−238	430	806	1030	1886	1630	2966	−184	−300
−100	−148	440	824	1040	1904	1640	2984	−157	−250
− 50	− 58	450	842	1050	1922	1650	3002	−129	−200
− 40	− 40	460	860	1060	1940	1660	3020	−101	−150
− 30	− 22	470	878	1070	1958	1670	3038	− 73	−100
− 20	− 4	480	896	1080	1976	1680	3056	− 46	− 50
− 10	+ 14	490	914	1090	1994	1690	3074	− 40	− 40
0	32	500	932	1100	2012	1700	3092	− 34	− 30
5	41	510	950	1110	2030	1710	3110	− 29	− 20
10	50	520	968	1120	2048	1720	3128	− 23	− 10
15	59	530	986	1130	2066	1730	3146	− 18	0
20	68	540	1004	1140	2084	1740	3164	− 15	5
25	77	550	1022	1150	2102	1750	3182	− 12	10
30	86	560	1040	1160	2120	1760	3200	− 9	15
35	95	570	1058	1170	2138	1770	3218	− 7	20
40	104	580	1076	1180	2156	1780	3236	− 4	25
45	113	590	1094	1190	2174	1790	3254	− 1	30
50	122	600	1112	1200	2192	1800	3272	+ 2	35
55	131	610	1130	1210	2210	1810	3290	4	40
60	140	620	1148	1220	2228	1820	3308	7	45
65	149	630	1166	1230	2246	1830	3326	10	50
70	158	640	1184	1240	2264	1840	3344	13	55
75	167	650	1202	1250	2282	1850	3362	16	60
80	176	660	1220	1260	2300	1860	3380	18	65
85	185	670	1238	1270	2318	1870	3398	21	70
90	194	680	1256	1280	2336	1880	3416	24	75
95	203	690	1274	1290	2354	1890	3434	27	80
100	212	700	1292	1300	2372	1900	3452	29	85
110	230	710	1310	1310	2390	1910	3470	32	90
120	248	720	1328	1320	2408	1920	3488	35	95
130	266	730	1346	1330	2426	1930	3506	38	100
140	284	740	1364	1340	2444	1940	3524	43	110
150	302	750	1382	1350	2462	1950	3542	49	120
160	320	760	1400	1360	2480	1960	3560	54	130
170	338	770	1418	1370	2498	1970	3578	60	140
180	356	780	1436	1380	2516	1980	3596	65	150
190	374	790	1454	1390	2534	1990	3614	71	160
200	392	800	1472	1400	2552	2000	3632	76	170
210	410	810	1490	1410	2570	2050	3722	83	180
220	428	820	1508	1420	2588	2100	3812	88	190
230	446	830	1526	1430	2606	2150	3902	93	200
240	464	840	1544	1440	2624	2200	3992	121	250
250	482	850	1562	1450	2642	2250	4082	149	300
260	500	860	1580	1460	2660	2300	4172	177	350
270	518	870	1598	1470	2678	2350	4262	204	400
280	536	880	1616	1480	2696	2400	4352	232	450
290	554	890	1634	1490	2714	2450	4442	260	500
300	572	900	1652	1500	2732	2500	4532	288	550
310	590	910	1670	1510	2750	2550	4622	316	600
320	608	920	1688	1520	2768	2600	4712	343	650
330	626	930	1706	1530	2786	2650	4802	371	700
340	644	940	1724	1540	2804	2700	4892	399	750
350	662	950	1742	1550	2822	2750	4982	427	800
360	680	960	1760	1560	2840	2800	5072	454	850
370	698	970	1778	1570	2858	2850	5162	482	900
380	716	980	1796	1580	2876	2900	5252	510	950
390	734	990	1814	1590	2894	3000	5432	538	1000

(Courtesy of *Metals Handbook*, Vol. 8, published by American Society for Metals, Metals Park, Ohio.)

APPENDIX B

MELTING POINTS OF THE ELEMENTS

Element	Symbol	Melting point, °F	Element	Symbol	Melting point, °F
Actinium	Ac	2900	Neodymium	Nd	1875
Aluminum	Al	1220	Neon	Ne	−416
Americium	Am	....	Neptunium	Np	....
Antimony	Sb	1167	Nickel	Ni	2651
Argon	A	−309	Niobium (Colum-		
Arsenic	As	1497	bium)	Nb	4380
Astatine	At	....	Nitrogen	N	−346
Barium	Ba	1300	Osmium	Os	4900
Berkelium	Bk	....	Oxygen	O	−362
Beryllium	Be	2340	Palladium	Pd	2829
Bismuth	Bi	520	Phosphorus	P	111
Boron	B	4200	Platinum	Pt	3224
Bromine	Br	19	Plutonium	Pu	....
Cadmium	Cd	610	Polonium	Po	1100
Calcium	Ca	1560	Potassium	K	145
Californium	Cf	....	Praseodymium	Pr	1715
Carbon	C	6700	Promethium	Pm	....
Cerium	Ce	1480	Protoactinium	Pa	5400
Cesium	Cs	82	Radium	Ra	1300
Chlorine	Cl	−150	Radon	Rn	−96
Chromium	Cr	3430	Rhenium	Re	5740
Cobalt	Co	2723	Rhodium	Rh	3571
Copper	Cu	1981	Rubidium	Rb	102
Curium	Cm	....	Ruthenium	Ru	4500
Dysprosium	Dy	2730	Samarium	Sm	1930
Erbium	Er	....	Scandium	Sc	2190
Europium	Eu	....	Selenium	Se	428
Fluorine	F	−370	Silicon	Si	2605
Francium	Fa	....	Silver	Ag	1760
Gadolinium	Gd	2460	Sodium	Na	208
Gallium	Ga	85	Strontium	Sr	1420
Germanium	Ge	1760	Sulfur	S	246
Gold	Au	1954	Tantalum	Ta	5425
Hafnium	Hf	3100	Technetium	Tc	4900
Helium	He	−456	Tellurium	Te	840
Holmium	Ho	2730	Terbium	Tb	621
Hydrogen	H	−435	Thallium	Tl	572
Indium	In	313	Thorium	Th	3300
Iodine	I	237	Thulium	Tm	....
Iridium	Ir	4449	Tin	Sn	449
Iron	Fe	2802	Titanium	Ti	3040
Krypton	Kr	−251	Tungsten (Wolfram)	W	6170
Lanthanum	La	1688	Uranium	U	2065
Lead	Pb	621	Vanadium	V	3150
Lithium	Li	367	Xenon	Xe	−170
Lutecium	Lu	....	Ytterbium	Yb	....
Magnesium	Mg	1202	Yttrium	Y	2700
Manganese	Mn	2273	Zinc	Zn	787
Mercury	Hg	−38	Zirconium	Zr	3362
Molybdenum	Mo	4760			

(From *Metals Handbook*, published by American Society for Metals, Metals Park, Ohio).

APPENDIX C

AISI-SAE ALLOY STEEL COMPOSITIONS

Manganese Steels

AISI Number	Chemical Composition Ranges and Limits, per cent								Corresponding SAE Number
	C	Mn	P max	S max	Si	Ni	Cr	Mo	
1330	0.28/0.33	1.60/1.90	0.040	0.040	0.20/0.35	—	—	—	1330
1335	0.33/0.38	1.60/1.90	0.040	0.040	0.20/0.35	—	—	—	1335
1340	0.38/0.43	1.60/1.90	0.040	0.040	0.20/0.35	—	—	—	1340
1345	0.43/0.48	1.60/1.90	0.040	0.040	0.20/0.35	—	—	—	1345

Nickel-Chromium Steels

AISI Number	C	Mn	P max	S max	Si	Ni	Cr	Mo	SAE
3140	0.38/0.43	0.70/0.90	0.040	0.040	0.20/0.35	1.10/1.40	0.55/0.75	—	3140
E3310	0.08/0.13	0.45/0.60	0.025	0.025	0.20/0.35	3.25/3.75	1.40/1.75	—	3310

Molybdenum Steels

AISI Number	C	Mn	P max	S max	Si	Ni	Cr	Mo	SAE
4012	0.09/0.14	0.75/1.00	0.040	0.040	0.20/0.35	—	—	0.15/0.25	4012
4023	0.20/0.25	0.70/0.90	0.040	0.040	0.20/0.35	—	—	0.20/0.30	4023
4024	0.20/0.25	0.70/0.90	0.040	0.035/0.050	0.20/0.35	—	—	0.20/0.30	4024
4027	0.25/0.30	0.70/0.90	0.040	0.040	0.20/0.35	—	—	0.20/0.30	4027
4028	0.25/0.30	0.70/0.90	0.040	0.035/0.050	0.20/0.35	—	—	0.20/0.30	4028
4037	0.35/0.40	0.70/0.90	0.040	0.040	0.20/0.35	—	—	0.20/0.30	4037
4042	0.40/0.45	0.70/0.90	0.040	0.040	0.20/0.35	—	—	0.20/0.30	4042
4047	0.45/0.50	0.70/0.90	0.040	0.040	0.20/0.35	—	—	0.20/0.30	4047
4063	0.60/0.67	0.75/1.00	0.040	0.040	0.20/0.35	—	—	0.20/0.30	4063

Chromium-Molybdenum Steels

AISI Number	C	Mn	P max	S max	Si	Ni	Cr	Mo	SAE
4118	0.18/0.23	0.70/0.90	0.040	0.040	0.20/0.35	—	0.40/0.60	0.08/0.15	4118
4130	0.28/0.33	0.40/0.60	0.040	0.040	0.20/0.35	—	0.80/1.10	0.15/0.25	4130
4135	0.33/0.38	0.70/0.90	0.040	0.040	0.20/0.35	—	0.80/1.10	0.15/0.25	4135
4137	0.35/0.40	0.70/0.90	0.040	0.040	0.20/0.35	—	0.80/1.10	0.15/0.25	4137
4140	0.38/0.43	0.75/1.00	0.040	0.040	0.20/0.35	—	0.80/1.10	0.15/0.25	4140
4142	0.40/0.45	0.75/1.00	0.040	0.040	0.20/0.35	—	0.80/1.10	0.15/0.25	4142
4145	0.43/0.48	0.75/1.00	0.040	0.040	0.20/0.35	—	0.80/1.10	0.15/0.25	4145
4147	0.45/0.50	0.75/1.00	0.040	0.040	0.20/0.35	—	0.80/1.10	0.15/0.25	4147
4150	0.48/0.53	0.75/1.00	0.040	0.040	0.20/0.35	—	0.80/1.10	0.15/0.25	4150

Nickel-Chromium-Molybdenum Steels

AISI Number	C	Mn	P max	S max	Si	Ni	Cr	Mo	SAE
4320	0.17/0.22	0.45/0.65	0.040	0.040	0.20/0.35	1.65/2.00	0.40/0.60	0.20/0.30	4320
4337	0.35/0.40	0.60/0.80	0.040	0.040	0.20/0.35	1.65/2.00	0.70/0.90	0.20/0.30	4337
E4337	0.35/0.40	0.65/0.85	0.025	0.025	0.20/0.35	1.65/2.00	0.70/0.90	0.20/0.30	—
4340	0.38/0.43	0.60/0.80	0.040	0.040	0.20/0.35	1.65/2.00	0.70/0.90	0.20/0.30	4340
E4340	0.38/0.43	0.65/0.85	0.025	0.025	0.20/0.35	1.65/2.00	0.70/0.90	0.20/0.30	E4340
4422	0.20/0.25	0.70/0.90	0.040	0.040	0.20/0.35	—	—	0.35/0.45	4422
4427	0.24/0.29	0.70/0.90	0.040	0.040	0.20/0.35	—	—	0.35/0.45	4427
4520	0.18/0.23	0.45/0.65	0.040	0.040	0.20/0.35	—	—	0.45/0.60	4520

Nickel-Molybdenum Steels

AISI Number	C	Mn	P max	S max	Si	Ni	Cr	Mo	SAE
4615	0.13/0.18	0.45/0.65	0.040	0.040	0.20/0.35	1.65/2.00	—	0.20/0.30	4615
4617	0.15/0.20	0.45/0.65	0.040	0.040	0.20/0.35	1.65/2.00	—	0.20/0.30	4617
4620	0.17/0.22	0.45/0.65	0.040	0.040	0.20/0.35	1.65/2.00	—	0.20/0.30	4620
4621	0.18/0.23	0.70/0.90	0.040	0.040	0.20/0.35	1.65/2.00	—	0.20/0.30	4621
4718	0.16/0.21	0.70/0.90	0.040	0.040	0.20/0.35	0.90/1.20	0.35/0.55	0.30/0.40	4718
4720	0.17/0.22	0.50/0.70	0.040	0.040	0.20/0.35	0.90/1.20	0.35/0.55	0.15/0.25	4720
4815	0.13/0.18	0.40/0.60	0.040	0.040	0.20/0.35	3.25/3.75	—	0.20/0.30	4815
4817	0.15/0.20	0.40/0.60	0.040	0.040	0.20/0.35	3.25/3.75	—	0.20/0.30	4817
4820	0.18/0.23	0.50/0.70	0.040	0.040	0.20/0.35	3.25/3.75	—	0.20/0.30	4820

APPENDIX C (CONTINUED)

AISI Number	Chemical Composition Ranges and Limits, per cent.								Corresponding SAE Number
	C	Mn	P max	S max	Si	Ni	Cr	Mo	
Chromium Steels									
5015	0.12/0.17	0.30/0.50	0.040	0.040	0.20/0.35	—	0.30/0.50	—	5015
5046	0.43/0.50	0.75/1.00	0.040	0.040	0.20/0.35	—	0.20/0.35	—	5046
5115	0.13/0.18	0.70/0.90	0.040	0.040	0.20/0.35	—	0.70/0.90	—	5115
5120	0.17/0.22	0.70/0.90	0.040	0.040	0.20/0.35	—	0.70/0.90	—	5120
5130	0.28/0.33	0.70/0.90	0.040	0.040	0.20/0.35	—	0.80/1.10	—	5130
5132	0.30/0.35	0.60/0.80	0.040	0.040	0.20/0.35	—	0.75/1.00	—	5132
5135	0.33/0.38	0.60/0.80	0.040	0.040	0.20/0.35	—	0.80/1.05	—	5135
5140	0.38/0.43	0.70/0.90	0.040	0.040	0.20/0.35	—	0.70/0.90	—	5140
5145	0.43/0.48	0.70/0.90	0.040	0.040	0.20/0.35	—	0.70/0.90	—	5145
5147	0.45/0.52	0.70/0.95	0.040	0.040	0.20/0.35	—	0.85/1.15	—	5147
5150	0.48/0.53	0.70/0.90	0.040	0.040	0.20/0.35	—	0.70/0.90	—	5150
5155	0.50/0.60	0.70/0.90	0.040	0.040	0.20/0.35	—	0.70/0.90	—	5155
5160	0.55/0.65	0.75/1.00	0.040	0.040	0.20/0.35	—	0.70/0.90	—	5160
E50100	0.95/1.10	0.25/0.45	0.025	0.025	0.20/0.35	—	0.40/0.60	—	50100
E51100	0.95/1.10	0.25/0.45	0.025	0.025	0.20/0.35	—	0.90/1.15	—	51100
E52100	0.95/1.10	0.25/0.45	0.025	0.025	0.20/0.35	—	1.30/1.60	—	52100
Chromium-Vanadium Steel									
6118	0.16/0.21	0.50/0.70	0.040	0.040	0.20/0.35	—	0.50/0.70	0.10/0.15	6118
6120	0.17/0.22	0.70/0.90	0.040	0.040	0.20/0.35	—	0.70/0.90	0.10 Min	6120
6150	0.48/0.53	0.70/0.90	0.040	0.040	0.20/0.35	—	0.80/1.10	0.15 Min	6150
Nickel-Chromium-Molybdenum—Triple-Alloy Steels									
8115	0.13/0.18	0.70/0.90	0.040	0.040	0.20/0.35	0.20/0.40	0.30/0.50	0.08/0.15	8115
8615	0.13/0.18	0.70/0.90	0.040	0.040	0.20/0.35	0.40/0.70	0.40/0.60	0.15/0.25	8615
8617	0.15/0.20	0.70/0.90	0.040	0.040	0.20/0.35	0.40/0.70	0.40/0.60	0.15/0.25	8617
8620	0.18/0.23	0.70/0.90	0.040	0.040	0.20/0.35	0.40/0.70	0.40/0.60	0.15/0.25	8620
8622	0.20/0.25	0.70/0.90	0.040	0.040	0.20/0.35	0.40/0.70	0.40/0.60	0.15/0.25	8622
8625	0.23/0.28	0.70/0.90	0.040	0.040	0.20/0.35	0.40/0.70	0.40/0.60	0.15/0.25	8625
8627	0.25/0.30	0.70/0.90	0.040	0.040	0.20/0.35	0.40/0.70	0.40/0.60	0.15/0.25	8627
8630	0.28/0.33	0.70/0.90	0.040	0.040	0.20/0.35	0.40/0.70	0.40/0.60	0.15/0.25	8630
8637	0.35/0.40	0.75/1.00	0.040	0.040	0.20/0.35	0.40/0.70	0.40/0.60	0.15/0.25	8637
8640	0.38/0.43	0.75/1.00	0.040	0.040	0.20/0.35	0.40/0.70	0.40/0.60	0.15/0.25	8640
8642	0.40/0.45	0.75/1.00	0.040	0.040	0.20/0.35	0.40/0.70	0.40/0.60	0.15/0.25	8642
8645	0.43/0.48	0.75/1.00	0.040	0.040	0.20/0.35	0.40/0.70	0.40/0.60	0.15/0.25	8645
8650	0.48/0.53	0.75/1.00	0.040	0.040	0.20/0.35	0.40/0.70	0.40/0.60	0.15/0.25	8650
8655	0.50/0.60	0.75/1.00	0.040	0.040	0.20/0.35	0.40/0.70	0.40/0.60	0.15/0.25	8655
8660	0.55/0.65	0.75/1.00	0.040	0.040	0.20/0.35	0.40/0.70	0.40/0.60	0.15/0.25	8660
8720	0.18/0.23	0.70/0.90	0.040	0.040	0.20/0.35	0.40/0.70	0.40/0.60	0.20/0.30	8720
8735	0.33/0.38	0.75/1.00	0.040	0.040	0.20/0.35	0.40/0.70	0.40/0.60	0.20/0.30	—
8740	0.38/0.43	0.75/1.00	0.040	0.040	0.20/0.35	0.40/0.70	0.40/0.60	0.20/0.30	8740
8742	0.40/0.45	0.75/1.00	0.040	0.040	.20/0.35	0.40/0.70	0.40/0.60	0.20/0.30	8742
8822	0.20/0.25	0.75/1.00	0.040	0.040	0.20/0.35	0.40/0.70	0.40/0.60	0.30/0.40	8822
E9310	0.08/0.13	0.45/0.65	0.025	0.025	0.20/0.35	3.00/3.50	1.00/1.40	0.08/0.15	9310
9840	0.38/0.43	0.70/0.90	0.040	0.040	0.20/0.35	0.85/1.15	0.70/0.90	0.20/0.30	9840
9850	0.48/0.53	0.70/0.90	0.040	0.040	0.20/0.35	0.85/1.15	0.70/0.90	0.20/0.30	9850
Silicon-Manganese Steels									
9255	0.50/0.60	0.70/0.95	0.040	0.040	1.80/2.20	—	—	—	9255
9260	0.55/0.65	0.70/1.00	0.040	0.040	1.80/2.20	—	—	—	9260
9262	0.55/0.65	0.75/1.00	0.040	0.040	1.80/2.20	—	0.25/0.40	—	9262

(From American Society for Metals, *Metals Handbook*, 8th Edition, 1961.)

APPENDIX C (CONTINUED)

BORON STEELS

(Steels in this category will be expected to have 0.0005 per cent minimum boron)

AISI Number	Chemical Composition Ranges and Limits, per cent								Corresponding SAE Number
	C	Mn	P max	S max	Si	Ni	Cr	Mo	
50B40	0.38/0.43	0.75/1.00	0.040	0.040	0.20/0.35	--	0.40/0.60	—	50B40
50B44	0.43/0.48	0.75/1.00	0.040	0.040	0.20/0.35	—	0.40/0.60	—	50B44
50B46	0.43/0.50	0.75/1.00	0.040	0.040	0.20/0.35	—	0.20/0.35	—	50B46
50B50	0.48/0.53	0.75/1.00	0.040	0.040	0.20/0.35	—	0.40/0.60	—	50B50
50B60	0.55/0.65	0.75/1.00	0.040	0.040	0.20/0.35	—	0.40/0.60	—	50B60
51B60	0.55/0.65	0.75/1.00	0.040	0.040	0.20/0.35	—	0.70/0.90	—	51B60
81B45	0.43/0.48	0.75/1.00	0.040	0.040	0.20/0.35	0.20/0.40	0.35/0.55	0.08/0.15	81B45
86B45	0.43/0.48	0.75/1.00	0.040	0.040	0.20/0.35	0.40/0.70	0.40/0.60	0.15/0.25	86B45
94B15	0.13/0.18	0.75/1.00	0.040	0.040	0.20/0.35	0.30/0.60	0.30/0.50	0.08/0.15	94B15
94B17	0.15/0.20	0.75/1.00	0.040	0.040	0.20/0.35	0.30/0.60	0.30/0.50	0.08/0.15	94B17
94B30	0.28/0.33	0.75/1.00	0.040	0.040	0.20/0.35	0.30/0.60	0.30/0.50	0.08/0.15	94B30
94B40	0.38/0.43	0.75/1.00	0.040	0.040	0.20/0.35	0.30/0.60	0.30/0.50	0.08/0.15	94B40

(From *Metals Handbook*, 8th edition, published by American Society for Metals, Metals Park, Ohio)

Those alloys listed in Appendix C with the prefix E are usually manufactured by the basic electric furnace method. All others are manufactured, as a rule, by the basic open-hearth process. However, when they are manufactured by the basic electric furnace process, it is essential to make proper adjustments in sulfur and phosphorus. All resulfurized steels above noted with minimum and maximum sulfur shown have good machinability.

APPENDIX D

AISI-SAE NONRESULFURIZED CARBON STEEL—1964

AISI No.	SAE No.	Ladle Chemical Composition Limits, per cent			
		C	Mn	P max	S max
C 1008	1008	0.10 max.	0.25/0.50	0.040	0.050
C 1010	1010	0.08/0.13	0.30/0.60	0.040	0.050
C 1011	—	0.08/0.13	0.60/0.90	0.040	0.050
C 1012	1012	0.10/0.15	0.30/0.60	0.040	0.050
C 1015	1015	0.13/0.18	0.30/0.60	0.040	0.050
C 1016	1016	0.13/0.18	0.60/0.90	0.040	0.050
C 1017	1017	0.15/0.20	0.30/0.60	0.040	0.050
C 1018	1018	0.15/0.20	0.60/0.90	0.040	0.050
C 1019	1019	0.15/0.20	0.70/1.00	0.040	0.050
C 1020	1020	0.18/0.23	0.30/0.60	0.040	0.050
C 1021	1021	0.18/0.23	0.60/0.90	0.040	0.050
C 1022	1022	0.18/0.23	0.70/1.00	0.040	0.050

APPENDIX D (CONTINUED)

AISI No.	SAE No.	Ladle Chemical Composition Limits, per cent			
		C	Mn	P max	S max
C 1023	1023	0.20/0.25	0.30/0.60	0.040	0.050
C 1024	1024	0.19/0.25	1.35/1.65	0.040	0.050
C 1025	1025	0.22/0.28	0.30/0.60	0.040	0.050
C 1026	1026	0.22/0.28	0.60/0.90	0.040	0.050
C 1027	1027	0.22/0.29	1.20/1.50	0.040	0.050
C 1029	—	0.25/0.31	0.60/0.90	0.040	0.050
C 1030	1030	0.28/0.34	0.60/0.90	0.040	0.050
C 1031	—	0.28/0.34	0.30/0.60	0.040	0.050
C 1033	1033	0.30/0.36	0.70/1.00	0.040	0.050
C 1035	1035	0.32/0.38	0.60/0.90	0.040	0.050
C 1036	1036	0.30/0.37	1.20/1.50	0.040	0.050
C 1037	1037	0.32/0.38	0.70/1.00	0.040	0.050
C 1038	1038	0.35/0.42	0.60/0.90	0.040	0.050
C 1039	1039	0.37/0.44	0.70/1.00	0.040	0.050
C 1040	1040	0.37/0.44	0.60/0.90	0.040	0.050
C 1041	1041	0.36/0.44	1.35/1.65	0.040	0.050
C 1042	1042	0.40/0.47	0.60/0.90	0.040	0.050
C 1043	1043	0.40/0.47	0.70/1.00	0.040	0.050
C 1045	1045	0.43/0.50	0.60/0.90	0.040	0.050
C 1046	1046	0.43/0.50	0.70/1.00	0.040	0.050
C 1049	1049	0.46/0.53	0.60/0.90	0.040	0.050
C 1050	1050	0.48/0.55	0.60/0.90	0.040	0.050
C 1051	—	0.45/0.56	0.85/1.15	0.040	0.050
C 1052	1052	0.47/0.55	1.20/1.50	0.040	0.050
C 1053	—	0.48/0.55	0.70/1.00	0.040	0.050
C 1055	1055	0.50/0.60	0.60/0.90	0.040	0.050
C 1060	1060	0.55/0.65	0.60/0.90	0.040	0.050
C 1070	1070	0.65/0.75	0.60/0.90	0.040	0.050
C 1078	1078	0.72/0.85	0.30/0.60	0.040	0.050
C 1080	1080	0.75/0.88	0.60/0.90	0.040	0.050
C 1084	1084	0.80/0.93	0.60/0.90	0.040	0.050
C 1085	1085	0.80/0.93	0.70/1.00	0.040	0.050
C 1086	1086	0.80/0.93	0.30/0.50	0.040	0.050
C 1090	1090	0.85/0.98	0.60/0.90	0.040	0.050
C 1095	1095	0.90/1.03	0.30/0.50	0.040	0.050

(Courtesy of United States Steel Corporation, Pittsburgh, Pa., *The Making, Shaping and Treating of Steel*, 1964 edition.)

Copper—when required in these steels is specified as an added element to a standard steel.

Lead —if and when required is specified as an added element to a standard steel as noted.

Silicon —when needed is usually added within the ranges and limits as noted below:

Carbon Steel Designations	*Silicon Ranges or Limits*
Up to C 1015 exclusive	0.10 max.
C 1015 to C 1025 inclusive	0.10 max., 0.10/0.20, or 0.15/0.30
Over C 1025 steel	0.10/0.20, or 0.15/0.30

APPENDIX E

TYPICAL HEAT TREATMENTS FOR AISI-SAE ALLOY STEELS*

Steel No.	Normalizing Temperature (°F)	Annealing Temperature (°F)	Hardening Temperature (°F)	Quenching Medium
1330	1600-1700	1500-1600	1525-1575	Water or oil
1335 1340	1600-1700	1500-1600	1525-1575	Oil
3130	1600-1700	—	1500-1550	Water or oil
3140	1600-1700	1450-1550	1500-1550	Oil
4037 4042	1600-1700	1525-1575	1500-1575	Oil
4047	1600-1700	1450-1550	1500-1575	Oil
4063	1600-1700	1450-1550	1475-1550	Oil
4130	1600-1700	1450-1550	1600-1650	Water or oil
4137 4140	1600-1700	1450-1550	1550-1600	Oil
4145 4150	1600-1700	1450-1550	1500-1600	Oil
4340	1600-1700	1450-1550	1475-1525	Oil
5046	1600-1700	1450-1550	1475-1500	Oil
5130 5132	1650-1750	1450-1550	1500-1550	Water, caustic solution, or oil
5135 5140 5145	1650-1750	1450-1550	1500-1550	Oil
5147 5150	1650-1750	1450-1550	1475-1550	Oil
50100 51100 52100	— —	1350-1450 1350-1450	1425-1475 1500-1600	Water Oil
6150	1650-1750	1550-1650	1600-1650	Oil
9255 9260 9262	1650-1750	1550-1650	1500-1650	Oil
8627 8630	1600-1700	1450-1550	1550-1650	Water or oil
8637 8640	1600-1700	1450-1550	1525-1575	Oil
8642 8645 8650	1600-1700	1450-1550	1500-1550	Oil
8655 8660	1650-1750	1450-1550	1475-1550	Oil
8735 8740	1600-1700	1450-1550	1525-1575	Oil
9840	1600-1700	1450-1550	1500-1550	Oil

* Courtesy American Society for Metals, *Metals Handbook*, Vol. 2, 1964.

APPENDIX F

AISI-SAE FREECUTTING STEEL COMPOSITIONS—1964*

Acid Bessemer Resulfurized Carbon Steels

AISI No.	SAE No.	Ladle Chemical Composition Limits, per cent			
		C	Mn	P	S
B 1111	1111	0.13 max	0.60/0.90	0.07/0.12	0.08/0.15
B 1112	1112	0.13 max	0.70/1.00	0.07/0.12	0.16/0.23
B 1113	1113	0.13 max	0.70/1.00	0.07/0.12	0.24/0.33

Open-Hearth Resulfurized Carbon Steels

AISI No.	SAE No.	Ladle Chemical Composition Limits, per cent			
		C	Mn	P max	S
C 1108	1108	0.08/0.13	0.50/0.80	0.040	0.08/0.13
C 1109	1109	0.08/0.13	0.60/0.90	0.040	0.08/0.13
C 1110	—	0.08/0.13	0.30/0.60	0.040	0.08/0.13
C 1113	—	0.10/0.16	1.00/1.30	0.040	0.24/0.33
C 1115	1115	0.13/0.18	0.60/0.90	0.040	0.08/0.13
C 1116	1116	0.14/0.20	1.10/1.40	0.040	0.16/0.23
C 1117	1117	0.14/0.20	1.00/1.30	0.040	0.08/0.13
C 1118	1118	0.14/0.20	1.30/1.60	0.040	0.08/0.13
C 1119	1119	0.14/0.20	1.00/1.30	0.040	0.08/0.13
C 1120	1120	0.18/0.23	0.70/1.00	0.040	0.08/0.13
C 1125	—	0.22/0.28	0.60/0.90	0.040	0.08/0.13
C 1126	1126	0.23/0.29	0.70/1.00	0.040	0.08/0.13
C 1132	1132	0.27/0.34	1.35/1.65	0.040	0.08/0.13
C 1137	1137	0.32/0.39	1.35/1.65	0.040	0.08/0.13
C 1138	1138	0.34/0.40	0.70/1.00	0.040	0.08/0.13
C 1139	1139	0.35/0.43	1.35/1.65	0.040	0.12/0.20
C 1140	1140	0.37/0.44	0.70/1.00	0.040	0.08/0.13
C 1141	1141	0.37/0.45	1.35/1.65	0.040	0.08/0.13
C 1144	1144	0.40/0.48	1.35/1.65	0.040	0.24/0.33
C 1145	1145	0.42/0.49	0.70/1.00	0.040	0.04/0.07
C 1146	1146	0.42/0.49	0.70/1.00	0.040	0.08/0.13
C 1151	1151	0.48/0.55	0.70/1.00	0.040	0.08/0.13

* *The Making, Shaping and Treating of Steel*, 1964 edition, Courtesy United States Steel Corporation.

Silicon. When silicon is required, the following ranges and limits are commonly used:

Standard Steel Designations	Silicon Ranges or Limits
Up to C 1113 excl.	0.10 max
C 1113 and over	0.10 max, 0.10/0.20 or 0.15/0.30

Lead. When required, lead is specified as an added element to a standard steel.

APPENDIX G

PERIODIC TABLE OF THE ELEMENTS

0	I	II	III	IV	V	VI	VII	VIII
	H 1 (1.0080)							**He** 2 (4.003)
He 2 (4.003)	**Li** 3 (6.940)	**Be** 4 (9.013)	**B** 5 (10.82)	**C** 6 (12.01)	**N** 7 (14.008)	**O** 8 (16.00)	**F** 9 (19.00)	**Ne** 10 (20.183)
Ne 10 (20.183)	**Na** 11 (22.991)	**Mg** 12 (24.32)	**Al** 13 (26.98)	**Si** 14 (28.09)	**P** 15 (30.975)	**S** 16 (32.066)	**Cl** 17 (35.457)	**A** 18 (39.994)

Transition and main-group elements:

0	a	a	a	a	a	a	a		VIII		b	b	b	b	b	b	b	0
A 18 (39.994)	**K** 19 (39.100)	**Ca** 20 (40.08)	**Sc** 21 (44.96)	**Ti** 22 (47.90)	**V** 23 (50.95)	**Cr** 24 (52.01)	**Mn** 25 (54.94)	**Fe** 26 (55.85)	**Co** 27 (58.94)	**Ni** 28 (58.71)	**Cu** 29 (63.54)	**Zn** 30 (65.38)	**Ga** 31 (69.72)	**Ge** 32 (72.60)	**As** 33 (74.91)	**Se** 34 (78.96)	**Br** 35 (79.916)	**Kr** 36 (83.8)
Kr 36 (83.8)	**Rb** 37 (85.48)	**Sr** 38 (87.63)	**Y** 39 (88.92)	**Zr** 40 (91.22)	**Cb** 41 (92.91)	**Mo** 42 (95.95)	**Tc** 43 (98)	**Ru** 44 (101.1)	**Rh** 45 (102.91)	**Pd** 46 (106.7)	**Ag** 47 (107.880)	**Cd** 48 (112.41)	**In** 49 (114.82)	**Sn** 50 (118.70)	**Sb** 51 (121.76)	**Te** 52 (127.61)	**I** 53 (126.91)	**Xe** 54 (131.30)
Xe 54 (131.30)	**Cs** 55 (132.91)	**Ba** 56 (137.36)	**La to Lu** 57 to 71 (138.92)	**Hf** 72 (178.68)	**Ta** 73 (180.95)	**W** 74 (183.86)	**Re** 75 (186.22)	**Os** 76 (190.2)	**Ir** 77 (192.2)	**Pt** 78 (195.09)	**Au** 79 (197.0)	**Hg** 80 (200.61)	**Tl** 81 (204.39)	**Pb** 82 (207.21)	**Bi** 83 (209.00)	**Po** 84 (210)	**At** 85 (211)	**Rn** 86 (222)
Rn 86 (222)	**Fr** 87 (223)	**Ra** 88 (226.05)	**Ac** 89 (227)	**Th** 90 (232.06)	**Pa** 91 (231.1)	**U** 92 (238.07)	**Np** 93 (237)	**Pu** 94 (242)	**Am** 95 (243)	**Cm** 96 (243)	**Bk** 97 (245)	**Cf** 98 (251)	**E** 99 (254)	**Fm** 100 (253)	**Mv** 101 (256)	**No** 102 (254)	**Lw** 103 (257)	
0	1	2	3	4	5	6	7	8	9	10	11	12	13	14	15	16	17	18

Rare Earth Metals

Ce 58 140.13	**Pr** 59 140.92	**Nd** 60 144.27	**Pm** 61 (145)	**Sm** 62 150.35	**Eu** 63 152.0	**Gd** 64 157.26	**Tb** 65 158.93	**Dy** 66 161.51	**Ho** 67 164.94	**Er** 68 167.27	**Tm** 69 168.94	**Yb** 70 173.04	**Lu** 71 174.99

APPENDIX H

HARDNESS OF METALS

Material ↓	High	Low	Material ↓	High	Low
Alloy Irons, Cast	700	130	Aluminum & Its Alloys, Sol'n Tr &		
Alloy Steels, H & T	627	217	Aged	150	73
Martensitic Stainless Steels, H & T	580	180	Naval Brass, Hard	150	130
Carbon Steels, H & T	495	174	Nickel Brasses & Bronzes (cast), Leaded	150	50
Stainless Steels (cast), H & T	470	185	Low Expansion Nickel Alloys, Ann	144	132
Alloy Steels, Carb Grades	429	248	Ingot Iron, CD	142	—
Nitriding Steels, H & T	415	230	Yellow Brass, Hard	140	—
Alloy Steels (cast)	400	150	Cobalt, Ann	138	122
Rhodium, CW	390	260	Cobalt (cast)	135	105
Duranickel, Age H	380	300	Low Brass, 80%, Hard	130	—
Nickel & Its Alloys (cast)	380	80	Red Brass, 85%, Hard	126	—
Nickel & Its Alloys (cast), Ann. & Aged	380	300	Palladium, CW	109	—
Iridium, CW	350	—	Commercial Bronze, 90%, Hard	107	—
Monel, Age H	350	290	Aluminum & Its Alloys, Hard	105	44
Osmium (cast)	350	—	Gilding, 95%, Hard	105	—
Nodular Irons	325	140	Wrought Irons, HR	105	97
Gray Irons	300	170	Platinum, CW	97	13
Heat Resistant Nodular Irons	300	140	Zinc Alloys (die cast)	90	82
Nickel Steels, CD	272	188	Aluminum & Its Alloys (cast)	85	40
Heat Resistant Alloys (cast), Ht Tr	270	185	Magnesium Alloys (cast), Sol'n Tr & Aged	84	73
Malleable Irons	269	110	Muntz Metal, Ann	82	—
Martensitic Stainless Steels, Ann	260	150	Zinc Alloys, CR	80	60
Nickel-Base Superalloys, Sol'n Tr	241	187	Tin Bronzes (cast), Leaded	80	60
Austenitic Stainless Steels, CW	240	—	Aluminum & Its Alloys, Ann	75	23
Aluminum Bronzes (cast), Ht Tr	235	180	Yellow Brasses (cast), Leaded	75	40
Free-Cutting Steels, CD	230	150	Tin Bronzes (cast), High Leaded	70	35
Carbon Steels, Carb Grades	229	149	Ingot Iron, Ann	69	—
Nickel Steels, HR	225	155	Magnesium Alloys (forged)	69	47
Yellow Brasses (cast), High Strength	225	80	Magnesium Alloys (cast)	65	50
Heat Resistant Alloys (cast)	223	160	Red Brasses (cast), Leaded	65	50
Manganese Steels, Ann	222	178	Magnesium Alloys (cast), Sol'n Tr	63	51
Ruthenium (cast)	220	—	Zinc Alloys, HR	61	51
Yellow Brass (cast), High Strength	220	80	Gold, CW	58	—
Carbon Steels (cast)	212	131	Platinum, Ann	52	38
Stainless Steels (cast), Ann	210	195	Zinc, HR	47	37
Austenitic Nodular Irons	200	140	Palladium, Ann	46	—
Aluminum Bronzes (cast)	195	120	Copper, Ann	40	—
Copper, Hard	194	—	Silver, Ann	35	25
Carbon Steels, V-Bearing	190	149	Lead-Base Babbitts (chill cast)	28	14
Ferritic Stainless Steels, CW	185	—	Tin-Base Babbitts (chill cast)	27	17
Austenitic Stainless Steels, Ann	170	150	Gold, Ann	25	—
Iridium, Ann	170	—	Pewter (cast)	23	—
Manganese Bronze, Half Hard	160	—	White Metal (cast)	20	—
Aluminum & Its Alloys (cast), Sol'n Tr			White Metal, Ann	17	—
& Aged	160	80	Hard Lead Alloys (chill cast)	15.4	7
Yellow Brass, Hard	160	—	Pewter, Ann	13	—
Rhodium, Ann	156	55	Lead & Its Alloys (extr)	12.4	5.1
Standard Malleable Irons	156	110	Hard Lead Alloys (rolled)	9.5	5.9
Cartridge Brass, 70%, Hard	154	—	Grade A Tin, Ann	7	—
Muntz Metal, Hard	151	—	Soft Lead (chill cast)	4.2	—

• Values represent high and low sides of a range of *typical* values.

(Courtesy of *Materials Selector Guide* from *Materials in Design Engineering*, published by Reinhold Publishing Corporation, mid-October 1966 issue.)

APPENDIX I

YIELD STRENGTH OF METALS[a]
1000 psi

Material	High	Low	Material	High	Low
Alloy Steels, H & T	288	76	Chromium Copper, Hard	55	—
Ultra High Strength Steels, Ht Tr	284	240	Ferritic Stainless Steels, Ann	55	35
Martensitic Stainless Steels, H & T	275	60	Commercial Bronze, 90%, Hard	54	—
Age Hardenable Stainless Steels, Sol'n Tr & Aged	225	42	Naval Brass, Half Hard	53	—
Titanium & Its Alloys	220	135	Free-Cutting Brass, Half Hard	52	—
Tungsten, Str Rel	220	—	Low Alloy, High Str Steels	50	42
Nitriding Steels, H & T	202	90	Aluminum & Its Alloys, Hard	50	22
Carbon Steels, H & T	188	58	Gilding, 95%, Hard	50	—
High Temperature Steels, H & T	186	117	Leaded Commercial Bronze, Half Hard	50	—
Alloy Steels, Carb Grades	178	62	Tantalum, Str Rel	48	—
Nickel-Base Superalloys, Sol'n Tr & Aged	170	92	Sulfur Copper, Half Hard	48	—
Alloy Steels (cast)	170	45	Aluminum Bronzes (cast)	45	27
Stainless Steels (cast), H & T	165	67	Copper, Hard	45	—
Beryllium-Copper, Hard	150	130	Thorium, CW	45	—
Titanium & Its Alloys, Ann	150	40	Magnesium Alloys	44	19
Cr-Ni-Fe Superalloys, Sol'n Tr & Aged	142	71	Silver, CW	44	—
Austenitic Stainless Steels, CW	140	75	Tellurium Copper, Half Hard	44	—
Columbium & Its Alloys, Str Rel	135	35	Cobalt (cast)	43	20
Nodular Irons	125	45	Aluminum & Its Alloys (cast), Sol'n Tr & Aged	42	20
Nickel-Base Superalloys (cast)	120	105	Low Expansion Nickel Alloys, Ann	40	33
Nickel & Its Alloys, Ann. & Age Hard	120	90	Nickel Brasses & Bronzes (cast), Leaded	40	15
Cobalt-Base Superalloys, Sol'n Tr & Aged	113	67	Standard Malleable Irons	40	32
Martensitic Stainless Steels, Ann	105	25	Austenitic Nodular Irons	38	32
Molybdenum & Its Alloys, Str Rel	105	82	Beryllium-Copper, Ann	35	25
Free-Cutting Steels, CD	100	60	Hafnium, Ann	32	—
Pearlitic Malleable Irons	100	45	Gold, CW	30	—
Zirconium & Its Alloys, CW	98	58	Magnesium Alloys (cast)	30	8
Hafnium, CW	96	—	Nickel Silvers, Ann	30	18
Heat Resistant Nodular Irons	95	45	Palladium, CW	30	—
Cr-Ni-Co-Fe Superalloys, Sol'n Tr & Aged	91	58	Tin & Aluminum Brasses, Ann	30	22
Nickel Silvers, Hard	90	74	Phosphor Bronzes, Ann	28	14
Yellow Brasses (cast), High Strength	90	25	Platinum, CW	27	—
Silicon Bronzes, Hard	88	50	Wrough tIrons, HR	27	—
Stainless Steels (cast)	85	31	Aluminum & Its Alloys (cast)	26	8
Heat Resistant Alloys (cast), Ht Tr	81	43	Tin Bronzes (cast), Leaded	26	16
Ferritic Stainless Steels, CW	80	45	Thorium, Ann	26	—
Aluminum & Its Alloys, Sol'n Tr & Aged	78	31	Uranium, Ann	25	—
Carbon Steels, Carb Grades	77	46	Red Brasses (cast), Leaded	24	12
Carbon Steels (cast)	75	35	Aluminum & Its Alloys Ann	23	4
Phosphor Bronzes, Hard	75	50	Cupro-Nickels, Ann	22	15
Zirconium Copper, Hard	75	48	Tin Bronzes (cast), High Leaded	22	11
Cupro-Nickels, Hard	73	—	Muntz Metal, Ann	21	—
Nickel-Base Superalloys, Sol'n Tr	72	52	Architectural Bronze (extr)	20	—
Aluminum B onzes (cast), Ht Tr	70	40	Forging Brass (extr)	20	—
Low Expansion Nickel Alloys, CW	70	—	Leaded Brasses, Ann	20	17
Ingot Iron, CD	69	—	Yellow Brasses (cast), Leaded	20	11
Nickel & Its Alloys, Ann	65	12	Ingot Iron, Ann	19	—
Carbon Steels, V-Bearing	65	45	Free-Cutting Brass, Ann	18	—
Cartridge Brass, 70%, Hard	63	—	Chromium Copper, Ann	15	—
Zirconium and Its Alloys, Ann	61	29	Yellow Brass, Ann	14	—
Carbon Steels, CB-Bearing	60	45	Low Brass, 80%, Ann	12	—
Tin & Aluminum Brasses, Half Hard	60	53	Cartridge Brass, 70%, Ann	11	—
Leaded Brasses, Hard	60	52	Commercial Bronze, 90%, Ann	10	—
Manganese Bronze (A), Half Hard	60	—	Copper, Ann	10	—
Silicon Bronzes, Ann	60	15	Gilding, 95%, Ann	10	—
Yellow Brass, Hard	60	—	Red Brass, 85%, Ann	10	—
Low Brass, 80%, Hard	59	—	Silver, Ann	8	—
Red Brass, 85%, Hard	57	—	Tin & Its Alloys, CR	6	2
Austenitic Stainless Steels, Ann	55	30	Platinum, Ann	5.5	—
Beryllium, Ann	55	45	Palladium, Ann	5	—
			Lead & Its Alloys	1.6	0.8
			Tin & Its Alloys, Ann	1.3	—

[a] Values represent high and low sides of a range of *typical* values at 0.2% offset.

(Courtesy of *Materials Selector Guide* from *Materials in Design Engineering*, published by Reinhold Publishing Corporation, mid-October 1966 issue.)

APPENDIX J

MACHINABILITY OF METALS°
1000 psi

Material ↓	Machin-ability Index^	Material ↓	Machin-ability Index^
Magnesium Alloys	500–2000	Ingot Iron	50
Aluminum Alloy (218-T), Cast	240	Stainless Steels (201, 202, 304, 309, 310, 316)	50
Free-Cutting Brass	200	Tool Steels (A)	50
Aluminum Alloy (2011)	200	Wrought Iron	50
Zinc	200	Low Alloy Steels, Cast	30–70
Aluminum Alloys (5052, 5056, 6061, 6063)	190	High Carbon Steels, Ann	43–53
Aluminum Alloys (3003, 3004)	180	Low Alloy Steels (23XX)	40–55
Aluminum Alloys (112, B-113, 750-T), Cast	180	Low Carbon Steels, HR	40–50
Sulfur Copper	180	Stainless Steels (420, 431)	45
Architectural Bronze	180	Low Alloy Steels (48XX)	45
High-Leaded Brass	180	Tool Steels (D)	45
Leaded Commercial Bronze	180	Copper, Electrolytic Tough Pitch	40–50
Leaded Copper	160	Tool Steels (M)	40
Forging Brass	160	Stainless Steels (440A, B, C)	40
Leaded Nickel Silver	160	19–9DL	40
Aluminum Alloy (2024)	150	Copper, 99.5%	40
Leaded Phosphor Bronze	100–200	Nickel Silvers	40
Aluminum Alloys (108, 122, A-356), Cast	140	Zirconium Copper	40
Aluminum Alloys (2014, 2017, 6051)	140	Chromium Copper	40
Low-Leaded Brass	140	Phosphor Bronzes (A, C, D, E)	40
Leaded Naval Brass	140	Cupro-Nickels	40
Leaded Muntz Metal	120	Gilding, 95%	40
Aluminum Alloy (7075)	120	Commercial Bronze, 90%	40
Leaded Silicon Bronze	120	Beryllium Copper	40
Leaded Naval Brass	120	Phosphorized Copper	40
Malleable Iron (standard)	120	Oxygen-Free Copper	40
Gray Iron (ferritic)	110	Titanium Alloys (A-55, A-70)	38
Nodular Iron	90–110	Low Alloy Steels (92XX)	36–38
Malleable Iron (pearlitic)	80–90	Tool Steels (H)	37
Aluminum Bronzes, Cast	60–100	Low Alloy Steels (61XX)	26–46
Stainless Steel (416)	80	Tool Steels (T)	34
Muntz Metal	80	16–25–6	31
Stainless Steel (303)	65	Titanium Alloy (A-110)	29
Medium Carbon Steels, Ann	65	A-286	27
Medium Carbon Steels, CW	60–67	Titanium Alloy (C-120)	26
Carbon Steels, Cast	55–70	Discaloy	25
Low Alloy Steels (40XX)	52–73	V-57	25
Low Alloy Steels (13XX)	59–62	Titanium Alloy (C-130)	24
Low Alloy Steels (51XX)	55–67	Incoloy 901	20
Stainless Steel (405)	60	Titanium Alloy (C-140)	20
Yellow Brass	60	Refractaloy 26	20
Red Brass, 85%	60	S-590	15–20
Silicon Bronzes (A, B)	60	Multimet, N-155	15
Tool Steels (W)	60	Inconel X	15
Naval Brass	60	Titanium Alloy (MST)	13
Cartridge Brass, 70%	60	Hastelloy B	12
Low Brass, 80%	60	HS 25, L-605	12
Tool Steels (L)	56	Hastelloy C	10
Low Alloy Steels (41, 43XX)	51–62	S-816	9
Stainless Steels (305, 347, 348, 302, 321, 403, 410)	55	Udimet 500	9
		Inconel 700	8
Tool Steels (S, O)	54	Inconel 713 C	6
Low Alloy Steels (86, 87XX)	45–61	HS 21	6
Low Carbon Steels, CW	45–60	HS 31, X-40	6

° Based on AISI B1112 = 100.

(Courtesy of *Materials Selector Guide* from *Materials in Design Engineering*, published by Reinhold Publishing Corporation, mid-October 1966 issue.)

APPENDIX K

Approximate Equivalent Hardness Numbers for Rockwell C Hardness Numbers for Steel(a)

Rockwell C-scale hardness No.	Diamond pyramid hardness No.	Brinell hardness No., 10-mm ball, 3000-kg load Standard ball	Hultgren ball	Tungsten carbide ball	Rockwell A-scale 60-kg load brale penetrator	Rockwell B-scale 100-kg load, 1/16-in. diam ball	Rockwell D-scale 100-kg load brale penetrator	15-N scale 15-kg load	30-N scale 30-kg load	45-N scale 45-kg load	Shore scleroscope hardness No.	Tensile strength (approx), 1000 psi	Rockwell C-scale hardness No.
68	940	...	...	...	85.6	...	76.9	93.2	84.4	75.4	97	...	68
67	900	...	...	...	85.0	...	76.1	92.9	83.6	74.2	95	...	67
66	865	...	...	...	84.5	...	75.4	92.5	82.8	73.3	92	...	66
65	832	...	...	739	83.9	...	74.5	92.2	81.9	72.0	91	...	65
64	800	...	...	722	83.4	...	73.8	91.8	81.1	71.0	88	...	64
63	772	...	...	705	82.8	...	73.0	91.4	80.1	69.9	87	...	63
62	746	...	...	688	82.3	...	72.2	91.1	79.3	68.8	85	...	62
61	720	...	...	670	81.8	...	71.5	90.7	78.4	67.7	83	...	61
60	697	...	613	654	81.2	...	70.7	90.2	77.5	66.6	81	...	60
59	674	...	599	634	80.7	...	69.9	89.8	76.6	65.5	80	326	59
58	653	...	587	615	80.1	...	69.2	89.3	75.7	64.3	78	315	58
57	633	...	575	595	79.6	...	68.5	88.9	74.8	63.2	76	305	57
56	613	...	561	577	79.0	...	67.7	88.3	73.9	62.0	75	295	56
55	595	...	546	560	78.5	...	66.9	87.9	73.0	60.9	74	287	55
54	577	...	534	543	78.0	...	66.1	87.4	72.0	59.8	72	278	54
53	560	...	519	525	77.4	...	65.4	86.9	71.2	58.6	71	269	53
52	544	500	508	512	76.8	...	64.6	86.4	70.2	57.4	69	262	52
51	528	487	494	496	76.3	...	63.8	85.9	69.4	56.1	68	253	51
50	513	475	481	481	75.9	...	63.1	85.5	68.5	55.0	67	245	50
49	498	464	469	469	75.2	...	62.1	85.0	67.6	53.8	66	239	49
48	484	451	455	455	74.7	...	61.4	84.5	66.7	52.5	64	232	48
47	471	442	443	443	74.1	...	60.8	83.9	65.8	51.4	63	225	47
46	458	432	432	432	73.6	...	60.0	83.5	64.8	50.3	62	219	46
45	446	421	421	421	73.1	...	59.2	83.0	64.0	49.0	60	212	45
44	434	409	409	400	72.5	...	58.5	82.5	63.1	47.8	58	206	44
43	423	400	400	400	72.0	...	57.7	82.0	62.2	46.7	57	201	43
42	412	390	390	390	71.5	...	56.9	81.5	61.3	45.5	56	196	42
41	402	381	381	381	70.9	...	56.2	80.9	60.4	44.3	55	191	41
40	392	371	371	371	70.4	...	55.4	80.4	59.5	43.1	54	186	40
39	382	362	362	362	69.9	...	54.6	79.9	58.6	41.9	52	181	39
38	372	353	353	353	69.4	...	53.8	79.4	57.7	40.8	51	176	38
37	363	344	344	344	68.9	...	53.1	78.8	56.8	39.6	50	172	37
36	354	336	336	336	68.4	(109.0)	52.3	78.3	55.9	38.4	49	168	36
35	345	327	327	327	67.9	(108.5)	51.5	77.7	55.0	37.2	48	163	35
34	336	319	319	319	67.4	(108.0)	50.8	77.2	54.2	36.1	47	159	34
33	327	311	311	311	66.8	(107.5)	50.0	76.6	53.3	34.9	46	154	33
32	318	301	301	301	66.3	(107.0)	49.2	76.1	52.1	33.7	44	150	32
31	310	294	294	294	65.8	(106.0)	48.4	75.6	51.3	32.5	43	146	31
30	302	286	286	286	65.3	(105.5)	47.7	75.0	50.4	31.3	42	142	30
29	294	279	279	279	64.7	(104.5)	47.0	74.5	49.5	30.1	41	138	29
28	286	271	271	271	64.3	(104.0)	46.1	73.9	48.6	28.9	41	134	28
27	279	264	264	264	63.8	(103.0)	45.2	73.3	47.7	27.8	40	131	27
26	272	258	258	258	63.3	(102.5)	44.6	72.8	46.8	26.7	38	127	26
25	266	253	253	253	62.8	(101.5)	43.8	72.2	45.9	25.5	38	124	25
24	260	247	247	247	62.4	(101.0)	43.1	71.6	45.0	24.3	37	121	24
23	254	243	243	243	62.0	100.0	42.1	71.0	44.0	23.1	36	118	23
22	248	237	237	237	61.5	99.0	41.6	70.5	43.2	22.0	35	115	22
21	243	231	231	231	61.0	98.5	40.9	69.9	42.3	20.7	35	113	21
20	238	226	226	226	60.5	97.8	40.1	69.4	41.5	19.6	34	110	20
(18)	230	219	219	219	...	96.7	...	...	...	...	33	106	(18)
(16)	222	212	212	212	...	95.5	...	...	...	...	32	102	(16)
(14)	213	203	203	203	...	93.9	...	...	...	...	31	98	(14)
(12)	204	194	194	194	...	92.3	...	...	...	...	29	94	(12)
(10)	196	187	187	187	...	90.7	...	...	...	...	28	90	(10)
(8)	188	179	179	179	...	89.5	...	...	...	...	27	87	(8)
(6)	180	171	171	171	...	87.1	...	...	...	...	26	84	(6)
(4)	173	165	165	165	...	85.5	...	...	...	...	25	80	(4)
(2)	166	158	158	158	...	83.5	...	...	...	...	24	77	(2)
(0)	160	152	152	152	...	81.7	...	...	...	...	24	75	(0)

(a) The values in bold face type correspond to the values in the joint SAE-ASM-ASTM hardness conversions as printed in ASTM E48, Table 2. Values in parentheses are beyond normal range and are given for information only.

Brinell Hardness Numbers (10-Mm Ball Diameter)

Indentation diam, mm	Load, kg 500	1000	1500	2000	2500	3000
2.00	158	316	473	632	788	945
2.05	150	300	450	600	750	899
2.10	143	286	428	572	714	856
2.15	136	272	409	544	681	817
2.20	130	260	390	520	650	780
2.25	124	248	373	496	621	745
2.30	119	238	356	476	593	712
2.35	114	228	341	456	568	682
2.40	109	218	327	436	545	653
2.45	104	208	314	416	522	627
2.50	100	200	301	400	500	601
2.55	96.3	193	289	385	482	578
2.60	92.6	185	278	370	462	555
2.65	89.0	178	267	356	445	534
2.70	85.7	171	257	343	429	514
2.75	82.6	165	248	330	413	495
2.80	79.6	159	239	318	398	477
2.85	76.8	154	231	307	384	461
2.90	74.1	148	222	296	371	444
2.95	71.5	143	215	286	358	429
3.00	69.1	138	208	276	346	415
3.05	66.8	134	201	267	334	401
3.10	64.6	129	194	258	324	388
3.15	62.5	125	188	250	313	375
3.20	60.5	121	182	242	303	363
3.25	58.6	117	176	234	293	352
3.30	56.8	114	171	227	284	341
3.35	55.1	110	166	220	276	331
3.40	53.4	107	161	214	267	321
3.45	51.8	104	156	207	259	311
3.50	50.3	101	151	201	252	302
3.55	48.9	97.8	147	196	244	293
3.60	47.5	95.0	143	190	238	285
3.65	46.1	92.2	139	184	231	277
3.70	44.9	89.8	135	180	225	269
3.75	43.6	87.2	131	174	218	262
3.80	42.4	84.8	128	170	212	255
3.85	41.3	82.6	124	165	207	248
3.90	40.2	80.4	121	161	201	241
3.95	39.1	78.2	118	156	196	235
4.00	38.1	76.2	115	152	191	229
4.05	37.1	74.2	112	148	186	223
4.10	36.2	72.4	109	145	181	217
4.15	35.3	70.6	106	141	177	212
4.20	34.4	68.8	104	138	172	207
4.25	33.6	67.2	101	134	167	201
4.30	32.8	65.6	98.5	131	164	197
4.35	32.0	64.0	96.0	128	160	192
4.40	31.2	62.4	93.5	125	156	187
4.45	30.5	61.0	91.5	122	153	183
4.50	29.8	59.6	89.5	119	149	179
4.55	29.1	58.2	87.0	116	145	174
4.60	28.4	56.8	85.0	114	142	170
4.65	27.8	55.6	83.5	111	139	167
4.70	27.1	54.2	81.5	108	136	163
4.75	26.5	53.0	79.5	106	133	159
4.80	25.9	51.8	78.0	104	130	156
4.85	25.4	50.8	76.0	102	127	152
4.90	24.8	49.6	74.5	99.2	124	149
4.95	24.3	48.6	73.0	97.2	122	146
5.00	23.8	47.6	71.5	95.2	119	143
5.05	23.3	46.6	70.0	93.2	117	140
5.10	22.8	45.6	68.5	91.2	114	137
5.15	22.3	44.6	67.0	89.2	112	134
5.20	21.8	43.6	65.5	87.2	109	131
5.25	21.4	42.8	64.0	85.6	107	128
5.30	20.9	41.8	63.0	83.6	105	126
5.35	20.5	41.0	61.5	82.0	103	123
5.40	20.1	40.2	60.5	80.4	101	121
5.45	19.7	39.4	59.0	78.8	98.5	118
5.50	19.3	38.6	58.0	77.2	96.5	116
5.55	18.9	37.8	57.0	75.6	95.0	114
5.60	18.6	37.2	55.5	74.4	92.5	111
5.65	18.2	36.4	54.5	72.8	90.8	109
5.70	17.8	35.6	53.5	71.2	89.2	107
5.75	17.5	35.0	52.5	70.0	87.5	105
5.80	17.2	34.4	51.5	68.8	85.8	103
5.85	16.8	33.6	50.5	67.2	84.2	101
5.90	16.5	33.0	49.6	66.0	82.5	99.2
5.95	16.2	32.4	48.7	64.8	81.2	97.3
6.00	15.9	31.8	47.8	63.6	79.5	95.5
6.05	15.6	31.2	46.9	62.4	78.0	93.7
6.10	15.3	30.6	46.0	61.2	76.7	92.0
6.15	15.1	30.2	45.2	60.4	75.3	90.3
6.20	14.8	29.6	44.4	59.2	73.8	88.7
6.25	14.5	29.0	43.6	58.0	72.6	87.1
6.30	14.2	28.4	42.8	56.8	71.3	85.5
6.35	14.0	28.0	42.0	56.0	70.0	84.0
6.40	13.7	27.4	41.3	54.8	68.8	82.5
6.45	13.5	27.0	40.5	54.0	67.5	81.0

(Courtesy of American Society for Metals, *Metals Handbook*, 8th edition.)

APPENDIX L

Trademark Name	Product	Manufacturer
Acrylite	acrylic	American Cyanamid Company
Adiprene	urethane rubber	E. I. du Pont de Nemours & Company
Agilene	polyethylene	American Agile Corporation
Agilide	PVC	American Agile Corporation
Alathon	polyethylene	E. I. du Pont de Nemours & Company
Alkathene	polyethylene	Imperial Chemical Industries, Ltd.
Ameripol	synthetic rubber*	Goodrich-Gulf Chemicals
Ampacet	polyethylene	American Molding Powder & Chemical Corporation
Arodure	urea resin	Archer Daniels Midland Company
Arothane	urethane foam	Archer Daniels Midland Company
Bakelite†	various plastics	Union Carbide Corporation
Beetle	urea-formaldehyde	American Cyanamid Company
Bexoid	cellulose acetate	B. X. Plastics, Ltd.
Blacar	polyvinyl chloride	Cary Chemicals, Inc.
Butacite	polyvinyl acetal	E. I. du Pont de Nemours & Company
Butvar	polyvinyl butyral	Shawinigan Resins Corporation
Celcon	acetal	Celanese Corporation of America
Chemigum	synthetic rubber*	Goodyear Tire & Rubber Company
Cumar	coumarone-indene resin	Allied Chemical Corporation
Cycolac	ABS	Marbon Chemical Division, Borg-Warner Corporation
Cycolon	ABS	Marbon Chemical Division, Borg-Warner Corporation
Cymel	melamine-formaldehyde	American Cyanamid Company
Dapon	diallyl phthalate	FMC Corporation
Delrin	acetal	E. I. du Pont de Nemours & Company
Durethene	polyethylene film	Sinclair-Koppers Company, Inc.
Durez†	various plastics	Durez Division, Hooker Chemical Corporation
Dyalon	urethane elastomer	Thombert, Inc.
Dylan	polyethylene	Sinclair-Koppers Company, Inc.
Dylene	polystyrene	Sinclair-Koppers Company, Inc.
Dylite	expandable polystyrene	Sinclair-Koppers Company, Inc.
El Rex†	various plastics	Rexall Chemical Company
Elvanol	polyvinyl alcohol	E. I. du Pont de Nemours & Company
Elvax	vinyl resin	E. I. du Pont de Nemours & Company
Epi-Rez	epoxy resin	Davoe & Raynolds Company
Epolite	epoxy resin	Rezolin, Inc.
Epon	epoxy resin	Shell Chemical Company
Escon	polypropylene	Enjay Chemical Company
Estane	polyurethane	B. F. Goodrich Chemical Company
Ethafoam	expanded polyethylene	Dow Chemical Company
Ethocel	ethyl cellulose	Dow Chemical Company
Exon	polyvinyl chloride	Firestone Plastics Company
Formvar	polyvinyl formal	Shawinigan Resins Corporation
Forticel	cellulose propionate	Celanese Corporation of America
Fortiflex	polyethylene	Celanese Corporation of America

Fostalite	polystyrene	Foster Grant Company, Inc.
Fostarene	polystyrene	Foster Grant Company, Inc.
Gelvatol	polyvinyl alcohol	Shawinigan Resins Corporation
Genpol	polyester	General Tire & Rubber Company
Genthane	polyurethane rubber	General Tire & Rubber Company
Geon	PVC	B. F. Goodrich Chemical Company
Glaskyd	glass-reinforced alkyd	American Cyanamid Company
Halon	fluorohalocarbon	Allied Chemical Corporation
Hetrofoam	fire-retardant polyurethane	Durez Division, Hooker Chemical Corporation
Hetron	fire-retardant polyesters	Durez Division, Hooker Chemical Corporation
Hi-fax	polyethylene	Hercules Powder Company
Hypalon	chlorosulfonated polyethylene	E. I. du Pont de Nemours & Company
Insular	polyvinyl chloride	Rubber Corporation of America
Irrathene	irradiated polyethylene	General Electric Company
Kel-F	poly CTFE	Minnesota Mining & Manufacturing Company
Kralastic	ABS	U.S. Rubber Company
Kynar	polyvinylidene fluoride	Pennsalt Chemicals Corporation
Laminac	polyester	American Cyanamid Company
Lexan	polycarbonate	General Electric Company
Linde	silicones	Union Carbide Corporation
Lucite	acrylic	E. I. du Pont de Nemours & Company
Lustran	ABS	Monsanto Company
Lustrex	polystyrene	Monsanto Company
Maraset	epoxy resin	Marblette Corporation
Marlex	polyolefins	Phillips Petroleum Company
Marvinol	PVC	U.S. Rubber Company
Merlon	polycarbonate	Mobay Chemical Company
Moplefan	polypropylene	Montecatini, Società Generale per l'Industria Mineraria e Chemiche
Mouldrite	phenolic and urea	Imperial Chemical Industries, Ltd.
Mylar	polyester film	E. I. du Pont de Nemours & Company
Nordel	ethylene-propylene rubber	E. I. du Pont de Nemours & Company
Oleform	polypropylene	Avisun Corporation
Olemer	propylene copolymer	Avisun Corporation
Opalon	PVC	Monsanto Company
Pelaspan	expandable polystyrene	Dow Chemical Company
Penton	chlorinated polyether	Hercules, Inc.
Petrothene	polyethylene	U.S. Industrial Chemicals Company
Plaskon†	various plastics	Allied Chemical Corporation
Plastacele	cellulose acetate	E. I. du Pont de Nemours & Company
Plexiglas	acrylic	Rohm and Haas Company
Pliovac	PVC	Goodyear Tire & Rubber Company
Plyophen	phenolic	Recihhold Chemicals, Inc.
Poly-Eth	polyethylene	Spencer Chemical Company
Polylite	polyester	Reichhoid Chemicals, Inc.
Pro-fax	polypropylene	Hercules, Inc.
Resimene	melamine-formaldehyde	Monsanto Company
Resinox	phenolic	Monsanto Company
Royalene	synthetic rubber*	U.S. Rubber Company
Rulon	fluorocarbons	Dixon Corporation of America
Saflex	polyvinyl butyral	Monsanto Company

Santofome	expanded polystyrene	Monsanto Company
Sicalit	cellulose acetate	Mazzucchelli Cell. s.p.a.
Silastic	silicone rubber	Dow Corning Corporation
Spenkel	polyurethane	Textron Division, Spencer Kellogg Company
Styrofoam	expanded polystyrene	Dow Chemical Company
Styron	polystyrene	Dow Chemical Company
Surlyn	ionomer	E. I. du Pont de Nemours & Company
Sylgard	silicone resins	Dow Corning Corporation
Sylplast	urea resin	FMC Corporation
Synpol	synthetic rubber*	Texas—U.S. Chemical Company
Synvarite	phenolic	Synvar Corporation
Tedlar	vinyl fluoride	E. I. du Pont de Nemours & Company
Teflon	poly TEE or FEP	E. I. du Pont de Nemours & Company
Tenite†	various plastics	Eastman Chemical Products
Tetra-Ria	urea resin	National Polychemicals, Inc.
Texin	polyurethane	Mobay Chemical Company
Tipox	epoxy resin	Thiokol Chemical Corporation
Tyril	styrene-acrylonitrile copolymer	Dow Chemical Company
Ultrathene	ethylene-vinyl acetate copolymer	U.S. Industrial Chemicals Company
Unox	epoxy resin	Union Carbide Corporation
Vibrin	polyester	U.S. Rubber Company
Viton	fluorinated rubber	E. I. du Pont de Nemours & Company
Vulcollan	polyurethane rubber	Mobay Chemical Company
Vygen	PVC	General Tire & Rubber Company
Vyram	vinyl resins	Monsanto Company
Zerlon	acrylic-styrene copolymer	Dow Chemical Company
Zetafin	olefin copolymer	Dow Chemical Company
Zytel	nylon	E. I. du Pont de Nemours & Company

*Trademark name for a series of synthetic rubbers, further identified by additional designations.
†General trademark for products.

APPENDIX M

HANDBOOKS

Handbooks: Although there are many handbooks with detailed information on a broad range of subjects, designed to assist the average person in search for metals information, perhaps the *Metals Handbook,* published by the American Society for Metals, Metals Park, Ohio 44073 is by far superior to all others. These include the following:

Volume 1. Properties and Selection of Metals (1961)
Volume 2. Heat Treating, Cleaning and Finishing (1964)
Volume 3. Machining (1967)
Volume 4. Forming (1969)
Volume 5. Forging and Casting (1970)
Volume 6. Welding and Brazing (1971)
Volume 7. Atlas of Microstructures of Industrial Alloys (1972)
Volume 8. Metallography and Phase Diagrams 1974)
Volume 9. Failure Analysis (1975)

Two Volume Source Book on Heat Treating: Vol. 1 Materials and Processes; Vol. 2 Production and Engineering Practices (American Society for Metals, Metals Park, Ohio 44073) 1976.

ASME Handbook: Metals Engineering—Design (McGraw-Hill, 1953)
ASME Handbook: Metal Properties (McGraw-Hill, 1954)
Cast Metals Handbook: American Foundrymen's Society 1957
Gray Iron Castings Handbook: Gray Iron Founders Society 1957
Rare Metals Handbook: Hampel, Clifford, Reinhold Press 1954
Handbook of Nonferrous Metallurgy: Liddell, D. M. McGraw-Hill 1945
Welding Handbook: American Welding Society, New York 1957
Engineering Alloys: Woldman, N. E. (Names Properties and Uses), American Society for Metals, Metals Park, Ohio 1954–1976

Index

Index